W9-AQE-486

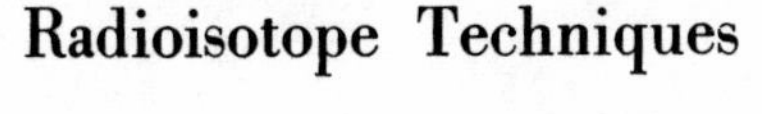

Radioisotope Techniques

Radioisotope Techniques

Ralph T. Overman

CHAIRMAN, SPECIAL TRAINING DIVISION
OAK RIDGE INSTITUTE OF NUCLEAR STUDIES

Herbert M. Clark

PROFESSOR OF PHYSICAL AND NUCLEAR CHEMISTRY
RENSSELAER POLYTECHNIC INSTITUTE

McGRAW-HILL BOOK COMPANY, INC.

New York Toronto London

1960

RADIOISOTOPE TECHNIQUES

 Library of Congress Catalog Card Number 59-10721

47950

VI

This book is dedicated to all whose purpose in searching for knowledge is to share it unselfishly with others and to use it with understanding for the benefit of their fellow men

Preface

In writing this book we have chosen as our goal the presentation of material that will permit a scientific investigator to use radioactive materials in his research program. Most problems associated with this work have to do with techniques for handling radioactive materials safely in the laboratory, performing proper and significant measurements of radioactivity, and interpreting the data obtained from such measurements. An understanding of the theory behind the techniques is desirable for responsible workers in the field. This book should serve not only as a guide for those teaching or studying in areas such as nuclear chemistry where the measurement of radioactivity is of importance, but also as a general guide for those who wish to apply radioisotope techniques to particular research fields.

The over-all division of the material into chapters and the sequence of chapters are based on experience we have gained in offering formal radiochemistry courses, as well as special training courses in basic radioisotope techniques. We recognize that one of the freedoms of a teacher is the determination of the order of presentation of topics. The arrangement we have followed, we believe, is sufficiently flexible to permit any presentation required by course schedules and available equipment. In almost any sequence it is difficult to avoid an occasional reference to material that is discussed fully in a later section.

In presenting experimental procedures, we have tried to encourage students to display initiative without forcing them to make decisions which (in the absence of experience) might lead to indefinite or discouraging results. Even so, the directions given for some experiments may be too specific. Whether this is the case depends upon many variables, including the background and caliber of the students and the scope and pace of the course. We have used the experiments in various combinations at two educational institutions but under quite different conditions. The qualifications of the trainees have varied from those of a college senior majoring in science to those of a scientist with several years of postdoctorate research experience.

More experiments are given than would normally be performed in a single course. This was done partly to enable instructors to select experiments according to equipment and space available and partly to increase the usefulness of the volume as a reference book. In some cases, alternative procedures are suggested in order to include both naturally occurring and artificially produced radioactive substances. Results of the experiments may be checked against the data given in text or reference books.

It is inevitable that certain details of the procedure may be subject to modification in accordance with the advances being made in the nuclear field. For example, at the present time there is a marked shift in emphasis on the type of detectors in use. Although most laboratories now employ Geiger counters for much of their work, scintillation counters are already commonplace in many centers. A modification of this type, however, would have relatively little effect on most experiments.

It was felt that the book would be more usable if experiments were collected at the end of each chapter rather than being interspersed in the text or collected in a separate section at the end. Each experiment consists of a short statement of the particular principle or technique to be studied, a list of equipment and materials needed, a statement of the procedure to be followed, and a section on analysis of the data. The last section is linked to the text material. A table of radioisotopes that can be used for all experiments and a list of equipment and materials required for the course are included in the Appendix. In many experiments we have used the classical procedures. This was done so that the experiments which are designed to illustrate principles and techniques might be performed without a high outlay for special reagents and equipment.

To illustrate various methods and techniques, a few examples are presented from the literature. To conserve space, the number of examples was limited, but not without difficulty, in view of the overwhelming number of publications dealing with radioactivity. Literature references for all names appearing in the text are given at the end of the chapter. Supplementary references are listed with particular attention to articles of a review character which permit students to extend their reading in specific fields. A general bibliography is included at the end of Chap. 1 and in Appendix J.

The authors have given considerable thought to the conduct of courses on the academic level. Although it is true that formal laboratory courses are frequently not desired at the graduate level, it is felt that some kind of formal laboratory periods are necessary for the most efficient presentation of the type of material outlined in this book. This is particularly important if the work is given on the advanced undergraduate level. Since there are numerous ways of organizing a course involving both laboratory techniques and background material, we have used several of these in conducting these programs.

The first method is illustrated by the intensive course at Oak Ridge and obviously would not be suited to normal academic presentation, although the time utilized approximated that of a university term. Another program, which one of us carried out, involved a graduate course comprising the theory and principles of nuclear chemistry given during one 15-week term as a prerequisite to the laboratory course offered during the subsequent term. An alternative program would be to combine all radioactivity work in a one-term course. The last method would usually require a reduction in laboratory hours of about 50 per cent and would be more difficult to plan in order to ensure the proper order of presentation of material needed for laboratory experiments. This method is satisfactory only if all students perform the experiments together or in a prescribed order. This might necessitate a larger outlay for equipment than the two-term program.

A few words should be said about the specific prerequisites for an academic course. These include basic undergraduate courses in elementary and analytical chemistry and the basic courses in college physics. Those who wish to derive maximum benefit should also have background course work in inorganic and in physical chemistry. A knowledge of organic chemistry is desirable in order to become familiar with certain applications of the tracer method. In general, we believe that formal courses dealing with radioisotope techniques are best given at the graduate or advanced undergraduate level.

In addition to students who wish to acquire an adequate understanding of the principles involved in work in this field, there are many workers in science, medicine, and engineering who use the tracer method in applied problems but who do not feel the necessity of understanding all the implications involved in using the tracer as a tool. We hope that this book may be useful to this group also, either in the study of material alone (under the guidance of highly trained persons in this field) or as the basis for presentation of technical courses in tracer techniques for those interested primarily in particular applications.

We wish to thank the many assistants and coworkers who have contributed to the development of this material and the preparation of the manuscript. These include the following present and former staff members of the Special Training Division of the Oak Ridge Institute of Nuclear Studies: Dr. C. L. Comar, R. H. Firminhac, Dr. John W. Jones,

Dr. R. G. Fluharty, Dr. Elizabeth Rona, Dr. M. Nold, Dr. C. S. Simons, Dr. L. K. Akers, and Dr. H. K. Ezell. Others who have made vital contributions to this work include Dr. H. M. Roth and Dr. K. Newton. We should like to give special thanks to S. R. Sapirie of the Atomic Energy Commission and Dr. W. G. Pollard, Executive Director of the Oak Ridge Institute of Nuclear Studies, whose sympathetic guidance in both personal and professional matters has been a major factor in the preparation of this book. The assistance of Miss Louise Markel and Miss Marion Garber, librarians at the Oak Ridge Institute of Nuclear Studies, is also gratefully acknowledged.

For secretarial assistance at Oak Ridge we are indebted to Miss Edith Wilson, Mrs. Abbie Logan, Mrs. Frances Neal, Mrs. Margaret Scott, and Miss Shirley Vowell; at Troy we are indebted to Miss Esther Wight, Mrs. Frances Feski, and Miss Anne Warren. We are additionally indebted to Miss Wight for encouragement during preparation of the manuscript.

We acknowledge with thanks the many helpful comments and suggestions offered by the participants of the Special Training Division courses and by the students at Rensselaer.

In recognition of a very important type of contribution, we should like to express our appreciation to our most understanding families, who struggled through the project with us.

Ralph T. Overman
Herbert M. Clark

Contents

1

Nuclear Radiations and Their Interactions with Matter

1-1. The Production of Radiation

Most of the radiations emitted by radioactive substances arise from changes in an atomic nucleus, although a few of these transformations involve the emission of X rays or electrons from the extranuclear electron levels. The radiations which are of interest to most laboratory workers include alpha particles, positive and negative beta particles (positrons and negatrons), gamma rays, X rays, and bremsstrahlen. The nature of these radiations, the ways in which they interact with matter, and their applications to scientific research form the basis of this study.

Alpha particles are emitted primarily by nuclei of high atomic number. These particles, which are identical to helium nuclei, consist of 2 protons and 2 neutrons. Their characterization in the laboratory is based on the relationships between their relatively large mass and the amount of energy which they possess when they are ejected from nuclei. Commonly they are emitted from natural radioactive materials with an energy of 3 to 8 million electron volts (Mev).* Alpha radiation is emitted from a given radionuclide, or radioisotope, with a discrete kinetic energy, and this energy is one of the identifying features of a given radioisotope.

If the nuclei of elements which occur in nature are investigated, it is

* An electron volt is the kinetic energy acquired by an electron falling through a potential difference of 1 volt. It is equivalent to 1.602×10^{-12} erg. The usual abbreviations for this and its 1,000-fold multiples are ev, kev, and Mev. The maximum energy of the electrons striking the target of a 200-kv X-ray machine would be 200 kev. The energies of chemical bonds are of the order of a few electron volts.

observed that these stable nuclei exhibit a certain pattern with respect to the ratios of the number of neutrons to the number of protons in them. This ratio is close to 1:1 in the lower-atomic-weight elements, but the ratio of neutrons to protons increases in stable elements of higher atomic weight. In the very heavy elements this neutron-proton ratio stability is retained but other factors are responsible for the emission of alpha particles, so that these nuclei are said to be unstable to alpha decay.

If, however, a nucleus is formed by the emission of an alpha particle or by the bombardment of a nucleus with a nuclear projectile, the neutron-proton ratio may differ from that of a stable nucleus of that particular element. If such a nucleus is formed with excess neutrons a change will take place in it to bring about a lower energy or a stable state. This change involves the transition of one of the neutrons into an electron, a proton, and a neutrino. The proton remains in the nucleus, increasing the atomic number by one unit while the electron and the neutrino are ejected from the nucleus. The electron which is formed in this process is called a negative beta particle or negatron and may be detected by its interaction with a suitable detector. The neutrino has essentially no interaction properties and was detected only after extremely complex experiments (1).

If the nucleus under consideration has a neutron-proton ratio lower than the stable forms of the element, two processes compete to return the nucleus to stability. One possibility is for a proton in the nucleus to combine with or "capture" an electron from one of the extranuclear electron levels. This electron is usually from the K level or shell, so the process is frequently referred to as the K-capture decay process. The term electron capture (abbreviated EC) is preferred since nuclei sometimes capture electrons from the second, or L, shell, etc. In this process no radiation except a neutrino is usually emitted from the nucleus, but X rays are emitted from the atom when the electron captured by the nucleus is replaced by an electron from a higher-energy level or a more distant electron. These are the characteristic X rays of the daughter or product atom.

When the amount of energy available in a nucleus with low neutron-proton ratios is at least 1.02 Mev or twice the rest mass of an electron, a second process may compete with electron capture. In this case a proton may transform into a positron, a neutron, and an antineutrino. (Technical distinctions may sometimes be made between a neutrino and an antineutrino.) As in the negative-beta case, the positron and the antineutrino are emitted, leaving the neutron in the nucleus. The "daughter" of a positron-emitting nucleus, then, has an atomic number one less than the parent.

Any of the processes mentioned above, involving transformations of nuclei, may leave the daughter nucleus with more energy than is normally possessed by the resulting stable nucleus. This excess energy may be emitted by such a nucleus in the form of electromagnetic energy or gamma radiation. This "cooling" process involves the emission of one or more monoenergetic photons from the excited nucleus. A study of nuclear spectroscopy gives considerable information about the structure of nuclei in much the same way that atomic spectroscopy has given information about atomic structure. Normally, the photon emission takes place in times of the order 10^{-12} sec after the daughter's stability ratio is attained. In some cases the gamma radiation may be delayed with half-lives ranging from 10^{-7} sec up to a few hours. Such relatively slow emissions of gamma rays are called isomeric transitions (abbreviated IT), and the two nuclear energy states are referred to as nuclear isomers. This is the only decay process in which gamma radiation is emitted without the emission of alpha particles, electrons, neutrinos, or other nuclear components, although gamma rays may be given off following the capture of various nuclear particles.

One further type of radiation might be mentioned. When fast-moving particles such as electrons enter the electrical field around a nucleus, the electron is accelerated by an amount varying with its kinetic energy and the charge or atomic number of the nucleus in the vicinity. In this process some of the energy is radiated as electromagnetic radiation called bremsstrahlung, or "braking radiation." Although electromagnetic in nature like gamma radiation, this radiation exhibits a continuous spectrum of energy. It is produced in high intensity in betatrons, X-ray tubes, and other electron accelerators. Bremsstrahlung production accounts for about 0.1 per cent of the electron interaction for P^{32} in matter of low atomic number, although the amount of its contribution varies with the energy of the radiation and the nature of the absorbing material as shown in Fig. 1-1.*

According to the brief description of the types of radioactive decay given above, it would appear that one would observe the emission of alpha particles, negatrons, or positrons with or without gamma rays from a radioactive source. It is found that this expectation must be modified in some cases because of atomic transformations subsequent to the nuclear decay. For example, either an X ray or gamma ray produced in the decay of a radioactive atom may interact with an electron in that atom and eject it instead of emitting the electromagnetic radiation expected. This interaction may be between an X ray and an extranuclear electron or between a gamma ray and an electron (usually

* For high-energy electrons the ratio of radiative to ionization loss in energy on passage through an absorber varies directly with the kinetic energy of the electron and the atomic number of the absorber.

a K- or L-level electron). Electrons ejected by these processes are called Auger electrons and conversion electrons respectively. They are usually designated by the symbol e^- to distinguish them from beta particles, for which the symbol β^- or β^+ is used. The Auger or conversion electrons differ from beta particles in being monoenergetic and having an energy corresponding to the difference between the photon energy and the binding energy of the ejected electron.

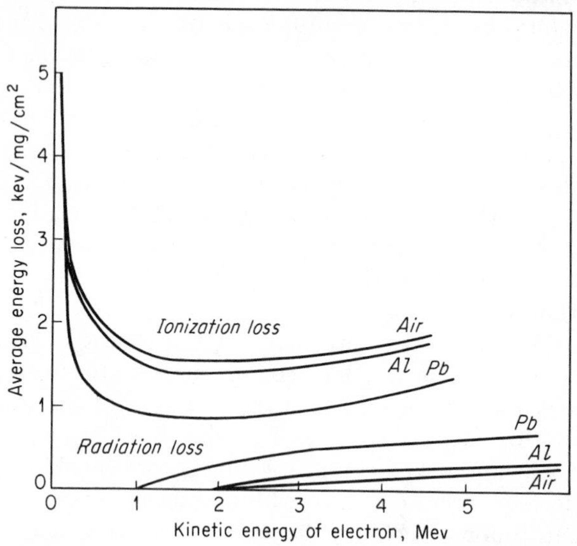

FIG. 1-1. Mass absorption losses for electrons in air, Al, and Pb. Upper three curves show losses by ionization. Lower three curves show bremsstrahlung production. [*From Evans* (2).]

1-2. The Spectra of Nuclear Radiations

Alpha and beta radiations are usually referred to as particulate radiation in contradistinction to electromagnetic radiation, although theoretical descriptions of matter make no such distinction. One difference between the two types of radiation as they are emitted from radioactive sources is the energy variation among particles from a given nuclear species. Alpha particles from a given species of nucleus are emitted with essentially the same energy for a given group, although some "straggling" is observed in examining alpha radiation from a source.

On the other hand, beta particles are ejected from any nuclear species having a continuous spectrum ranging from zero energy up to a certain maximum value which is characteristic of that nuclear species. The beta-ray spectrum can be obtained experimentally by using one of several types of instruments. Several of these instruments have been described by Hine (3), and a detailed description of the techniques and interpretation of the data is included in an excellent book by Siegbahn (4). The beta-ray spectrum of P^{32} is shown in Fig. 1-2. Even though the particles are emitted in a spectral distribution, the common practice is to stipulate the maximum energy of the beta particles corresponding to the separation of the energy levels in the radioactive parent and the

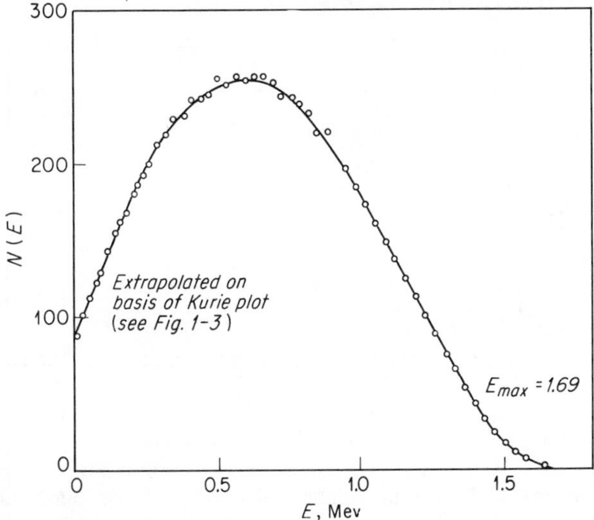

FIG. 1-2. Plot of the number of particles emitted from a sample of P^{32} as a function of their energy. [*From Ketelle and Brosi* (6).]

daughter. This is frequently abbreviated E_{max} and is the value listed for "the" beta-ray energy in tabulations of data. As can be seen from an inspection of the curve, it is rather difficult to obtain the true "end point" or maximum energy of the radiation. To obtain the maximum energy in practice, Kurie, Richardson, and Paxton (5) have developed a method for this determination by a linear extrapolation, as shown in Fig. 1-3. Most single beta spectra, when transformed into the Kurie plot, exhibit a linear form except for the effects of beta particles scattered from the material surrounding the sample mount. There are, however, some beta spectra which show a greater abundance of low-energy electrons than in the usual case. In research involving a calculation of the amount of energy transferred to a system, such as a problem involving biological dosimetry or the initiation of chemical reactions, it is important to know the actual shape of the curve if the average energy is needed for the calculations. The normal beta-ray curve is said to arise in "allowed" beta-decay processes, and those having deviations in the low-energy region are said to belong to one of the several classes of "forbidden" transitions.

One of the important simplifications which is generally valid is that the shapes of beta-ray spectra are essentially the same. This is strictly true only for allowed beta spectra, although certain portions of the curves retain their similarity for many spectra.* As a result, different spectra could be superimposed on one another by a proper translation in the energy scale. This fact simplifies many of the problems associated

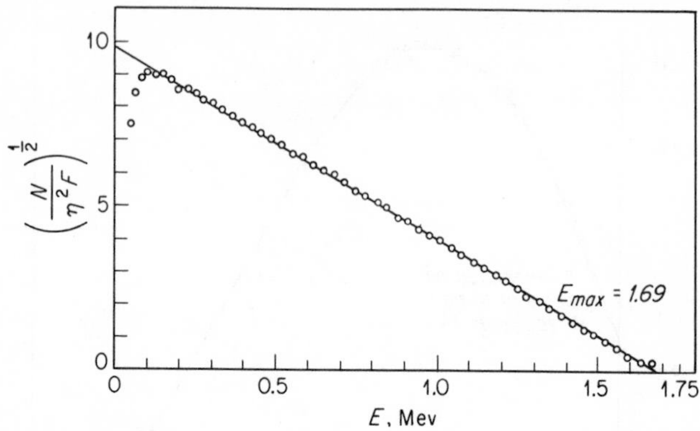

FIG. 1-3. Kurie plot of data of Fig. 1-2 for P^{32}, in which N is the disintegration rate, η is the momentum of the particle, and F is a complex Fermi function which is dependent on the atomic number and energy. [*From Ketelle and Brosi* (6).]

with beta-ray measurement. For example, the rough generalization can be made that the average energy (E_{av}) of the beta rays from a radionuclide which undergoes an allowed transition has a ratio of about 0.35 to 0.4 to the maximum energy. The experimentally determined values for the average to maximum energy ratios for a number of isotopes have been collected by Marinelli, Brinckerhoff, and Hine (7). A few values are included in Table 1-1. Since many more low-energy electrons are ejected from forbidden transitions, the ratio of average to maximum energy is correspondingly lower. For first forbidden transitions the ratio might be of the order of 0.31, whereas second forbidden spectra give ratios of the order of 0.26. The differences are of relatively little importance for most radioactive tracer work.

* There seems to be some indication from further investigation of the Fermi beta-ray-decay theory (2) that beta-ray spectra with low (less than 0.5 Mev) maximum energies do not exhibit geometrical maxima in their curves. Such curves may exhibit a steady drop from the positive intercept. There are also intermediate cases in which a slight maximum is observed at a low energy. Even in these cases the observed curves correspond to the shape of the high-energy end of the otherwise characteristic spectrum.

1-3. Decay Schemes

A convenient method of indicating schematically the information about the type of radiation given off by a nucleus is a decay or disintegration scheme. The usual diagram is a plot of energy against atomic number, although no scale is used. Usually, the symbol and mass number of the nuclide are written on a short horizontal line. The type of transformation is then represented by an arrow either to the right or to the left depending on whether a negative or positive particle is emitted or an orbital electron captured. The arrow terminates at another horizontal line to represent the daughter nucleus. If the daughter nuclide is left in an excited state after the particle emission or capture, the gamma rays which are emitted are indicated by vertical lines (sometimes undulating to indicate waves) drawn to the base line or ground energy state. The maximum kinetic energy of the emitted particles and the energy of the gamma radiation are written near the appropriate arrow. In the case of electron capture, the symbol EC is usually written on the arrow without any indication of energy values. For positron emission many authors show a vertical line labeled $2m_0c^2$ to indicate the amount of energy required to create an electron pair. In nuclei where more than one decay path is found, the percentage of decays following a given path is likewise indicated near the arrow when known.

TABLE 1-1

MAXIMUM AND AVERAGE BETA-RAY ENERGIES FOR SELECTED RADIOISOTOPES*

Radioisotope	E_{max}	E_{av}	$\frac{E_{av}}{E_{max}}$
Na^{22}	0.575	0.225	0.39
Na^{24}	1.39	0.540	0.39
P^{32}	1.71	0.695	0.40
Fe^{59}	0.46	0.150 } 0.120	0.32
	0.255	0.085 }	0.30
Cu^{64}	0.578 β^-	0.175 } 0.205	0.33
	0.659 β^+	0.265 }	0.40
I^{130}	1.03	0.360 } 0.270	0.35
	0.61	0.195 }	0.32
I^{131}	0.595	0.205	0.34
RaE	1.17	0.330	0.28
UX_2	2.32	0.865	0.37

* From Marinelli, Brinckerhoff, and Hine (7).

Examples of various types of decay schemes are given in Fig. 1-4. These illustrate the following:

1. P^{32}: Decay is by pure negatron emission, $E_{max} = 1.707$ Mev.
2. Cs^{137}: Predominant mode is negatron emission to produce the

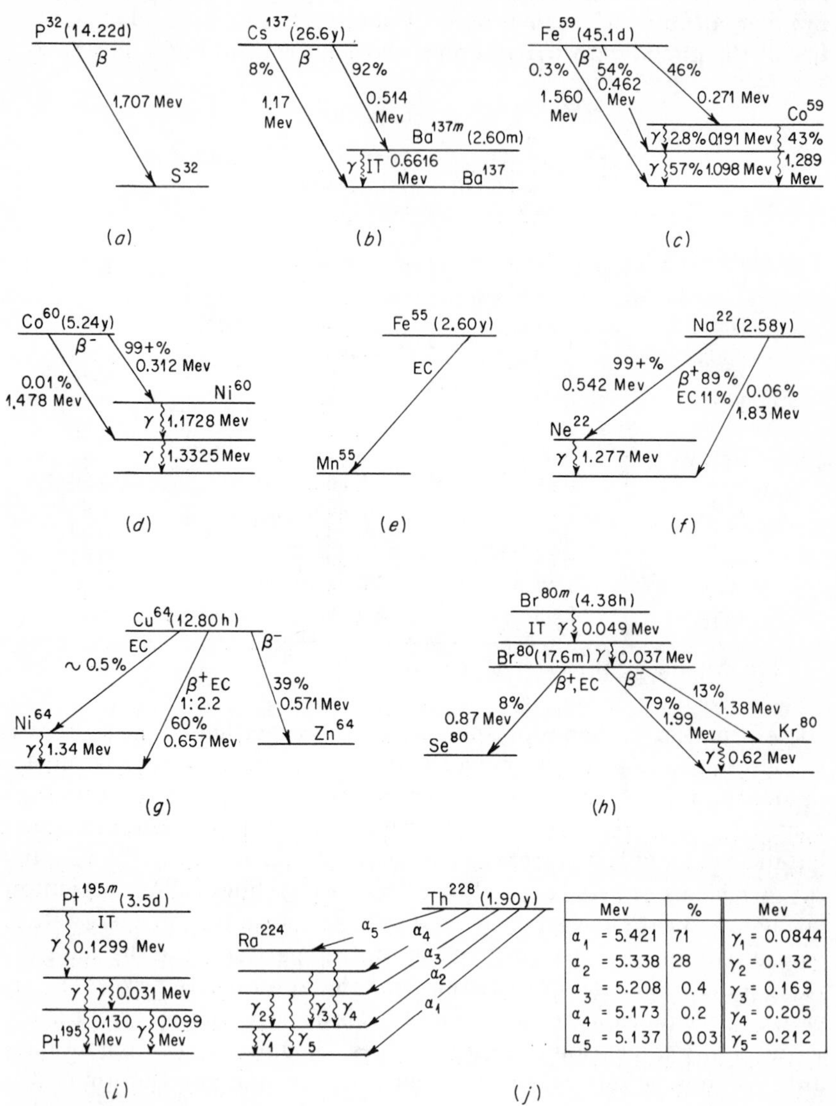

Mev	%	Mev
α_1 = 5.421	71	γ_1 = 0.0844
α_2 = 5.338	28	γ_2 = 0.132
α_3 = 5.208	0.4	γ_3 = 0.169
α_4 = 5.173	0.2	γ_4 = 0.205
α_5 = 5.137	0.03	γ_5 = 0.212

FIG. 1-4. Examples of decay schemes. [*Based on Strominger, Hollander, and Seaborg* (12).]

2.60-min isomer, Ba^{137m}, which undergoes isomeric transition and is the source of the well-known 0.66-Mev gamma ray associated with Cs^{137}; 8 per cent of the Cs^{137} nuclei decay by negatron emission directly to the ground state of Ba^{137}.

3. Fe^{59}: Following the 0.271-Mev negatron transition there is an immediate transition to the ground state of Co^{59} by two branches; the gamma transition directly to the ground state predominates.

4. Co^{60}: Essentially all 5.24-year Co^{60} nuclei decay by way of the 0.312-Mev negatron transition, which is followed immediately by 2 photons in cascade.

5. Fe^{55}: Decay is entirely by electron capture; weak photoelectrons and Mn X rays are emitted, with the latter appearing unconverted in about 25 per cent of the transitions.

6. Na^{22}: Essentially all 2.58-year Na^{22} nuclei decay to excited Ne^{22} nuclei, which emit 1.277-Mev photons; positron emission is about eight times more frequent than electron capture.

7. Cu^{64}: Electron capture accounts for 42 per cent, negatron emission for 39 per cent, and positron emission for 19 per cent of the disintegrations of Cu^{64}; a photon is emitted following decay of about 5 out of each 1,000 Cu^{64} nuclei.

8. Br^{80m}: Isomeric transition to the 17.6-min Br^{80} is accompanied by two weak photons which are highly converted; the Br^{80} decays predominantly to the ground state of Kr^{80}.

9. Pt^{195m}: Isomeric transition of the 3.5-day isomer to stable Pt^{195} is accompanied by photons which are highly converted. (Although not illustrated, IT and decay with change in atomic number may occur competitively, for example, Sr^{85m}.)

10. Th^{228} (RdTh): Five groups of alpha particles are emitted; the predominant mode is to the ground state of Ra^{224}; the other modes involve emission of one or more photons en route to Ra^{224} in the ground state.

Some published diagrams also indicate gamma-ray conversion coefficients and the extent of fluorescence following electron capture. In the case of the diagram for I^{131} given in Chap. 7, about 73 per cent of the emissions of the 80-kev gamma ray are internally converted, and the radiations which may be observed from this emission are the conversion electrons. In the next section mention is made of the process in which positrons are annihilated to produce one or usually two annihilation photons. These appear as gamma rays of 0.511-Mev energy. These photons are always observed experimentally but are not represented in the decay scheme since they arise in interactions subsequent to the nuclear decay process.

Extensive tabulations of this type of decay information are available in several publications (8–13). The importance of these diagrams in shielding calculations is outlined in a publication by Morgan (14). Their importance to the standardization of radioactivity is discussed in Chap. 7.

1-4. Interactions of Alpha and Beta Radiation with Matter

Two factors of importance in the diminution of radiation intensity are the inverse-square law and the probability of the absorption of the radiation in matter. The first is a geometrical factor and is not related to the absorption of the radiation itself. The second factor depends on the type and energy of the radiation and the nature of the absorbing material.

All charged particulate radiation of any type loses its energy by interacting with matter in essentially the same way. This interaction is based primarily on the interaction between the particles and the electrons in the atoms of the absorbing matter. The attractive or repulsive forces are sufficiently great either to excite an electron within the atom or to remove an electron from the atom. If the electron is removed, the resulting negative electron and the positively charged ion are called an ion pair. Each radiation particle gives up a portion of its energy by the formation of a long succession of ion pairs. Likewise a portion of the energy is used to raise some of the atoms to excited states by raising their electrons to higher-energy levels. There is no complete agreement on the relative importance of ionization and excitation processes in the biological or chemical effects of radiation, although it has been estimated that they may each contribute approximately 50 per cent of the observed radiation effects in a typical case. (See Chap. 2.)

When radiation passes through air, it has been found that, on the average, the production of an ion pair requires about 35 ev. This means that particulate radiation will create about 30,000 ion pairs for each million electron volts which the incident particle possesses. Actually, the number of ion pairs formed per unit path length, called the specific ionization, increases considerably as the particle slows down. At the end of its path the specific ionization increases by a factor of from 2 to 7 over its initial value, as shown for a typical case in Fig. 1-5, which is the well-known Bragg curve (16). The height of the curve is determined by the length of time spent in the vicinity of the atom as the charged particle slows down. The specific ionization of alpha radiation is of the order of 25 or more times higher than for beta radiation of the same energy because of the former's large mass and double charge. As a result the thickness of material required to stop the radiation from a given nuclide, or the range of the alpha particle, is relatively small and well defined, since the radiation is monoenergetic. This radiation does exhibit "straggling," however, which complicates the determination of a precise range value. Fairly good techniques are available for the determination of the range in a few materials, however, and curves showing the relation between the range and energy of alpha radiation in air and aluminum are given in Fig. 1-6. Most naturally occurring alpha-ray emitters emit particles in the range of 3 to 8 Mev which have ranges in air from approximately 3 to 8 cm.

The path, or track length, of an electron having a given energy is much longer than that of an alpha particle of the same energy. In addition, the lower mass of the electron permits much greater deviations

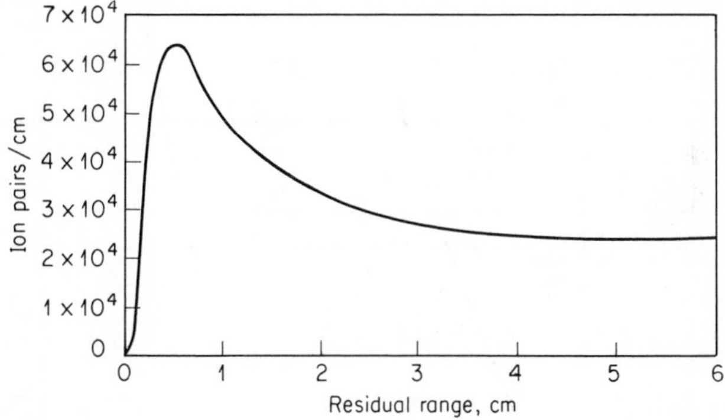

FIG. 1-5. Bragg curve for specific ionization of alpha particles in air at 15°C and 760 mm Hg. [*From Bragg* (16).]

from a straight-line path. This, together with spectral distribution of beta particles, makes the determination of the beta-ray range considerably more difficult. The term range for beta particles also has a somewhat different meaning in that it defines the thickness of a filter necessary to stop the maximum-energy beta radiation. In general, the attenuation, or stopping power, of material for particle radiation is nearly independent of the atomic number of the material.

Positive beta-ray particles, or positrons, also use up their kinetic energy in the formation of ions in a manner similar to that for negatrons except that attractive rather than repulsive forces cause the ionization. Positrons are characterized, however, by a different end state. Negative electrons occupy any available energy level after they lose their kinetic energy. When positrons lose their kinetic energy, they combine with a negative electron. This interaction causes the annihilation of both electrons with the transformation of their rest mass into electromagnetic radiation. This annihilation radiation usually consists of two gamma-ray photons of 0.511 Mev energy which are given off at a 180°

angle to one another. They are frequently called gamma rays, but "annihilation photons" is becoming an accepted term. As noted earlier, such annihilation radiation is always observed in the vicinity of a

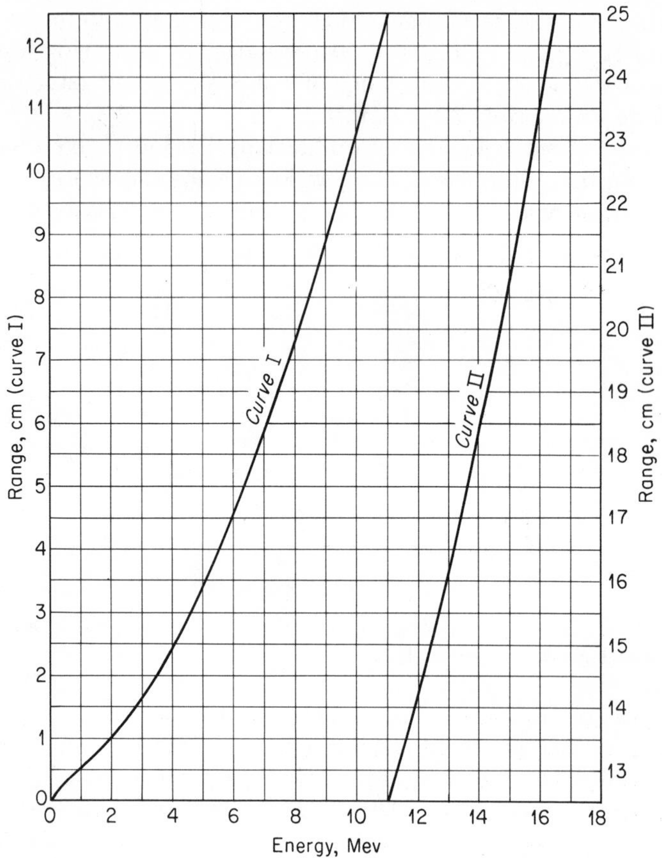

FIG. 1-6a. Range of alpha particles in air. [*From Aron, Hoffman, and Williams* (15).]

positron-emitting source, but the gamma radiations are not included in tabulations of radiations emitted from a given nuclide since they arise in the matter surrounding the source.

1-5. Interactions of Electromagnetic Radiation with Matter

Electromagnetic radiation has a much lower probability of interacting with matter than particulate radiation has. Although the precise values of the specific ionizations depend markedly on the energy of the radiation and the kind of absorbing material, typical relative values for alpha, beta, and gamma radiation having the same initial energy might be 2,500, 100, and 1 respectively. The mechanism of the interaction of

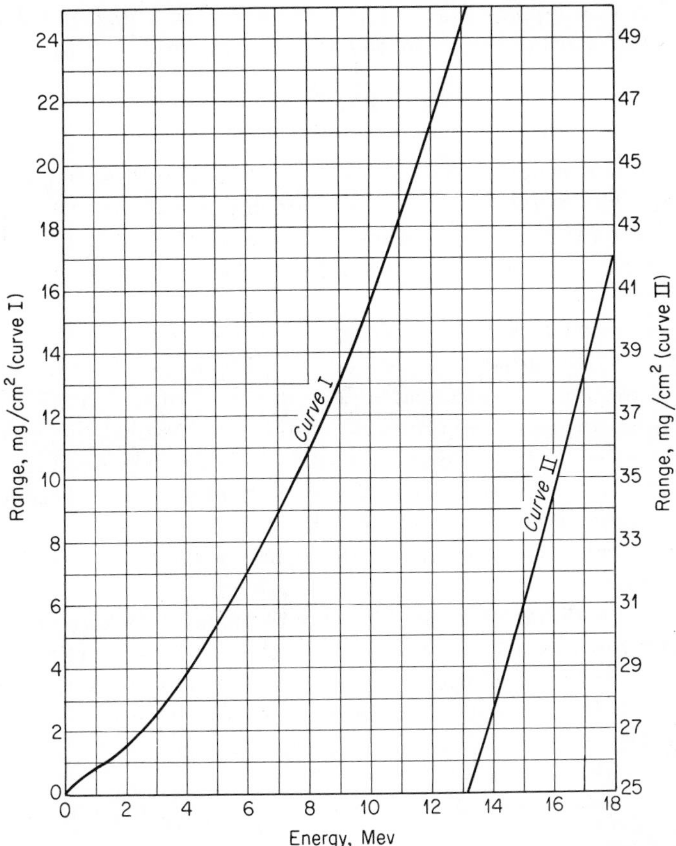

FIG. 1-6b. Range of alpha particles in aluminum. [*From Aron, Hoffman, and Williams* (15).]

photons with matter differs considerably from that of particulate radiation. Whereas charged particles interact directly to produce ions, photons may interact in one of several different ways. Although a distinction is usually made between "ionizing," or particulate, radiation and electromagnetic radiation in respect to the nature of the primary interaction, the distinction loses its force if the secondary effects are considered. Since electrons are set in motion or are produced following gamma-ray interaction, the ultimate effects of this interaction are the same as for beta radiation.

Though most of the considerations involved in the attenuation of the radiation from a gamma-ray source involve the problems of interaction with matter, it should be pointed out that the diminution of the radiation with distance is a very important factor. This is usually referred to as the "inverse-square law." The intensity I at a distance d from a point source or other uncollimated source is given by

$$I = \frac{k}{d^2}$$

in which k is a proportionality constant (equal to intensity at a unit distance). The usual test of this relationship is a plot of the intensity against the square of the distance from the source. It is valid for distances which are large compared with the dimensions of the detector and the source.

In the case of a parallel or collimated beam of gamma rays, there is no diminution of the radiation intensity except by interaction between the radiation and matter in the path. The intensity of such a beam is proportional to the number of photons per unit time passing through a unit area perpendicular to the beam. The amount of energy passing is equal to the sum of the products of the numbers of photons and their energies passing at that time, or if each photon has the same energy, the intensity is proportional to the product of the total number and energy of the photons.

For such a collimated beam of monochromatic electromagnetic radiation, the intensities at various points in the absorbing medium can be calculated. If I_0 is the intensity at the incident surface of the stopping material, I is the intensity after passing through a thickness x, and μ is the total absorption coefficient, the intensity is given by

$$I = I_0 \exp(-\mu x) \qquad \text{or} \qquad \frac{I}{I_0} = \exp(-\mu x) \tag{1-1}$$

The absorption coefficient is a constant whose value depends on the kind of material and the energy of the photons in the beam. Linear absorption coefficients are in units of reciprocal centimeters, and mass absorption coefficients may be expressed as square centimeters per gram. Mass absorption coefficients may be calculated from the linear absorption coefficient by dividing the latter by the density of the absorbing medium. It should be noted that the absorption coefficient is a measure of the probability of occurrence of an interaction process. This gives the fraction of the number of photons lost per centimeter or per gram per square centimeter by the particular process under discussion. The mass absorption coefficient is useful in comparing effects in materials of different density, whereas the linear absorption coefficient gives results which translate directly into a linear thickness of an absorbing material.

Equation (1-1) is generally assumed to be valid for the total diminution of the beam. However, it is frequently helpful to consider the different processes which contribute to the total absorption coefficient.

The first of the three processes, the photoelectric interaction, is important for low-energy (up to about 1 Mev) photons and high-atomic-number materials and is the effect utilized in photoelectric cells. In this case, the photon interacts with an atom and ejects an electron which is more or less tightly bound to the atom. The entire energy of the quantum of radiation is transferred to the atom, which subsequently ejects an orbital electron. The electron is ejected with a kinetic energy equal to the difference between the energy of the incident photon and the binding energy of the electron. This may be expressed by

$$E_{\text{kin}} = h\nu - W \tag{1-2}$$

in which E_{kin} is the kinetic energy of the ejected electron, $h\nu$ is the energy of the incident photon, and W is the work necessary to remove the electron from the atom, i.e., its binding energy. The relationship of the photoelectric absorption coefficient, the energy of the radiation, and the atomic number of the material absorbing the radiation is given by

$$\tau = 0.0089 \frac{\rho}{A} 4.1Z\left(\frac{12.4}{E}\right)^n \tag{1-3}$$

where τ is in reciprocal centimeters, ρ is the density of the material, E is the energy of the radiation in thousands of electron volts,* Z is the mean atomic number of the material, A is the mean atomic weight, and n is a constant which has a value of 3.05 for nitrogen, carbon, and oxygen and 2.85 for the elements from sodium to iron in the periodic table. Values are not well determined for the remaining elements. It is evident that this process is strongly dependent on the energy of the radiation and the nature of the stopping material.

For electromagnetic radiation of higher energy or for material of lower atomic number, the Compton interaction process becomes relatively more important. In this process the photon imparts a portion of its energy to a substantially free electron. The energy of the incident gamma ray is then divided between the kinetic energy of the electron and a lower-energy photon in a manner which somewhat resembles the

* X rays are frequently characterized by their wavelengths in angstroms in tables of X-ray data. The energy and wavelength are related by the equation $E = 12.4/\lambda$, in which E is the X-ray energy in thousands of electron volts and λ is in angstroms. See Appendix E for a table of characteristic X-ray values for the elements.

billiard-ball type of collision. Sometimes the probability or absorption coefficient for this interaction is subdivided into two factors, one involving the electron and the other the scattered photon radiation. The Compton absorption coefficient σ_a represents the probability of the energy being transferred to the electron, and the Compton scattering coefficient σ_s represents the probability of the energy being scattered as a lower-energy photon. In some cases it is important to distinguish between the two coefficients, since the scattered radiation still appears in the system as electromagnetic radiation giving rise to additional Compton or photoelectric interactions in the absorbing medium. This factor is important in laboratory shielding and measurement problems. The relationship of the Compton absorption coefficients, the atomic number of the absorbing material, and the energy of the radiation is given by

$$\sigma = \sigma_a + \sigma_s = NZ(f_a + f_s) \tag{1-4}$$

in which N is the number of atoms per cubic centimeter, Z is the atomic number (number of electrons per atom), and f_a and f_s are functions of the energy which can be derived from the Klein-Nishina (17) theory of the process.

The energy $h\nu'$ of a photon scattered by the Compton process is given by

$$h\nu' = \frac{h\nu}{1 + (h\nu/m_0c^2)(1 - \cos\phi)} \tag{1-5}$$

where $h\nu$ is the energy of the incident photon, m_0c^2 is the rest energy of the Compton recoil electron, and ϕ is the angle between the scattered and incident photons. The Compton interaction is the most probable process of interaction in lead for gamma-ray energies between about 0.5 and 5 Mev.

A third process by which high-energy photons may interact with matter is by pair production. This is the conversion of the photon into a negatron and a positron, and may occur (usually in the vicinity of a nucleus) if the energy of the photon is at least 1.02 Mev. This quantity is the sum of the rest energies of the two particles, that is, $2m_0c^2$. Any additional photon energy is imparted to the electrons as kinetic energy. The electrons interact subsequently with matter in the manner described above under particulate radiation.

The relationship of the pair-production probability κ, the atomic number of the absorbing medium, and the energy of the radiation is given by

$$\kappa = aNZ^2(E - 1.02) \tag{1-6}$$

in which κ is the absorption coefficient, a is a proportionality constant,

N is the number of atoms per cubic centimeter, Z is the atomic number, and E is the energy of the photon in Mev.

Additional details of the interaction processes are discussed by Fano (18), by Fluharty (19), and extensively by Evans (2). Various absorption coefficients are plotted for aluminum and lead in Figs. 1-7 and 1-8. Similar curves may be drawn for other kinds of absorbing materials,

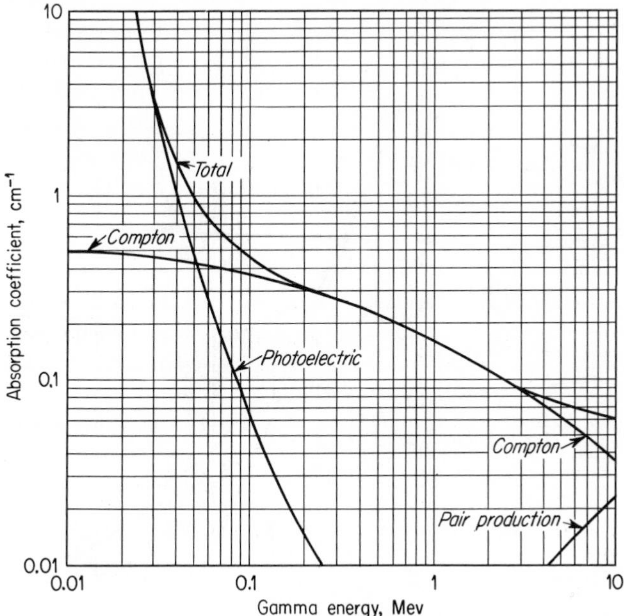

FIG. 1-7. Linear absorption coefficient vs. photon energy for aluminum, including partial absorption coefficients. (*From G. R. White, Natl. Bur. Standards Circ.* 583, 1957.)

using methods described in the literature cited above. The total absorption coefficient μ_0 may be used as a first approximation in "good" geometry (see Chap. 6) for calculations of shielding and dosage. This is the arithmetic sum of the various components

$$\mu_0 = \tau + \sigma + \kappa \tag{1-7}$$

Laboratory calculations frequently are made on the basis of the "half-thickness," or "half-value layer," which can be related to the absorption coefficient by

$$X_{1/2} = \frac{0.693}{\mu_0} \tag{1-8}$$

in which $X_{1/2}$ is the thickness of material which reduces the radiation intensity by one-half. This is valid if one assumes that the radiation absorption is a simple exponential function. This assumption would be valid for "good" geometry or for a collimated source. It is sometimes useful to calculate the amount of material which diminishes the intensity to another arbitrarily determined fraction such as the tenth value, $X_{1/10}$, which is the thickness that reduces the intensity to one-tenth of that of the original.

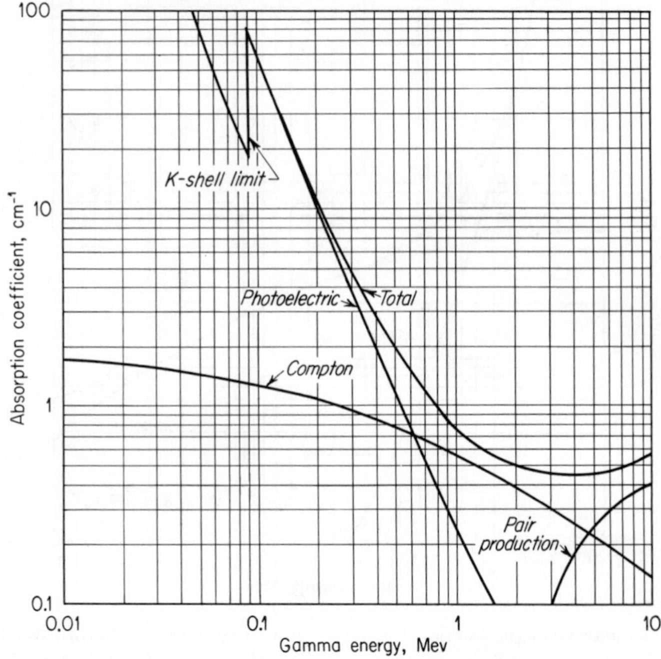

FIG. 1-8. Linear absorption coefficient vs. photon energy for lead, including partial absorption coefficients. (*From G. R. White, Natl. Bur. Standards Circ.* 583, 1957.)

Chapter 6 outlines details of laboratory practice involving the characterization and shielding problems. Half-thickness curves corresponding to Figs. 1-7 and 1-8 are given in that chapter.

1-6. Radiation Units

There are two fundamental units which occur in many discussions of radioisotope utilization. One of these units is a measure of the disintegration rate of a given sample or source of radioactive material. The other is a measure of the radiation dose particularly as it can be related to biological damage, as in shielding problems.

It would be proper to use the term disintegrations per unit time as the measure of the "activity" of a given sample. Since the number of such disintegrations per minute or per second is usually quite high for most samples, it is convenient to choose another term, the curie, to simplify the usage. This unit was originally defined as the quantity of radon in equilibrium with 1 g of radium. Early measurements of the disintegration rate of radon gave values in the neighborhood of 3.7×10^{10} alpha particles per second. The curie was then defined as a sample of naturally radioactive material with this disintegration rate. More recent measurements of the decay rate of the radon in equilibrium with 1 g of radium give a value of $(3.608 \pm 0.028) \times 10^{10}$ dps. However, the curie has been officially redefined (20) as any radioactive source with a decay rate of 3.700×10^{10} dps, and it is no longer limited to use with naturally occurring radioactive elements. A millicurie and a microcurie are one-thousandth and one-millionth of a curie respectively.

The effect of radiation is determined by the energy which is transferred to the system, whether it be a biological system requiring shielding or a chemical system in which it is desired to increase the energy available. Two units are in common use for expressing the energy transmitted to a system, and several additional terms are derived from these. The two basic terms are the roentgen, which has been in use, and the rad, which is making its bid for acceptance as a more recent official adoption.

The roentgen, abbreviated r, was officially defined by the International Radiological Congress in Chicago in 1937 as "the quantity of X or gamma radiation such that the associated corpuscular emission per 0.001293 gram of air produces, in air, ions carrying one electrostatic unit of quantity of electricity of either sign" (20). (The mass of air referred to is 1 cm^3 of dry air at STP.) There are several significant aspects of the definition:

1. The unit is limited to "that type of radiation" which limits the use to X or gamma radiation, and does not permit it to be used for alpha, beta, neutron, or other radiation types.

2. The definition limits the effect to that produced by the "associated corpuscular emission," which includes photoelectrons, Compton electrons, and electron pairs.

3. The effect is limited to that produced in air. This includes the air surrounding the cubic centimeter in which the primary interaction took place. It also limits the definition to the interactions in air and not in tissue or other material.

4. One esu involves the production of 2.093×10^9 ion pairs, since the charge on an electron is 4.8×10^{-10} esu. An electron in air requires about 35 ev to produce 1 ion pair; so this number of ion pairs requires

the dissipation of about 6.8×10^{10} ev/cm^3 of air. A roentgen, then, transfers 6.8×10^4 Mev energy to the electrons per cubic centimeter of air, or 5.24×10^7 Mev/g of air. Likewise, since there is 1.6×10^{-12} erg/ev, the energy dissipated per gram of air is 83.8 ergs.

5. The roentgen is not a measure of intensity. For example, if a source gives off 1,000 photons/cm^2/sec at 1 Mev and another source gives off 500 photons/cm^2/sec at 2 Mev, the intensity in both cases is 1,000 Mev/cm^2/sec. However, the extent of the interaction between 1-Mev photons and 2-Mev photons with air is not equal, so that the number of roentgens per hour from the two sources is not the same. The difference can be calculated from proper absorption coefficients.

Since the definition of the roentgen is limited to the effects of X or gamma radiation, it was considered necessary to devise an equivalent unit to describe the effects of other types of radiation on materials such as biological tissue. A unit which has been in common use for several years is the roentgen equivalent physical (abbreviated rep), which is defined as the dose of any ionizing radiation which produces the energy absorption of 93 ergs/g in tissue. The value of 93 ergs/g was chosen because of the difference in absorption characteristics of tissue as compared with air. Since there are different absorption characteristics for different energy radiations, the unit was defined to correlate the effects of particulate radiations and 250-kev X rays.

The second unit used as a measure of the energy transferred to a system is the rad. The unit was adopted in 1954 by the International Commission on Radiation Protection since the rep unit was too highly dependent on the energy of the electromagnetic radiation. The rad is defined as the absorption of 100 ergs/g and is thus not directly related to the roentgen. A more extensive discussion of these and other units such as the rem is included in Chap. 4, and a compilation and a discussion of these have been prepared by K. Z. Morgan (21).

Cited References

1. Reines, F., and C. L. Cowan, Jr.: Neutrino Physics, *Phys. Today,* vol. 10, no. 8, pp. 12–18, August, 1957.
2. Evans, R. D.: "The Atomic Nucleus," McGraw-Hill, New York, 1955.
3. Hine, G. J.: Beta- and Gamma-ray Spectroscopy. I, *Nucleonics,* vol. 3, no. 6, pp. 32–42, December, 1948; II, vol. 4, no. 2, pp. 56–66, February, 1949.
4. Siegbahn, K. (ed.): "Beta- and Gamma-ray Spectroscopy," Interscience, New York, 1955.
5. Kurie, F. N. D., J. R. Richardson, and H. C. Paxton: Further Data on the Energies of Beta-rays Emitted from Artificially Produced Radioactive Bodies, *Phys. Rev.,* vol. 49, p. 203, 1936.
6. Ketelle, B. H., and A. R. Brosi: private communication.

7. Marinelli, L. D., R. F. Brinckerhoff, and G. J. Hine: Average Energy of Beta-rays Emitted by Radioactive Isotopes, *Revs. Modern Phys.*, vol. 19, pp. 25–28, January, 1947.
8. Ajzenberg, F., and T. Lauritsen: Energy Levels of Light Nuclei. IV, *Revs. Modern Phys.*, vol. 24, pp. 321–402, October, 1952.
9. Way, K., et al.: Nuclear Data, *Natl. Bur. Standards Circ.* 499 and Supplements 1–3, 1950–1952.
10. "Nuclear Data Sheets," National Academy of Sciences–National Research Council, Washington, 1958.
11. Strominger, D., and J. M. Hollander: Decay Schemes, *U.S. Atomic Energy Comm. Rept.* UCRL-8289, June, 1958.
12. Strominger, D., J. M. Hollander, and G. T. Seaborg: Table of Isotopes, *Revs. Modern Phys.*, vol. 30, pp. 585–904, 1958.
13. Way, K., W. King, C. L. McGinnis, and R. van Lieshout: Nuclear Level Schemes, $A = 40$–$A = 92$ (Covering the Elements Ca–Zr), *U.S. Atomic Energy Comm. Rept.* TID-5300, 1955.
14. Morgan, G. W.: "Some Practical Considerations in Radiation Shielding," U.S. Atomic Energy Commission, Isotopes Division Circular B-4, Oak Ridge, Tenn., 1948.
15. Aron, W. A., B. G. Hoffman, and F. C. Williams: Range-Energy Curves, *U.S. Atomic Energy Comm. Rept.* AECU-663, 2d rev., 1951.
16. Bragg, W. H.: Ionisation of Various Gases by α-particles, *Phil. Mag.*, vol. 13, pp. 333–357, March, 1907.
17. Klein, O., and Y. Nishina: Über die Streuung von Strahlung durch freie Elektronen nach neuen relativistischen Quantendynamik von Dirac, *Z. Physik*, vol. 52, pp. 853–868, 1929.
18. Fano, U.: Gamma-ray Attenuation. I, Basic Processes, *Nucleonics*, vol. 11, no. 8, pp. 8–12, August, 1953; II, Analysis of Penetration, vol. 11, no. 9, pp. 55–61, September, 1953.
19. Fluharty, R. G.: Interaction of Isotopic Radiation with Matter. I, *Nucleonics*, vol. 2, no. 5, pp. 28–40, May, 1948; II, vol. 3, no. 1, pp. 46–56, July, 1948.
20. Report of the International Commission on Radiological Units and Measurements, *Natl. Bur. Standards Handbook* 62 (supersedes Handbook 47), 1957.
21. Morgan, K. Z.: Maximum Permissible Internal Dose of Radionuclides: Recent Changes in Values, *Nuclear Sci. and Eng.*, vol. 1, pp. 477–500, December, 1956.

Supplementary References

"American Institute of Physics Handbook," McGraw-Hill, New York, 1957.

Aston, F. W.: "Mass Spectra and Isotopes," 2d ed., Longmans, New York, 1942.

Auger, P.: Sur les rayons secondaires produits dans un gaz par des rayons X, *Compt. rend.*, vol. 180, pp. 65–68, 1925.

Bethe, H. A.: "Elementary Nuclear Theory: A Short Course on Selected Topics Given at the Research Laboratory of the General Electric Company at Schenectady," 2d ed., Wiley, New York, 1956.

——— and R. F. Bacher: Nuclear Physics. A. Stationary States of Nuclei, *Revs. Modern Phys.*, vol. 8, pp. 82–229, April, 1936.

Bitter, F.: "Nuclear Physics," Addison-Wesley, Reading, Mass., 1950.

Blatt, J. M., and V. F. Weisskopf: "Theoretical Nuclear Physics," Wiley, New York, 1952.

Bohr, N., and J. A. Wheeler: The Mechanism of Nuclear Fission, *Phys. Rev.*, vol. 56, pp. 426–450, Sept. 1, 1939.

Brown, H.: Quantum Mechanics for Nuclear Technology. I, *Nucleonics*, vol. 1, no. 1, pp. 34–41, September, 1947; II, Derivations of Some Basic Nuclear Concepts, vol. 1, no. 3, pp. 45–53, November, 1947.

———: A Table of Relative Abundances of Nuclear Species, *Revs. Modern Phys.*, vol. 21, pp. 625–634, October, 1949.

Chadwick, J.: "Radioactivity and Radioactive Substances," 4th ed. (revised by J. Rotblat), Pitman, London, 1953.

Compton, A. H., and S. K. Allison: "X-rays in Theory and Experiment," Van Nostrand, Princeton, N.J., 1935.

Condon, E. U.: Foundations of Nuclear Physics, *Nucleonics*, vol. 1, no. 1, pp. 3–11, September, 1947.

Cook, G. B., and J. F. Duncan: "Modern Radiochemical Practice," Oxford, New York, 1952.

Cork, J. M.: "Radioactivity and Nuclear Physics," 3d ed., Van Nostrand, Princeton, N.J., 1957.

Curie, M.: "Recherches sur les substances radioactives," Gauthier-Villars, Paris, 1904.

Darrow, K. K.: "Atomic Energy," Wiley, New York, 1948.

Devons, S.: "Excited States of Nuclei," Cambridge, New York, 1949.

Dushman, S.: "Fundamentals of Atomic Physics," McGraw-Hill, New York, 1951.

Ellis, C. B.: On Closed Shells in Nuclei, *Phys. Rev.*, vol. 74, p. 1547, Nov. 15, 1948.

Evans, R. D.: Radioactivity Units and Standards, *Nucleonics*, vol. 1, no. 2, pp. 32–43, October, 1947.

Faires, R. A., and B. H. Parks: "Radioisotope Laboratory Techniques," Pitman, London, 1958.

Feather, N.: "An Introduction to Nuclear Physics," Cambridge, New York, 1936.

———: "Nuclear Stability Rules," Cambridge, New York, 1952.

Feenberg, E.: "Shell Theory of the Nucleus," Princeton University Press, Princeton, N.J., 1955.

Fermi, E.: "Nuclear Physics: A Course Given by Enrico Fermi at the University of Chicago" (notes compiled by J. Orear, A. H. Rosenfeld, and R. A. Schluter), University of Chicago Press, Chicago, 1950.

Finkelnburg, W.: "Atomic Physics," McGraw-Hill, New York, 1950.

Fluegge, S.: "An Introduction to Nuclear Physics," Interscience, New York, 1946.

Friedlander, G., and J. W. Kennedy: "Nuclear and Radiochemistry," Wiley, New York, 1955.

Gamow, G.: "Atomic Energy in Cosmic and Human Life: Fifty Years of Radioactivity," Cambridge, New York, 1946.

——— and C. L. Critchfield: "Theory of Atomic Nucleus and Nuclear Energy Sources," Oxford, New York, 1949.

Glasstone, S.: "Principles of Nuclear Reactor Engineering," Van Nostrand, Princeton, N.J., 1955.

———: "Sourcebook on Atomic Energy," Van Nostrand, Princeton, N.J., 1958.

——— and M. C. Edlund: "The Elements of Nuclear Reactor Theory," Van Nostrand, Princeton, N.J., 1952.

Goodman, C. D. (ed.): "The Science and Engineering of Nuclear Power," vol. I, 2d ed., Addison-Wesley, Reading, Mass., 1952.

———: "The Science and Engineering of Nuclear Power," vol. II, Addison-Wesley, Reading, Mass., 1949.

Green, A. E. S.: "Nuclear Physics," McGraw-Hill, New York, 1955.

Hahn, O.: "New Atoms, Progress and Some Memories," Elsevier, New York, 1950.

Haissinsky, M.: "La Chimie nucleaire et ses applications," Masson, Paris, 1957.

Halliday, D.: "Introductory Nuclear Physics," 2d ed., Wiley, New York, 1955.

"Handbook of Chemistry and Physics" (revised at frequent intervals), Chemical Rubber Publishing Company, Cleveland.

Heisenberg, W.: "Nuclear Physics," Philosophical Library, New York, 1953.

Heitler, W.: "The Quantum Theory of Radiation," 3d ed., Oxford, New York, 1954.

Herzberg, G.: "Atomic Spectra and Atomic Structure," Dover, New York, 1944.

Hume-Rothery, W.: "Electrons, Atoms, Metals, and Alloys," 2d ed., Philosophical Library, New York, 1955.

Huntley, H. E.: "Nuclear Species," St. Martin's, New York, 1954.

Kaplan, I.: "Nuclear Physics," Addison-Wesley, Reading, Mass., 1955.

Kohman, T. P.: Atomic Species Redefined, *Nucleonics*, vol. 1, no. 2, p. 43, October, 1947.

———: The Limits of Beta-stability, *Phys. Rev.*, vol. 73, pp. 16–21, Jan. 1, 1948.

Konopinski, E. J.: Beta-decay, *Revs. Modern Phys.*, vol. 15, pp. 209–245, October, 1943.

Lange, N. A. (compiler): "Handbook of Chemistry" (revised at frequent intervals), McGraw-Hill, New York.

Lapp, R. E., and H. L. Andrews: "Nuclear Radiation Physics," 2d ed., Prentice-Hall, Englewood Cliffs, N.J., 1954.

Lauritsen, T.: Energy Levels of Light Nuclei, Nuclear Science Series Preliminary Report 5, National Research Council, Committee on Nuclear Science, Washington, 1949.

———, W. A. Fowler, and C. C. Lauritsen: Energy Levels of Light Nuclei, *Nucleonics*, vol. 2, no. 4, pp. 18–29, April, 1948.

Mattauch, J.: "Nuclear Physics Tables," Interscience, New York, 1946.

Mayer, M. G.: Radioactivity and Nuclear Theory, *Ann. Rev. Phys. Chem.*, vol. 3, pp. 19–38, 1952.

———: On Closed Shells in Nuclei, *Phys. Rev.*, vol. 74, pp. 235–239, Aug. 1, 1948.

——— and J. H. D. Jensen: "Elementary Theory of Nuclear Shell Structure," Wiley, New York, 1955.

Millikan, R. A.: "Electrons (+ and −), Protons, Neutrons, Mesotrons, and Cosmic Rays," rev. ed., University of Chicago Press, Chicago, 1947.

Milner, C. J.: Model of Nuclear Structure, *Nucleonics*, vol. 4, no. 1, pp. 56–59, January, 1949.

Moon, P. B.: "Artificial Radioactivity," Cambridge, New York, 1949.

Nordheim, L. W.: On Spins, Moments, and Shells in Nuclei, *Phys. Rev.*, vol. 75, pp. 1894–1901, June 15, 1949.

Perlman, I., and J. M. Hollander: Radioactivity and Nuclear Structure, *Ann. Rev. Phys. Chem.*, vol. 5, pp. 119–138, 1954.

Pollard, E.: Measurement of Nuclear Energy Change Values, *Nucleonics*, vol. 2, no. 4, pp. 1–17, April, 1948.

——— and W. L. Davidson: "Applied Nuclear Physics," 2d ed., Wiley, New York, 1951.

Present, R. D.: The Liquid-drop Model for Nuclear Fission, *Nucleonics*, vol. 3, no. 3, pp. 25–31, September, 1948.

Primakoff, H.: Introduction to Meson Theory, *Nucleonics*, vol. 2, no. 1, pp. 2–11, January, 1948.

Purkayastha, B. S.: Fission of Atomic Nuclei. I, Transuranium Elements, *Nucleonics*, vol. 3, no. 5, pp. 2–21, November, 1948; II, vol. 3, no. 6, pp. 2–22, December, 1948.

Rasetti, F.: "Elements of Nuclear Physics," Prentice-Hall, Englewood Cliffs, N.J., 1936.

Richtmyer, F. K., and E. H. Kennard: "Introduction to Modern Physics," 5th ed., McGraw-Hill, New York, 1955.

Rosenfeld, L.: "Nuclear Forces," North Holland, Amsterdam, 1948.

Rossi, B. B.: "High-energy Particles," Prentice-Hall, Englewood Cliffs, N.J., 1952.

Rothman, S. C. (ed.): "Constructive Uses of Atomic Energy," Harper, New York, 1949.

Rutherford, E., J. Chadwick, and C. D. Ellis: "Radiations from Radioactive Substances," Cambridge, New York, 1930.

Seaborg, G. T.: Artificial Radioactivity, *Chem. Revs.*, vol. 27, pp. 199–282, 1940.

Segrè, E. (ed.): "Experimental Nuclear Physics," vols. I and II, Wiley, New York, 1953.

Semat, H.: "Introduction to Atomic Physics," 3d ed., Rinehart, New York, 1955.

Shankland, R. S.: "Atomic and Nuclear Physics," Macmillan, New York, 1955.

Slater, J. C.: "Modern Physics," McGraw-Hill, New York, 1955.

Smyth, H. de W.: "Atomic Energy for Military Purposes: The Official Report on the Development of the Atomic Bomb under the Auspices of the U.S. Government, 1940–1945," Princeton University Press, Princeton, N.J., 1945.

Sneed, M. C., J. L. Maynard, and R. C. Brasted: "Comprehensive Inorganic Chemistry," vol. I, "Principles of Atomic and Molecular Structure, Theoretical and Applied Nuclear Chemistry, the Actinide Series," Van Nostrand, Princeton, N.J., 1953.

Stephens, W. E. (ed.): "Nuclear Fission and Atomic Energy," Science Press, Lancaster, Pa., 1948.

Stranathan, J. D.: "The 'Particles' of Modern Physics," McGraw-Hill–Blakiston, New York, 1942.

Strong, J., et al.: "Procedures in Experimental Physics," Prentice-Hall, Englewood Cliffs, N.J., 1938.

Sullivan, W. H: "Trilinear Chart of Nuclear Species," 2d ed., Wiley, New York, 1956.

Tolansky, S.: "Introduction to Atomic Physics," 4th ed., Longmans, London, 1956.

Turkevich, A.: Radioactivity and Nuclear Theory, *Ann. Rev. Phys. Chem.*, vol. 4, pp. 119–142, 1953.

Weizsäcker, C. F. von: "Die Atomkerne, Grundlagen und Anwendungen ihrer Theorie," Akademische Verlagsgesellschaft, Leipzig, 1937 (reprinted by Edwards, Ann Arbor, Mich., 1944).

Whitehouse, W. J., and J. L. Putman: "Radioactive Isotopes," Oxford, New York, 1953.

2

The Detection of Radiation

2-1. Radiation Detectors

Ion-collection Detectors. *Ion-collection Phenomena.* Since the interaction of the various types of radiation with matter is accompanied by ionization, the obvious method of detecting the radiation is by collecting the ions produced. Since the fundamentals of the behavior of electrons in electrical circuits have been so well developed, it is a relatively simple matter to design a device which can collect the ions formed by the radiation. The essential features of such a device are an electrode system, in which the ions may be collected, and a circuit through which the current passes when ions are attracted to the charged electrodes. Although plate electrode systems can be used, other geometrical arrangements are possible, and more frequently a cylindrical geometry is utilized. This incorporates a wire, or electrode, in the center of a cylinder, which acts as the other electrode and is separated from the central wire, or electrode, by an efficient insulator. These electrodes are connected through a suitable resistance which permits a potential difference to be applied to the electrodes, as shown in Fig. 2-1. The resistance may be one which is inserted into the circuit, or it may be only the parts of the circuit themselves (i.e., the tubes and wiring).

Although ionization is produced when radiation passes through any kind of matter, one of the most suitable mediums from which the ions can be collected is a gas. If a cylinder containing a central electrode, as described above, is filled with a gas, and a source of radiation is brought into the vicinity so that the radiation passes through the gas and causes ionization in it, these ions are attracted to the electrodes. If, for example, the center wire is charged positively with respect to the outer electrode, any negative ions formed will migrate to the center electrode and the positive ions will migrate to the wall. Since the negative ions are usually electrons, they will cause a charge to be collected on the center wire as they arrive.

Under suitable conditions, a current may pass from the center wire through the external circuit to the other electrode. Consequently, the basic problem of the detection of radiation resolves itself into one of the detection and measurement of small currents arising from the ion collection in the detector system.

There are two problems which must be considered in the study of the detection of ionizing radiation. These are the problem as to the behavior of the ion in the tube as a function of the collection voltage, and the

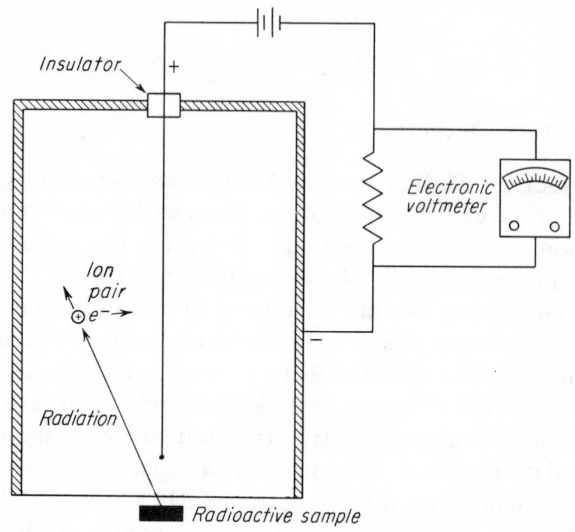

FIG. 2-1. Schematic diagram of generalized ion-collection device.

problem involved in the detection of very small currents in the external system of the instrument.

Electrode Voltage. To study this problem, one may determine the amount of charge which is collected on an electrode as a function of the potential across the electrode system. For a given geometrical arrangement of the electrodes, the charge collected after the passage of the particles may vary because of the different numbers of ions formed by the particles as they traverse the gas in the collecting system. This may be the result of either differing specific ionization for the two radiations or a difference in the path length of the particle in the sensitive volume of the detector.

If a curve is plotted showing the amount of charge collected on the electrode as a function of voltage, it will appear as in Fig. 2-2. The passage of an alpha particle through the detector is shown in the upper curve, and the passage of a beta particle through it is shown in the lower curve. It is found that at very small voltages only a fraction of the number of ions formed in the detector may be collected because the weak electrostatic field allows some of the ions to recombine before they are collected. As the voltage increases, the field increases proportionately and all the ions produced inside the detector are collected. This

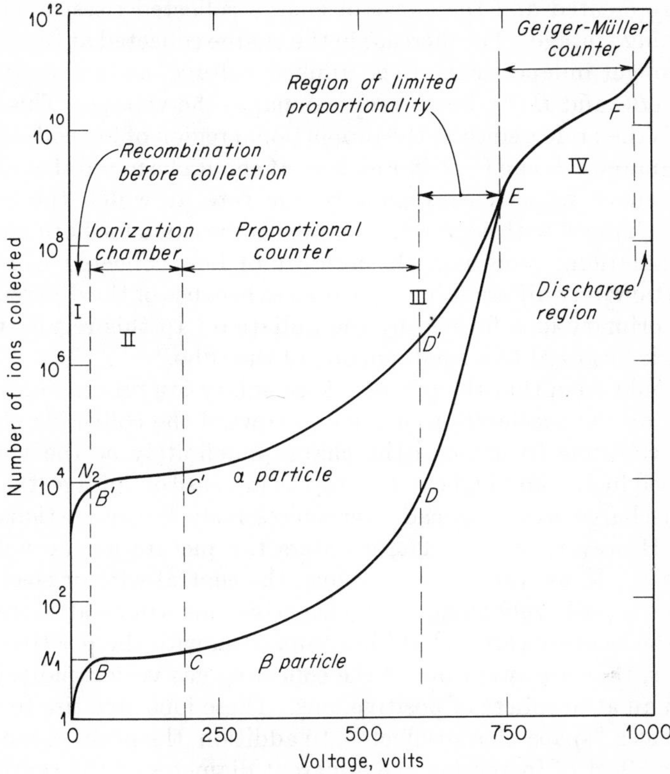

FIG. 2-2. Curves of pulse height vs. applied voltage to illustrate ionization, proportional, and Geiger-Müller regions of operation. (*Adapted from C. G. Montgomery and D. D. Montgomery, J. Franklin Inst., vol.* 231, *p.* 447, 1941.)

is shown by a leveling off of both curves so that both represent the collection of a constant charge as the voltage is increased for several hundred volts. These plateaus are called "saturation" values, or the region of saturation voltage, and are indicated by the segments BC for the beta and $B'C'$ for the alpha radiation.

In each case, the saturation plateau continues as the voltage is increased, as long as all the so-called "primary" ions are being collected. A voltage is then reached at which the primary ions are accelerated in the field of the center electrode to such a point that they may produce secondary ionization by their interaction with other gas molecules. The result is that more ions reach the collecting electrode than were formed in the original collisions and the amount of charge collected increases over the saturation value. This process is called gas amplification.

If the voltage is increased above this point, more and more secondary ions are created and the curve of charge collected rises rapidly with increasing voltage. The increase in the charge collected at the electrode is no longer independent of the applied voltage, as in the saturation region (BC and $B'C'$), but is proportional to the voltage. This voltage range is then referred to as the proportional region of ion collection and is designated CD and $C'D'$ in Fig. 2-2. It should be noted that the slope of the curve which corresponds to the rate at which the collected charge changes with increasing voltage is the same for both alpha and beta radiation. However, the number of ions collected will remain proportionately different in the two cases because of the different number of primary ions formed by the radiation. In this region, the discharge is localized to a small portion of the tube.

It would seem that the process of secondary-ion production which is caused by the acceleration of the ions toward the collecting electrode would continue to increase the charge indefinitely as the voltage is increased higher and higher. During the increase of voltage, the ionization discharge would spread over successively larger portions of the tube. However, another factor enters the picture as the voltage is increased. If, as was assumed above, the central wire or electrode of the tube is positively charged, the negative ions will be attracted to it. Since the electrons are so light in comparison with the positive atomic residues, they are swept out of the collecting gas very rapidly, leaving behind an atmosphere of positive ions. These ions give rise to what is known as a "space-charge effect." In addition, the positive-ion sheath has the effect of increasing the apparent diameter of the central electrode which reduces the electrostatic field intensity in the tube. The result is that an upper limit of voltage is reached at which these factors effectively limit the number of ions which may be collected at the positive electrode. This means that the multiplication of secondary ionization cannot continue to increase indefinitely with increasing voltage.

This region in which there is not a strict proportionality between the voltage and the amount of charge collected is called the limited proportional region and is shown as the segment DE and $D'E$ in Fig. 2-2. In this region, the slope of the curves for the two types of radiation is not the same because of the limiting value of the amount of charge that can be collected imposed by the particular characteristics of the tube in use.

If the voltage is increased still further, one finds that the charge collected is not at all dependent on the type of radiation or the number of primary ions initially formed, but only on the voltage applied to the electrode. In this region, the field intensity about the center electrode is so high that any ion formed, whether of primary or secondary origin, can be accelerated enough to cause additional ionization in the gas. A chain reaction is thus instituted, and an "avalanche" of ions is created in the tube. In principle, any particle giving rise to a single ion pair in a detector operating above this particular voltage would be sufficient to cause the collection of the same amount of charge at the electrode as a particle giving rise to many thousands of ion pairs initially. The actual charge collected from either type of radiation does increase slowly as the voltage is further increased, but its amount does not depend on the type of radiation or the energy of the particle which causes the initial ionization. This region was first investigated by Geiger and has since been called the "Geiger region" of ion collection. This is represented by the segment EF in Fig. 2-2.

If the voltage on the collecting electrode is further increased, a limit is reached at which the tube discharges in a "continuous" manner. (With many types of Geiger tubes, permitting the tube to discharge in such a way damages it. This should be guarded against, but if it happens inadvertently, the voltage should be immediately lowered to a safe value.)

Instrument Types. There are three standard types of detectors based on this collection system. Detectors which operate in the ionization region in which the voltage is insufficient to cause gas amplification are known as ionization chambers. The most common of these are gold-leaf and gold-plated quartz-fiber electroscopes. The latter have an ocular system for accurately observing the fiber position. Typical laboratory instruments of this type are the Landsverk and the Lauritsen electroscopes and direct-reading pocket dosimeters.

The usual form of these instruments is a hollow cylinder or sphere with a central electrode. It is particularly important that the central electrode be well insulated from the outer case, which acts as the oppositely charged electrode. In many instruments the central electrode is held at ground potential with the outer case at a positive potential of a few hundred volts. The voltage may be supplied either by batteries or, as in the Landsverk electroscope, by a friction charger. This means that the positive ions created in the gas of the chamber move to the center electrode and the electrons move to the outer case. For a typical voltage the electrons might drift at the rate of about 10^5 cm/sec, while the positive ions would move about 100 cm/sec. Since the electronic charge is 1.60×10^{-19} coulomb, the current produced in an ionization chamber might be of the order of 10^{-17} amp. It is not possible for such currents to be measured directly on a galvanometer; so some other current measurement system is employed.

Most ionization chambers permit the radioactive sample to be introduced directly into the sensitive volume of the detectors, either as a flat plate on which the solid sample is mounted or in the form of a gas in which the direct ionization current can be measured. The latter is particularly sensitive for C^{14} and tritium since no absorption of their weak radiation in the solid sample is observed. However, it is also possible to use ion chambers as detectors of external gamma radiation. Gamma-ray chambers of this type are usually filled to higher pressure. A particularly useful filling for this type of chamber is sulfur hexafluoride, which liquefies at a relatively low pressure. This type of chamber is used in gamma logging of oil wells and in reactors.

The primary construction difference between an ionization chamber and a detector operating in either the proportional region or the Geiger region is the larger center electrode in the ion chamber. The smaller wire in the Geiger and proportional counter permits a higher voltage gradient in the vicinity of the wire. Frequently mixtures of gases are employed in order to obtain suitable ion-collection properties and voltages which are within the range of ordinary high-voltage supplies. In principle, a detector of this type may function either as a proportional counter or as a Geiger counter, but in practice the filling-gas and voltage ranges are selected for optimum operation in only one region since a proportional counter must be used with very much greater external amplification. Typical filling gases for proportional counters are methane, carbon dioxide, and a commercial mixture, P-10, which is a mixture of argon and methane.

Since the usual form of these counters is cylindrical with a central electrode, the electrostatic field at a distance d from the center of the chamber is given as

$$E = \frac{V}{d} \ln \frac{r_2}{r_1} \tag{2-1}$$

in which E is the field strength, V is the voltage across the electrode system, r_1 is the radius of the wire, and r_2 is the radius of the cylinder. The central wire is usually made positive with the outer case at ground. The electrons will move to the central wire and the positive ions migrate to the outer envelope. Gas amplifications in proportional counters of the order of 10^3 or 10^4 are reached, the limiting requirement being that the electron must be accelerated sufficiently between collisions to reach a kinetic energy greater than the ionization potential of the gas.

The voltage necessary to operate in the proportional region increases with higher gas pressure and with a higher ionization potential of the gas in the sensitive volume. The operating voltages are between 1,500 and 5,000 volts, but the system usually requires an external amplifier to obtain pulses that can be measured satisfactorily.

Detectors operating in the Geiger region (sometimes referred to as Geiger-Müller or G-M counters) are characterized by having a sufficiently high voltage across the electrodes so that the gas amplification in the detector is of the order of 10^7. Under these conditions the discharge covers the entire length of the central wire and all the output pulses are of the same size or height. Typical operating voltages are in the range of 1,000 to 2,000 volts, although some type of filling mixtures may permit operation between 700 and 1,000 volts. The gas fillings for Geiger counters are usually mixtures of argon and ethanol, helium and isobutane, or neon and an organic halide. Although formerly tubes were operated at a total pressure of the order of 0.1 atm, many detectors are now constructed to operate near atmospheric pressure.

One of the problems inherent in Geiger counting is the fact that the positive ions move so slowly toward the walls of the detector as to cause the tube to be inoperative for a long time between successive pulses. Another related problem is that of the multiple pulses which may occur when electrons are produced by the radiation emitted by the ions as they collect electrons from the walls in becoming neutral atoms again. The electron would trigger the detector again unless some means of stopping the discharge in a short time were used. Some of the early approaches to "quenching" the discharge employed external electronic circuits which lowered the voltage instantaneously during the positive-ion collection period. More recently the standard procedure has been to introduce an organic quenching gas. These polyatomic molecules dissociate in absorbing the deexcitation radiation from the ions. Since the organic molecules are used up in the quenching process, there is a finite lifetime for detectors quenched by this type of additive. A relatively recent development is the use of halogen-quenched tubes in which the halogen recombines after the quenching process. This type of tube thus has an "infinite" life, although it has some disadvantages for certain laboratory uses.

The problems associated with the various types of ion-collection detectors in actual laboratory operations will be considered later. A general discussion of the construction and operation of these devices is given in a number of books and papers including those of Price (1), Jordan (2), Korff (3), Strong (4), and Wilkinson (5). The volume by Price is particularly valuable with respect to all types of radiation detectors.

Scintillation Detectors. *The Scintillation Process.* A type of detector which has come into extensive use during the last few years and which differs in principle from the ion-collection devices is the scintillation counter. This is a modernized version of the spinthariscope, which was one of the first detection instruments used. It is particularly useful for gamma-ray measurement because of its high detection efficiency for gamma rays when certain scintillators are used.

It was pointed out in Chap. 1 that, when gamma radiation interacts with matter, there are three competing possibilities. These processes are the photoelectric, Compton interaction, and pair-production processes.

It will be remembered that in the photoelectric process essentially all the energy of the gamma-ray photon is transferred to the electron which is ejected. Likewise, in the pair-production process the gamma-ray energy goes into the formation of a pair of electrons and imparts kinetic energy to them. In the Compton interaction, on the other hand, only part of the energy of the incident photon is transferred to the electron, since a scattered photon of lower energy is also produced. It is important to note that at least one electron is associated with each interaction.

These electrons, as well as those involved in beta and alpha interactions, lose energy when passing through matter either by ionization or by the excitation of the atoms through which they are passing. Although much of radiation-detection instrumentation employs the ionization-collection principle, there are a number of substances in which the excitation process can be utilized for this detection. Substances which absorb such excitation energy and reemit the energy in the form of light photons are called phosphors. One of the earliest known was ZnS, which scintillates on being irradiated with alpha rays and which served as the basis for the spinthariscope mentioned above. There are a number of phosphors which can be excited and which emit a certain fraction of the total energy absorbed as blue visible light. This light wavelength corresponds to about 3 ev.

The fundamental basis of this type of measurement is that the number of photons produced is proportional to the energy of the electron if one assumes that all the electronic energy is dissipated within the phosphor. This assumption is reasonable since an electron may be absorbed in a cubic millimeter of common phosphor. For example, if the electron has 1 Mev kinetic energy after the gamma-ray interaction and if we assume that 5 per cent of this energy is transferred to visible light, and if we also assume that the excitation process takes 10 ev, this would mean the occurrence of 100,000 excitation processes, which would give rise to about 5,000 photons. It is the detection of these photons which gives the measured signal. Although it is possible to detect the flash of light from such a number of photons by visual means, this method of detection was not highly developed until the perfection of the photomultiplier tube, which could convert the light flashes to electrons and amplify the resulting pulse.

Although the light which is observed is not dependent on the origin of the electron in the initial interaction process, it is apparent that a different response is found for photoelectrons and Compton electrons in relation to the initial gamma-ray energy. The total energy of the process is the same, but the amount of energy transferred to the phosphor differs in the two cases if the Compton scattered photon is not absorbed in the phosphor. This is often the case since the volume of the phosphor is usually relatively small compared with the interaction probability of the photons. Consequently, the number of photons observed from a gamma-ray source is dependent on the overall size or volume of the phosphor. Thus, the total amount of light emitted is proportional to the absorbed energy and not to the incident energy. Quite extensive treatment of the theory of the scintillation process is given by Birks (6), Swank (7), Hardwick and McMillan (8), and Jordan and Bell (9).

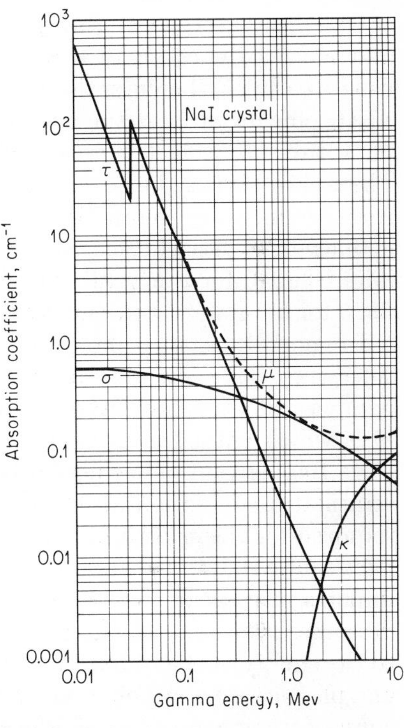

FIG. 2-3. Gamma absorption coefficients for sodium iodide vs. gamma-ray energy. (*From W. H. Jordan, Ann. Rev. Nuclear Sci., vol.* 1, *p.* 221, 1951.)

Types of Scintillation Phosphors. The two general types of phosphors are solids, which may be either inorganic or organic, and liquids. The common solid phosphors are sodium iodide with a slight trace of Tl as an excitant, anthracene, stilbene, and "loaded" plastic. Each of these has special advantages for certain types of problems, but since the greatest need has been for high-efficiency gamma-ray detection, much of the contemporary work is centered around NaI(Tl) crystals. It is particularly valuable because of its high density (3.67 g/cm^3) and its high atomic number (53 for iodine). Typical values for the absorption coefficients for this type of crystal are given in Fig. 2-3. The primary advantage of the inorganic crystals is their higher density, which is mainly responsible for the higher stopping power and thus the greater counting efficiency for gamma rays. However, some of the heavy phosphors, such as ZnS, are not transparent to their own emission and thus are not practical for gamma-ray detection since they cannot be used in thick layers. The alkali halides and particularly NaI are characterized by the high density, high light output, transparency, and suitable index of refraction.

One disadvantage of NaI(Tl) crystals is that they are hygroscopic and must be encased in a watertight envelope. Consequently, it is usual to "can" the crystals in aluminum with a thin layer of MgO or Al_2O_3 powder around the crystal (except at the face adjacent to the phototube) to reflect the escaping light back toward the phototube. These crystals may be purchased in either the canned or uncanned form from a number of manufacturers either as solid crystals or with holes in one face to permit their use as a "well"-type detector. Typical prices might be $50 for a crystal 1 in. in diameter, $300 for a 2-in. crystal, $800 for a 3-in. crystal, and $2,000 for a 5-in. cylinder.

In general, organic phosphors are used for beta radiation detection since they have low atomic numbers. They have lower efficiency for gamma radiation but have 100 per cent efficiency for measuring beta rays which enter the crystal. Since Geiger-Müller detectors likewise have 100 per cent efficiency for beta radiation, little is gained by using scintillation detection for them since the light covering which may be required for the crystal may of necessity have more absorption for the particulate radiation than the window of a G-M detector. However, an important use can be made of the scintillation detector for energy determination since the light produced in the phosphor is proportional to the energy of the radiation. Specially shaped crystals of anthracene and plastics are now being used rather extensively for beta-ray spectroscopy of weak sources, since the sample can be placed in a high solid angle with respect to the detector.

One of the most rapidly developing areas in applied nuclear science is that of the use of liquid-scintillation systems. These systems are of particular interest in beta-ray detection since the detector is a 4π solid-angle detector and does not exhibit radiation loss in the sample itself. The sample to be measured is dissolved in a liquid-scintillator solution which is then viewed by a photomultiplier tube.

There are a number of possible combinations of scintillator phosphors and solvents, but typical solutes are *p*-terphenyl and diphenyloxazole dissolved in benzene, toluene, or xylenes, although these solvents must sometimes be mixed with alcohol or dioxane to increase their water solubility. Since some of these materials do not phosphoresce in the visible region, it is sometimes necessary to add compounds which can absorb the excitation energy and reemit it at a wavelength which can be detected by the phototube. The process may be considered as a chain of events in which the radiation excites the solvent molecules, which transfer the excitation energy to the scintillator molecules (present in a concentration of about 0.5 per cent). The energy is then transferred to the "shifter" molecule (at a concentration of about 0.001 per cent), which then emits the light. This light is made to match the response curve of the photomultiplier, which may be sensitive in the region between 3,000 and 7,000 angstroms. An interesting variation on the liquid-scintillation detector is a plastic solution in which the solvent for the scintillator is a solid. One such detector is a solution of *p*-terphenyl in polystyrene. These systems are used mostly as thin wafers for beta detection, although they can be used for large-volume detectors since they are considerably cheaper than large crystals of NaI(Tl) and can be machined to any shape. Several groups are using plastic detectors up to 16 in. in diameter for anticoincidence radiation shields.

Although liquid-scintillation-detector systems are widely used, particularly for C^{14} and tritium counting, many of the pulses from such low-energy beta radiation are very small and may be in the range of the random electrical impulses in the photomultiplier tube. It is frequently desirable to place the detector system in a deep-freeze unit to minimize the random pulses in the circuit. Commercial liquid-scintillation systems are available that use a deep-freeze unit, but measurements can be made at room temperature using conventional laboratory glassware which may then be made lighttight with masking tape. One large laboratory uses a refrigeration unit, but instead of placing the entire sample inside, the cooling fluid is pumped through a jacket surrounding the phototube. Such a system is quite convenient and has the advantage of the refrigerating unit. A description of a typical laboratory procedure is given in Sec. 2.3.

One other factor which is of importance in all scintillation detectors is the decay period of the light emitted. It is obvious that, for very fast counting, this factor must be considered although for routine laboratory work the electronic circuitry is usually the controlling factor in determining the maximum counting rate. Table 2-1 shows a summary of scintillation phosphors as published in the literature of the Harshaw Chemical Company. Additional material of interest on the characteristics of various scintillators is found in papers by Swank (10), Sangster and Irvine (11), and Hayes, Ott, and Kerr (12).

The Photomultiplier Tube. The scintillator itself is only a portion of the scintillation detector since it is necessary to obtain an electronic signal from the phosphor. Although the first use of the photomultiplier tube for this purpose was by Blau and Dreyfus (13) in 1945, the recent rapid development of these tubes has been in large part responsible for the success of the scintillation technique. The photomultiplier tube as shown in Fig. 2-4 is an envelope containing a material used as a photocathode. The photocathode is frequently made from silver-magnesium and cesium-antimony alloys. One manufacturer claims that an

TABLE 2-1

PHYSICAL CONSTANTS OF SELECTED SCINTILLATION PHOSPHORS

Type	Density	Refractive index	Pulse height (% anthracene)	Decay përiod (mean lifė), sec	Wave-length of maximum emission, A	Principal applications
Plastic	1.04	1.581	40–70	4.0×10^{-9}	4,300	Gamma, alpha, beta, fast *n*
Liquid	0.88	1.504	78	2.8×10^{-9}	3,920	Alpha, beta (internal counting, low temperature)
Gel	0.88	1.496	50	2.6×10^{-9}	4,300	Alpha, beta (internal counting)
Pb (5%) loaded liquid	0.93	1.505	25	1.1×10^{-9}	4,300	Gamma
Anthracene	1.25		100	3.2×10^{-8}	4,470	Gamma, alpha, beta, fast *n*
Stilbene	1.16	1.626	60	4.0×10^{-9}	4,100	Gamma, alpha, beta, fast *n*
NaI(Tl)	3.67	1.775	230	0.25×10^{-6}	4,130	Gamma
ZnS(Ag)	4.09	2.356	300	2×10^{-7}	4,500	Alpha, beta

efficiency of 20 per cent in photoelectron production may be reached with a combination of several elements. The principal suppliers of these tubes are RCA and Du Mont in the United States and EMI in England. The cost ranges from \$50 to \$500 for commercially available tubes.

One primary requirement for the photocathode is that it must be in an envelope which transmits the ultraviolet or visible radiation from the phosphor. The phototube is frequently placed adjacent to the phosphor, but occasionally a "light piper" of Lucite or other transparent plastic is used to transmit the light from the phosphor to the phototube. When the light impinges on the photocathode, a photoelectron of 1 to 2 ev energy is ejected with approximately 5 to 10 per cent efficiency. That is, a photoelectron is ejected from the photocathode for every 10 to 20 incident photons. These photoelectric emissions are in competition with thermionic emissions, which give rise to the background impulses in the tube, or the tube "noise." It is to minimize the thermionic emission that cooling of the tube is helpful when high sensitivity is desired.

After the emission of the photoelectrons, it is necessary to amplify the photoelectric current. This is done by focusing the photoelectrons on the first of a series of dynodes. These are electrodes which are so arranged that the electrons from each preceding stage are focused on the next. Each dynode in the series is at a potential (of the order of 100 volts in a typical case) higher than that of the preceding dynode; this causes the production of secondary electrons at the next dynode surface. Since the envelope is evacuated, there is no absorption of electrons and a large amplification factor is attained. If one assumed, for example, that the voltage across each dynode in the series is sufficient to cause the appearance of two secondary electrons for each primary electron per stage and if one also assumed 100 per cent efficiency in the focusing at each stage, a tube with 10 dynodes would have an over-all amplification factor of 1,024. Commercial tubes have 6 to 14 dynodes with secondary emission ranging from 3 to 5 electrons per stage.

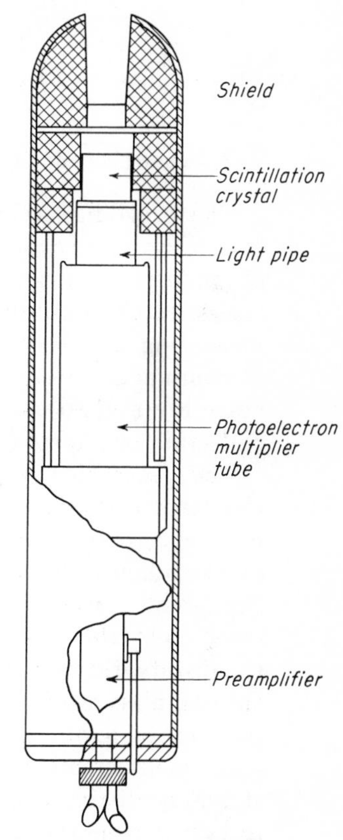

FIG. 2-4. Schematic diagram of probe type of scintillation detector. (*Courtesy Nuclear Chicago Co.*)

It is apparent from the foregoing discussion that the scintillation counter is a proportional device and has the advantages and limitations of such counters. It is difficult to obtain an over-all efficiency figure for these detectors because of the wide variation in the efficiencies observed at the various steps in the process, ranging from the initial interaction of the radiation to the final signal output from the phototube.

Since the initial interaction probability varies with the incident photon energy, the values shown in Table 2-2 may be considered typical for the over-all electron multiplication in a detector. The output of the phototube is passed through conventional amplifiers and scalers for measurement. A number of surveys of the scintillation field are available, with papers by Morton (14, 15) and the *Nucleonics* survey (16) being suggested as starting points for further reading.

TABLE 2-2

ELECTRON MULTIPLICATION IN TYPICAL SCINTILLATOR DETECTOR

For 1 photon absorbed in crystal at given energy, Mev	*Number of electrons produced at tube output*
1	250,000
2	500,000
3	750,000

2-2. Associated Electronic Equipment

The foregoing section surveyed the principle of operation of the radiation detectors in common use. Ambiguity sometimes arises over the use of the term "counter." In some laboratories, the counter refers only to the detector or counter tube. In others, the detector and associated measuring and recording equipment are referred to as the counter. Recommended usage is to use the term counter to refer to the entire assembly and to use the term detector or counter tube for the ion-collection or phosphor-photomultiplier system.

The electronic equipment which is used to permit the registration of the detector signal will vary, of course, with the type of instrument in use and the experimental data required. In general, there are two types of instrumentation necessary depending on the nature of the signal from the detector. If it is desired to determine the number of pulses which are received by the detector in a given time (corresponding to a measure of the disintegration rate of the sample), a pulse counter may be used. If the cumulative effect of the radiation is the quantity desired, it is often more useful to obtain a measure of the total ionization current. Such an instrument could be called an integrating instrument, although this should be distinguished from a device which sums the number of pulses in a given time and which could be called a pulse-integrating device. In this section a brief description of the salient features of the various components which make up these two types of instruments will be given, and in the next section various typical combinations of these into practical laboratory measuring systems will be described.

Pulse Counters. The precise difference between pulse counters and integrating instruments involves a distinction between their resolving times (Sec. 2-3), but for the present purpose it is assumed that the quantity desired is the number of pulses per unit time. A block diagram of a pulse counter is given in Fig. 2-5. The detector may be of any of the types described in Sec. 2-1.

High-voltage Supplies (High-tension Sets). One unit which all electronic radiation detectors require is a high-voltage source. For some of the electroscopes this may be a 90-volt battery or a friction-charging mechanism, but most instruments require an electronic voltage source of some type. Most of these devices consist of a high-voltage transformer, rectifier, and one or more voltage-regulation tubes for control. High-voltage supplies may be designed to furnish 500 to 5,000 volts depending on their intended use. In general, it is better to have voltage supplies of 2,500 volts for use with Geiger-Müller counters, although many tubes do not require this. Since a number of commercial tubes

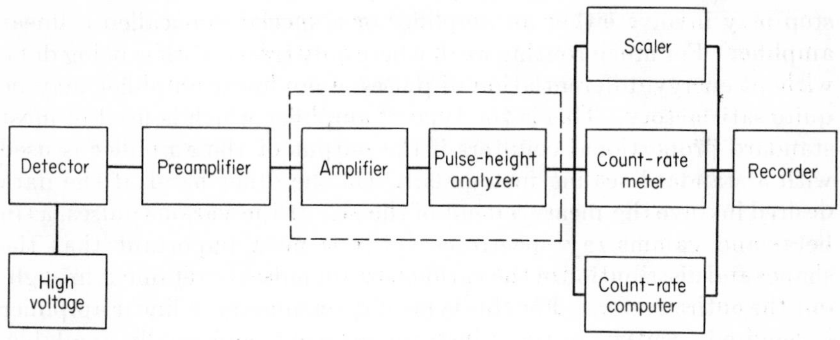

FIG. 2-5. Schematic diagram of pulse counter.

may operate above 1,500 volts, the higher-voltage source is recommended when purchasing basic instrumentation. Proportional counters are usually equipped with 5,000-volt supplies, which is adequate for most operations. Radio-frequency (r-f) supplies are not often used except for portable or field instruments, which do not require high precision. Most commercial high-voltage units in the United States will operate satisfactorily on line voltages between 90 and 135 volts, the output voltage being regulated to within 0.01 per cent. Much better regulation is required for proportional counters and scintillation counters than for Geiger-Müller instruments.

Preamplifiers, Amplifiers, and Linear Amplifiers. Although G-M counters may produce a sufficiently large pulse of electrons to be accepted by a data-registration unit, the other types of ion-collection and scintillation systems do not. For these instruments it is necessary to amplify the pulse in one or more steps. If the pulse put out by the detector is quite small (of the order of a few millivolts), the high impedance of the detector usually makes it necessary to mount a preamplifier near the detector, since the weak pulse may be lost in the cable connecting the detector to the following part of the instrument. Another factor which is sometimes important is the "shape" of the pulse, i.e., the change in the number of electrons in motion in the circuit with time. If the characteristic of the circuits to be used with the detector does not correspond to the shape of the pulse in the circuit, it is sometimes necessary to use the preamplification stage as a "pulse-shaping" step rather than as an amplification step. This stage may use a "cathode follower," which matches the signal to the impedance of the conducting cable. Proportional counters and scintillation counters commonly make use of a preamplifier and cathode-follower combination which may have an amplification factor of 20 to 30.

In many circuits another amplification step is also necessary. This step may involve either an amplifier or a special unit called a linear amplifier. For much routine work where only tracer work is being done without energy differentiation of pulses, a nonlinear amplifier may be quite satisfactory. This is the type of amplifier which is used in most standard proportional counters if the output of the amplifier is used with a standard scaling instrument. On the other hand, if the data desired involve the measurement of the size of the various pulses, as in beta- and gamma-ray spectrometry, it is most important that the shapes and distribution of the various sizes of pulses be retained throughout the entire system. For this type of spectrometry, a linear amplifier is required. Several of these instruments are commercially available, but the two types developed by the Oak Ridge National Laboratory and commonly referred to as an A-1 or a DD amplifier are quite satisfactory.*

Integral Pulse-height Selectors (*Discriminators*). Since any electrical system will have small random noise signals, it is apparent that the differentiation between the true pulses and the random noise pulses is necessary in data-registering devices. These pulses attain some maximum pulse amplitude which corresponds to the largest electron current occurring within the lifetime of the pulse. This maximum amplitude of the pulse is generally referred to as the pulse height. A pulse-height selector is an electronic circuit which blocks or discards all pulses below some set amplitude. Such circuits are a part of all pulse-registering devices and allow one to register true pulses and reject noise pulses. The pulse amplitude required to pass through the pulse-height selector is the "input sensitivity" of the circuit.

In any type of proportional counting it is frequently necessary to know the number of pulses exceeding some variable setting of the pulse-height selector (PHS), i.e., the number of pulses exceeding several

* Commercial instruments built according to these specifications refer to National Laboratory prints and specifications ORNL-Q1593 for the DD-2 amplifier and ORNL-1326 for the A-1-D amplifier.

selected settings of the PHS. Frequently this is possible by maintaining a fixed setting of the PHS and varying the detector voltage so that the entire pulse-height spectrum is expanded or contracted. A more desirable way is to have an accurate control (a precision variable resistor) on the PHS which allows a variation of the input sensitivity. These discriminators are frequently calibrated in volts although, in general, there is only a constant ratio between the dial reading and the corresponding pulse height in volts.

Differential Pulse-height Selectors (Analyzers). Successive subtractions of the integral pulse-height spectrum as determined from a complete series of discriminator settings would yield the differential pulse-height spectrum. A less tedious method of obtaining such a

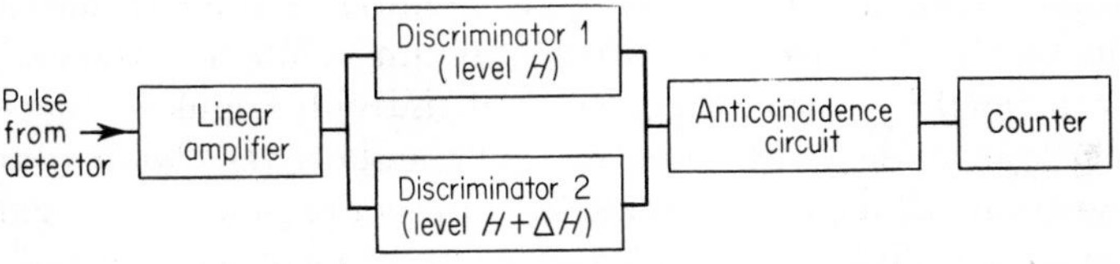

FIG. 2-6. Block diagram of a differential pulse-height analyzer. [*From Price* (1).]

differential spectrum is the inclusion of a differential pulse-height selector (analyzer) in the circuit. An analyzer is composed of two discriminators and one "anticoincidence" circuit, as shown by the block diagram of Fig. 2-6. Discriminator 1 is set to accept smaller pulses. In this circuit any pulse too small to pass discriminator 1 will then be too small to pass discriminator 2, so that such a pulse gives no output to the anticoincidence circuit and thus no output from the analyzer.

On the other hand, a pulse large enough to pass either discriminator 1 or discriminator 2 will give a pulse from each to the anticoincidence circuit. The anticoincidence circuit is designed so that, when two pulses arrive simultaneously, both are blocked and no output signal is registered. Those pulses large enough to pass discriminator 1 but not large enough to pass discriminator 2 will allow one pulse to pass the anticoincidence circuit. This single pulse is also passed on by the anticoincidence circuit. The effect of the analyzer is that only pulses occurring within some selected interval of pulse heights are allowed to pass on to the data-registering device. The voltage separation of the two discriminators is known as the "window," or "bin," width.

Instruments of this type allow the determination of the pulse-height spectrum, i.e., the number of pulses occurring within each pulse-height increment. Each pair of single discriminators and the associated anticoincidence circuit operates as a single channel analyzer. More complex instruments are capable of simultaneously recording the number of pulses occurring in 20, 256, or even several thousand channels. Any one pulse, of course, can fall in only one channel, but the totals found in some interval of time indicate the spectrum of pulses which occurred. Some of these instruments resolve pulses as close as 1½ to 3 μsec. The study of short-lived isotopes is greatly simplified and extended by the use of multichannel analyzers. A comprehensive description or survey of pulse-height analyzers is beyond the scope of this book, but papers by Robinson (17), Van Rennes (18), and Higinbotham (19) will serve as a starting point for those interested in the details of these devices.

Data Registration. The data from the detector system and its associated equipment are most frequently presented on a scaler, although various types of counting-rate computing instruments may be used. The object of each of these devices is to indicate the number of pulses put out by the detector system per unit time. Much of the early work was performed by attempting to count individual pulses, but a major advance was made by Higinbotham, Gallagher, and Sands (20) with a scaling circuit which could divide the number of pulses recorded by the register by a scaling factor such as 8, 64, or some other power of 2. This circuit is known as a "flip-flop" circuit which uses electronic tubes in either an "on" or an "off" position. This has been found to be an extremely stable circuit and has been the basis of most of the scalers developed up to the present time. These scalers have the disadvantage of the power of 2 for the scaling factor, since the numbers must be multiplied by a nondecimal factor. A table containing multiples of 64 and 256 is given in the Appendix. Binary scalers are preferred by many investigators because of their reliability, the ease of determining the faulty component when trouble develops, and the lower maintenance required.

From the standpoint of the technician or other person making the readings from a scaler, it is obvious that there is great advantage in instruments utilizing a decimal scaling factor. In the past, most "decade" scalers have made use of a binary circuit but have attempted to reset the mechanism after 10 pulses have been received. This may lead to considerable maintenance difficulty by requiring additional electronics components to reset the circuit. Typical difficulties with these scalers are skipping, or repeating, counts, in addition to the problem of determining just which component is malfunctioning.

Somewhat newer developments in decade scaling systems use glow transfer tubes or beam-switching tubes. These are true decade scaling devices and are characterized by having 10 stable positions. The beam-switching, or magnetron, tubes are faster but have been somewhat more expensive. Glow transfer tubes are slower but are satisfactory for routine counting with Geiger-Müller detectors. Some manufacturers have combined a good "decade strip" using a modified binary circuit for the initial scaling factor with glow transfer tubes for higher scaling factors.

Since the information desired from most types of radiation-detection equipment is the counting rate, one of the early developments was that of a direct-counting rate meter. This instrument electronically determines the average rate at which pulses are generated by the detector. In these instruments it is important that the size of the pulse be made uniform. The plate current in the final tube is read directly on a meter. Since the fluctuations may be high in such a meter, it is a usual practice to place a resistor and capacitor in the circuit to smooth out the variations. Since time must be allowed for the capacitor to become charged, there is a delay in the response of a rate meter. Commercial instruments usually have a switch with which to select various "time constants." The greater fluctuation is observed with a short time constant. The paper by Bousquet (21) gives interesting comparisons between counting-rate meters and scalers. A discussion of the statistical problems associated with their use is included in Chap. 3.

Several types of instruments are available which calculate the counting rate in a somewhat different fashion from a true counting-rate meter. One of these employs a clock-driven computer, and another permits a capacitor to charge for a given length of time, e.g., 100 sec, and indicates the number of pulses received in the time interval. These instruments are usually calibrated directly in counting rate.

For qualitative measurements it is frequently desirable to have an audio system with a speaker which may indicate the impulses by a popping sound. These devices are frequently found in survey instruments where it is not practical to watch the meter constantly. An interesting deviation on an audio system has been described by Harris, Bell, and Francis (22). This makes use of a frequency variation in the sound rather than the actual rate of the "popping." In this device, the pitch of the sound rises with an increase in counting rate. It is probable that this will find extensive use in instruments used for radiation scanning purposes.

One other type of data registration might be mentioned. This is the direct display of the pulse rate or size on an oscilloscope. This is frequently done for maintenance or trouble-shooting purposes, but there are interesting examples of using the oscilloscope as a registration system. Usually the information is displayed on the screen visually, but various methods have been developed to make records of the oscilloscope trace by photographic means or by activating a photoelectric recording device.

Accessory Instrumentation. A number of types of accessories may be used in conjunction with the apparatus described above. Since it is frequently desirable to make a permanent record of the results of an experiment, it is frequently very useful to make a recording of the data. This is not easy with scalers, but it is usually quite simple to make a recording of the data from a counting-rate meter using a strip-chart recorder. Two types are in common use. One is a direct recording of the data as exemplified by the Esterline-Angus recorder. The other utilizes a potentiometer either as a direct-reading or as a null-point recorder. The Brown recorder is a common example of this type.

A modification of this type of recorder which can be used with a pulse counter of any type is the pulse scanner, which has found considerable use in medical practice when it is desirable to determine relative concentrations, e.g., in the scanning of a thyroid uptake pattern or the localization of a brain tumor. These are usually devices which make an imprint on a chart by mechanical or electrical means when a certain number of counts have been accumulated. The density of the imprints permits a direct visualization of the concentration of the radioactive material in the system.

Another useful addition to conventional laboratory apparatus used for industrial problems is that of a feedback control. Recent estimates, for example, have given an indication of very high industrial savings using various types of gauges in industrial factory process control. These are essentially detection instruments which not only give information about the process as a function of the radiation intensity measured but are also equipped with feedback control circuits. When the radiation intensity varies, an appropriate compensation is automatically signaled to the controls of the machinery. An example of this is the cigarette-density gauge, which automatically controls the density of the cigarette as measured by the attenuation of a beam of radiation.

Another somewhat different type of accessory instrumentation is represented by coincidence and anticoincidence circuits. These are auxiliary in the sense that they are not routinely used by laboratory investigators using isotopes as tracers. They are coming into much more extensive use as various types of analyzers are becoming available. These circuits may utilize one of two designs. One such circuit operates on the basis that, if all of a group of electronic tubes sharing a common plate resistance are simultaneously turned off, the voltage at the plates rises to the voltage of the supply, whereas if even one is still on, the plate voltage stays quite low. Events happening in coincidence in two or more counters produce this large voltage change. The other common circuit is based on the fact that, if two pulses are superimposed, the total voltage can reach only double that of each one when exact coincidence occurs. Technical descriptions of these circuits are given by Elmore and Sands (23). These circuits have extensive use in spectrometry and in other specialized areas in nuclear science. A typical example of their use is given by Mandeville and Scherb (24).

Integrating Measurement Devices. The foregoing discussion has to do with pulse counters. It is sometimes desirable to employ instruments which measure the cumulative effect of ionization. These are characterized by the use of collection voltages in the saturation or ionization region, as shown in Fig. 2-2. Although these instruments may give a measure of the total amount of charge collected, this quantity is not often the information required. Rather, the rate of radiation emission is wanted which is usually proportional to the rate of charge collection or the rate of ion collection.

In order to determine the rate at which ions are collected by a given electrode system, one of two general methods is used. In the first method, the actual rate of the charging or discharging of an electrical capacitance is measured. This may be done simply, as in the case of the discharge of a gold-leaf or quartz-fiber electroscope, or, more elegantly, by the actual use of a capacitor in an electrical circuit. In this method, the rate of drift of the leaf or of a needle of an electrometer is used as a measure of the rate of charge collection and is thus a measure of the rate at which the radiation is affecting the detector. A galvanometer is not used directly since it cannot usually detect a current corresponding to less than about 10^{-9} amp, whereas the current generated by the detection of a beta particle may be as low as 10^{-17} amp.

The second general method of current measurement involves the use of the well-known Ohm's law. (All current measurements utilize this law, but some are not directly evident.) This law is usually expressed in the following form:

$$V = IR \tag{2-2}$$

in which V is the voltage produced by a current I passing through a resistance R.

In this method of ionization-current measurement, the current from the detector is passed through a resistor and the corresponding voltage drop across the resistor is measured. The deflection of the voltmeter is then proportional to the amount of ionization being collected by the detector electrode. This voltage would vary if the rate at which the radiation passed through the detector changed and would also vary with different types of radiations as a result of their different specific ionizations in the detector tube.

It is easily seen that the rate-of-drift method measures the time required to collect a given amount of charge. The potentiometer or

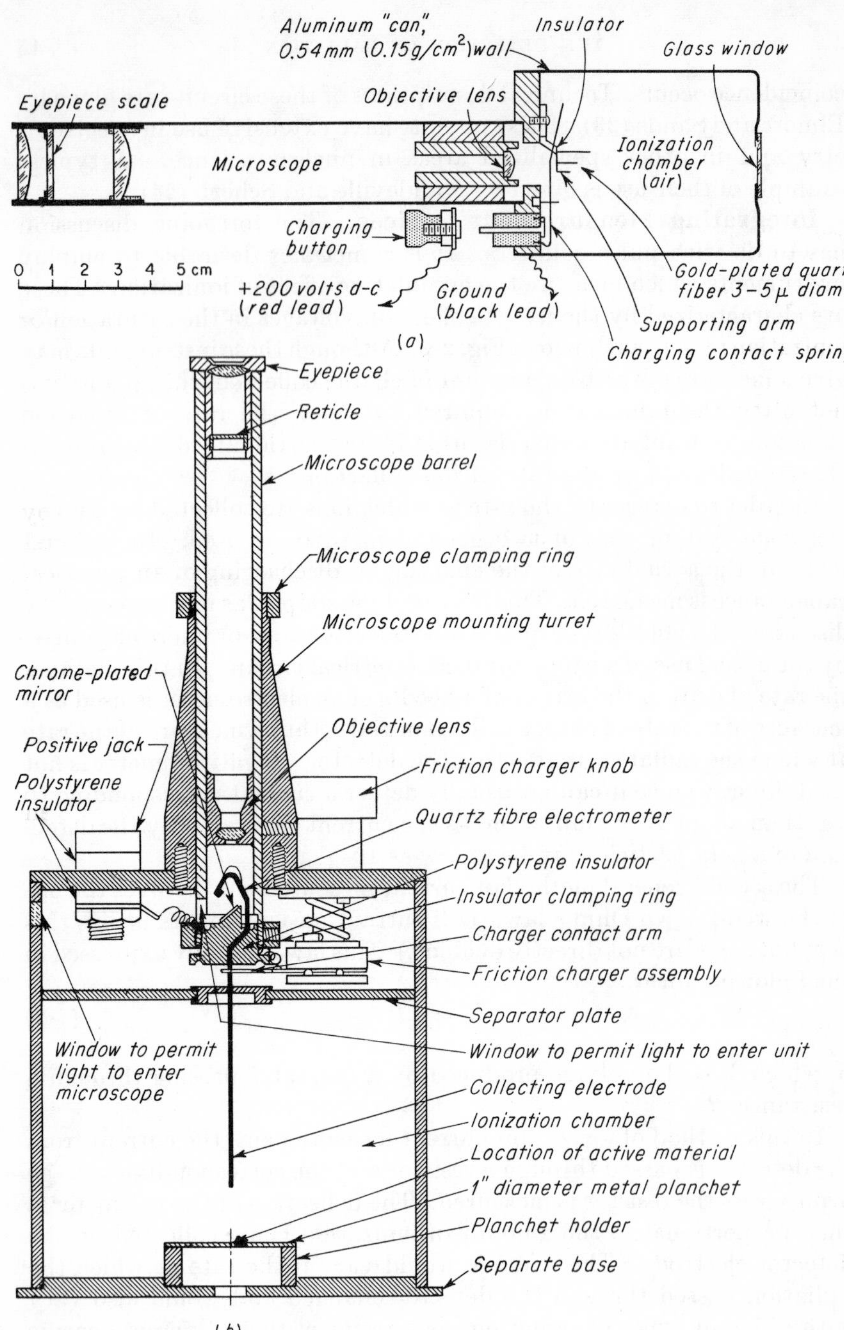

FIG. 2-7. (*a*) Schematic diagram of the Lauritsen electroscope. (*From C. S. Garner, J. Chem. Educ., vol. 26, p. 542, 1949.*) (*b*) Schematic diagram of the Landsverk electroscope. (*Courtesy of Landsverk Co.*)

voltage reading then gives a measure of the steady-state ionization being produced at a given time by the passage of ionizing radiation through the detector. Neither of these methods measures directly the number of particles passing through the detector but gives only the total effect of the radiation on the detector.

Although the principle of the detector operation is the same for all integrating ionization chambers, many different methods are used in the laboratory for making and recording measurements with such chambers. One of the simplest of these instruments is the classical gold-leaf electroscope which is frequently used for demonstration, although it has not been used extensively in research.

More recent modifications of the design of electroscopes and those which show considerable promise for public-health work are the widely used Lauritsen electroscope (Fig. 2-7*a*) and the Landsverk sample analyzer. In this type of instrument, the gold leaf of the older electroscope is replaced by a gold-plated quartz fiber. Schematic representations of these instruments are shown in Fig. 2-7. In these instruments the fiber is charged with a battery, a rectifier, or a friction-charging mechanism. Through the eyepiece can be seen an illuminated scale with a visible cross hair. After being charged, the fiber is on the zero mark on the scale. If a radioactive source is brought near the instrument or placed in the sample-measuring position, the fiber will move back toward the discharge position at a rate nearly proportional to the intensity of the radiation entering the chamber. The reading may then be expressed in scale divisions per unit time. The background may be determined by allowing the fiber to drift over the scale in the same manner with no radioactivity in the vicinity of the chamber. Since the instrument is sometimes not linear over the entire scale, it is usual to take a reading over a certain part of the scale and use, for comparison, readings taken over the same portion.

The apparent activity of the sample is then proportional to the difference between the reciprocal time required for the measurement of the source and that required for the background over a given region of the scale:

$$A \propto \frac{1}{t_{\text{sample}}} - \frac{1}{t_{\text{background}}} \tag{2-3}$$

The fiber instrument is quite simple to operate and is considered to be among the most reliable and rugged detection instruments available for laboratory or field use. It has the distinct advantage of being able to measure a wide range of apparent activities in various samples but is somewhat tedious to use for extended periods of time, as it is necessary to watch the fiber through the telescope ocular.

The direct-reading electroscope is reasonably sensitive, but considerably greater sensitivity may be acquired by using an electrometer to measure the ion current from the ionization chamber. A number of very satisfactory electrometers have been in use for several years. Included in this category are those of the Lindemann type, the string electrometer, various modifications of the quadrant electrometer, and various types of vacuum-tube electrometers.

The vacuum-tube type has been used in many laboratories because of its relative simplicity of operation and because the measurements may be made either by visual determination of the rate of drift of a galvanometer needle, by the deflection of the needle if the resistor method is used, or by some type of recording system. The basic circuits of these electrometers employ one of several types of electrometer vacuum tubes, such as the General Electric FP 54, the Victoreen VX 32, or the Raytheon CK 571 AX. Similar circuits are commonly used with portable ionization-chamber monitoring devices.

The resistances that are utilized in this type of circuit are frequently selected in powers of 10, ranging from 10^8 to 10^{12} ohms, to give satisfactory readings on common voltmeters. These are usually quite satisfactory instruments for laboratory or field use, although they are not so sensitive as some other types of instruments. The statistical fluctuations at very small currents are quite troublesome.

One of the difficulties in work with electrometers has been in the instability of d-c amplifiers. To circumvent this, an interesting type of circuit has been developed which is called the dynamic-capacitor electrometer (often called the vibrating-reed electrometer). In this device, a metallic reed is driven at a fixed frequency such as 400 cycles/sec. The ionization current is superimposed on the fixed-frequency signal, giving an alternating current with an amplitude proportional to the ion current. Such signals may then be amplified by suitable a-c amplifiers which are quite stable. The amplified ionization-current signal is then separated and measured either by the rate-of-drift method or by determining the potential drop across a resistor. This instrument has been described by Palevsky, Swank, and Grenchik (25) and is one of the most stable instruments in use. It is used extensively for the measurement of isotopes like C^{14} and tritium in the gaseous state.

2-3. Standard Laboratory Instrumentation Systems

In this section an outline will be given of various typical laboratory combinations of the units described in the previous sections. There are a great variety of ways in which the various components can be used together depending on the type of isotope under study, the nature of the problem, and the facilities available to the worker. There are several experimental factors which are common to all systems.

A few preliminary questions in regard to practical laboratory problems are sometimes raised. A brief résumé of some of these is given below:

1. Is a variable discriminator necessary on standard counting units? Variable discriminators have no use in G-M counting systems since no energy differentiation is possible. They are quite useful for proportional counters and thus may be included on a general-purpose scaler which might be used for several types of systems.

2. Is a 60-cycle test switch useful on a scaler? This is a most useful device to determine if the scaler is registering properly. It should register 3,600 cpm if the scaler is operating accurately. If the line frequency is not exactly at 60 cycles, the variation should be constant.

3. Are automatic or preset features desirable? Preset total-count switches and preset timers have considerable usefulness when many samples are to be run or when the counting time for the samples is long. These devices permit the investigator to do other work while the counter is operating. From statistical considerations a preset count device is better than a preset timer since each sample is counted to the same statistical accuracy.

Preset timing is useful if the samples are sufficiently active that statistical variation is not significant. In general, the more automation included in the system the greater the potential maintenance problem becomes. This statement applies also to automatic resetting devices for the scalers. In most laboratories it is doubtful if the time saved justifies the extra cost and maintenance problems of introducing the automatic devices. It might well be worthwhile in laboratories in which a large number of samples are run daily.

4. What are the sources of extraneous counts? In addition to the difficulties inherent in the counter itself, if it fails to operate properly, one may find that extraneous counts may come from the timers used, from the resetting mechanisms in the instrument itself or others in the room, from calculating machines being used in the vicinity, from neon lights, from X-ray machines in the neighborhood, or from samples of radioactive material (shipments or radioactive wastes) being transported or stored near the counter.

General Problems. *Background Radiation.* One of the ever-present difficulties in the field of radiation measurement is the "background," or natural, radiation present. There are several sources of this radiation. The earth receives a more or less steady stream of high energy (10 to 1,000 Bev) particles, largely protons from space. When these particles interact in the upper atmosphere, neutrons, mesons, and gamma rays are formed. Gamma radiation is usually all that is observed at the earth's surface. There is variation in the cosmic-ray background at various altitudes, typical ratios being 1, 5, and 75 at altitudes of sea level, 15,000 ft, and 55,000 ft respectively. There is also a latitude effect, more cosmic radiation being observed at the earth's poles than at the equator. At sea level, cosmic-radiation intensity averages about 2 ion pairs/cm^3/sec, which corresponds to about 0.1 mr/day. (See Chap. 4 for permissible exposure levels.)

In addition to the cosmic radiation, other contributions are made to the background by the naturally radioactive radioisotopes in the earth, air, water, and in the body. Rocks and minerals contain small amounts of Rb^{87}, La^{138}, and Sm^{147} besides K^{40}, uranium, thorium, and their radioactive daughters. The largest amounts of radioactivity in the air arise from radon, thoron, and their daughters. These amount to about 10^{-10} μc/cm^3. The decay products of these gases are solids and are brought down as a natural "fallout" by rain and by temperature inversions. Drinking water contains traces of uranium, radium, and radon in concentrations of 10^{-9} to 10^{-10} μc/ml, although some spring waters contain 1,000 times this concentration. Milk contains about 6×10^{-8} μc K^{40}/ml. It might be interesting to note that the average human body contains an equilibrium concentration of 380,000 dpm of K^{40}, 150,000 dpm of C^{14}, and 14,000 dpm of radium. It is also true that fallout from nuclear-weapons tests adds a certain amount of radioactivity, primarily in the form of Sr^{90} and Cs^{137}, to these quantities. However, it is agreed that the greatest danger from such fallout is ingestion rather than external radiation. Such ingestion may produce minor radiation exposure to the bones or other organs concentrating strontium. The effects of such exposure, including genetic effects, are controversial when predicted on the basis of present knowledge.

In most tracer work, the background is not significant because the work is usually carried out with large enough amounts of radioactive materials to make the background statistically insignificant. However, in some work such as radiocarbon dating and other low-level counting procedures, extreme care must be taken to minimize the background effect. This may be done by extensive shielding, by choosing construction materials with low contamination, and by the use of anticoincidence counters. Although it is not possible to eliminate its effect entirely, various attempts to minimize the background have been described by Kulp (26), Libby (27), and Johnston (28). (See Chap. 10 for low-level counting discussion.)

For all routine work, the background reading should be measured under the operating conditions chosen and subtracted from the measured reading on the sample, taking proper care to treat the data statistically (see Chap. 3). For certain types of instruments, particularly proportional and scintillation counters, a refinement of this simple background subtraction technique is desirable. With these instruments, the counting rate will differ for various operating voltages or discriminator settings, and it is to the advantage of the investigator to obtain the best working conditions possible. Since the background varies at different voltage settings on these detectors, background measurements should be made over the range of usual operating voltages. This may give a curve as in Fig. 2-8*a*. Another curve should then be plotted using the sample under investigation. A typical curve is shown in Fig. 2-8*a*. Since it is apparent that both background and the sample vary, Loevinger and Berman (29) have suggested plotting the ratio of the square of the sample rate to the background rate as a function of the applied voltage, as in Fig. 2-8*b*. The proper operating voltage is taken to be the maximum in this curve. This technique may be used to determine the best operating voltage for any proportional instrument when energy differentiation is not desired. (See Chap. 3 for other criteria.)

Operational Plateaus. When it is intended to make measurements of radiation with a typical Geiger instrument, several other concepts must be kept in mind. Although it is theoretically conceivable that a given detector tube could operate in several of the voltage regions, in practice the detectors are used either as ionization chambers or as proportional or Geiger counters.

Because of the structural limitations imposed by the restrictions of the electrostatic fields in high-voltage counters and because of the limitations imposed by the electronics that are necessary to record counts on a mechanical register, there is a voltage minimum below which most proportional and Geiger counters will not operate. The voltage which is necessary to obtain a large enough pulse to record the impulse is called the threshold voltage and is a characteristic of a particular type of Geiger tube filling and the instrument used. The same phenomenon is observed with proportional counters. The first step in operating a counter, then, is to determine this threshold voltage by bringing an active sample into the vicinity of the detector and turning the voltage up until the impulses start registering in the counter.

For Geiger tubes, if the operator then continues to raise the voltage while the sample is in the same position relative to the detector and while it is giving off particles at a constant rate, a voltage is reached at which the counting rate begins to level off after rising rather sharply at the threshold. This plateau may continue for several hundred volts as the voltage is raised higher. The plateau terminates with an abrupt rise in counting rate when the counter goes into discharge and counts in a "continuous" fashion. If this happens inadvertently, the detector should not be left at this discharge voltage but should be immediately turned down into the plateau region to avoid ruining the tube. The Geiger region for many tubes is in the voltage range of 1,000 to 2,000 volts, although this varies markedly with the tube and its filling. The

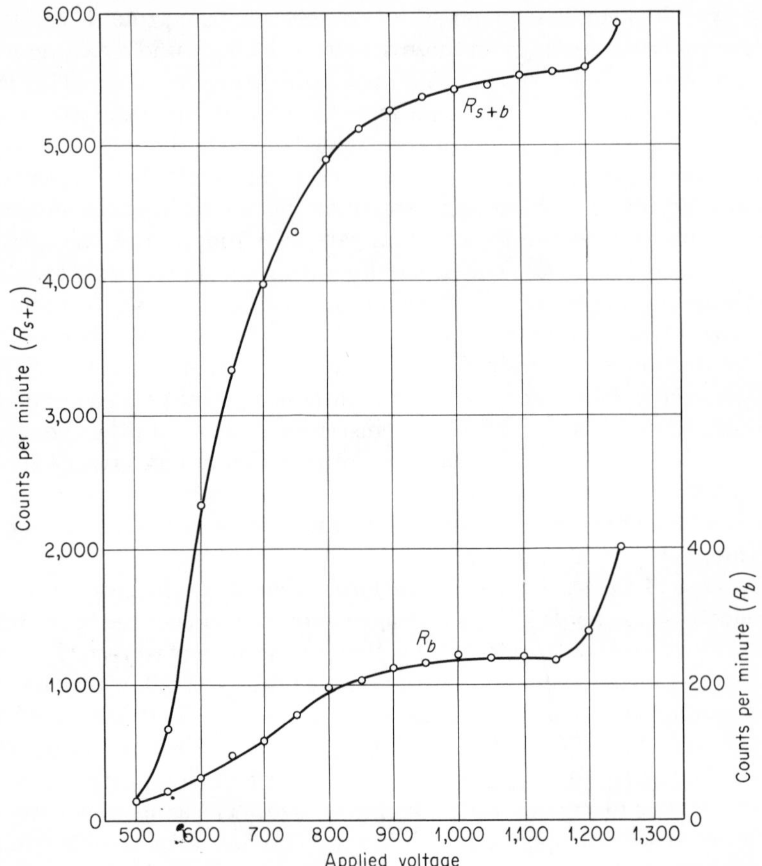

FIG. 2-8*a*. Counting rate for Co^{60} source and for background; NaI scintillation counter.

nature and length of the plateau is one of the most important characteristics of this type of detector. The advantage of this plateau is that the sensitivity of the instrument is fairly independent of small changes in the high voltage. For laboratory and tracer work a tube is considered satisfactory if it has a plateau with a variation in counting rate (slope of the curve) of not greater than 5 per cent/100 volts. For portable or field instruments, 10 per cent/100 volts is not uncommon in many commercial models. A typical plot of counting rate as a function of voltage showing the plateau is given in Fig. 2-9. The operating voltage is usually selected at 75 to 100 volts above the threshold.

Although many investigators are familiar with the plateau of a Geiger

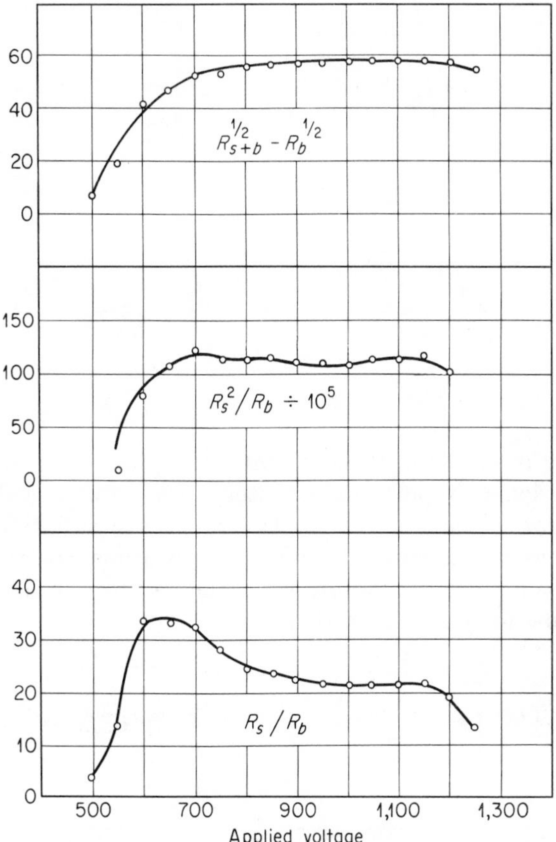

FIG. 2-8*b*. Criteria for selecting operating potential (based on Fig. 2-8*a*).

tube, it should be pointed out that proportional counters also have plateaus which may extend over 1,000 volts. In other words, for a given type of radiation, a point is reached at which all the radiation particles are detected and an increase in voltage causes no change in the number of impulses registered. If two types of particles are being emitted from the sample (such as alpha and beta radiation), one plateau will be observed for the alpha particles, and then with higher voltages the Geiger plateau is observed in which both types of ionizing particles are registered. Alpha radiation of varying energies may cause "steps"

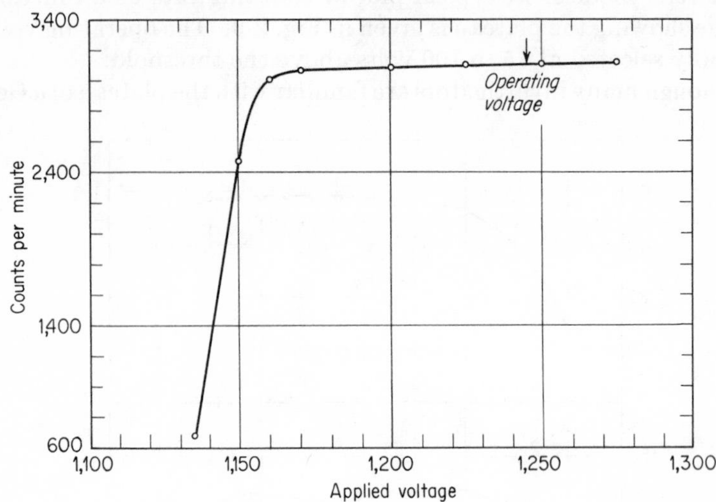

FIG. 2-9. Characteristic curve for a G-M tube.

in the plateau of the ionization region. A typical counting-rate-vs.-voltage curve for a proportional counter is shown in Fig. 2-10. This characteristic of "discrimination" between types of radiation, together with the increased counting rates which are possible as a result of the shorter dead time, are the factors which make proportional counting highly desirable for many investigations.

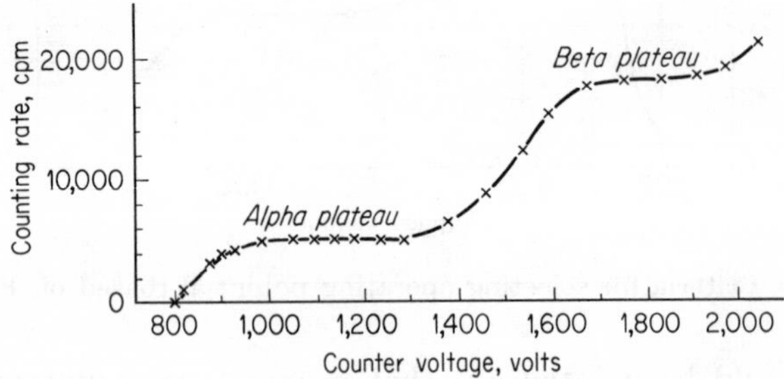

FIG. 2-10. Counting rate vs. counter voltage for a flow-type proportional counter with a National Bureau of Standards RaD-E-F source. [*From Price* (1).]

Resolving Time and Coincidence Correction. Most tracer work with radioactivity is performed by comparing the rates of radiation emission of two or more samples, with little regard for the total amount of ionization produced. As indicated earlier, a basic difference between pulse and integrating types of detectors is the length of time during which the instrument is permitted to collect and register the ionization current. Any ion-collection instrument is characterized by a "time constant," so that a long time constant prohibits the registration of individual ionization bursts. Such a device would measure either an average value of the current or the total current passing in a given length of time. If the instrument has a short time constant, individual ionization bursts can be detected and the total number of such bursts can be registered. Price (1) and Elmore and Sands (23) have given detailed descriptions of the problems associated with the time constants of various circuits.

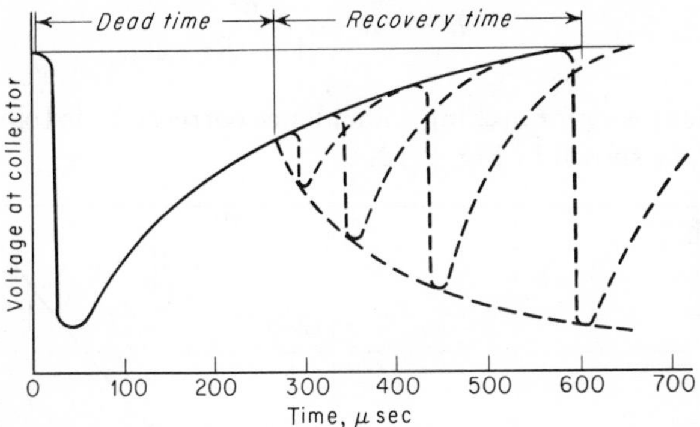

FIG. 2-11. Illustration of dead time in a typical G-M tube. (*From H. G. Stever, Phys. Rev., vol.* 61, *p.* 38, 1942.)

The resolving time of a counter is the minimum time interval between events which can be registered. The loss of counts caused by failure to distinguish successive events is called the "coincidence loss." Although the collection time for the electrons in a Geiger tube is of the order of a microsecond, the tube might require several hundred microseconds for the positive ions to be collected. The time, following an event in the tube, in which the tube gives no pulse or has no response to an ionizing event is the dead time of the tube. This dead time is determined by the construction of the tube and the voltage applied across it. Since the tube has some response before it regains its normal electric field, the pulses occurring immediately after the dead time will be smaller than normal. The time required for the tube to recover sufficiently to give a pulse large enough to be registered in the counting circuit is the resolving time. This is determined by the sensitivity of the counting circuit, the tube voltage, and the dead time. The oscilloscope trace (Fig. 2-11) shows the response of a typical Geiger tube.

The coincidence correction (to be added to the observed counting rate) may be computed from the experimentally determined resolving time τ. If the circuit registers R events per minute, it is inoperative for

$R\tau$ min each minute. If R' particles arrive per minute, then the number of these which will not be detected is $R' - R$, or $R'R\tau$. In terms of the observed counting rate R, the true rate R' is given by the following equation:

$$R' = \frac{R}{1 - R\tau} \qquad (2\text{-}4)$$

The coincidence correction $(R' - R)$ is then found to be

$$R' - R = \frac{\tau R^2}{1 - R\tau} \qquad (2\text{-}5)$$

A convenient way for making coincidence corrections is to plot $R' - R$ against R, as shown in Fig. 2-12.

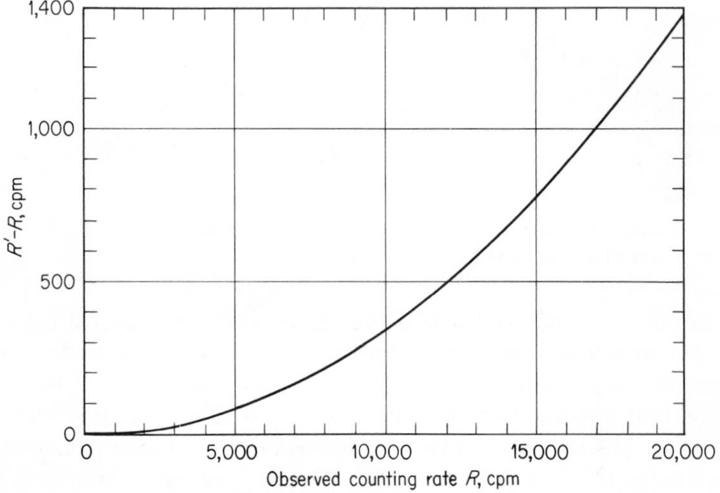

FIG. 2-12. Coincidence-correction curve for a G-M tube with $\tau = 208\ \mu$sec.

The coincidence correction may also be expressed as a percentage of the observed counting rate. This relationship is given by the following:

$$\text{Coincidence correction, } \% = 100 \times \frac{R' - R}{R} = 100 \times \frac{R\tau}{1 - R\tau} \qquad (2\text{-}6)$$

If the observed counting rate is expressed in thousands of counts per minute, this expression for the percentage coincidence correction is then

$$\text{Coincidence correction, } \% = \frac{(R/1{,}000) \times 10^5\tau}{1 - R\tau} \qquad (2\text{-}7)$$

As an example, for $\tau = 300$ μsec, or 5 μmin, the per cent correction is approximately

$$\% \text{ correction} \approx \frac{R}{1{,}000} \times 0.5 \tag{2-8}$$

neglecting the R in the denominator. (Neglecting the $R\tau$ in the denominator introduces an error of about 12 per cent in the correction at 20,000 cpm.) For a detector with this resolving time the coincidence loss is about 5 per cent at a counting rate of 10,000 cpm or a 10 per cent loss at 20,000 cpm. A curve for an actual detector should be plotted for precise work.

A simple way to evaluate τ is by the "paired-source" method. Four counting rates are required: background, R_b; one beta source, R_1; the second source, R_2; and the sources counted simultaneously, R_{12}. The approximate resolving time may then be calculated from the following equation:

$$\tau = \frac{R_1 + R_2 - R_{12} - R_b}{R_1{}^2 - R_1{}^2 - R_2{}^2} \cong \frac{R_1 + R_2 - R_{12} - R_b}{2R_1R_2} \tag{2-9}$$

Direct determination of the resolving time by use of an oscilloscope is recommended where the equipment is available. This topic is considered in detail in a number of references, including a paper by Borkowski (30).

One of the advantages of a proportional counter arises from its short resolving time. A G-M tube may have a resolving time of 200 to 600 μsec, whereas proportional detectors range from 10^{-8} to 10^{-5} sec for their resolving time. Consequently, a counter operating in the proportional region may accept a million or more impulses per minute with negligible loss, whereas most Geiger-Müller counters have considerable loss at above 10,000 cpm. The coincidence-correction curve shown in Fig. 2-12 is for a G-M tube having a resolving time of 208 μsec.

One of the factors which must be borne in mind is that each component of a counter system has its independent resolving time. For pulse counters the longest resolving time in the system is the limiting factor on the speed of response and should be ascertained if high counting rates are expected. For example, manufacturers of equipment frequently specify the resolving time of the detector and not that of the entire counting system. The techniques that are used to determine resolving times of detectors are well illustrated for scintillation detectors in a paper by Kelley, Bell, Davis, and Lazar (31).

Measurement Systems without Energy Differentiation. For routine tracer work many detection systems are entirely satisfactory, and the decision as to which system to use is determined primarily by the availability of various types of apparatus. In other cases, the type of radiation emitted by the source is the controlling factor. Practical points will be made here regarding the advantages, limitations, and special features and forms of the common types of detection systems.

Ionization Chambers. Measurements may be made with ionization chambers with either pulse-counting or integrating circuits. The chambers themselves may be made in a variety of forms, two of them being shown in Fig. 2-13. These are chambers that may be used for

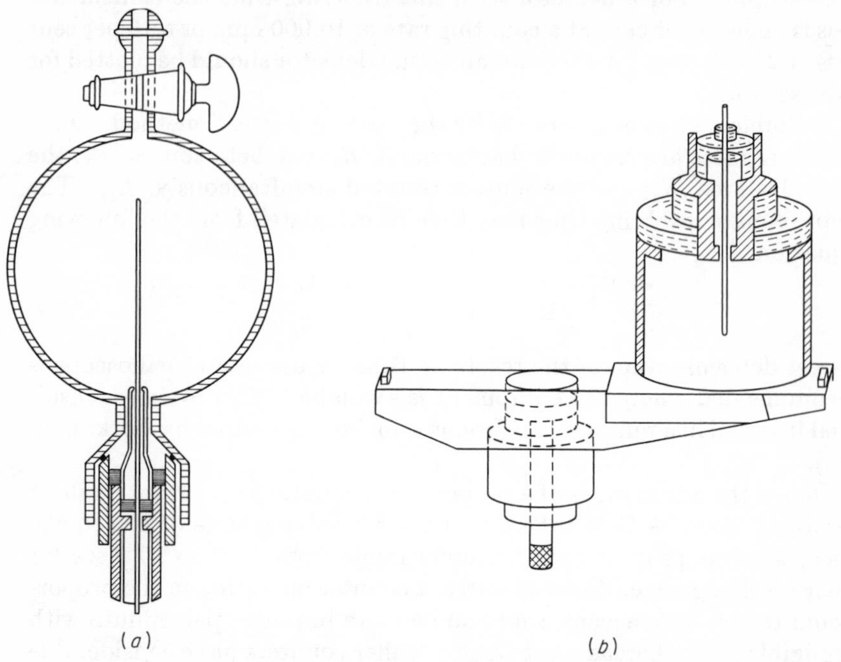

FIG. 2-13. Diagrams of two types of ionization chambers. (*a*) Chamber for measuring gaseous samples; (*b*) chamber for measuring solid samples.

measuring gaseous samples or solid samples and are connected to either a vacuum-tube or a dynamic-capacitor electrometer circuit. The electrometer gives readings by either the rate-of-drift or the constant-deflection method. Another type which has been used extensively is a high-pressure spherical chamber. An excellent example of this type has been described by Shonka and Stephenson (32), as modified by Borkowski (30). An excellent general discussion of ionization chambers and counters is given by Price (1) and by Rossi and Staub (33). A typical example of their use in C^{14} problems is given by Janney and Moyer (34).

Proportional Counters. It has been pointed out that there are several features of proportional detectors which give rise to their use. One of these is the short resolving time, which permits high counting rates with low coincidence loss. Another is the possibility of differentiating the sizes of pulses and thus of performing both differential counting and energy determinations.

Commercially available proportional counters are usually operated at atmospheric pressure using a gas-flow or gas-purging system and a windowless counting chamber. Although these counters are used frequently for the measurement of low-energy beta-ray samples, the significant feature in much of their use is that the detector has no window and has a resulting higher counting yield for the low-energy beta particles. Windowless proportional-flow counters are more commonly used than windowless G-M tubes. Some laboratories use proportional detectors in many forms. They are also used frequently in special standardization problems, as discussed in Chap. 7, and for alpha counting.

Proportional-counting systems employ several components in addition to the proportional detector itself. Since the pulses are small, it is always necessary to use an amplifier stage, and in some cases a preamplifier is advisable. A very stable high-voltage supply is also required since the instrument is not usually operated on the same type of "plateau" as is observed in Geiger-Müller counters. The pulses are registered on a standard scaler.

It is usual to purchase a "proportional" counter which includes a high-voltage supply with very good voltage control, an amplifier, and scaler in one chassis. This unit may be used with either a gas-type proportional detector or a scintillation proportional detector, although care should be taken to make certain that the sign of the pulse from the detector (positive or negative) is proper for the electronic system accepting it. In scintillation counters, the type of pulse will depend on the wiring of the dynode circuits in the tube base. A discriminator and a pulse-height analyzer are included in some proportional-counting systems.

Examples of proportional-counting systems and the advantages and limitations of their use are given by Bernstein and Ballentine (35), Nader, Hagee, and Setter (36), and Robinson (37).

Geiger-Müller Counters. G-M counters have been popular instruments during the past several years because they are relatively inexpensive, do not require high stability in their voltage control, and require little extra amplification. The usual apparatus consists of a G-M detector, the high-voltage supply, and scaling circuit. A general survey of G-M systems was published by Price (1) and Brown (38), although there are a great many papers on the theory and operation of these systems, a number of which are included in the supplementary references in this chapter. There have been no recent major changes in

G-M systems except in the development of new and different types of detectors. A few typical types are shown in Fig. 2-14. A variety of these are described in a *Nucleonics* survey (39).

Laboratory G-M detectors are frequently of the end-window variety or the glass-wall type. The detectors which have been used for measuring liquid samples are usually either dip counters which may be

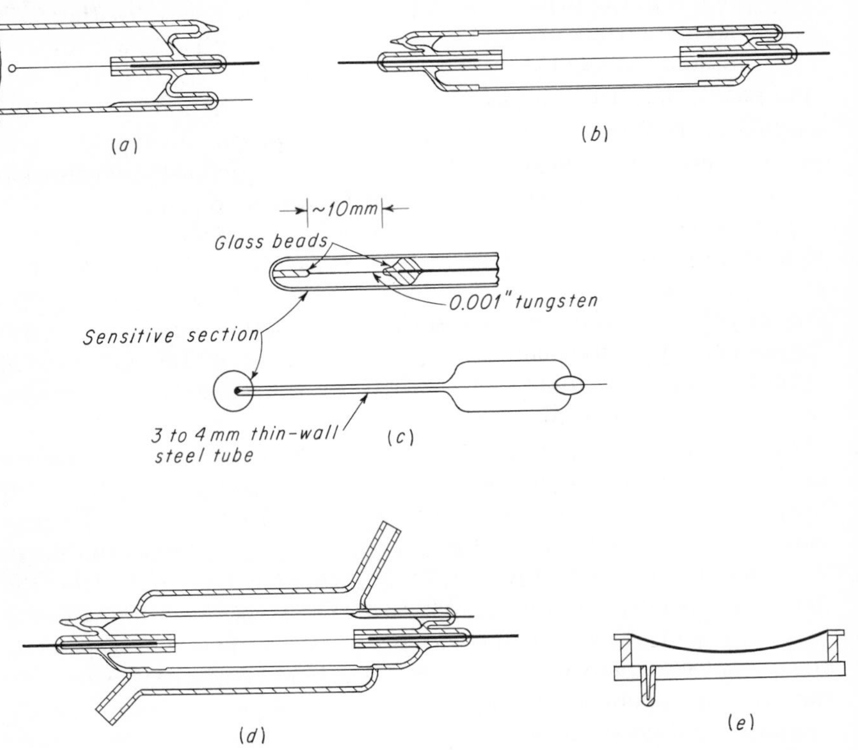

FIG. 2-14. Various Geiger-Müller tubes. (*a*) Bell type; (*b*) cylindrical type; (*c*) needle counter; (*d*) jacketed tube; (*e*) parallel-plate type. [*From Price* (1).]

immersed in the liquid or liquid-jacketed counters which have the solution passed around the detector for higher efficiency. These are probably used less at the present time since they become contaminated by the active liquid rather readily. End-window counters are still used quite extensively for laboratory work since they can be fabricated with windows of very-low-density thickness ($\sim$1 mg/cm^2). The thinnest glass-wall detectors usually have about 30 mg/cm^2 density thickness and are not suitable for low-energy beta-emitting isotopes such as C^{14}. There are a number of types of tubes in which a radioactive gas is measured inside the detector with high efficiency. Examples of special applications are given in papers by Libby (40) and Eidinoff (41). Several examples of G-M tubes are shown in Fig. 2-14.

Recent interesting developments include that of employing a ring of G-M detectors around a sample holder to form a "well" counter. Reasonably high counting yields can be obtained in this way because of the high solid angle formed by the counting tubes. Another important development in the field of isotope utilization is that of using a metal-wall G-M tube as the standard detector for many industrial applications. The walls and baffles of these tubes are of a high-atomic-number metal. As a result, they are quite rugged and give relatively high efficiency for gamma measurement. It is problematic whether large G-M detectors or scintillation detectors have the advantage for routine industrial use, but both are being used extensively.

Scintillation Counters (Well Type). Scintillation counters may be used either with energy differentiation (see next section) or as instruments to measure gross counting rates. The most common type of non-energy differentiation detector is the scintillation well counter which consists of a crystal [usually NaI(Tl)] in which a small hole is bored to permit entry of a small sample vial. This has the advantage that samples of any size or shape (up to the size of the well) may be used and the counting geometry is not changed materially. In most work, liquid samples are used; this saves considerable time by not requiring the evaporation of a sample. When the scintillation counter is used in this way, all that is required is the detector, a high-voltage supply, the amplifier, and scaler. As in the other counting systems, the scintillation "counter" usually contains all of these components except the detector in a single unit. The operating voltage may be determined by plotting the ratio of the square of the sample rate to the background as described above. This operating voltage will frequently be different from the operating voltage suggested by the manufacturer. There is considerable advantage in the use of energy differentiation even with well counters to get more significant results. It can be shown in many cases that more meaningful data can be obtained using a pulse-height analyzer in conjunction with a crystal, even though the actual counting rate at a given energy may be considerably lower than the gross counting rate as determined by a routine measurement with a well counter. This difference may be particularly important when scattering of radiation is a factor to be considered. Considerable effort is being expended to determine the relative merits of counting systems for various laboratory problems. A paper by Weisburger and Lipner (42) gives a specific evaluation of this problem.

Cloud Chambers and Bubble Chambers. Two techniques of radiation measurement which are quite useful for special problems are those of the Wilson cloud chamber and the more newly developed bubble chamber. Both of these operate on the principle that ionization produced by radiation will cause a physical effect under certain conditions in special systems. The cloud chamber requires the production of proper atmospheric conditions inside the chamber to produce supersaturation of air with water or a suitable organic vapor. In the expansion type of chamber the supersaturation is caused instantaneously by a sudden expansion of the system. Any charged radiation passing through the system during the expansion process may cause a condensation of vapor particles along the radiation path. With suitable illumination, pictures may be taken of these events. A more recent variation is the continuous cloud chamber, in which a chamber is kept at a very cold (dry ice) temperature on one side and at room temperature on the other. An absorbent pad is saturated with alcohol or other volatile material on the warm side. As the vapor meets the cold layer, a supersaturation takes place at the interface. Again, if ionization is produced in this supersaturated zone, a track will be produced which can be observed and photographed. An interesting compilation of cloud-chamber photographs has been prepared by Gentner, Maier-Leibnitz, and Bothe (43).

The bubble chamber is based on the principle that radiation impinging on liquid hydrogen may cause localized boiling to take place along the path of the radiation. As in the other types of chambers, photographs of these tracks may be taken. A survey of both cloud chambers and bubble chambers has been published by Fretter (44). These techniques have been used much more in experimental physics than in the fields of applied radiation problems.

Chemical Dosimetry and Radiation Chemistry. It has been observed for many years that both chemical and physical changes are brought about by the passage of radiation through matter. Radiation chemistry, the investigation of these chemical changes, gives a basis for another method in the detection and measurement of radiation. Radiation chemistry is particularly important since it is correlated with much of the biological effect of radiation. Radiation chemistry differs from photochemistry in that photochemical reactions involve the interaction between a quantum of radiation and a single specific molecule. Radiation chemistry deals with a generalized effect of radiation on all the molecules in the ionization path.

It was pointed out in Chap. 1 that the two processes involved in dissipating radiation energy are ionization and excitation. If the electron to which energy is transferred is ejected from the atom, the process is one of ionization. If the electron is merely raised to a higher energy state but still retained in the atom, it is called excitation. Either of these processes may give rise to radiation effects. For some time, attempts have been made to determine whether chemical (and biological) effects are produced by a direct hit on the molecule, which reacts, or by secondary effects. Recent work indicates that nearly all of these effects are brought about by secondary reactions occurring in the neighborhood of the affected molecule or cell component.

In general, different types of reactions are observed with "fast" and "slow" radiation particles. The "fast" or light particles include X rays, gamma rays, beta rays, and high-speed electrons; the "slow" or heavy particles produce a higher specific ionization and include alpha rays, neutrons, and accelerated charged particles such as protons and deuterons.

Because of the unique significance of water to the functioning of biological systems and to the development of nuclear reactors and because of its importance in general chemical theory, the radiolysis (radiation-induced decomposition) of water has been the most thoroughly studied of all chemical systems. A number of competing reactions may be observed. Among those produced primarily by heavy radiation particles are the following:

$$2H_2O \rightarrow H_2 + H_2O_2 \qquad (a)$$

$$2H_2O \rightarrow 2H + H_2O_2 \qquad (b)$$

The predominating basic reaction for light particles is probably the following:

$$2H_2O \rightarrow H_2 + 2OH \qquad (c)$$

One of the significant phenomena in these reactions is seen to be the production of free radicals which will subsequently react with other radicals or molecules of the solvent or any solute present. These decomposition reactions may be reversed by a back reaction between the free radicals and the decomposition products. The back reaction is inhibited by the presence of impurities in the water and by an excess of hydrogen peroxide or of oxygen, but it is favored by the presence of excess hydrogen. The reactions observed depend upon many different factors such as ionization density and the type of radiation, and much experimental work is being done with these systems. The results, although complicated, can be correlated qualitatively by the following mechanisms:

$$H_2O \rightarrow H_2,\ H_2O_2,\ H,\ OH$$

$$OH + H_2 \rightarrow H_2O + H \qquad (d)$$

$$H + H_2O_2 \rightarrow H_2O + OH \qquad (e)$$

$$OH + H_2O_2 \rightarrow H_2O + HO_2 \qquad (f)$$

$$HO_2 + HO_2 \rightarrow H_2O_2 + O_2 \qquad (g)$$

$$H + O_2 \rightarrow HO_2 \qquad (h)$$

Reactions (*d*) and (*e*) represent a chain reaction which is the most important factor in reversing the radiolysis. Reactions (*f*) and (*h*) stop the chain reaction, as do molecules of solutes present.

Free radicals may be described essentially as fragments containing an odd number of electrons. They have a fleeting existence, but it is assumed that most chemical and biological effects are brought about by the reactions of these aqueous free radicals with the other materials in the system. In general, oxidizable solutes will be oxidized by OH radicals and reducible solutes will be reduced by H radicals.

If a chemical system is to be used to measure the passage of radiation, an ideal system should have several characteristics, among which are the following:

1. The chemical product resulting from the radiation should be one which can be accurately measured by a convenient method.
2. The amount of change produced by a given amount of radiation should be independent of the energy and type of radiation, the rate of dose, and the concentration of the reactant and product.
3. The system should be reproducible and easily made from shelf reagents.
4. The amount of chemical reaction should be proportional to the radiation dose.

Of the various reactions which might be considered, several useful systems have been developed for laboratory and field use. The most common of these can be grouped into three classes:

1. Aqueous systems in which a direct oxidation or reduction can take place. Examples of this are the oxidation of ferrous sulfate or the reduction of ceric sulfate in 0.8 *N* sulfuric acid.
2. Aqueous solutions of halogenated hydrocarbons which form hydrogen ions on radiolysis. The pH change can usually be measured by the inclusion of an indicator dye in the system.
3. Solid systems such as the use of silver phosphate glass in which the silver is reduced by the action of the radiation and can be determined with a fluorophotometer.

The oxidation of ferrous sulfate was suggested by Fricke and Morse (45) in 1928 and has been studied extensively since that time. The reaction is considered to be the following:

$$15.6\mathrm{Fe}^{++} + 3.7\mathrm{O}_2 + 15.6\mathrm{H}^+ \xrightarrow{100\text{ ev}} 15.6\mathrm{Fe}^{3+} + 0.4\mathrm{H}_2 + 7.4\mathrm{H}_2\mathrm{O}$$

It should be noted that reactions of this type are frequently written using fractional coefficients as indicated above. This coefficient, which is called the *G* value for a substance, is defined as the number of ions or molecules of that substance involved in the reaction per 100 ev absorbed by the system. The coefficient 15.6 for the $FeSO_4$ indicates that 15.6

ferrous ions are oxidized per 100 ev absorbed. The yield of ferric ion is a direct measure of the energy absorbed by both ionization and excitation processes.

As an example of the use of the ferrous sulfate system, Weiss, Allen, and Schwarz (46) describe a procedure for this type of dosimetry. They suggest dissolving 2 g of $FeSO_4$ or $Fe(NH_4)_2(SO_4)_2 \cdot 6H_2O$ and 0.3 g of NaCl in 110 cm^3 of concentrated (95 to 98 per cent) H_2SO_4. To this is added enough distilled water to make 5 liters of solution. Sufficient solution to fill a spectrophotometer cell is placed in glass or polystyrene sample containers having at least 8 mm inside diameter. The duration of the irradiation period should be accurately noted.

The determination of the ferric ion produced could be made with any suitable chemical determination, but the direct measurement of its light absorption is the method most commonly used. The absorption band at 305 μ is preferred for the measurement. The optical density D of the sample is compared with that of the irradiated solution at the given wavelength. The spectrophotometer should be thermostatted for best results because of the high temperature coefficient of the extinction coefficient.

The dose rate R is given by

$$R\ (\text{r/hr}) = \frac{10^9}{\epsilon Y} \frac{D_s - D_b}{\text{time}} \tag{2-10}$$

in which ϵ is the molar extinction coefficient, Y is the ferrous sulfate yield in units of micromoles per liter per 1,000 r, D_s and D_b are the optical densities of the sample and blank respectively, and time is given in hours. These authors use a value for ϵ of 2,174 at 23.7°C. The G value for this system corresponds to a yield Y of about 16 μmoles/1,000 r. This system is considered to be satisfactory for a total dose range of 4,000 to 4,000,000 r. Similar dosimeter systems make use of ceric sulfate solutions.

Dosimeters making use of halogenated hydrocarbons may be either two-phase or single-phase systems. Several of these are described by Taplin (47). Perhaps the most highly developed two-phase system is that of a resorcinol-stabilized chloroform–bromocresol purple mixture. These dosimeters are capable of sensitivities down to 25 to 50 r. Single-phase systems have a marked limitation or sensitivity, but this can be overcome by the use of trichloroethylene and a dye such as phenol red which has end points bracketing neutrality. Since phenol red systems must be kept free from CO_2, special techniques are required in the preparation of the dosimeter ampoules. One of the problems in these dosimeter systems is that of thermal stability. The single-phase phenol red systems withstand exposure in a water bath at 50 to 60°C for at least a month and for 2 weeks at 70°C. Two-phase systems of similar sensitivity decompose within a few minutes at 100°C, last only a few hours at 70°C, and last 2 weeks at 50°C. Both types are stable at less than 37°C for many months.

To calculate the G values for chloroform or related compounds it is necessary to convert ionization (r) values to energy units (electron volts) per gram in order to convert micromilliequivalents of acid formed per milliliter to the number of acid molecules per gram or milliliter. The factors involved in this type of calculation are the following:

1. 35 ev is required to produce 1 ion pair in air.
2. 1.61×10^{12} ion pairs are produced per roentgen per gram of air.
3. 6.02×10^{23} molecules are equivalent to 1 g of H.
4. ρ (density) of chloroform is 1.498.

If the yields are measured in micromilliequivalents per milliliter per roentgen, the number of acid molecules formed per milliliter per roentgen is obtained by multiplying the yield by the factor $6.02 \times 10^{23} \times 10^{-9}$, or 6.02×10^{14}. Since the photons from radium or Co^{60} are absorbed in chlorinated hydrocarbons or water essentially entirely by the Compton process, 1 g of the chlorinated hydrocarbon will absorb nearly the same energy per roentgen as air, which is $1.61 \times 10^{12} \times 35$ ev, or 56.4×10^{12} ev. Since the density of chloroform is 1.498, the energy absorbed per milliliter of chloroform per roentgen is 84.6×10^{12}. For the general case

$$G = \frac{6.02 \times 10^{14} \times A \times 10^{2}}{56.4 \times 10^{12} \times \rho}$$

For example, for 0.1 μmeq/ml/r for chloroform,

$$G = \frac{6.02 \times 10^{14} \times 0.1 \times 10^{2}}{56.4 \times 10^{12} \times 1.498} = 73.6$$

The dosimeters described above are usually quite satisfactory for laboratory work involving the calibration of large sources, for various types of biological systems, and for use in problems of food and drug sterilization. A recent development in field monitoring for military and civil-defense use is the use of small wafers of phosphate glass which are considerably more rugged than the liquid systems. They have the additional advantage that they can be localized in chemical or biological systems. They have been described by Davison, Goldblith, and Proctor (48). In this device the silver ion in the Ag_3PO_4 in the glass is reduced to metallic silver. This induces fluorescence in the glass which is proportional to the absorbed energy. The fluorescence can be measured with a photocell and a photomultiplier tube. This dosimeter has a very high sensitivity peak at about 0.08 Mev and does not respond linearly below 0.200 Mev. It is used primarily with high-energy gamma-ray sources. A blank reading must be made and the result subtracted from that for the pellet. Comparisons of some of the features and applications which are characteristic of the various dosimeter systems are given in Table 2-3.

Measurement Systems with Energy Differentiation. As was pointed out earlier, most routine work with radioisotopes makes use only of the measurement of the relative counting rates of various samples. For this purpose, energy differentiation is frequently not necessary. On the other hand, much modern work makes use of energy differentiation either for the identification of a certain material in a sample or more particularly for the identification of a specific radiation in the presence of other radiation. A number of these techniques are finding extensive application in medical and industrial practice.

Proportional Counters. The most straightforward differentiating device in use is the proportional counter, which makes the differentiation by the voltage control or a simple discriminator. In some cases, as in the differentiation of alpha and beta radiation (although this is a pulse-height and not strictly an energy-differentiation technique), the measurement of one type of radiation can be made in the presence of the other by measuring the heavier ionizing alpha particles at a low voltage and then measuring the combined alpha-plus-beta counting rate at a higher voltage and obtaining the beta counting rate by difference.

The advantages of proportional-counting systems over ionization chambers are several: the pulses are larger, so that the amplifier can be somewhat more simple; more capacitance can be permitted in the cable between the detector and amplifier; the interference and amplifier noise are less troublesome; and the resolving time is much faster. The advantages over G-M counting are primarily in the resolving time and the differentiation feature, and the advantages over scintillation counting lie in the better response characteristics and resolution in the low-energy region. For example, proportional counters produce one ion pair for each 35 ev of particle energy, whereas a scintillation counter produces a photoelectron for approximately 1,000 ev of particle energy. Proportional counters can thus detect particles of much lower energy than scintillation counters.

Commercially available proportional counters are usually equipped with some type of windowless (or ultrathin window) detector suitable for placing samples directly in the sensitive volume. Proportional counters usually require a fairly good amplifier, a high-voltage supply up to 5,000 volts, and a scaler or counting-rate meter equipped with a

TABLE 2-3

SYNOPSIS OF USEFUL APPLICATIONS OF CHEMICAL DOSIMETERS FOR THE MEASUREMENT OF X and γ RADIATION

Applications	Radiation source	Factors influencing radiation response			Preferred dosimeter
		Energy spectrum	Dose rate, r/min	Dose range, r	
Civil defense	Atomic explosion	1.0–5.0 Mev	10^1–10^5	0–600	Single- or two-phase hydrocarbon
		0.1–1.0 Mev	10^{-3}–10	0–100	Single-phase
		Above 200 kev broad	To 10^6	10^6	Phosphate glass
Biological studies	250-kv X rays	Broad	1–100	10^2–10^3	Single-phase
	β and γ	Above 200 kev broad	70	5–14,000	Phosphate glass
Depth dose and tumor measurement	Co^{60} γ rays	1.1–1.3 Mev	10–100	500–5,000	Single-phase
	Million-volt X rays	Broad	10–100	500–5,000	Single-phase
Food sterilization by radiation	Co^{60} γ rays	1.1–1.3 Mev	To 10^5	2×10^4–5×10^6	$FeSO_4$, $Ce(SO_4)_2$
					Two-phase (10^4–10^6 r)
	Fission products	0.6–1.2 Mev			
Calibration of γ-ray sources	Co^{60} γ rays	1.1–1.3 Mev	To 10^5	2×10^4–5×10^6	$FeSO_4$, $Ce(SO_4)_2$
	Fission products	0.6–1.2 Mev			Two-phase

discriminator. The operation of most proportional counters is quite similar to the operation of a standard Geiger-Müller counter except for the use of the discriminator for selecting the pulse heights.

Beta and Gamma-ray Spectrometers. Scintillation spectrometers have been developed relatively recently and for much general work have taken the place of magnetic-lens spectrometers. The latter are still used for precise beta-ray energy determinations. Scintillation spectrometers have been used quite extensively for both beta- and gamma-ray energy determination, although their introduction for work with gamma radiation has revolutionized the field of gamma-ray spectrometry.

A typical scintillation spectrometer for measuring beta-ray spectra might consist of an anthracene crystal (either solid, split, or with a well drilled in it) cemented to one end of a Lucite cylinder, the other end being cemented to a standard photomultiplier tube. A piece of 0.2-mil aluminum foil is used to cover the crystal except on the exposed end, which is covered by a foil of approximately 0.2 mg/cm^2 as a beta-ray window. The entire assembly is then mounted inside a lighttight metal can. The high-voltage supply may be either batteries or an electronically regulated supply. The pulses must be amplified with a good linear amplifier and fed into a single or multichannel analyzer. The output of the analyzer then operates one or more scalers or counting-rate registration devices. Further details on the interpretation of the results are available in the excellent books by Siegbahn (49) and Price (1). An interesting simplification of a number of the energy-determination problems has been described by Marshall (50).

This type of spectrometer can be easily modified for use as a gamma-ray spectrometer by use of a thallium-activated sodium iodide crystal or other suitable gamma-ray scintillation detector. The crystals are usually sealed in an aluminum can, sometimes with a Lucite "light piper" transmitting the light to the photomultiplier tube. Essentially the same type of amplifiers, high-voltage supply, and registration devices is used for both beta- and gamma-ray spectrometry. The application of these instruments has been quite powerful in the elucidation of decay schemes, and most investigations of these schemes now use this technique. A survey of some of the problems of low-energy gamma scintillation spectrometry is given by Borkowski (51), and typical spectra and a discussion of some of the results in the characterization of radiation are given in Chap. 6. One particularly interesting development is that of a relatively inexpensive single-unit spectrometer which has obtained wide acceptance in the medical and industrial fields. This is called the "medical spectrometer" and was designed by Francis, Bell, and Harris (52). This type of instrument is highly recommended for routine use where high stability and precision are relatively

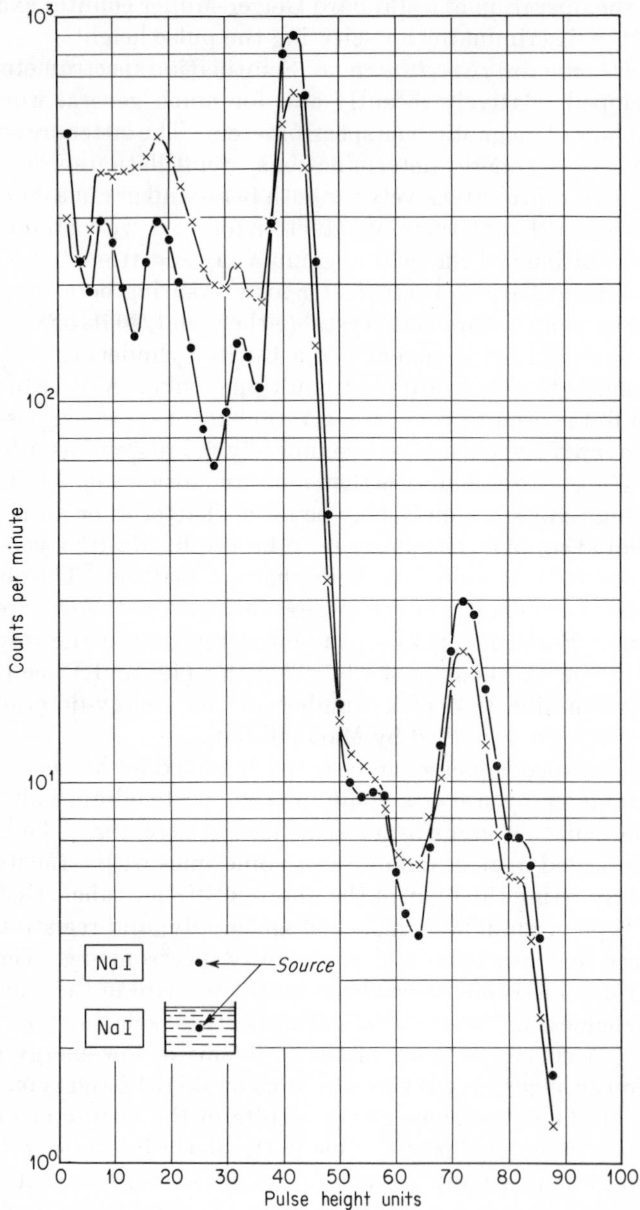

FIG. 2-15. Spectrum of I^{131} showing increase in Compton scattering by placing source in water. ●, unscattered source; x, source placed in water. [*Replotted from Francis, Bell, and Harris* (52).]

unimportant. Figure 2-15 shows a typical spectrum taken with various types of scattering material in the vicinity of an I^{131} source.

It was pointed out in an earlier section that the light pulse emitted by a scintillation crystal is proportional to the energy absorbed in the crystal. For example, if all the energy from a monoenergetic source of 1 Mev were absorbed, a spectral line at 1 Mev should be observed in an ideal instrument. However, since the instrument is not ideal and statistical problems exist, a Gaussian distribution about 1 Mev would actually be observed. Likewise, since a Gaussian distribution of electron energies would occur in the cathode and in the light pulses from the crystal, the resultant distribution is a composite of these Gaussian curves. This type of line spectrum is demonstrated by the photoelectric interaction process, so that gamma-ray spectra will usually show a sharp maximum called the photoelectric peak.

The Compton interactions which have a strong angular dependence give rise to electrons in the crystal of less than maximum energy. As a result of these photoelectric and Compton processes, a simple gamma-ray spectrum is characterized by a photopeak at the highest energy point and a broad lower-energy region corresponding to the Compton electrons interacting in the crystal. This is further complicated by Compton photons being scattered from the materials surrounding the crystal back into the crystal. Consequently, since scattered radiation is lower in energy, the only part of the spectrum which does not represent the scattered radiation is the total energy or the photopeak. The relationship between the intensity of the Compton portion of the spectrum and the photopeak depends greatly on the size of the crystal. Figure 2-16 shows the effect of the size of the crystal on the shape of the spectrum for the typical case. In general, small crystals are adequate for the detection of low-energy photons, but for high-energy determination large crystals are much more useful for efficient measurements.

If it is desired to determine how much total activity is in the source, it is quite possible to calibrate the instrument to determine the counting rate under the photopeak. With an appropriate size of analyzer window, this counting rate would be independent of scattering radiation in the vicinity of the crystal. A technique is described in Chap. 7 for the absolute measurement of gamma-ray activity by determining the probability of a maximum-energy interaction in a given size of crystal and calculating the efficiency of detection for that energy. A relative measurement could be made by counting in the peak region and calibrating the apparatus with a sample of known strength.

The background in a scintillation spectrometer varies with the energy, since it is caused by naturally radioactive materials and cosmic radiation. The cosmic radiation gives rise to very-high-energy pulses

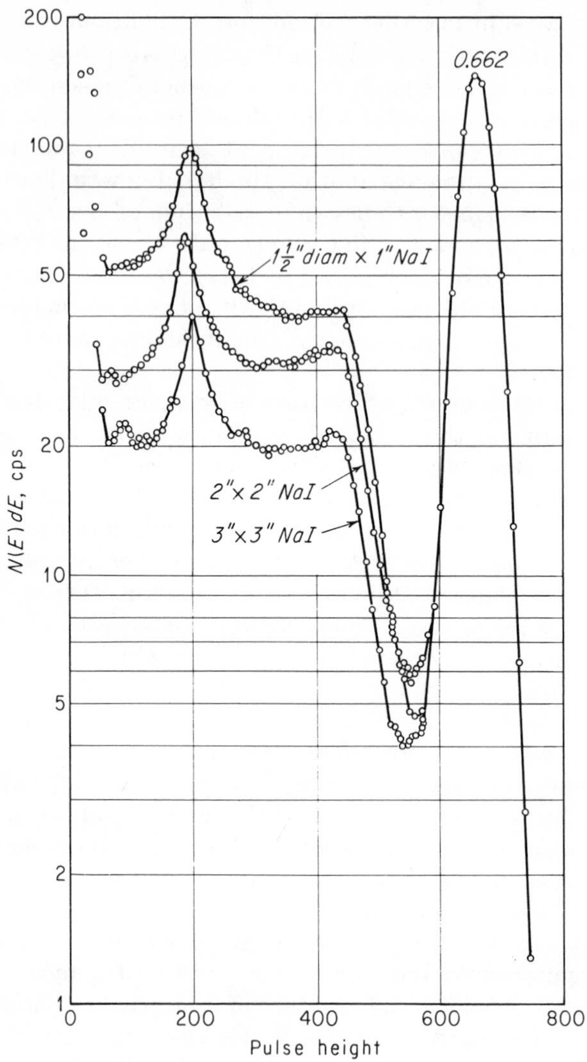

FIG. 2-16. Effect of detector size on Compton electron distribution. Cs^{137} gammas; source distance, 10 cm. (*From R. L. Heath, Scintillation Spectrometry—Gamma Ray Spectrum Catalogue, U.S. Atomic Energy Comm. Rept.* IDO 16408.)

and is not very significant in the region of interest in most radioisotope measurements. The two gamma rays of most importance in the background are those from ThC″, with an energy of 2.62 Mev, and K^{40}, with an energy of 1.46 Mev. It is apparent that the background should be measured as a function of energy before doing spectrometric calculations. That is, the background should be subtracted for each energy or pulse-height setting of the pulse-height analyzer instead of attempting to subtract an over-all background rate. The sample-to-background ratio method of determining the optimum setting for the window width and the pulse-height analyzer is often used in this connection. For a spectrometer with a 3-in. crystal and a 4-in. lead shield, the background might be 14 cpm for the area under a peak at 0.84 Mev (Mn^{56}), compared with a reading of 0.14 cpm for the area under a 2.76-Mev peak (Na^{24}).

It is quite evident that spectrometric techniques will be developed quite highly within the next several years for both routine and highly specialized problems. There are a number of problems in special fields of interest such as medical practice, where extensive measurements are made of iodine uptake in the thyroid glands. It is probable that satisfactory empirical techniques will be developed which will take into consideration the problems referred to here. Likewise, industrial practice will find these instruments of considerable value in many plant and development problems.

Liquid-scintillation Systems. Mention has been made previously of the principles and materials used in the liquid-scintillation systems. A procedure of Guinn and Wagner (53) will be described as a more or less typical scheme for putting this technique into practice, although papers by Williams, Hayes, Kandel, and Rogers (54), Hayes, Rogers, and Langham (55), and Rosenthal and Anger (56) give other procedures which can be used by workers in different fields. A rather specialized treatment of measuring natural radiocarbon is given by Hayes, Anderson, and Arnold (57) which is of interest to those doing radiocarbon dating work (see also Chap. 10).

Guinn and his coworkers have used a dual-channel coincidence apparatus utilizing in a small-sized freezer unit. In this technique, two photomultiplier tubes are fixed at right angles to one another, with their faces bonded to the flat surface of a Lucite sample holder using high-viscosity silicone. The lead-shielded assembly and a sample rack with holders for a number of samples are mounted in the refrigerator. The Lucite sample holder is painted white for reflection except the surface attached to the photocathode. The refrigerator is usually held at −5°C. The sample bottles are standard cylindrical weighing bottles which are 40 mm in diameter and 80 mm high with ground-glass stoppers.

Although the bottle holds about 75 ml, only 25 ml of liquid scintillator is ordinarily used with sample volumes ranging from 1 to 40 ml.

In this apparatus, the amplifier and other parts of the circuit are located outside the refrigerator. The circuits are arranged so as to permit either single measurements or coincidence counting rates from the two detectors to reduce the "noise" from the photomultipliers. At $-5°C$, the noise counting rate of each photomultiplier tube may be from 10,000 to 30,000 cpm. With the coincidence circuit operating, the counting rate is usually only 20 to 50 cpm. Without refrigeration, the single-channel counting-rate noise might be 100,000 cpm.

In this procedure, the proper volume of liquid sample (or weight of solid sample) is transferred into a sample bottle and stirred with the proper amount of liquid scintillator until a homogeneous solution is obtained. The samples are placed in the rack in the refrigerator for 30 min before measuring. This permits them to cool and allows their short-lived phosphorescence to decay. The use of a glove port permits interchange of the samples without opening the refrigerator. This also permits changing the sample without lowering the phototube voltage, which would be necessary to prevent excessive counting rates if light fell on the tubes.

Usually, all samples are counted in an identical manner, with the same sample size, same amount of liquid scintillator solution, high voltage, and amplifier gain. If this is not possible, cross calibration is necessary. For example, if certain samples of tritium-labeled material are aqueous and some are organic, the aqueous samples may be counted in a water-miscible medium such as toluene-ethanol or toluene-dioxane, and the organic samples can be counted with three times greater efficiency in toluene. A cross calibration between the two scintillator systems can then be carried out.

Guinn and Wagner also point out in what way various operational problems may be solved. (See also Sec. 5-4.)

1. *Sample insolubility:* perform simple chemical conversion, e.g., combustion to water, burning C^{14} samples to CO_2 (it is seldom worthwhile to convert gases to liquids for scintillation counting); count samples at lower concentration if they have partially frozen out; count samples in a scintillating gel.

2. *Colored samples:* count the sample twice, before and after the addition of a small amount of standard solution of the same isotope (internal standard).

3. *Fluorescence quenching:* use small amount of sample in large amount of scintillator; use internal standard method; flush with nitrogen (although variation of counting rate after flushing is considerable).

4. *Drift in gain* (important for tritium, less so for other beta emitters):

count standard sample periodically and normalize sample counting rates to standard; use very stable high-voltage supply and, if possible, leave voltage on the photomultiplier at all times.

5. *Effect of liquid volume:* use same size sample or cross-calibrate.

6. *Variation of sample bottles:* use bottles very nearly the same size; calibrate each bottle with known volume of scintillator (particularly for tritium).

7. *Static charges* (shown by a high initial counting rate, followed by rapid approach to steady correct rates, usually within a few minutes): make several successive 1-min counts until rate is constant; use "antistatic" compound; use aluminum cell with two glass windows.

Portable Instruments. Electrometers for ionization chambers as well as G-M and scintillation counters can all be made portable with built-in power supplies. In general, the pulse counters equipped with a counting-rate meter are most useful for the detection of sources of radioactive contamination and for locating radioactive material deposits. They are not usually highly accurate for the determination of the radiation intensity for a wide range of gamma-ray energy in meeting radiological safety requirements, although they may be calibrated against radium. Readings on the instrument are not independent of gamma-ray energy. These instruments usually have several ranges, permitting them to be read from a few counts per minute up to 15,000 to 20,000 cpm.

Portable ionization chambers are somewhat less sensitive than portable G-M counters. However, if they are calibrated for gamma radiation, the readings are fairly reliable over a wide range of gamma-ray energies and may give adequate information for radiation protection. Neither type of portable instrument gives significant readings for alpha or beta radiation, although ionization chambers and pulse counters are available with thin windows for the detection of alpha and beta radiation. Most laboratory ion-chamber instruments read from a few milliroentgens per hour up to several roentgens per hour, although they may be modified to read higher.

Two of the widely used personnel protection devices are the pocket chamber and the pocket dosimeter. These ion chambers are charged at the beginning of a work period, and the residual charge is determined at the end of the period. The loss in charge is proportional to the radiation which has been received. Pocket dosimeters are direct-reading quartz-fiber electroscopes. They have the advantage that they can be read directly and do not require auxiliary readers. These instruments are quite useful, but film badges are used in most laboratories for permanent records of radiation exposure.

Many of these instruments were given popular names by workers on the Manhattan Engineering Project. Several typical portable instruments are shown in Fig. 2-17.

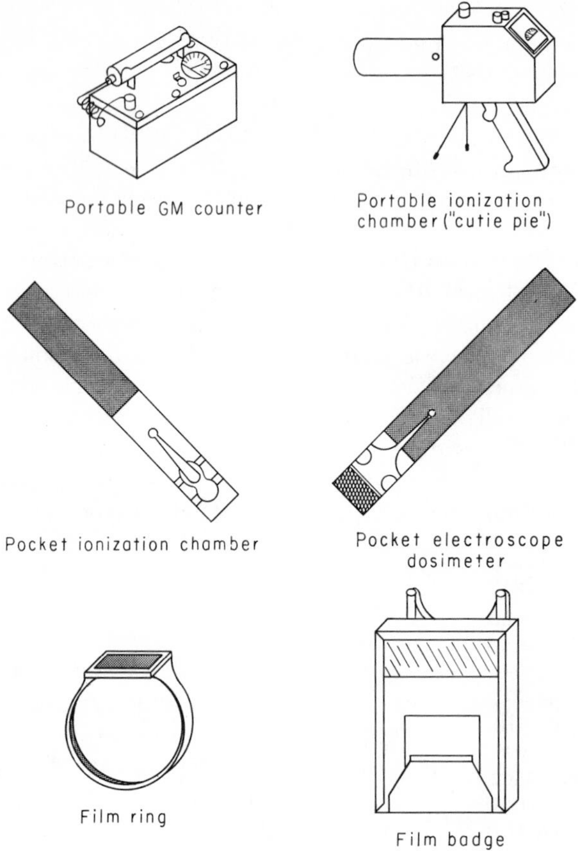

FIG. 2-17. Portable radiological safety instruments.

2-4. Photographic Emulsions and Autoradiography

It is well known that photographic film is affected by nuclear radiation. Film is used primarily for two purposes and in reality is a type of nuclear "instrumentation." It may be used either in the form of a film badge or ring to determine how much radiation has been accumulated or as a data-registration device or a localizing detector, as in the case of an autoradiogram. For personnel monitoring, the density of the blackening may be compared with that for a calibrated film. Table 2-4 gives a list of various types of commercially available films which are useful for radiation measurement in personnel monitoring. The list is taken from National Bureau of Standards Handbook 57 (58). It also shows the extension of useful exposure range by the use of two developers.

Of the two general methods of using film for data registration, little need be said of the routine use of photographs for recording all types of scientific results. However, an interesting publication by Powell and Occhialini (59) shows various examples of the ways in which photographs have been used in nuclear physics.

TABLE 2-4

PHOTOGRAPHIC EMULSIONS USEFUL FOR RADIATION MEASUREMENT IN PERSONNEL MONITORING WITH EXTENSION OF USEFUL EXPOSURE RANGE BY THE USE OF TWO DEVELOPERS

Film type	Approximate useful exposure range, r (X radiation of about 600 kev for 5 min development at 20°C)	
	In Kodak Liquid X-ray Developer	In Ansco Reprodol Developer
Ansco High Speed X-ray	0.1–10	10–100
Ansco Superay A	0.5–20	10–800
Ansco Non-Screen	0.1–8	5–500
Ansco Commercial	2.5–20	20–300
Ansco Reprolith Ortho	25–1,000	250–3,000
Dupont Type 502	0.3–10	10–100
Dupont Type 510	1–50	25–400
Dupont Type 606	20–700	200–2,000
Kodak Type 5302	20–700	200–3,000
Kodak Type 548-0 (single-coated)	5,000–40,000	10,000–100,000

One of the most powerful tools available to the radioisotope worker is the technique known as radioautography, or preferably autoradiography. A discussion of the etymology and use of these terms is given in a very comprehensive volume by Boyd (60), which is a most useful reference for workers in all scientific fields even though its main emphasis is on biology and medicine. The techniques which are outlined in that book can be very readily adapted to a wide variety of problems in all fields of science. There are a number of books and papers dealing with the theory and general practice of autoradiography, ranging from the detailed volume by Boyd and one by Yagoda (61) to various survey papers by Axelrod (62), Beiser (63), Goldschmidt-Clermont (64), and Norris and Woodruff (65).

Autoradiography may be defined as the recording of the distribution of radioactivity in a specimen by means of photographic emulsions. The technique has been in use since Becquerel first detected radioactivity. The components of any film or plate are (1) the sensitive material (usually a silver halide), (2) a dispersal medium for the sensitive material (usually gelatin), and (3) the emulsion base, which is cellulose acetate for most films and glass for slides.

A number of factors are important in determining which emulsion should be used for a particular problem. Some of these may be listed as follows:

1. Sensitivity to type of radiation of interest. Some emulsions are satisfactory for alpha particles, and some for both alpha and beta, whereas practically none is very sensitive to gamma radiation. The relative efficiency of interaction for the three types of radiation for emulsions may be of the order of 10,000, 1,000, and 10 to 100 for alpha, beta, and gamma radiation respectively.

2. Grain size. For high resolution one must use a fine-grain emulsion. However, the resolution or the ability to differentiate between adjacent active areas does not correlate with sensitivity, since large-grain emulsions are usually sensitive, whereas fine-grain emulsions are relatively insensitive.

3. Grain concentration. This is important in sensitivity. For example, an X-ray film may have the sensitive material present to about 15 per cent by weight, whereas a fine-grain nuclear emulsion may have 48 to 50 per cent by weight. Since the latter concentration corresponds to about 80 per cent by volume, the probability of a particle striking a grain in this emulsion is quite high.

4. Emulsion thickness. The thicker the emulsion the poorer the resolution of the film.

5. Background effect. The background should be as low as possible compatible with the results desired.

It is apparent that the choice of an emulsion is always a compromise among the various factors mentioned.

A number of types of emulsions are available in the United States and other countries. The best known United States manufacturers are Eastman Kodak, Ansco, and Dupont, although Kodak probably has more varieties of emulsions available for these purposes. European suppliers are Kodak, Ltd. (England), Kodak Pathe (France), Gevaert (Belgium), Ilford (England), and Agfa (Germany). Table 2-5 lists pertinent information for typical emulsions as supplied by Eastman Kodak. Similar information can be obtained from the other manufacturers mentioned.

The problem of estimating the exposure period for autoradiograms has been studied extensively. An example of such a procedure for calculating exposure periods is given by Wainwright, Anderson, Hammer, and Lehman (66). However, the general impression of most laboratory workers is that the empirical determination of this information is more generally reliable. Although an approximation might be that between 2 and 10 million beta particles per square centimeter are required to produce a usable specimen, it is usually more satisfactory to make a series of exposures. Not only is it desirable to obtain at least one usable autoradiogram, but also it is frequently desirable to have several lengths

TABLE 2-5*a*

KODAK EMULSIONS COMMONLY USED IN GROSS AUTORADIOGRAPHY*

Kodak no-screen film	Most sensitive of all X-ray film; relatively poor resolution; high background; large grain; low concentration
Kodak Type K X-ray film	Slightly less sensitivity than no-screen; large grain size; relatively poor resolution; high background
Kodak Blue Brand X-ray film (also Type F)	About one-third as sensitive as no-screen; smaller grain size; fair resolution; fairly low background
Kodak Type A X-ray film	About one-sixth as sensitive as no-screen; small grain size; good resolution; low background
Kodak Type M X-ray film	About one-twentieth as sensitive as no-screen; grain size and resolution about the same as Type A

* All these emulsions are double-coated; i.e., there is a cellulose acetate film base about 130 μ thick with a layer of photographic emulsion approximately 35 μ thick on each side. *Kodak Rapid X-ray Developer* is recommended for developing these films. They should be fixed in *Kodak X-ray Fixer* or *Kodak Acid Fixer.*

TABLE 2-5*b*

KODAK EMULSIONS COMMONLY USED IN MICROSCOPIC AUTORADIOGRAPHY*

Kodak NTA	Registers alpha tracks; relatively insensitive to beta and gamma radiation
Kodak NTB	Registers alpha tracks and also beta tracks of 30 kev or less
Kodak NTB-2	Registers alpha tracks and beta tracks up to 1 Mev; higher-energy beta radiation shows as random grains; relatively insensitive to gamma radiation
Kodak NTB-3	Registers all alpha tracks and beta tracks up to energies of 2 Mev

* These nuclear emulsions are coated on glass plates of any size specified. The emulsion thickness can be obtained in any thickness from 10 to 200 μ. However, for most purposes a thickness of more than 25 μ is not recommended. Minimum order is one dozen plates.

Table 2-5c

Kodak Emulsions for Special Problems

Kodak Autoradiographic Plates, No Screen	The regular no-screen emulsion coated on 1- by 3-in. glass plates; available only in 25-μ thickness; useful where level of activity is low and high resolution is insignificant
Kodak Autoradiographic Plates, Type A	Usual Type A X-ray emulsion coated on 1- by 3-in. glass plates; available only in 25-μ thickness; better resolution than with no-screen plates; about one-sixth as sensitive
Kodak 35-mm autoradiographic permeable-base stripping film	Available in 5-ft rolls; sensitivity between those of NTA and NTB; available in 5-μ thickness only
Kodak Autoradiographic Stripping Film, Type NTB	Emulsion thickness 10 μ; impermeable-base stripping film; available on 4- by 5-in. sheets
Liquid emulsions	Write to manufacturer for information
Pellicles	These are sheets of emulsion 1 by 3 in. or 4 by 5 in. and are 250 μ thick; emulsions available are NTA, NTB, NTB-2, and NTB-3
Kodak Fine Grain Autoradiography Stripping Plate AR.10	Emulsion layer 5 μ thick on a gelatin layer of 10 μ; under favorable conditions a resolution of 2 μ may be obtained

of exposure to emphasize various areas in the final picture. Accurate log-book records should likewise be made on each experiment. Entries should include an indication of the reading on a laboratory monitor on each specimen, the type of film used, the length of exposure, and an indication of the outcome of the exposure together with notations of any other pertinent observations.

There are clearly a number of sources of error in this technique. Boyd has an extensive discussion of the following 20 possible errors:

1. Leaching of activity
2. Displacement of tissue components and chemical components
3. Uneven thickness of the specimen
4. Light fogging of the emulsion
5. Fingerprints
6. Static discharges
7. Wetting the emulsion
8. Pressure effects and scratches
9. Contraction of the emulsion around the edges
10. Chemical effects (chemograms)
11. Diffusion of atoms and molecules

12. Nonradioactive radiation from the specimen (photoluminescence)
13. Cerenkov radiation
14. Stray radiation from other sources
15. Displacement of the image
16. Distortion of the emulsion
17. Errors in processing (lack of agitation, temperature, etc.)
18. Removal of silver grains by staining
19. Aggregates of grains
20. Errors in handling films

A number of papers of special interest in the autoradiographic techniques are included in the supplementary references to this chapter. Boyd has a bibliography of about 700 papers published before January, 1953, listed and cross-indexed in an ingenious fashion. These are primarily papers having to do with biological and medical uses of the technique, but workers in other fields will find the list quite helpful. Many of the survey papers in the list of tracer applications in Chap. 10 indicate the usefulness of this tool in widely different areas of scientific interest.

Experiment 2-1
Characteristics and Calibration of a Quartz-fiber Electroscope

The quartz-fiber electroscope is a relatively rugged and inexpensive integrating type of radiation detector. It is reliable and can be designed to give accurate results but is relatively insensitive when compared with a G-M tube or a scintillation detector. As a laboratory instrument it can be used to compare the activity of sources in the multimicrocurie and millicurie range. As other radiation detectors have gained in popularity in research, the quartz-fiber electroscope has found its main application in the form of pocket dosimeters for personnel monitoring.

Although commonly used for the detection of gamma radiation, electroscopes can be equipped with thin windows to allow passage of beta radiation or can be designed to accept an internal source. In any event, precautions must be taken to prevent damage of the fiber by air currents.

Apparatus and Materials

Quartz-fiber electroscope, e.g., Lauritsen type* (a pocket dosimeter can be used, but with reduced accuracy)

* C. S. Garner, The Lauritsen Quartz-fiber Electroscope, *J. Chem. Educ.*, vol. 26, pp. 542–546, 1949.

Charging unit (variable voltage)
Timer
Light source to illuminate the electroscope scale
Sources of gamma radiation—one or two standard sources and a source of the same radioactive material having an "unknown" strength, for example, Co^{60}, Ra^{226} with daughters, I^{131} as capsules or solutions in glass ampoules or some other convenient form
Source holder, e.g., a wire cradle or device with minimum material to scatter radiation from the source
Meter stick
Shelf support, aluminum or lead absorbers, suitable sources if absorption measurements are to be made

Procedure

If the available sources permit, arrange the electroscope and source holder so that (1) full-scale deflection of the fiber can be observed in a reasonable length of time with the most intense source in position, and (2) the fiber moves across about one-half of the scale in 30 to 45 min with the weakest source in position. (If possible, the strengths of the various sources should fall within a single decade.) Make suitable provisions for maintaining constant the position of the source holder relative to the electroscope while the sources are being compared.

Place one of the sources in position (remove all other sources from the vicinity of the electroscope) and charge the electroscope according to the instructions for the particular instrument available. It is not necessary to attempt to set the fiber at exactly zero in this experiment. Allow the fiber to move about 1 division and then start the timer. For a scale having 10 numbered divisions divided into tenths, it is convenient to take full scale as 100 marked divisions and estimate the fiber position to the nearest tenth of a division.

Take readings of the fiber position at regular time intervals, e.g., 2 min for a slowly moving fiber (say, 2 divisions/min) to 30 sec for a rapidly moving fiber (say 10 or more divisions per minute). Measure the rate of drift of the fiber for each source and for normal background in the absence of sources.

Measure the distance between the electroscope and the source (center to center), and with the most intense source in the holder establish the rate of drift for the source when the distance is increased twofold, threefold, fourfold, etc., as time permits.

If a shelf support and absorbers are available, measure the rate of drift for a source without and with absorbers in position. Beta-ray and gamma-ray absorption curves can be obtained as for Expts. 6-1 and 6-4. Absorption measurements, however, are especially time-consuming with an electroscope, and such measurements serve to emphasize the advantages of other detectors for rapid measurements with weak sources.

Analysis of Data

Tabulate the scale readings at various times for each sample and plot the data on linear graph paper. From the data for the source for which the fiber traversed the full scale, determine the range of linear response of the fiber. Typical curves are shown in Fig. 2-18.

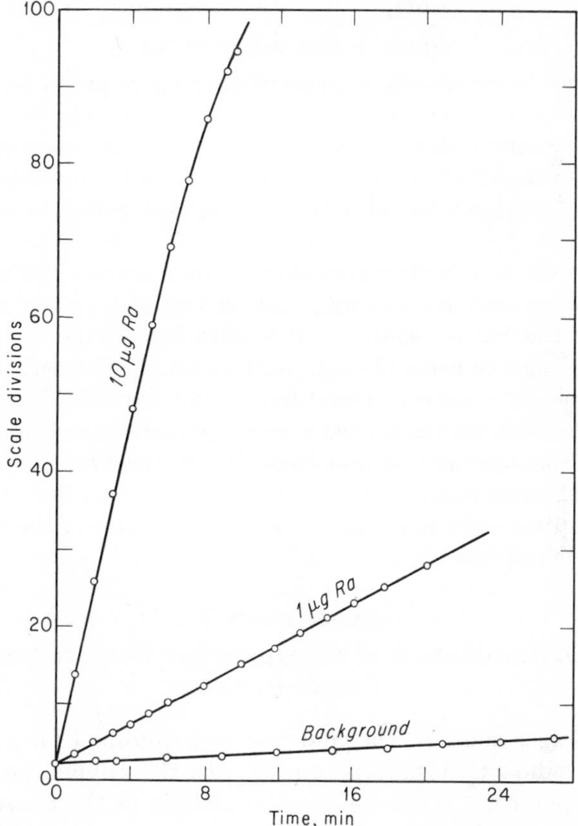

FIG. 2-18. Linearity response of quartz-fiber electroscope (Expt. 2-1).

Find the rate of drift in divisions per minute in the region of linear response for each source and for background. Subtract the background rate from the observed rate for each source to obtain the net rate for each source.

In the range of linear response,

$$\text{dpm} = K \times (\text{net divisions/min})$$

where K is the calibration constant which depends upon (1) the intrinsic efficiency of the electroscope functioning as an ionization chamber, (2) the nature of the radioactive source type and energy of emitted radiation, (3) the distance between the source and the electroscope, and (4) self-absorption in the source and absorption in the source container or mount. For two sources, 1 and 2, of the same radioactive material compared under identical circumstances,

$$\frac{\text{dpm}_1}{\text{dpm}_2} = \frac{(\text{net divisions/min})_1}{(\text{net divisions/min})_2}$$

Sources may be compared in terms of the time required for the fiber to move between two specified scale divisions in the region of linear response. The source strengths are then, of course, inversely proportional to the times required. In general, however, better precision is obtainable when the time interval is fixed rather than the scale interval for a moving fiber.

Compare the source strengths of the known sources and interpret the results, taking into account information available on the errors in the values for the known sources. Calculate the source strength of the "unknown" source using the standard which most closely resembles it, when a choice is possible. (See Chap. 7 and Expt. 7-2.)

From the data for the source which was placed at various measured distances from the electroscope, compare the observed decreases in rate of drift with those computed from the inverse-square law. Consider the effect of finite source size and the sensitive volume of the electroscope on the observed results.

Experiment 2-2
Determination of the Operating Potential of a Geiger Counter

For a Geiger counter, the counting rate obtained for a given fixed source of radioactive material varies with the applied potential. An operating potential is selected on the plateau of the curve where the counting rate is relatively insensitive to voltage change. (See Fig. 2-9.)

Apparatus and Materials

Geiger tube
Scaler with timer and register
Radioactive source of suitable counting rate, e.g., long-lived reference source (Expt. 5-1)

Linear graph paper (millimeter scale)
Straight edge

Procedure

Turn on the scaler according to the procedure recommended by the manufacturer. The high-voltage setting should be at the minimum.

Place the radioactive sample in position on a shelf or near the detector.

Turn the count switch to the "on" position and increase the high voltage until the starting potential is reached. Reset the register and timer and count 1 to 2 min or longer if necessary to obtain at least 5,000 counts.

Determine the counting rate as a function of voltage as follows:

1. *Initial rise.* Take 10- to 20-volt increments. Accumulate as many counts per point as is feasible for the counting rates observed along the rise.
2. *On plateau.* Take 25- to 50-volt increments. Accumulate at least 10,000 counts per point.
3. *Discharge region.* If this region is reached, lower the applied potential immediately. If the plateau is at least 150 volts wide, it is not necessary to find the high-voltage end of the plateau.

Analysis of Data

As the data are obtained, prepare a plot (on linear paper) of the counting rate as a function of applied potential. Prepare a copy on a scale suitable for mounting on the Geiger-tube housing.

Select and indicate the operating potential on the curve. Also label the curve, indicating:

1. Geiger-tube serial numbers
2. Geiger-tube window thickness
3. Date
4. Type of source and shelf
5. Name or initials

Experiment 2-3

Determination of the Resolving Time of a Geiger Counter

The determination of the resolving time is best accomplished with a "triggered" oscilloscope. If this instrument is not available, this experiment is instructive in making these determinations.

Apparatus and Materials

Geiger tube
Scaler and timer

Paired semicircular sources or material for preparation as described below

Blank source mounts (one circular and one semicircular)

Procedure

Paired sources for use with end-window counters may be prepared by depositing radioactive material (a beta emitter) in a small area on each of two semicircular mounts prepared by cutting a 1-in. flat copper planchet into two equal parts. Any long-lived, fairly high-energy beta emitter of high specific activity may be applied, e.g., RaD-E-F. The quantity of material used should be chosen to give a counting rate of not less than 7,000 cpm for each half. The upper limit will probably be determined by possible register losses when the sources are counted together. In addition to the usual identification the samples should be labeled 1 and 2 or R and L (for right and left).

Background should be counted with a blank disk in place. Next, one of the sources and a blank half disk should be counted. Then, the blank should be replaced by the second half-disk source without disturbing the first one, and the two counted together. Finally, the first source should be replaced by the blank without disturbing the second. About 30,000 to 40,000 counts should be accumulated for each of the three measurements involving sources.

If time permits, repeat once or twice following the same sequence of measurements.

Analysis of Data

Calculate τ according to Eq. (2-9). If the measurements were repeated, find an average value for τ. Calculate the coincidence correction for counting rates up to the limit of the scaler and register.

Plot the coincidence correction as a function of counting rate. Consider the advantages and disadvantages of linear, semilog, and log-log plots. Estimate the error in τ and the resulting error in $R' - R$. Show why the sources should be such as to make R_1 and R_2 as large as possible within the range of the instrument.

Experiment 2-4

Determination of the Operating Characteristics of a Windowless Gas-flow Proportional Counter

The type of instrument to be studied will detect alpha, beta, and gamma radiation. Samples are placed inside the sample chamber, which has 2π geometry (a counting yield of 51 per cent for alpha particles; 50 per cent plus backscattering for beta particles; about 1 per cent for gamma rays, except for very-low-energy rays for which the yield is greater than 1 per cent). (See Chap. 7 and Expt. 7-2.)

Apparatus and Materials

Proportional counter: windowless, gas-flow, or purging type
Source of alpha and beta radiation, e.g., NBS RaD-E-F source
Long-lived U_3O_8 reference source (Expt. 5-1)
Copies of excerpts from manufacturer's instruction manual

Procedure

Follow carefully the manufacturer's instructions for operating the counter. Using a standard RaD-E-F source, measure the counting rate at various applied voltages, using 50-volt increments of voltage. Follow the operating curve to the end of the beta plateau, plotting the curve as data are obtained.

Choose an alpha and beta-gamma operating potential. Measure the beta-gamma counting rate of the U_3O_8 reference source, prepared in Expt. 5-1 if it can be introduced into the counting chamber conveniently.

Measure the alpha and the beta-gamma background rates.

Analysis of Data

Prepare a plot of the counting rate as a function of applied potential through the alpha and beta-gamma (proportional and Geiger) regions. Label the curve at the operating potentials.

From (1) the nature of the RaD-E-F radiations, (2) the source construction, and (3) the counting yield for the chamber, compare the observed net alpha and beta rates for the standard sample with those expected. Explain any discrepancies.

From the net counting rate of the U_3O_8 source and the alpha counting yield, calculate the effective disintegration rate for the source.

Experiment 2-5

Characteristics of a Gamma-detecting Scintillation Counter

The type of scintillation detector to be studied consists of a thallium-activated sodium iodide crystal optically coupled to a multiplier phototube. The crystal may or may not have a well. Samples may be contained in screw-cap vials (or sealed ampoules) which can be placed in a holder near the crystal if it is of the solid type or in a test tube and lowered into the crystal if it is of the well type.

Selection of an operating potential (for a given amplifier gain and discriminator-bias voltage setting) of a gamma scintillation counter is not so straightforward as for a Geiger counter. The slope of the plateau for a source is greater, usually, than for a Geiger counter, and there is no plateau for background. Furthermore, the length and slope of the plateau for a source depend upon the source strength. Commonly, the length decreases and the slope increases with decreasing source strength. The various criteria used to select the optimum operating potential are discussed in Secs. 2-3 and 3-3.

The detection coefficient or counting yield Y will depend upon the various factors discussed in Chap. 7. To a major extent the value of Y is determined by the factors G and f_E. For a well-type crystal, G approaches 4π. The intrinsic efficiency for gamma rays f_E depends upon the size of the crystal and the gamma-ray energy, but it is roughly an order of magnitude greater than that for a thin-window Geiger or proportional tube.

Gamma scintillation counters can be used to measure the activity of high-energy beta emitters by detection of bremsstrahlung. The sample may be counted as a liquid contained in a suitable vial.

Apparatus and Materials

- Scintillation detector
  - Sodium iodide crystal, solid or well type
  - Necessary associated electronic equipment: preamplifier, well-regulated high-voltage power supply, scaler or counting-rate meter
  - Timer
- Sources of gamma radiation, e.g., Co^{60}, I^{131} (if possible, one or more standard sources)
- Source of relatively high-energy beta radiation, e.g., P^{32}
- Source containers—vials, test tubes

Procedure

Turn on the counter according to the operating instructions for the instrument.

Place a source in position. **Caution:** If a well-type crystal is being used, be extremely careful to lower the sample gently and take all precautions to avoid contamination of the crystal.

Measure the counting rate as a function of the applied potential. Plot the data as soon as each measurement is completed. *Do not* increase the applied potential far beyond the high-voltage end of the plateau into the region of rapid rise in counting rate, and *in any case* do not allow the applied potential to exceed the maximum value recommended for the multiplier phototube.

Remove the source, place an empty source container in position, and measure the background rate over the same range of applied potential.

If time permits, (1) find the characteristic curve for one or more additional sources, e.g., sources of the same radionuclide differing in strength or sources of different radionuclides, and (2) compare the counting rates attainable when equal aliquots of the radionuclide available are counted with the scintillation counter and with a thin-window Geiger or proportional counter.

Analysis of Data

1. Prepare a plot showing the counting rate as a function of the applied potential for the gamma source or sources and for background.
2. Evaluate the slope of the plateau in per cent per 100 volts for each radionuclide.
3. Prepare a second plot of the criteria for optimum operating potential as a function of applied potential.
4. If data are available for a standard source, calculate the detection coefficient for the particular radionuclide and the particular measurement conditions.

Experiment 2-6
Introduction to Autoradiography

It was by means of the photographic plate that radioactivity was discovered by Becquerel in 1896. The photographic emulsion was, then, the first detector used for nuclear radiation, and it is still one of our most important nuclear-radiation detectors. It is used for studying (1) single nuclear events, e.g., high-energy reactions which produce tracks, and (2) the geography and geometry of radioactive material located in or on an object, e.g., radioiodine in tissue, and for measuring radiation dosage, e.g., as film-badge dosimeters.

In this experiment photographic film is used to show the location of a beta-emitting radioactive material on the surface of a metal planchet and within a plant leaf. (See Fig. 2-19.)

Apparatus and Materials

Radioactive sources
Eastman No-Screen X-ray film or equivalent as pieces 1 by 3 in. and 1½ by 1½ in. contained in two identified lightproof boxes
Microscope slides, 1 by 3 in.
Cardboard backing, 1 by 3 in. and 1½ by 1½ in.
Black paper, 3 by 5 in. and 3 by 3 in.
Saran wrap (or equivalent), 2 by 3 in.
Box of labels
Scotch tape

Scissors
Tweezers
Darkroom facilities
  X-ray developer and fixer solutions, acetic acid for short stop, wash water
  Trays, tongs
  Darkroom light with filter for X-ray film
  Clock
Printing paper and necessary photographic solutions
Printing frame
Ferrotype tin for glossy prints

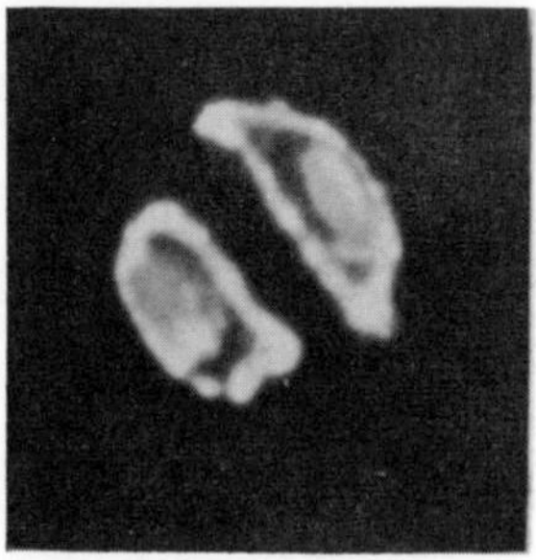

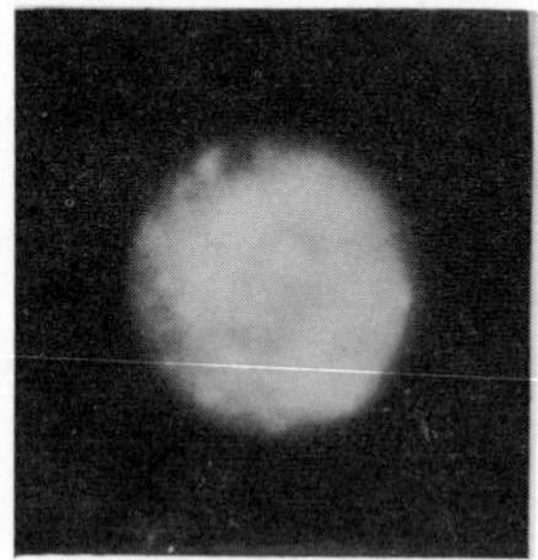

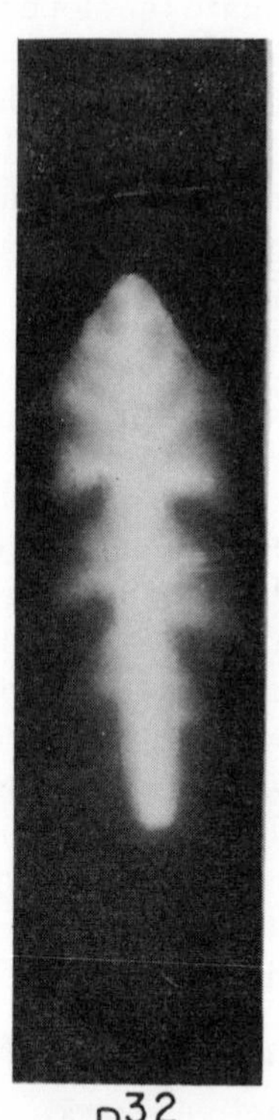

FIG. 2-19. Typical autoradiograms (Expt. 2-6).

Procedure

Plant Leaf. If the plant has not been previously prepared, place a young plant, e.g., dandelion, tradescantia, or tomato, in a container such as a test tube containing water and the radioactive material, e.g., phosphorus 32. Only the roots should be immersed in the liquid. Generally a few microcuries will be required, but the exact amount needed to provide suitable uptake for a convenient exposure time (in the range of 3 to 24 hr) will depend upon the individual plant and the uptake time.

With tweezers remove a leaf or a portion of a leaf somewhat smaller in area than the 1- by 3-in. glass slide. Place the leaf on the glass slide and, with the leaf flat and completely uncurled, wrap the slide and leaf in a single piece of Saran foil with the excess foil under the glass slide. Mount at least one additional leaf in the same manner.

Obtain an estimate of the rate of emission of beta rays from each leaf by using a suitable calibrated counter or counting-rate meter, and then take the mounted leaves into the darkroom and, with the yellow light turned on, place a piece of labeled film over one of the leaves. (The film may be labeled by cutting off corners, by notching the edge near a corner, or by punching a number of holes near one corner with a pin. At all times handle the film on the edge to avoid leaving fingerprints on the *two* emulsions.) Place a piece of cardboard over the film; center the slide, film, and cardboard; and then wrap the assembly tightly in a piece of paper. Wrap the assembly in two pieces of black paper so that the inner and outer overlaps do not come together. Seal the outer fold with Scotch tape and place a label on the other side of the packet. Label the packet indicating type of plant, radioactive material, your name, date, and time of day. Follow the same procedure for the additional leaves.

Estimate the exposure time on the assumption that the integrated beta flux should be about 10^6 per square centimeter of film. If three leaves are available, expose one for the estimated time, one for a shorter time, and one for a longer time in order to demonstrate the effect of exposure time. In selecting the range of exposure times take into consideration the general response characteristics of photographic emulsion.

At the end of the exposure time, process each film according to the manufacturer's recommended procedure. Care must be taken during the developing step to prevent the emulsion from sticking to the bottom of the tray. After the film has been thoroughly dried, prints should be prepared and mounted along with the film for the report.

What do you conclude about the uptake and distribution of radioactive material in the plant after examination of the autoradiogram?

Sources on Flat Planchets. Take at least two flat covered sources, e.g., U_3O_8 reference source and a pair of split RaD-E-F sources, and mount each in a manner similar to that used for the leaf in the previous part. Use 1½- by 1½-in. cardboard squares in place of the glass slide, omit the Saran foil, and place the film over the top of the source. Place a piece of cardboard over the film and wrap the assembly with paper.

Estimate the exposure time from the counting rate of each source. Process the film and prepare prints as for the plant leaves.

What do you conclude about the uniformity of the deposit of radioactive material and the quality of each source as a "point" source?

Cited References

1. Price, W. J.: "Nuclear Radiation Detection," McGraw-Hill, New York, 1958.
2. Jordan, W. H.: Detection of Nuclear Particles, *Ann. Rev. Nuclear Sci.*, vol. 1, pp. 209–226, 1952.
3. Korff, S. A.: "Electron and Nuclear Counters: Theory and Use," 2d ed., Van Nostrand, Princeton, N.J., 1955.
4. Strong, J., et al.: "Procedures in Experimental Physics," Prentice-Hall, Englewood Cliffs, N.J., 1943.
5. Wilkinson, D. H.: "Ionization Chambers and Counters," Cambridge, New York, 1950.
6. Birks, J. B.: "Scintillation Counters," McGraw-Hill, New York, 1953.
7. Swank, R. K.: Recent Advances in Theory of Scintillation Phosphors, *Nucleonics*, vol. 12, no. 3, pp. 14–19, March, 1954.
8. Hardwick, E. R., and W. G. McMillan: Study of the Scintillation Process, *J. Chem. Phys.*, vol. 26, pp. 1463–1470, June, 1957.
9. Jordan, W. H., and P. R. Bell: Scintillation Counters, *Nucleonics*, vol. 5, no. 4, pp. 30–41, October, 1949.
10. Swank, R. K.: Nuclear Particle Detection (Characteristics of Scintillators), *Ann. Rev. Nuclear Sci.*, vol. 4, pp. 111–140, 1954.
11. Sangster, R. C., and J. W. Irvine, Jr.: Study of Organic Scintillators, *J. Chem. Phys.*, vol. 24, pp. 670–715, April, 1956.
12. Hayes, F. N., D. G. Ott, and V. N. Kerr: Liquid Scintillators. II. Pulse-height Comparison of Secondary Solutes, *Nucleonics*, vol. 14, no. 1, pp. 42–45, January, 1956.
13. Blau, M., and B. Dreyfus: Multiplier Photo-tube in Radioactive Measurements, *Rev. Sci. Instr.*, vol. 16, pp. 245–248, 1945.
14. Morton, G. A.: Recent Developments in the Scintillation Counter Field, *IRE Trans. on Nuclear Sci.*, vol. NS-3, no. 4, pp. 122–135, November, 1956.
15. Morton, G. A.: Recent Developments in the Scintillation Counter Field, *Proc. Intern. Conf. Peaceful Uses Atomic Energy, Geneva, 1955*, vol. 14, pp. 246–259, United Nations, New York, 1956.
16. Scintillation Counting—1956, *Nucleonics*, vol. 14, no. 4, pp. 36–64, April, 1956.
17. Robinson, K. W.: Pulse-height Resolution, *Nucleonics*, vol. 10, no. 3, pp. 34, March, 1952.
18. Van Rennes, A. B.: Pulse Amplitude Analysis in Nuclear Research. I, *Nucleonics*, vol. 10, no. 7, pp. 20–27, July, 1952; II, vol. 10, no. 8, pp. 22–28, August, 1952; III, vol. 10, no. 9, pp. 32–38, September, 1952; IV, vol. 10, no. 10, pp. 50–56, October, 1952.
19. Higinbotham, W. A.: Survey of Pulse Height Analyzers, *IRE Trans. on Nuclear Sci.*, vol. NS-3, no. 4, pp. 3–8, November, 1956.
20. Higinbotham, W. A., J. Gallagher, and M. Sands: Model 200 Pulse Counter, *Rev. Sci. Instr.*, vol. 18, pp. 706–715, October, 1947.
21. Bousquet, A. G.: Counting Rate Meters versus Scalers, *Nucleonics*, vol. 4, no. 2, pp. 67–76, February, 1949.

22. Harris, C. C., P. R. Bell, and J. E. Francis: Aural Counting-rate Indicator, *Nucleonics*, vol. 15, no. 9, pp. 152–153, September, 1957.
23. Elmore, W. C., and M. Sands: "Electronics: Experimental Techniques," McGraw-Hill, New York, 1949.
24. Mandeville, C. E., and M. V. Scherb: Nuclear Disintegration Schemes and the Coincidence Method, *Nucleonics*, vol. 3, no. 4, pp. 2–12, October, 1948.
25. Palevsky, H., R. K. Swank, and R. Grenchik: Design of Dynamic Condenser Electrometers, *Rev. Sci. Instr.*, vol. 18, pp. 298–314, May, 1947.
26. Kulp, J. L.: Low-level Counting, Key to Advances in Radiocarbon Dating, *Nucleonics*, vol. 12, no. 12, pp. 19–21, December, 1954.
27. Libby, W. F.: "Radiocarbon Dating," 2d ed., University of Chicago Press, Chicago, 1955.
28. Johnston, W. H.: Low-level Counting and the Future of Isotopic Tracers, *Proc. Intern. Conf. Peaceful Uses Atomic Energy, Geneva, 1955*, vol. 14, pp. 149–155, United Nations, New York, 1956.
29. Loevinger, R., and M. Berman: Efficiency Criteria in Radioactivity Counting, *Nucleonics*, vol. 9, no. 1, pp. 26–39, July, 1951.
30. Borkowski, C. J.: Instruments for Measuring Radioactivity, *Anal. Chem.*, vol. 21, pp. 348–352, 1949.
31. Kelley, G. G., P. R. Bell, R. C. Davis, and N. H. Lazar: Intrinsic Scintillator Resolution, *IRE Trans. on Nuclear Sci.*, vol. NS-3, no. 4, pp. 57–58, November, 1956.
32. Shonka, F. R., and R. J. Stephenson: Simplified Ionization Chamber, *U.S. Atomic Energy Comm. Rept.* IDA-7 (Isotopes Division Circular A-7).
33. Rossi, B. B., and H. H. Staub: "Ionization Chambers and Counters: Experimental Techniques," McGraw-Hill, New York, 1949.
34. Janney, C. D., and B. J. Moyer: Routine Use of Ionization Chamber Method for C^{14} Assay, *Rev. Sci. Instr.*, vol. 19, pp. 667–674, October, 1948.
35. Bernstein, W., and R. Ballentine: Gas Phase Counting of Low Energy Beta-emitters, *Rev. Sci. Instr.*, vol. 21, pp. 158–162, February, 1950.
36. Nader, J. S., G. R. Hagee, and L. R. Setter: Evaluating the Performance of the Internal Counter, *Nucleonics*, vol. 12, no. 6, pp. 29–31, June, 1954.
37. Robinson, C. V.: Improved Methane Proportional Counting Method for Tritium Assay, *Nucleonics*, vol. 13, no. 11, pp. 90–91, November, 1955.
38. Brown, S. C.: Theory and Operation of Geiger-Müller Counters. I, The Discharge Mechanisms, *Nucleonics*, vol. 2, no. 6, pp. 10–22, June, 1948; II, Counters for Specific Purposes, vol. 3, no. 2, pp. 50–64, August, 1948; III, The Circuits, vol. 3, no. 4, pp. 46–61, October, 1948.
39. New Forms of Geiger-Mueller Counters, *Nucleonics*, vol. 13, no. 9, p. 77, September, 1955.
40. Libby, W. F.: Measurement of Radioactive Tracers, Particularly C^{14}, S^{35}, T, and Other Long-lived Low-energy Activities, *Anal. Chem.*, vol. 19, pp. 2–6, 1947.
41. Eidinoff, M. L.: Measurement of Radiocarbon as Carbon Dioxide inside Geiger-Müller Counters, *Anal. Chem.*, vol. 22, pp. 529–534, April, 1950.
42. Weisburger, J. H., and H. J. Lipner: Which I^{131} Counting System Is Best for Laboratory Use? *Nucleonics*, vol. 12, no. 5, pp. 21–23, May, 1954.
43. Gentner, W. H., H. Maier-Leibnitz, and W. Bothe: "An Atlas of Typical Expansion Chamber Photographs," Interscience, New York, 1954.
44. Fretter, W. B.: Nuclear Particle Detection (Cloud Chambers and Bubble Chambers), *Ann. Rev. Nuclear Sci.*, vol. 5, pp. 145–178, 1955.

45. Fricke, H., and S. Morse: The Action of X-rays on Ferrous Sulfate Solutions, *Phil. Mag.*, vol. 7, pp. 129–141, 1929.
46. Weiss, J., A. O. Allen, and H. A. Schwarz: Use of the Fricke Ferrous Sulfate Dosimeter for Gamma-ray Doses in the Range 4 to 40 Kr, *Proc. Intern. Conf. Peaceful Uses Atomic Energy, Geneva, 1955*, vol. 14, pp. 179–181, United Nations, New York, 1956.
47. Taplin, G. V.: Development of Direct-reading Chemical Dosimeters for Measurement of X, Gamma, and Fast Neutron Radiation, *Proc. Intern. Conf. Peaceful Uses of Atomic Energy, Geneva, 1955*, vol. 14, pp. 227–231, United Nations, New York, 1956.
48. Davison, S., S. A. Goldblith, and B. E. Proctor: Glass Dosimetry, *Nucleonics*, vol. 14, no. 1, pp. 34–39, January, 1956.
49. Siegbahn, K: "Beta- and Gamma-ray Spectroscopy," Interscience, New York, 1955.
50. Marshall, J. H.: How to Figure Shapes of Beta-ray Spectra, *Nucleonics*, vol. 13, no. 8, pp. 34–38, August, 1955.
51. Borkowski, C. J.: Low Energy Gamma Scintillation Spectrometry, *IRE Trans. on Nuclear Sci.*, vol. NS-3, no. 4, pp. 71–76, November, 1956.
52. Francis, J. E., P. R. Bell, and C. C. Harris: Medical Scintillation Spectrometry, *Nucleonics*, vol. 13, no. 11, pp. 82–88, November, 1955.
53. Guinn, V. P., and C. D. Wagner: Routine Liquid Scintillation Counting of Single and Multiplex Beta Activities, Paper P-567, prepared for presentation at the American Chemical Society meeting, 1957.
54. Williams, D. L., F. N. Hayes, R. J. Kandel, and W. H. Rogers: Preparation of C^{14} Standard for Liquid Scintillation Counter, *Nucleonics*, vol. 14, no. 1, pp. 62–64, January, 1956.
55. Hayes, F. N., B. S. Rogers, and W. H. Langham: Counting Suspensions in Liquid Scintillators, *Nucleonics*, vol. 14, no. 3, pp. 48–51, March, 1956.
56. Rosenthal, D. J., and H. O. Anger: Liquid Scintillation Counting of Tritium and C^{14} Labeled Compounds, *Rev. Sci. Instr.*, vol. 25, pp. 670–674, July, 1954.
57. Hayes, F. N., E. C. Anderson, and J. R. Arnold: Liquid Scintillation Counting of Natural Radiocarbon, *Proc. Intern. Conf. Peaceful Uses Atomic Energy, Geneva, 1955*, vol. 14, pp. 188–192, United Nations, New York, 1956.
58. National Bureau of Standards Handbook 57, August, 1954.
59. Powell, C. F., and G. P. S. Occhialini: "Nuclear Physics in Photographs," Oxford, New York, 1947.
60. Boyd, G. A.: "Autoradiography in Biology and Medicine," Academic Press, New York, 1955.
61. Yagoda, H. J.: "Radioactive Measurements with Nuclear Emulsions," Wiley, New York, 1949.
62. Axelrod, D. H.: The Radioautographic Techniques, *Advances in Biol. and Med. Phys.*, vol. 2, pp. 134–170, 1951 (also published as *U.S. Atomic Energy Comm. Rept.* UCRL-579).
63. Beiser, A.: Nuclear Emulsion Technique, *Revs. Modern Phys.*, vol. 24, pp. 273–311, October, 1952.
64. Goldschmidt-Clermont, Y.: Photographic Emulsions, *Ann. Rev. Nuclear Sci.*, vol. 3, pp. 141–170, 1953.
65. Norris, W. P., and L. A. Woodruff: The Fundamentals of Radioautography, *Ann. Rev. Nuclear Sci.*, vol. 5, pp. 297–326, 1955.
66. Wainwright, W. W., E. C. Anderson, P. C. Hammer, and C. A. Lehman: Simplified Autoradiography Exposure Calculations, *Nucleonics*, vol. 12, no. 1, pp. 19–21, January, 1954.

Supplementary References

Allen, Augustine O.: A Survey of Recent American Research in the Radiation Chemistry of Aqueous Solutions, *Proc. Intern. Conf. Peaceful Uses Atomic Energy, Geneva, 1955*, vol. 7, pp. 513–520, United Nations, New York, 1956.

Bejdl, W.: Ist die Autoradiographie als histologische Untersuchungsmethode anwendbar? *Anat. Anz.*, vol. 99, no. 6/9, pp. 124–129, 1952.

Berg, W. F.: Autoradiography, *Med. Biol. Illus.*, vol. 1, pp. 95–99, April, 1951.

Bleuler, E., and G. J. Goldsmith: "Experimental Nucleonics," Rinehart, New York, 1952.

Bourne, G. H.: Autoradiography, *Biol. Revs. Cambridge Phil. Soc.*, vol. 27, pp. 108–131, 1952.

Brownell, G. L., and H. S. Lockhart: CO_2 Counter Techniques for C^{14} Measurement, *MIT Tech. Rept.* 30, 1949 (also published as *U.S. Atomic Energy Comm. Rept.* NP-1079).

Clark, G. L.: "Applied X-rays," 4th ed., McGraw-Hill, New York, 1955.

Cobb, J., and A. K. Solomon: The Detection of Beta-radiation by Photographic Film, *Rev. Sci. Instr.*, vol. 19, pp. 441–447, July, 1948.

Coltman, J. W., and F. H. Marshall: Some Characteristics of the Photomultiplier Radiation Detector, *Phys. Rev.*, vol. 72, p. 528A, Sept. 5, 1947.

Compton, A. H., and S. K. Allison: "X-rays in Theory and Experiment," Van Nostrand, Princeton, N.J., 1935.

Curran, S. C.: "Luminescence and the Scintillation Counter," Butterworth, London, 1953.

——— and J. D. Craggs: "Counting Tubes: Theory and Applications," Academic Press, New York, 1949.

Eccles, W. H., and F. W. Jordan: Trigger Relay, *Electrician*, vol. 83, p. 298, September, 1919.

Eidinoff, M. L.: Measurement of Radiocarbon as CO_2 in Geiger-Muller Counters, *Science*, vol. 108, pp. 535–536, Nov. 12, 1948.

Engstrom, R. W.: Some Recent Developments in Multiplier Phototubes, *Nucleonics*, vol. 12, no. 3, p. 26, March, 1954.

Evans, T. C.: Selection of Radioautographic Technique for Problems in Biology, *Nucleonics*, vol. 2, no. 3, pp. 52–58, March, 1948.

Fitzgerald, P. J.: Radioautography in Cancer, *Cancer*, vol. 5, pp. 166–194, January, 1952.

———, M. L. Eidinoff, J. E. Knoll, and E. B. Simmel: Tritium in Radioautography, *Science*, vol. 114, pp. 494–498, Nov. 9, 1951.

Ghelardi, R. P., and C. H. Brown: Electronic Instruments for Use with Geiger-Muller Tubes, *Nucleonics*, vol. 1, no. 1, pp. 50–59, September, 1947.

Gomberg, H. J.: A New High Resolution System of Autoradiography, *Nucleonics*, vol. 9, no. 4, pp. 28–43, October, 1951.

Gorbman, A.: Radioautography in Biological Research, *Nucleonics*, vol. 2, no. 6, pp. 30–43, June, 1948.

Graves, A. C., and D. K. Froman (eds.): "Miscellaneous Physical and Chemical Techniques of the Los Alamos Project: Experimental Techniques," McGraw-Hill, New York, 1952.

Gray, L. H.: The Ionization Method of Measuring Neutron Energy, *Proc. Cambridge Phil. Soc.*, vol. 40, pp. 72–102, March, 1944.

Gross, J., R. Bogoroch, N. J. Nadler, and C. P. Leblond: The Theory and Methods of the Radioautographic Localization of Radioelements in Tissues, *Am. J. Roentgenol. Radium Therapy*, vol. 65, pp. 420–458, March, 1951.

Hayes, F. N., and R. G. Gould: Liquid Scintillation Counting of Tritium-labeled Water and Organic Compounds, *Science*, vol. 117, pp. 480–483, May 1, 1953.

———, D. G. Ott, V. N. Kerr, and B. S. Rogers: Liquid Scintillators. I, Pulse Height Comparison of Primary Solutes, *Nucleonics*, vol. 13, no. 12, pp. 38–41, December, 1955.

Healea, M.: Bibliography: Radiation Measurement, *Nucleonics*, vol. 2, no. 2, pp. 63–65, February, 1948.

———: Bibliography: Counting Circuits and Secondary Emission, *Nucleonics*, vol. 2, no. 3, pp. 66–74, March, 1948.

Heller, D. A., and J. G. Hamilton: Radioautography: Technic, in O. Glasser (ed.), "Medical Physics," vol. II, pp. 817–823, Year Book Publishers, Chicago, 1950.

Herz, R. H.: Autoradiography, *Med. Radiography Photography*, vol. 26, pp. 46–51, 84, 1950.

Hine, G. J.: Beta- and Gamma-ray Spectroscopy. I, *Nucleonics*, vol. 3, no. 6, pp. 32–42, December, 1948; II, vol. 4, no. 2, pp. 56–66, February, 1949.

Hofstadter, R.: Crystal Counters. I, *Nucleonics*, vol. 4, no. 4, pp. 2–27, April, 1949; II, vol. 4, no. 5, pp. 29–43, May, 1949.

Hughes, D. J.: "Pile Neutron Research," Addison-Wesley, Reading, Mass., 1953.

Kallmann, H.: Luminescent Counters, *Research* (*London*), vol. 2, pp. 62–68, February, 1949.

———: Scintillation Counting with Solutions, *Phys. Rev.*, vol. 78, pp. 621–622, June 1, 1950.

Kannerstein, M.: Radioautography: A Brief Review of Various Aspects and Applications with Special Reference to Thyroid Neoplasms, *J. Newark Beth Israel Hospital*, vol. 3, pp. 269–286, October, 1952.

Kelsey, F. E.: An Internal Geiger Counter for the Assay of Low Specific Activity Samples of Carbon 14 and Other Weak Beta Emitters in Biological Samples, *Science*, vol. 109, pp. 566–567, June 3, 1949.

Lauritsen, C. C., and T. Lauritsen: A Simple Quartz Fiber Electrometer, *Rev. Sci. Instr.*, vol. 8, pp. 438–439, November, 1937.

Lawson, R. W., and V. F. Hess: Erfahrungen und Spezialergebnisse bei der Zahlung von Alpha-Teilchen, *Sitzber. Akad. Wiss. Wien*, vol. 127, sec. IIa, pp. 599–629, 1918.

Lazar, N. H., R. C. David, and P. R. Bell: Peak Efficiency of NaI(Tl) Crystals for Gamma Rays from 0.150 to 7.5 MEV, *IRE Trans. on Nuclear Sci.*, vol. NS-3, no. 4, pp. 136–137, November, 1956.

Lewis, W. B.: "Electrical Counting, with Special Reference to Counting Alpha and Beta Particles," Cambridge, New York, 1942.

Liebson, S. H., and H. Friedman: Self-quenching Halogen-filled Counters, *Rev. Sci. Instr.*, vol. 19, pp. 303–306, May, 1948.

Lindemann, F. A., A. F. Lindemann, and T. C. Keeley: New Form of Electrometer, *Phil. Mag.*, vol. 47, pp. 577–583, March, 1924.

Montgomery, C. G., and D. D. Montgomery: Geiger-Muller Counters, *J. Franklin Inst.*, vol. 231, pp. 447–467, May, 1941; vol. 231, pp. 509–545, June, 1941.

Morton, G. A.: The Scintillation Counter, *Advances in Electronics*, vol. 4, pp. 69–107, 1952.

Murray, R. LeR.: "Introduction to Nuclear Engineering," Prentice-Hall, Englewood Cliffs, N.J., 1954.

Neher, H. V., and W. W. Harper: A High Speed Geiger-counter Circuit, *Phys. Rev.*, vol. 49, pp. 940–943, June 15, 1936.

Neher, H. V., and W. H. Pickering: Modified High Speed Geiger Counter Circuit, *Phys. Rev.*, vol. 53, p. 316, Feb. 15, 1938.

Practical Aspects of Radioactivity Instruments, *Nucleonics*, vol. 8, no. 6, supplement, pp. 1–32, June, 1951.

Reynolds, G. T.: Solid and Liquid Scintillation Counters, *Nucleonics*, vol. 10, no. 7, pp. 46–53, July, 1952.

Simons, C. S.: Instrumentation for an Agricultural Radioisotope Laboratory, *Atomics*, vol. 3, pp. 288–292, November, 1952.

Taylor, D.: "The Measurement of Radio Isotopes," Methuen, London, 1951.

Verkert, B.: Autoradiography in the Surface Phenomena, *Nucleonics*, vol. 14, pp. 60–64, July, 1956.

Wagner, C. D., and V. P. Guinn: For Low Specific Activity Use Scintillation Counting, *Nucleonics*, vol. 13, no. 10, pp. 56–59, October, 1955.

Wainwright, W. W.: Detail and Survey Radioautographs, *Science*, vol. 109, pp. 585–587, June 10, 1949 (also published in *N.Y. J. Dentistry*, vol. 20, pp. 309–319, 1950).

West, D.: Energy Measurements with Proportional Counters, *Progr. in Nuclear Phys.*, vol. 3, pp. 18–62, 1953.

Wilson, R. R., D. R. Corson, and C. P. Baker: Particle and Quantum Detectors, *U.S. Atomic Energy Comm. Rept.* NP-1889, 1950.

Wing, J., and W. H. Johnston: Method for Counting Tritium in Tritiated Water, *Science*, vol. 121, pp. 674–675, June 3, 1955.

3

Errors in Radioactivity Measurements

3-1. Sources of Error

An important part of a report of the results of any experiment is an indication of the reliability of the results. This is particularly important when slightly different results would lead to major changes in the interpretation of the results. Moreover, the planning of an experiment should be influenced by the degree of reliability expected for the results. In this chapter we shall consider first the estimation of errors in general and then errors which are characteristic of radioactivity measurements.

General Sources of Error. The results of experiments involving radioactivity are subject, of course, to the usual errors arising from common laboratory manipulations. Such errors might result from:

1. Measurement of volume and weight
2. Losses resulting from chemical separations
3. Losses resulting from transfer operations
4. Impurities—chemical and radiochemical
5. Preparation of radioactive sources—variations due to chemical instability: absorption of moisture; chemical exchange of isotopes, e.g., CO_2 in air with $BaC^{14}O_3$; nonuniformity of area, thickness, etc.
6. Arithmetical calculations

Errors Characteristic of Radioactivity Measurements. The very nature of the process of radioactive decay and the properties of the radiation emitted lead to errors in radioactivity measurements which are not found, for example, in the usual chemical measurements. The following are some of these sources of uncertainty:

1. Random disintegration process and, therefore, random emission of radiation from a source
2. Detection of the nuclear radiation
   a. Performance of the detector

(1) Failure to resolve events at high counting rates—coincidence losses

(2) Variation in performance due to changes in temperature, voltage applied, efficiency, aging (Geiger tube)

(3) Erratic performance—spurious counts, photosensitivity, "memory" effect, charge accumulation on internal sources

(4) Variation in natural background and variation in "laboratory" background due to changes in location or shielding of large sources in the laboratory

b. Performance of auxiliary equipment

(1) Erratic performance of electronic equipment—electronic "noise," "noise" from power line or vibration, electronic oscillation, failure of scaling circuit, etc.

(2) Coincidence losses in scaler (normally negligible relative to losses in detector)

(3) Erratic performance of mechanical register or other recording device

(4) Erratic performance of timing device

3. Radiation-measurement technique

a. Variation in radiation intensity reaching the detector resulting from interaction of the radiation with matter before reaching the detector

(1) Absorption of beta rays in the window or wall of the detector, cover over the source, and air

(2) Absorption of gamma rays with the production of secondary radiation

(3) Self-absorption of radiation

(4) Scattering and backscattering of radiation

b. Variation in radiation intensity reaching the detector due to uncertainties in positioning radioactive sources relative to the detector

The relative importance of each of the various factors listed above varies with the type of detector, type of radiation, nature of the experiment, i.e., whether relative or absolute measurements are involved, etc. A given experimental result will have an over-all, observed uncertainty resulting from one or more of these factors.

3-2. General Treatment of Errors

Classification of Errors. The errors listed above could be classified as either (1) systematic or determinate errors or (2) accidental or indeterminate errors. The former are minimized by applying known correction or calibration factors. For example, allowance for a chemical yield less than 100 per cent can be made on the basis of results obtained for a standard sample. Similarly the efficiency of a radiation detector may be determined by calibration of the detector with a standard source of radiation.

Even when allowance is made for all systematic errors, the values obtained from a set of supposedly identical experiments will show some variation. For example, samples measured with a very carefully calibrated pipette will show small variations in volume even when extreme care is exercised. These accidental errors are minimized by experimental technique. When they are treated in accordance with probability considerations, it is possible to express an experimental result with an error for which a probability of occurrence may be assigned. It should be pointed out that even the correction or calibration factors applied to minimize systematic errors are subject to accidental errors inherent in their determination.

Accidental or Indeterminate Errors. Before continuing with accidental errors, it is necessary to examine the definition of the term "error." General usage of the term is not consistent with its precise definition. It will be recalled that an error ϵ in a measured value X is defined as follows:

$$\epsilon = X - T \tag{3-1}$$

where T is the true or correct value. The magnitude of ϵ is a measure of the accuracy of the measured value. Actually, the true value is never known with absolute certainty, so that an error, so defined, can never be calculated. Instead, the difference between each measured value of a set of measurements and the best approximation to the true value is calculated. If only accidental errors are assumed, the best approximation to the true value is the arithmetic mean value $\bar{X}$ of the set of measurements. The difference x, referred to as a deviation, is given by the expression

$$x = X - \bar{X} \tag{3-2}$$

The value of the arithmetic mean of a set of n measurements is obtained from the usual equation

$$\bar{X} = \frac{\sum^{n} X_i}{n} \tag{3-3}$$

The magnitude of the deviation x for a particular measured value is an indication of the precision or reproducibility of the result. General usage is such that a measure of precision is also taken as a satisfactory measure of accuracy. It is true, of course, that good accuracy demands good precision, but, on the other hand, good precision does not guarantee high accuracy. For example, a set of measured values may show very little scatter about the average value, but the average value itself may differ greatly from the *true* value because of a systematic error such as an error in calculation or an incorrect calibration factor. Conversely, when the average value is a good approximation for the true value, not too much harm results from using the term "error" in the broad sense.

If the frequencies of occurrence of values obtained in a very large number of identical measurements subject to random accidental errors are plotted along the ordinate and the corresponding values along the abscissa, a frequency-distribution curve is obtained. Such a curve is generally bell-shaped, with the mean value as the most probable value having a frequency of occurrence at the peak of the curve. The detailed

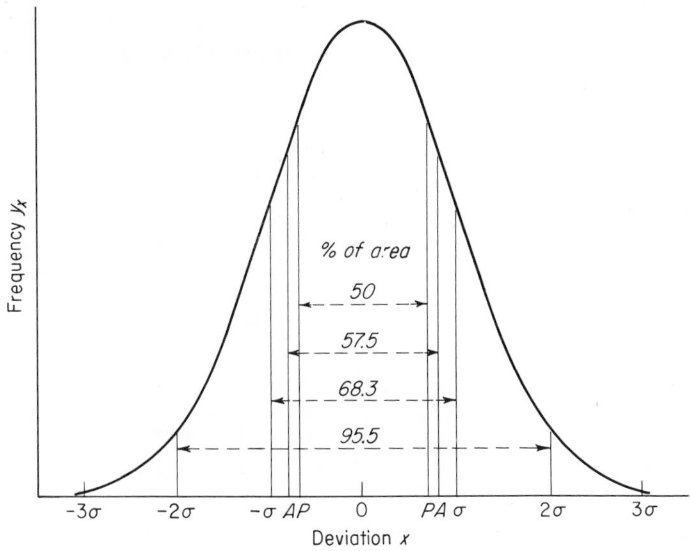

FIG. 3-1. Normal distribution function.

shape, i.e., symmetry, width, etc., of the distribution curve depends upon several factors and will differ from one type of experiment to another. A plot of the frequency of occurrence of deviations from the mean has the same shape and differs only in the units of the abscissa. A typical frequency curve for deviations is shown in Fig. 3-1.

Several distribution laws have been formulated to represent frequency-distribution curves. The three laws which have found considerable application are (1) the normal distribution, (2) the binomial distribution, and (3) the Poisson distribution. Each of these distributions has its own specific applications, but because it is relatively easy to handle mathematically, the normal law is frequently used as an approximation for the other two. Both the binomial and the Poisson distributions approach the normal law as a limit.

The Normal-distribution Law. According to the normal-distribution law, positive and negative deviations of a given magnitude are equally likely and the occurrence of large deviations is less probable than that of small ones. This corresponds to a symmetrical bell-shaped curve, with the most probable value the arithmetic average. From the distribution curve for the deviations of a set of measured values about the average, the probability may be calculated for the occurrence of a deviation as large as or larger than some specified value. Several measures of precision or "errors" are used to indicate the reliability of a result. Three of the more common ones are (1) the standard deviation (SD), (2) the average error (AE), and (3) the probable error (PE). For any measured value X in a set of n measured values having a mean $\bar{X}$, these precision measures are defined as follows:

(1)
$$\mathrm{SD} = \sigma_X = \left[\frac{\sum^{n}(X - \bar{X})^2}{n-1}\right]^{1/2} \tag{3-4}$$

or
$$\sigma_X = (\overline{X^2} - \bar{X}^2)^{1/2} \tag{3-5}$$

(2)
$$\mathrm{AE} = A_X = \frac{\sum^{n}|X - \bar{X}|}{n} = 0.7979\sigma_X \tag{3-6}$$

(3)
$$\mathrm{PE} = P_X = 0.6745\sigma_X \tag{3-7}$$

Equation (3-5), which is a convenient form when a calculating machine is used, may be derived from Eq. (3-4) if $n - 1$ is replaced by n, which it approximates for a large value of n. The three errors have been indicated in Fig. 3-1. (It will be observed that the standard deviation is at the point of inflection of either side of the distribution curve.) The average error is generally used in quantitative analytical chemistry. Both the average and the probable errors are used in physical chemistry. For radioactivity measurements both the probable error and the standard deviation are used, although two other designations are preferred by some investigators. These are the nine-tenths error (NTE) and the $^{95}/_{100}$ error, which are equal respectively to $1.645\sigma_X$ and $1.960\sigma_X$. The standard deviation, in terms of which all other errors may be expressed, is a very important statistical concept.

Suppose that the mean of a given set of measurements is reported as $\bar{X} \pm \sigma_X$, or $\bar{X} \pm P_X$. One might inquire about the significance of these two expressions and the difference between them. The two errors σ_X and P_X differ not only in their magnitudes but also in their associated probabilities. Thus for σ_X, assuming a normal distribution, there is a probability of 68.3 per cent, i.e., 683 chances out of 1,000, that a single measured value in the given set with mean $\bar{X}$ will *not* show a deviation from the mean by more than the amount σ_X. Expressed differently, there is a 31.7 per cent probability that a single measured value will deviate from the average by more than σ_X. Or one may say that for the given set of measurements the chance of observing a deviation of a single measured value from the mean by an amount less than or equal to σ_X is 68.3 per cent. On the other hand, for the probable error $(0.674\sigma_X)$, the probability of a deviation greater or less than P_X for a single measured value is 50 per cent.

The basis for assigning these probability values is the normal distribution, which is represented by the equation

$$y_x = \frac{1}{\sqrt{2\pi}\sigma_X} \exp\left[-\frac{(X - \bar{X})^2}{2(\sigma_X)^2}\right] \tag{3-8}$$

In this equation y_x is the frequency or the probability coefficient—the ordinate in Fig. 3-1. An increment of area $y_x\,dx$ under the curve is an element of probability and represents the probability of an error between x and $x + dx$. Since there is unit probability that a deviation lies between $+\infty$ and $-\infty$, we know that

$$\int_{-\infty}^{+\infty} y_x\,dx = 1 \tag{3-9}$$

The probability $P(x)$ of observing a deviation of $\pm x$ (between $+x$ and $-x$) is given by

$$P(x) = \int_{-x}^{x} y_x\,dx \tag{3-10}$$

and since the normal-distribution curve is symmetrical, we may also write

$$P(x) = 2\int_{0}^{x} y_x\,dx \tag{3-11}$$

When x is equal to σ_X, the area between the inflection points at $\pm\sigma_X$ is 68.3 per cent of the total area under the curve. Tables of the error integral are given in several of the standard reference texts on statistical analysis (1–3) and in various professional handbooks (4). The probabilities associated with a few errors expressed in terms of the standard deviation, that is, $\epsilon = K\sigma_X$, are listed in Table 3-1.

It should be clear, then, that the larger the error specified, the greater the chance that a measured value will deviate from the mean by less than the value, or the less the chance (area not included between $\pm\epsilon$ under the curve) that the specified error will be exceeded. It is important, therefore, to indicate which of the many precision measures is being reported with an experimental result. Too often report writers leave this to the imagination of the reader.

TABLE 3-1

PROBABILITY OF OBSERVING AN ERROR WHICH IS LESS THAN OR EQUAL TO $\epsilon = K\sigma_X$

K		$P(\epsilon \leq K\sigma_X)$, %
0.5		38.3
0.674	(PE)	50.0
0.797	(AE)	57.5
1.000	(SD)	68.3
1.645	(NTE)	90.0
1.960	($^{95}\!/_{100}$E)	95.0
2.000		95.5
3.000		99.73
4.000		99.99

The Binomial-distribution Law. For probability studies on processes such as flipping a coin or casting a die, the binomial distribution may be applied. Thus, if the probability that an event will happen is p and the probability that it will not happen is q, where $q = 1 - p$, then the probability that the event will happen a times and will not happen b times in n trials is

$$p(a) = \frac{n!}{a!b!} p^a q^b \tag{3-12}$$

This is a discontinuous frequency distribution which is in general asymmetric except when p and q are equal. The expected mean value of a is equal to np, and the standard deviation from the expected mean is equal to $(npq)^{1/2}$.

When n is large, the binomial law may be approximated by an exponential expression which is essentially the same as the continuous normal-distribution law. The normal law then becomes an approximation for the binomial law provided that n is large and p and q are about equal, so that $(npq)^{1/2}$ is large compared with $q - p$. When n is large and p is very small, the binomial law reduces approximately to the Poisson distribution.

The Poisson-distribution Law. The expression for the Poisson distribution may be derived directly from probability considerations or indirectly as a limiting case of the binomial distribution. If for a specified change in some variable, e.g., a given interval of time, the probability p that an event will happen is very small and if the probability q that it will not happen approaches unity, then in a large number of trials n the probability that the event will happen a times is

$$p(a) = \frac{e^{-\bar{a}}\bar{a}^a}{a!} \tag{3-13}$$

In this expression $\bar{a}$ is the expected mean and is equal to np. (In practice $\bar{a}$ is approximated by the arithmetical average of a set of measured values.) The Poisson distribution is discontinuous, with a standard deviation equal to $(np)^{1/2}$ or $(\bar{a})^{1/2}$. This simple relationship between the standard deviation and the mean is an important one, since the frequency distribution of values or deviations is determined entirely by the mean. Furthermore, as indicated later in this chapter, this provides a simple basis for calculating the precision measure for measured values in a set for which the Poisson distribution applies. Examples of applications of the Poisson distribution include (1) counts on bacterial culture for a specified area and (2) the number of alpha particles from a long-lived radionuclide counted in a specified interval of time. (In the latter application the total number of atoms is large and the fraction disintegrating very small.) For increasing values of $\bar{a}$, the maximum of the distribution curve becomes sharper and the normal law may be used as an approximation provided large deviations (tails of the curve) are not considered.

Error in the Mean. Returning to the case of a mean value reported with a standard deviation* ($\bar{X} \pm \sigma_X$), it will be recalled that σ_X is the standard deviation for a single measured value in a set having a mean $\bar{X}$. It is indicative of the scattering within the original set of measured values, i.e., the width of the distribution curve. In general, it is of more interest to have an estimate of the reliability of the mean itself. The most probable value would then be reported as $\bar{X} \pm \sigma_{\bar{X}}$. We now have an indication of the way in which the members of a set of mean values obtained from sets of measured values obtained in a similar manner would be distributed about the grand mean of the means. Thus, if the grand mean M is calculated from m means, then for a normal distribution

$$\sigma_{\bar{X}} = \left[\frac{\sum^{m} (\bar{X}_i - M)^2}{m - 1}\right]^{1/2} \tag{3-14}$$

As one would expect, the uncertainty in the mean of a single set of measured values showing accidental variations decreases with increasing number of measurements in the set. The standard deviation in the mean of a set of n measured values, expressed in terms of the standard deviation of a measured value, is

$$\sigma_{\bar{X}} = \frac{\sigma_X}{n^{1/2}} \tag{3-15}$$

* Note that the random uncertainty in an error itself may be estimated formally, but there is seldom justification for using more than one or possibly two significant figures for the error.

$$\sigma_{\bar{X}} = \left[\frac{\sum^{n} (X_i - \bar{X})^2}{n(n-1)}\right]^{1/2} \tag{3-16}$$

As may be seen from Table 3-2, there is a practical limit to the improvement of the mean as n is increased. As before, we may write

$$P_{\bar{X}} = 0.6745\sigma_{\bar{X}} \tag{3-17}$$

Relative errors such as $P_{\bar{X}}/\bar{X}$ and $\sigma_{\bar{X}}/\bar{X}$ are also used quite frequently.

Similarly, for the grand mean, the standard deviation is less than that for a single mean in accordance with the expression

$$\sigma_M = \left[\frac{\sum^{m} (\bar{X}_i - M)^2}{m(m-1)}\right]^{1/2} = \frac{\sigma_{\bar{X}}}{m^{1/2}} \tag{3-18}$$

TABLE 3-2

VARIATION OF THE RATIO OF THE STANDARD DEVIATION OF THE MEAN TO THAT OF A SINGLE MEASURED VALUE AS A FUNCTION OF THE NUMBER OF MEASURED VALUES n

n	$\sigma_{\bar{X}}/\sigma_X$	n	$\sigma_{\bar{X}}/\sigma_X$
2	0.71	8	0.35
3	0.58	9	0.33
4	0.50	10	0.32
5	0.45	20	0.22
6	0.41	50	0.14
7	0.38	100	0.10

Weighted Measurements. So far we have considered the error calculation for the case in which all measured values and means are considered to have equal weight. That is, it is assumed that any one measurement or mean is as reliable as any other. There are cases, especially in radioactivity measurements, for which it may be known that the measured values are not all equally reliable. If the result of one particular measurement is known to be exceptionally reliable, it should be assigned a weighting factor which makes it relatively more important in the calculation of the mean. Each measured value X_i in a set is assigned a weighting factor w_i, which in effect makes it equivalent to w_i values whose average is X_i with a weighting factor of unity. The weighting factors are arbitrary numbers which express the extent to which the experimenter believes some of the measured values are more reliable than others. Commonly, as in analytical chemistry, the experiments are designed to provide measured values of equal weight, that is, $w = 1$ for each value.

The mean for a series of unequally weighted values becomes

$$\bar{X} = \frac{\sum^{n} w_i X_i}{\sum^{n} w_i} \tag{3-19}$$

Since the weighting factor merely places a relative importance on each value, some one value may be assigned a weight of unity. For the value of unit weight, the standard deviation is

$$\sigma_X(w = 1) = \left[\frac{\sum^{n} w_i(X_i - \bar{X})^2}{n - 1}\right]^{1/2} \tag{3-20}$$

The standard deviation for any one of the other measured values X_i is

$$\sigma_{X_i} = \frac{\sigma_X(w = 1)}{(w_i)^{1/2}} \tag{3-21}$$

since the error in a single measured value varies inversely as the square root of its weighting factor. The corresponding standard deviation in the mean of the weighted values becomes

$$\sigma_{\bar{X}} = \frac{\sigma_X(w = 1)}{\left(\sum^{n} w_i\right)^{1/2}} = \left[\frac{\sum^{n} w_i(X_i - \bar{X})^2}{(n - 1)\sum^{n} w_i}\right]^{1/2} \tag{3-22}$$

if the mean is considered to be equivalent to a single value with weighting factor $\sum^{n} w_i$. For a set of measurements of equal weight, Eqs. (3-19), (3-20), and (3-22) reduce to Eqs. (3-3), (3-4), and (3-16) respectively and Eq. (3-21) reduces to an identity.

Frequently a final experimental result is obtained by combining the means of several sets of measured values to obtain a grand mean. Since the reliabilities of the individual means may not be identical, a weighting factor w_i' is required for each. These factors are assigned in accordance with the condition that the factors are inversely proportional to the square of the standard deviation (or any other precision measure) for each mean. The weighted grand mean M of m means becomes

$$M = \frac{\sum^{m} w_i' \bar{X}_i}{\sum^{m} w_i'} \tag{3-23}$$

with the standard deviation of a mean about the grand mean expressed as follows:

$$\sigma_{\bar{X}}(w' = 1) = \left[\frac{\sum^{m} w_i'(\bar{X}_i - M)^2}{m - 1}\right]^{1/2} \tag{3-24}$$

and

$$\sigma_{\bar{X}_i} = \frac{\sigma_{\bar{X}}(w' = 1)}{(w_i')^{1/2}} \tag{3-25}$$

For the grand mean itself, the appropriate relationship is

$$\sigma_M = \left[\frac{\sum^m w_i'(\bar{X}_i - M)^2}{(m - 1)\sum^m w_i'}\right]^{1/2} = \frac{\sigma_{\bar{X}}(w' = 1)}{\left(\sum^m w_i'\right)^{1/2}} = \frac{1}{\left[\sum^m (1/\sigma_{\bar{X}_i}{}^2)\right]^{1/2}} \tag{3-26}$$

Equations (3-24) and (3-26) reduce to Eqs. (3-14) and (3-18) for means of equal weight.

There may be some question about the validity of combining the means from various sets of measured values by using these equations which take into account only accidental errors. For example, the measurements may have been performed on different instruments or in different laboratories and may therefore contain systematic errors which could not be detected from any one set of values. As a rule, if the difference between two means is more than two or three times greater than the standard deviation of the difference as calculated from the rules for the propagation of errors [Eq. (3-28)], then the difference is probably not due to accidental errors. Other tests are described by Worthing and Geffner (1), who also discuss the problem of combining two means which differ more than expected. The weights of these means are frequently assigned arbitrarily after a consideration of factors such as the known reliability of different methods of measurement which may be involved.

Propagation of Errors. When the quantity Q is evaluated indirectly by calculation from directly measured quantities containing errors, the reliability of the calculated value is found by applying the theory of propagation of errors. As a general case we may write $Q = f(X, Y, \ldots)$, where X, Y, . . . are *independent* variables. The uncertainty (expressed as the variance) in Q resulting from uncertainties in X, Y, . . . is given by the equation

$$\sigma_Q{}^2 = \left(\frac{\partial Q}{\partial X}\right)^2 \sigma_X{}^2 + \left(\frac{\partial Q}{\partial Y}\right)^2 \sigma_Y{}^2 + \cdots \tag{3-27}$$

The standard deviation for Q is found by taking the square root of this expression. The equations for the following specific cases may be obtained from Eq. (3-27) in a straightforward manner.

Addition or Subtraction

If $\quad Q = X + Y \quad$ or $\quad X - Y$

then $\quad \sigma_Q = (\sigma_X{}^2 + \sigma_Y{}^2)^{1/2} \qquad (3\text{-}28)$

If $\quad Q = aX + bY$

then $\quad \sigma_Q = (a^2\sigma_X{}^2 + b^2\sigma_Y{}^2)^{1/2} \qquad (3\text{-}29)$

Multiplication or Division

If $$Q = XY \qquad \text{or} \qquad X/Y$$

then $$\sigma_Q{}^2 = Y^2\sigma_X{}^2 + X^2\sigma_Y{}^2 = (XY)^2\left(\frac{\sigma_X{}^2}{X^2} + \frac{\sigma_Y{}^2}{Y^2}\right)$$

or $$\sigma_Q{}^2 = \left(\frac{X}{Y}\right)^2\left(\frac{\sigma_X{}^2}{X^2} + \frac{\sigma_Y{}^2}{Y^2}\right)$$

and finally $$\frac{\sigma_Q}{Q} = \left(\frac{\sigma_X{}^2}{X^2} + \frac{\sigma_Y{}^2}{Y^2}\right)^{1/2} \tag{3-30}$$

Powers and Roots

If $$Q = X^n$$

then $$\sigma_Q{}^2 = (nX^{n-1}\sigma_X)^2 = \left(nX^n\frac{\sigma_X}{X}\right)^2$$

and $$\frac{\sigma_Q}{Q} = \frac{n\sigma_X}{X} \tag{3-31}$$

Logarithms

If $$Q = \ln X$$

then $$\sigma_Q = \frac{\sigma_X}{X} \tag{3-32}$$

For common logarithms, $\sigma_Q = 0.434\sigma_X/X$.

Rejection of Suspected Values. It is not uncommon to find in a set of measured values one value which deviates from the average by what appears to be an abnormally large amount. The question then arises as to whether or not a mean value closer to the true value could be obtained if the suspected value were rejected from the set. Various criteria for the rejection of data are in common usage. For example, some investigators reject a value which has a deviation from the mean greater than $2\sigma_X$; others use $3\sigma_X$ or even $4\sigma_X$ as limits. The probabilities of occurrence of such deviations are, respectively, 5 in 100, 3 in 1,000, and 1 in 10,000, as indicated in Table 3-1.

Chauvenet's criterion is preferred by most investigators. It takes into account the number of measured values in the set. Thus, for a set of n measured values a value is rejected if the probability of observing a deviation from the mean as large as or larger than that actually observed for the value in question is not greater than $1/2n$. In applying this test, reference is usually made to a table in which a limiting maximum value of the ratio of the observed deviation for a suspected value to one of the precision measures for the set is given for various values of n. Table 3-3 is an abbreviated table of this type. If the calculated value of x/σ_X for the suspected value exceeds that in the table for the corresponding value of n, the value is rejected. The procedure may be repeated successively using each new mean value to eliminate other suspected results, although the test is not very meaningful when n is less than 5.

TABLE 3-3

CHAUVENET'S CRITERION FOR REJECTION OF A SUSPECTED VALUE HAVING A DEVIATION x

n	x/σ_X	n	x/σ_X
3	1.37	10	1.97
4	1.53	20	2.24
5	1.64	30	2.39
6	1.73	40	2.50
7	1.80	50	2.57
8	1.87	100	2.80
9	1.91		

Test for Random Distribution of Data. It is frequently desirable to determine whether or not the observed frequency distribution for a given set of measured values corresponds to one of the distribution laws. In other words, it is of interest to know if the observed variations are reasonably consistent with expectation. Several tests, described in treatises on the theory of statistics, are employed for this purpose. The chi-square test is relatively simple to use and has wide application.

At least two definitions of chi squared, χ^2, are to be found in the many treatises on the theory of statistics. In one case it is defined in terms of the frequency of occurrence of measured values. Thus the value X_1 may have an observed frequency f_1 (appears f_1 times in the set of n values), and X_2 a frequency f_2, etc. If an assumption is made about the nature of the distribution, expected or theoretical frequencies $f'_1, f'_2, \ldots$ can be calculated. These expected frequencies may be based on a priori information concerning the distribution expected, i.e., normal, binomial, Poisson, or they may be estimated approximately from the data. The definition of χ^2 then becomes

$$\chi^2 = \sum^{n} \frac{(\text{deviation of observed from expected frequency})^2}{\text{expected frequency}}$$

$$= \frac{(f_1 - f'_1)^2}{f'_1} + \frac{(f_2 - f'_2)^2}{f'_2} + \cdots$$

The second definition of χ^2 involves the true variance V_X. The true variance is defined as for $\sigma_X{}^2$ except that deviations are from the true mean rather than the arithmetical mean. For a large number of measurements $\sigma_X{}^2$ approaches V_X. When expressed as an equation, the definition becomes

$$\chi^2 = \sum^n \frac{(X_i - \bar{X})^2}{V_X} \tag{3-33}$$

For the case of a Poisson distribution this assumes the form

$$\chi^2 = \sum^n \frac{(X_i - \bar{X})^2}{\bar{X}} \tag{3-34}$$

In either case χ^2 is a measure of the correspondence between the distribution assumed and that observed. Chi squared itself has a frequency distribution. This is not a normal distribution since it depends upon the number of measured values or rather the number of "degrees* of freedom." The probability of observing a value of χ^2 equal to or greater than a specified value is associated with the area under the distribution curve. Values of this probability have been calculated and tabulated for various values of χ^2 and either the number of degrees of freedom or the number of measured values. Chi-square probability is shown in Fig. 3-2 as a function of χ^2 and the number of measured values. From the observed value of χ^2 and the degrees of freedom one finds from the graph a value of $P(>\chi^2)$, which is the probability of finding a value of χ^2 as great as or greater than that observed. A very low value of P is taken to mean a very poor agreement between the theoretical spread of data and that observed. The lowest value of P acceptable is a matter of choice for the investigator. Two commonly used values are 0.05 and 0.01, although 0.001 is also used. These are referred to as levels of significance. Thus for $P = 0.01$, the chance of obtaining a value as large as or larger than χ^2_{obs} is only 1 in 100.

Examples of the application of the χ^2 test are given in the standard texts on the theory of statistics. It may be used to detect faulty operation of a radiation detector such as a G-M tube.

3-3. Errors Resulting from Fluctuations in the Rate of Radioactive Disintegration—Application of the Poisson Distribution

It has been known since the early days of radioactivity that the fluctuations associated with radioactive decay are properly described by the Poisson-distribution law. The applicability of the Poisson-distribution law has been discussed by many authors (1, 3, 5–11). Agreement with the Poisson-distribution law may be shown experimentally

* Degrees of freedom equal n minus the number of constants estimated from the data and equal $n - 1$ for most cases, where the mean value used to calculate the deviations is the single constant.

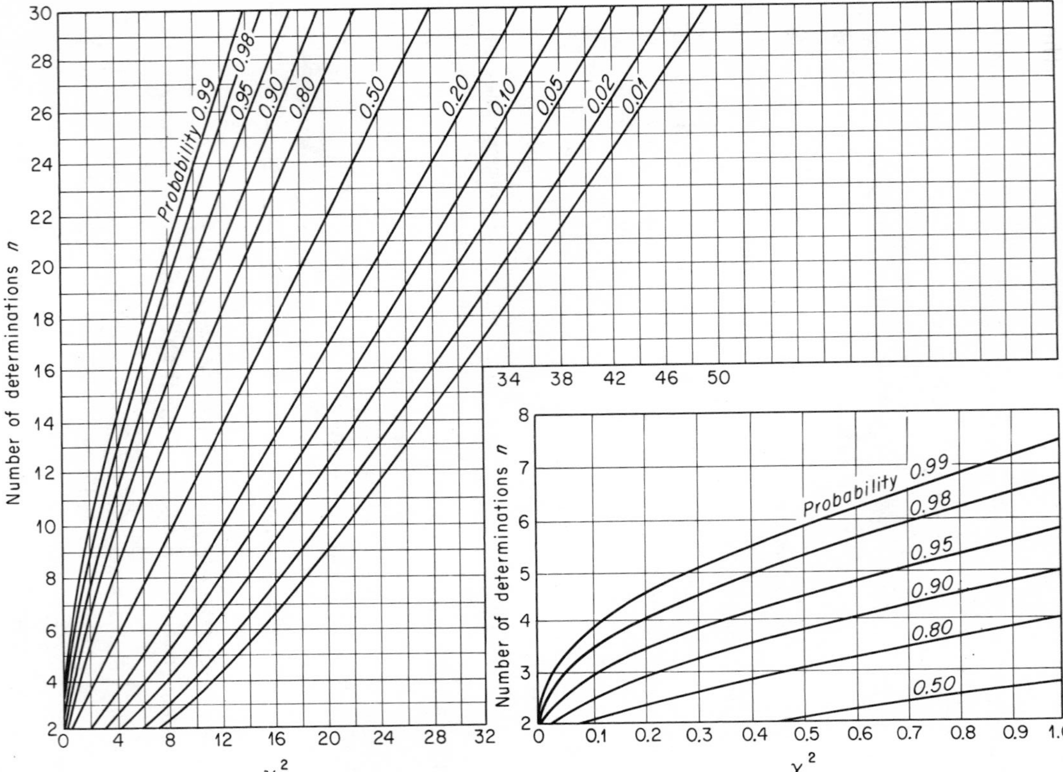

FIG. 3-2. The χ^2 distribution. The probability that the variations in a series of counting determinations are due to the randomness of the disintegration process. n, number of determinations. [*From Jarrett* (13).]

by measuring either (1) the time interval between successive pulses, i.e., particles counted, or (2) the total number of pulses received in a given time interval. For the latter experiment it is found that there is a random variation in the number of disintegrations or particle counts (a constant fraction of the number of disintegrations during the experiment) in a fixed time interval for a sample of long-lived* radioactive material.

Probability Calculations. The following symbols will be used in developing the statistics equations:

R = apparent or measured activity or observed counting rate,† e.g., counts per minute, an average for the counting period

$R = YA$

where A = absolute disintegration rate

Y = counting yield or detection coefficient, a constant for a given measurement

t = time interval for a measurement

$S = Rt$ = total number (integer) of counts received in time interval t

Suppose the measured values of the total number of counts observed for repeated measurements for a given time interval are $S_1, S_2, \ldots, S_i, \ldots, S_n$, with an average value $\bar{S}$. Then from Eq. (3-14) we obtain

$$P(S_i) = \frac{e^{-\bar{S}}\bar{S}^{S_i}}{S_i!} \tag{3-35}$$

for the probability of observing S_i counts in a given interval of time if $\bar{S}$ is the average number of counts for the interval. As an example, assume that $\bar{S} = 500$ counts when $t = 5$ min. We may then calculate the probability of observing a value such as 490 counts in 5 min. Then

$$P(490) = \frac{e^{-500}(500)^{490}}{490!}$$

By using tables of logarithms of factorials [see Fry (3) for example], we find that $P(490) = 1.7 \times 10^{-2}$. Similarly, $P(500) = 1.8 \times 10^{-2}$ and $P(400) = 4.4 \times 10^{-7}$. For all possible values of $P(S_i)$ it is true that $\sum_0^\infty P(S_i) = 1$; hence the probability for any one value of S_i is small and becomes smaller, the larger the value of $\bar{S}$.

* Long-lived to the extent that the per cent change in the number of radioactive atoms is negligible during the experiment.

† The symbol R without a subscript will be used also for (1) electrical resistance (but for this meaning it will generally appear in the resistance-capacitance product RC or current-resistance product IR) and (2) chromatographic constant (Chap. 9).

Rutherford, Geiger and Bateman (5) found excellent agreement between the observed frequency and that calculated as above from the Poisson distribution for the case of counting the number of alpha particles striking a fluorescent screen during 2,608 intervals of 7.5 sec each. Their results are also discussed by Wilks (12). This treatment of the fluctuations is general, of course, for any type of nuclear radiation entering any type of detector.

Errors in Data Obtained with a Resolving (Scaler-type) Counter. *Standard Deviation in the Total Number of Counts.* In practice we are not so much interested in the above probabilities as we are in the reliability of a measured value. The standard deviation for a single measured value in a set may be calculated quite simply, since for a Poisson distribution, as pointed out in Sec. 3-2, it is equal to the square root of the mean value. Thus we have

$$\sigma_{S_i} = (\bar{S})^{1/2} \tag{3-36}$$

It is important to note that, because of this property of a Poisson distribution, we can calculate a precision measure for a single measured value even when it is the only value, that is, $n = 1$. A measured value which is known to come from a set whose distribution is characterized by the Poisson law may be used not only as an estimate of the mean, but also for the calculation of a precision measure. As an example we might return to the previous instance and assume that for some reason we are unable to obtain more than one measured value, namely, 490 total counts. Recalling that for accidental errors small deviations are more probable than large ones, we may assume that a single value is not far from the mean. Then

$$\sigma_{S_i} \cong (S_i)^{1/2} \tag{3-37}$$

and for fractional SD

$$\frac{\sigma_{S_i}}{S_i} \cong \frac{1}{(S_i)^{1/2}} \tag{3-38}$$

For $S_i = 490$ we find $\sigma_{490} = \pm 22$ counts, which means that there is a 68.3 per cent chance that another measurement of 5 min duration would result in a value between 468 and 512 counts. The value would then be reported with its SD as 490 ± 22 counts, where the uncertainty refers *only* to that which might arise from fluctuations in decay rate. By comparison, if the mean is 500 counts, the standard deviation in a single measured value would be $(500)^{1/2}$, which is still ± 22 counts. In contrast, for a normal distribution, a single measured value serves only as an approximation for the mean and from it alone we have no way to estimate a precision measure.

Since the Poisson distribution is approximated (graphically and analytically) by the continuous normal distribution in the region near the mean, we use tables of the normal error function to relate to the standard deviation all the commonly used precision measures with their probabilities.

From Eq. (3-15) it follows that the standard deviation in the mean $\bar{S}$ of a set of n measured values of total counts is

$$\sigma_{\bar{S}} = \left(\frac{\bar{S}}{n}\right)^{1/2} \tag{3-39}$$

and the fractional SD is then

$$\frac{\sigma_{\bar{S}}}{\bar{S}} = \frac{1}{(n\bar{S})^{1/2}} \tag{3-40}$$

Standard Deviation in a Counting Rate. The uncertainty in a measured counting rate R_i or in the rate at which nuclear radiation reaches the detector depends upon the total number of events observed. It is important to remember that the Poisson distribution applies directly to the total number of events for a fixed time interval rather than the rate of occurrence. Therefore, to calculate the standard deviation in a measured rate we start with Eq. (3-36) and introduce the measurement time t, which is common to all measurements. This leads to

$$\sigma_{S_i} = (\bar{R}t)^{1/2} \tag{3-41}$$

and

$$\sigma_{R_i} = \frac{\sigma_{S_i}}{t} = \left(\frac{\bar{R}}{t}\right)^{1/2} \tag{3-42}$$

where $\bar{R}$ is the mean rate. If we have just one measured rate, Eq. (3-37) leads to

$$\sigma_{R_i} \cong \left(\frac{R_i}{t_i}\right)^{1/2} \tag{3-43}$$

and for the fractional SD

$$\frac{\sigma_{R_i}}{R_i} \cong \frac{1}{(R_i t_i)^{1/2}} \tag{3-44}$$

As expected, σ_{R_i} decreases with increasing time of measurement.

As an example, it is a simple matter to show by means of Eqs. (3-38) and (3-44) that, in order to reduce the relative standard deviation to 1 per cent for any one measured value S_i or R_i, it is necessary to record 10,000 counts regardless of the value of R_i. Figure 3-3 may be used to find the per cent standard deviation for an observed total number of counts or the total number of counts required to obtain a maximum specified per cent standard deviation in a single measured value of either the rate or the total number of counts.

The standard deviation in the mean of n measured rates obtained from measurements of equal time is

$$\sigma_{\bar{R}} = \left(\frac{\bar{R}}{nt}\right)^{1/2} \tag{3-45}$$

A question which frequently arises concerns the relative merits of making several identical measurements of the counting rate of a sample as compared with making a single measurement over a time interval equal to the sum of those for the repeated measurements. As an example we shall compare $\sigma_{\bar{R}}$ for a set of ten 2-min measurements with

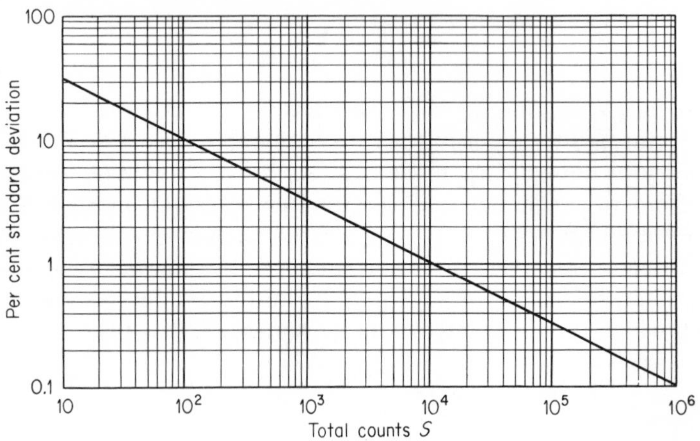

FIG. 3-3. Per cent standard deviation (SD) as a function of the total number of counts.

that for one 20-min measurement. Taking a value of $\bar{R}$ equal to 1,250 cpm, we find for the set of measurements $\sigma_{\bar{R}} = \pm 8$ cpm from Eq. (3-45) and for the single measurement $\sigma_R = \pm 8$ cpm from Eq. (3-43). As one might expect, the results are the same for essentially the same total number of counts. In general, however, it is preferable to make at least two or three measurements on a sample since unexpectedly poor precision would indicate faulty operation of the instruments. This might not be detected during a single measurement. It must be emphasized, however, that in the above comparison errors in timing were neglected. Very short measurements, e.g., 1 min or less, are to be avoided in accurate work since they may introduce significant errors in timing.

Standard Deviation in a Net Counting Rate. The apparent activity of a radioactive source is found by subtracting the ever-present background rate from the observed sample-plus-background rate. The background rate is measured separately and has an uncertainty of its own. It is generally assumed that the background rate resulting from (1) radioactive contaminants in materials of construction and (2) cosmic rays fluctuates in a random manner, so that the Poisson distribution may be applied. We may write for σ_{R_b}, the standard deviation in the background rate measured for a time t_b,

$$\sigma_{R_b} = \left(\frac{R_b}{t_b}\right)^{1/2} \tag{3-46}$$

In accordance with Eq. (3-28) the standard deviation in the net counting rate R_s for a sample is

$$\sigma_{R_s} = (\sigma^2_{R_{s+b}} + \sigma^2_{R_b})^{1/2}$$

or

$$\sigma_{R_s} = \left(\frac{R_{s+b}}{t_s} + \frac{R_b}{t_b}\right)^{1/2} \tag{3-47}$$

where R_{s+b} is the observed sample-plus-background rate corrected for coincidence losses and t_s is the measurement time for the sample. The standard deviation in the sample rate depends, then, upon both the time for sample measurement and that for background-rate measurement. When R_{s+b} is large in comparison with R_b, a long background measurement is not needed for most purposes to make the error contribution from the background rate negligible. On the other hand, when R_{s+b} is comparable to R_b, both t_s and t_b must be very long for small values of σ_{R_s}. In planning an experiment where the error in the background rate is an important factor, we may wish to know the answer to one or both of the following questions: (1) If R_b and R_{s+b} are known approximately (R_b from daily records and R_{s+b} from expectation or from a brief rough measurement or estimate) and if there is available a specified length of time t_t during which both R_{s+b} and R_b must be measured, how should the total time be allocated? (2) Assuming that R_{s+b} and R_b are known approximately, how much time is required for the sample measurement and the background measurement for a specified maximum fractional standard deviation in the net rate of the sample?

The answer to the first question is obtained as shown by Jarrett (13) by setting

$$\frac{d\sigma_{R_s}}{dt} = 0$$

for a minimum error. Using Eq. (3-47) and the relationship for the three time intervals, namely,

$$t_t = t_s + t_b \tag{3-48}$$

we find that

$$\frac{t_s}{t_b} = \left(\frac{R_{s+b}}{R_b}\right)^{1/2} \tag{3-49}$$

The values of t_s and t_b are found by combining this equation with Eq. (3-48) and using the values of t_t, R_b, and R_{s+b}. Thus if $t_t = 30$ min, $R_b = 20$ cpm, and $R_{s+b} = 80$ cpm, we find $t_s = 20$ min and $t_b = 10$ min. This leads to a value of 0.04 for $(\sigma_{R_s})/R_s$. Any other division of the time would lead to a larger error in R_s. Values for the ratio t_s/t_b for various values of R_{s+b}/R_b may be obtained from the curve of Fig. 3-4.

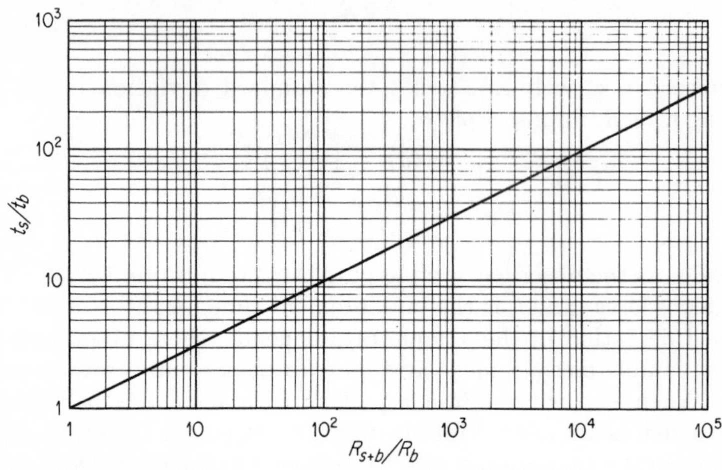

FIG. 3-4. Graph showing the most efficient distribution of counting time between sample and background. R_{s+b}, counting rate of sample plus background; R_b, counting rate of background; t_s, length of time of sample-plus-background count; t_b, length of time of background count.

In answering the second question we must find t_t, t_s, and t_b when R_b, R_{s+b}, and a specified fractional standard deviation, which we shall call g, are known. The relationship between g and these other quantities is

$$g = \left(\frac{R_{s+b}/t_s + R_b/t_b}{R_s^2}\right)^{1/2} \tag{3-50}$$

We have already shown that the most efficient division of the available measurement time is given by Eq. (3-49). Combining the latter equation with Eq. (3-50) and solving for t_s leads to

$$t_s = \frac{R_{s+b} + (R_b R_{s+b})^{1/2}}{g^2 R_s^2} \tag{3-51}$$

Plots of t_s vs. R_b for selected values of R_{s+b} and g equal to 0.01 and of t_s vs. R_{s+b} for selected values of R_b and $g = 0.10$ are shown in Figs. 3-5 and 3-6 respectively. For other values of g, t_s may be obtained by dividing the t_s corresponding to a 1 per cent SD by the (desired per cent SD)^2 or by multiplying the t_s corresponding to a 10 per cent SD by 100/(desired

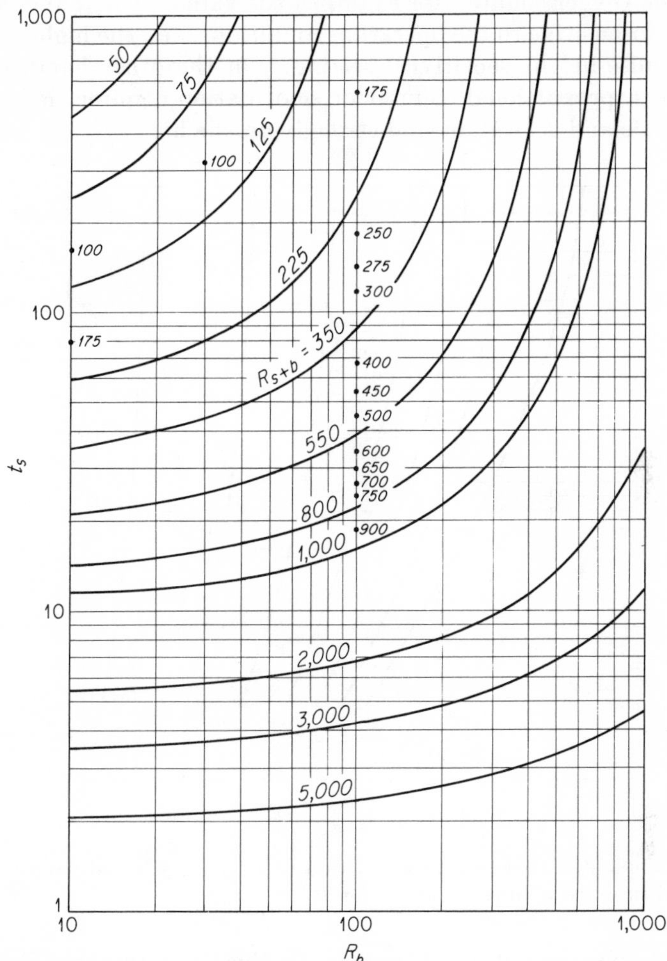

FIG. 3-5. Sample counting time as a function of the background rate for selected values of R_{s+b} and a 1 per cent SD for R_s.

per cent SD)^2. If, for example, we take $R_{s+b} = 80$ cpm and $R_b = 20$ cpm and let $g = 0.05$, we find $t_s = 14$ min. From Fig. 3-4 or by means of Eq. (3-49) we find the corresponding value of t_b to be 7 min. The figures may be used to establish appropriate counting schedules involving a minimum of time for a specified statistical reliability when the counting rate of a radioactive source is relatively close to background.

Selection of Optimum Operating Conditions for a Counter. In the selection of optimum counting times discussed in the previous section it was assumed that the sample and the background counting rates are fixed.

For a given Geiger counter, for example, the values of R_{s+b} and R_b are relatively insensitive to the operating conditions, i.e., the high-voltage and the pulse-height sensitivity setting. On the other hand, if the detector is a proportional counter or scintillation counter, R_{s+b} for a given sample and R_b will depend strongly on the high voltage and the

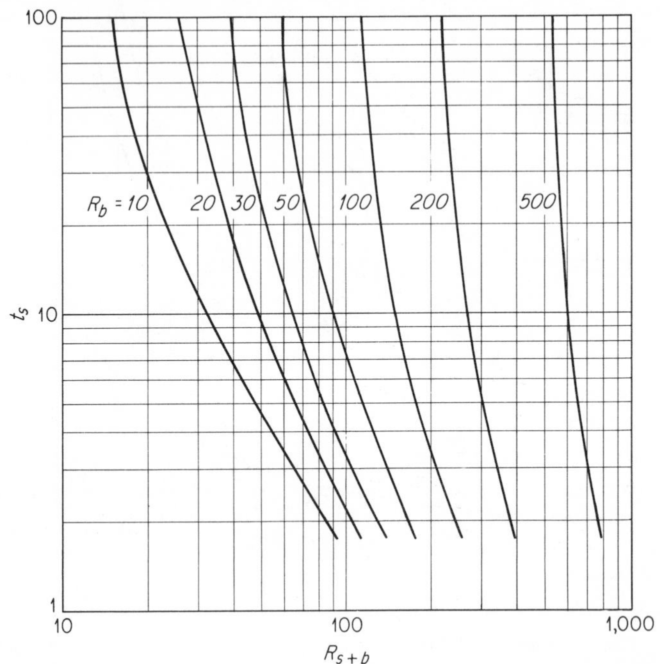

FIG. 3-6. Sample counting time as a function of R_{s+b} for selected values of the background rate and a 10 per cent SD for R_s.

pulse-height discrimination. Moreover, for these counters the efficiency (particles or photons counted per particle or photon reaching the sensitive region of the detector) depends upon the type and energy spectrum of the radiation being detected. Thus the sample rate and the background rate do not change by the same amount when the operating conditions are changed.

Various criteria have been used to select the optimum operating conditions for proportional and scintillation counters. They all involve plotting a suitable function of the sample and background counting rates vs. an instrumental variable. As examples, the discriminator setting may be varied for a given high-voltage setting or the high voltage may be varied for a given discriminator setting. The latter case is the common one for scintillation counters used without pulse-height analysis. In any case the optimum value for the variable is taken to be that which gives the maximum value of the function.

A function which many workers use is R_s/R_b. It is based more or less on intuition. When counting time is the important parameter, however, the mathematical expressions used in the previous section can serve as the basis for obtaining expressions for optimizing the operating conditions. Loevinger and Berman (14), for example, have derived such expressions and recommend that the operating conditions be adjusted until R_s^2/R_b is a maximum. This criterion is independent of the strength of the source, but it depends upon the radiation spectrum of the radionuclide. Outteridge (15) uses $R_{s+b}^{1/2} - R_b^{1/2}$ as the criterion to be maximized. For weak sources (relative to background) this is approximately equal to $R_s/2R_b^{1/2}$ and becomes equivalent to the criterion of Loevinger and Berman which is best suited for weak sources. The function $(R_{s+b}^{1/2} - R_b^{1/2})$ varies with source strength and can be used to find the optimum conditions for a particular source.

Plots of the three criteria are shown in Fig. 2-8*b* for an NaI scintillation counter. The use of the maximum value of R_s/R_b usually results in a lower operating potential and a longer counting time for the same relative error than would be obtained from either of the other two criteria. This is more pronounced for weak sources. For strong sources, that is, $R_s/R_b = 100$ or greater, the difference is less important since the counting times are shorter. Slightly shorter times are required when $R_{s+b}^{1/2} - R_b^{1/2}$ rather than R_s^2/R_b is used to select the operating voltage for strong sources; otherwise these two criteria differ very little.

It should be recognized that these several criteria do not take into account instability or faulty operation of counters. Furthermore, whenever the detector is modified in any way, the optimum operating conditions must be redetermined.

Comparison of Counters. A common problem is that of selecting the best counter from a variety of counters which could be used to count sources of a given radionuclide. Perhaps the first inclination would be to choose the one with the highest sensitivity, i.e., the one which has the highest net counting rate per unit disintegration rate of the source. The relative merits of two given counters, however, vary with the strength of the source. In order to take this into account various criteria for comparing counters have been derived. Thomas (16) defines a factor of merit M for one counter in terms of another in terms of the ratio of the counting times required to obtain equal statistical accuracy. The factor of merit for counter 2 in terms of counter 1 for strong sources where background is negligible is given by

$$M_2 = \frac{(R_s)_2}{(R_s)_1}$$

This is the same as the ratio of sensitivities for a given source. When the source is weak, i.e., much less than background, the factor of merit becomes

$$M_2 = \frac{(R_s)_2^2}{(R_s)_1^2} \frac{(R_b)_1}{(R_b)_2}$$

In either case counter 2 is the better one if M_2 is greater than unity.

According to Loevinger and Berman the counter which has the greater sensitivity and the larger value of R_s^2/R_b is the better one. If the counter with the greater sensitivity has the smaller value of R_s^2/R_b, it is disadvantageous for sufficiently weak sources.

Outteridge compares $R_{s+b}^{1/2} - R_b^{1/2}$ for two counters and selects the counter with the larger value for the source strength of interest.

When samples of low apparent activity necessitate the expenditure of long measurement times for both the background rate and for the sample, it is generally preferable to divide the time for measuring the background rate into two parts and measure the background rate before and after measurement of the sample rate. Any drift in the background rate over a period of a few hours is then less serious, since a mean value is obtained in this way. When several samples requiring long measurement time are counted in series, it is common practice to alternate the background and sample measurements.

It is not possible to decrease the background rate indefinitely by shielding, so that for sources having extremely low counting rates special measurement techniques such as those based on anticoincidence counting are necessary. The anticoincidence method has been used by Libby (17) for determining the natural C^{14} content of various materials.

For proportional and scintillation counters it is sometimes possible to adjust the circuit parameters so that the ratio of efficiencies of the counter for detecting radiation from the sample and background radiation remains constant. Based on measurements of the counting rate of a reference source and a knowledge of the relative rates of the reference source and background, changes in the background rate can be calculated from changes in the rate of the reference source without repeated long measurements of the background rate.

Errors in Data Obtained with a Counting-rate Meter. The errors discussed in the preceding sections apply to measurements made with resolving counters in which the average counting rate of a source of constant strength during the period of observation is calculated from a register reading, a scaling factor, and an elapsed time. The average counting rate for a given detection system may be obtained also by means of a counting-rate meter in which the random pulses from the detector are shaped uniformly and then applied to an integrating circuit (tank capacitor of capacitance C shunted with a resistance R), where the average voltage developed is proportional to the average counting rate. The average voltage is measured with a vacuum-tube voltmeter which operates either a panel meter or a pen-and-ink recorder. A comparison of the scaler-type counters and counting-rate meters has been made by Bousquet (18).

The uncertainty in the counting rate measured with a counting-rate meter arises not only from the random disintegration of the radioactive source, but also from the dependence of an observed rate on the immediately preceding rate and the accuracy of the mechanical indicating or recording meter. A counting rate may be determined as a single instantaneous rate, as an average of several successive readings, or as an average based on a continuous recording over a period of time.

Before observations of the counting rate can be made with a counting-rate meter, a steady-state output must be attained. The time required to reach steady state depends upon the following variables: (1) the magnitude of the change in rate when the rate is changed, (2) the new average counting rate, and (3) the time constant RC of the integrating circuit. If the initial rate is zero, the time required to reach steady state for a constant source is given by the expression (10)

$$t_{ss} = RC[0.394 + \tfrac{1}{2} \ln 2R(RC)] \tag{3-52}$$

in terms of the RC time constant and the observed rate R [equal to R_{ss} in Eq. (3-53)]. Steady state is approached exponentially according to the relation

$$R = R_{ss}\left(1 - \exp \frac{-t}{RC}\right) \tag{3-53}$$

where R_{ss} is the steady-state rate. The value of t given by Eq. (3-52) corresponds to approaching the steady-state rate within less than one probable error associated with statistical fluctuations. Equilibrium times calculated according to Eq. (3-52) are shown as a function of the counting rate for several values of RC in Fig. 3-7. In practice, the time required to reach steady state can be shortened by equipping the counting-rate meter with a manually operated device for rapidly charging or discharging the integrating capacitor in anticipation of the new steady-state value.

For a rate based on a single observation of a counting-rate meter in *steady state*, the fractional standard deviation is

$$\frac{\sigma_R}{R} = \frac{1}{[R(2RC)]^{1/2}} \tag{3-54}$$

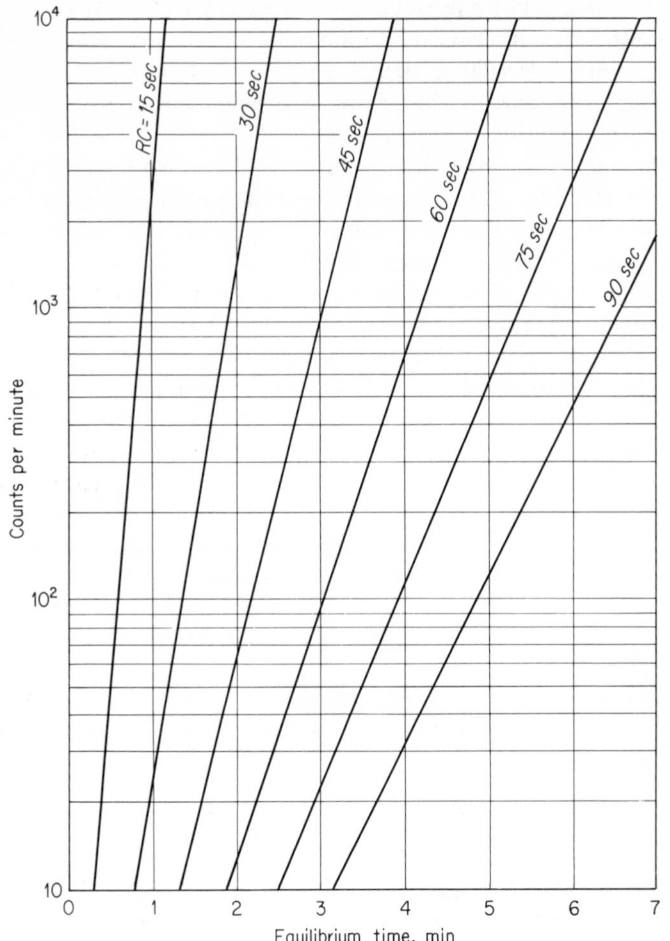

FIG. 3-7. Equilibrium time as a function of counting rate for various time constants for a counting-rate meter.

The larger the time constant, the smaller the standard deviation of a single observation of the rate, corresponding to integration of a larger number of pulses over a longer period of time.

When a series of counting-rate meter observations is made of the counting rate for a source of constant activity, the values are not independent (because of the memory effect of the integrating circuit) unless the interval of time between successive observations is much, e.g., five times, greater than the time constant of the integrating circuit. For the mean of n independent instantaneous observations the standard deviation is equal to that in a single value divided by $n^{1/2}$ as indicated in Eq. (3-15). An equation for the standard deviation of the mean of a series of successive observations which are not independent is given by Evans (10).

When the counting rate is evaluated from a pen-and-ink recording, the standard deviation depends upon the recording time t'. If t' is much longer than the RC time constant for the rate meter, the fractional deviation in the average rate may be obtained from the equation

$$\frac{\sigma_{\bar{R}}}{\bar{R}} = \frac{1}{(\bar{R}t')^{1/2}} \tag{3-55}$$

which is analogous to Eq. (3-44). The value of $\bar{R}$ can be obtained from the recording by the usual procedure of drawing a line through the tracing so that the area enclosed by the tracing above the line equals that below.

Errors in a net counting rate, etc., are calculated in accordance with the general rules for propagation of errors.

For an ionization chamber used as an integrating detector the error analysis is more complicated, as indicated by Evans (10) and Calvin et al. (19).

Experiment 3-1
Statistical Aspects of Nuclear-particle Counting (Pulse Counters)

It is the purpose of this experiment to illustrate:

1. The reproducibility of nuclear-particle counting
2. Two methods of calculating the standard deviation for counting-rate data
3. The agreement or disagreement between σ_R based on the radioactivity process alone and σ_R based on the observed over-all deviations
4. The effect of experimental technique on precision

Apparatus and Materials

Radiation-detection equipment—detector, scaler, register, timer
Radioactive material—may be alpha, beta, or gamma emitter, depending on detection equipment; a convenient beta emitter is P^{32}
Source mounting and covering material, e.g., flat copper planchets or cupped steel planchets; aluminum foil, collodion, etc.
Micropipette
Heat lamp

Procedure

Prepare and label three samples as nearly identical as possible (including centering of droplet of the activity-containing liquid) without rinsing the micropipette. Prepare a fourth sample, identical with the first three except that the micropipette should be rinsed and the activity in the rinse water added to the central droplet according to the procedure described in Sec. 5-2.

After the appropriate "warm-up" time for the counter, measure the background rate for 10 to 15 min with a blank source mounted in place.

For the three identical samples, count one sample ten times in succession for equal times without disturbing it; count each of the other two samples three times. Similarly, count the fourth (rinsed pipette) sample three times. The same time and a count of about 10,000 counts should be taken for each measurement. (The initial sample size and shelf position should be chosen so that each measurement will require 2 to 4 min.)

Repeat the background measurement and, if time permits, make two or three successive measurements, all for the same length of time as for the first measurement.

Analysis of Data

After applying appropriate coincidence corrections, but before subtracting background from the sample rates,

1. Calculate the average and the standard deviation of measured values σ_R in two ways, i.e.,

$$\sigma_R = \left[\frac{\sum^{n}(R_i - \bar{R})^2}{n-1}\right]^{1/2} \qquad \text{and} \qquad \sigma_R = \left(\frac{\bar{R}}{t}\right)^{1/2}$$

for (*a*) the set of 10 repeated measurements, (*b*) the first three values of the set of 10, (*c*) the three sets of three repeated measurements, (*d*) the background measurements.

2. Calculate the standard deviation of the average of each set of repeated measurements (four sources and background), using the average of the first three measurements for the sample measured 10 times.

3. Calculate a grand average for the equally weighted averages of triplicate measurements for the three identical samples, and calculate σ_M for the grand average.

4. Calculate the grand average of the average rates of the three identical samples using the average based on 10 measurements for the one sample, weighting each average inversely as its dispersion σ_R^2. Calculate σ_M. Compare M and σ_M with the values obtained in (3).

Using the grand average obtained in (4) for the gross sample rates of the three identical samples and the average background rate, calculate the grand average net counting rate and its standard deviation. Report the activity of the solution* (e.g., counts per minute per microliter) used to prepare the sources.

Compare the standard deviations calculated in two ways for the various measured values. Show how source-preparation error, i.e., pipette error and position variation, contribute to a difference between the two sets of σ_R values. Draw conclusions about:

1. The performance of the counting equipment
2. Variations in source preparation
3. Effect of rinsing the micropipette

Apply the chi-square test to the set of 10 measurements.

Experiment 3-2
Statistical Aspects of Nuclear-particle Counting (Counting-rate Meters)

It is the purpose of this experiment to illustrate:

1. The reproducibility of nuclear-particle counting
2. Two methods of calculating the standard deviation for counting-rate data
3. The agreement or disagreement between σ_R for radioactivity fluctuations and σ_R for observed over-all deviations
4. The effect of experimental technique on precision
5. Special characteristics of counting-rate meters

See also Expt. 3-1.

Apparatus and Materials

Radiation-detection equipment—detector, counting-rate meter, auxiliary timer
Radioactive material—a convenient beta emitter is P^{32}
Source mounting and covering material
Micropipette
Heat lamp

Procedure

Prepare three samples as nearly identical as possible (including centering of droplet of the activity-containing liquid) without rinsing the

* When the calibration of the detector is known, calculate disintegrations per second or microcuries per microliter. If the sources were prepared from a solution obtained by dilution of a stock solution, calculate the activity of the stock solution.

micropipette. Prepare a fourth sample, identical with the first three except that the micropipette should be rinsed and the activity in the rinse water added to the central droplet according to the procedure described in Sec. 5-2.

It may be advisable to check the calibration of the meter by means of the internal calibration circuit commonly provided.

If the *RC* time constants are not known for the various count-per-minute ranges of the meter, they may be estimated in the following way. With a source in position near the detector the counting rate varies with time according to Eq. (3-53); hence *RC* may be evaluated by observing R at various times until R_{ss} is reached for a fixed constant source. If the meter cannot be readily zeroed by means of a switch at $t = 0$, the source should be rapidly positioned near the detector or rapidly uncovered by removing an absorber.

From preliminary rough measurements, obtain values for the counting rates of background and the sources. Calculate, by means of Eq. (3-52), the time required to reach steady state for background and for the sources.

Make a single observation of the steady-state background rate.

Place one of the three identical samples in position near the detector and, after steady state has been reached, make 10 observations of the counting rate at intervals such that the values are independent. Similarly, make observations in triplicate for the remaining three samples.

Repeat the background measurement and, if time permits, make two or three successive independent observations.

Analysis of Data

The methods are those given in Expt. 3-1, except that Eq. (3-54) should be used to find σ_R arising from fluctuations in the decay rate.

Experiment 3-3

Statistical Fluctuations in Nuclear-particle Counting over Extended Periods of Time

Statistical analysis of the counting data for a long-lived source counted over a period of several months can be used to check the performance of counting equipment. Similarly a statistical analysis of background rates observed over an extended period can be used to indicate how well the detector is shielded with respect to large portable sources, accelerators, radioactive fallout or rainout from nuclear-weapons tests, etc.

Apparatus and Materials

Radiation-detection equipment
Long-lived source (see Expt. 5-1)

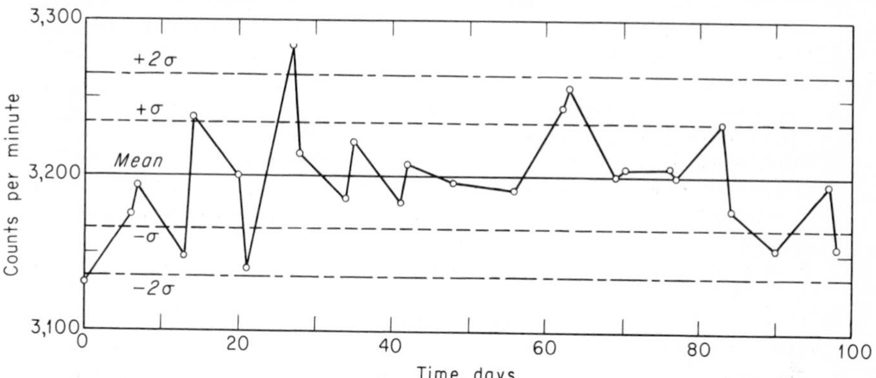

FIG. 3-8. Variation of counting rate of U_3O_8 reference source with time.

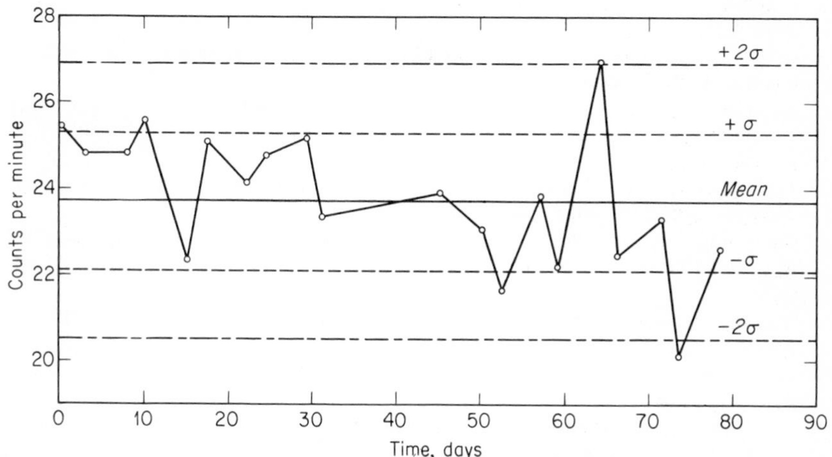

FIG. 3-9. Variation of background with time (Geiger counter).

Procedure

For preparation of a long-lived source, see Expt. 5-1.

Background data taken whenever samples are counted should be assembled for plotting on linear graph paper.

Analysis of Data

Examine linear plots of the data for background and for the long-lived source for trends and for deviations from the mean of σ, 2σ, and 3σ. (See Figs. 3-8 and 3-9.)

Cited References

1. Worthing, A. G., and J. Geffner: "Treatment of Experimental Data," Wiley, New York, 1943.
2. Crumpler, T. B., and J. H. Yoe: "Chemical Computations and Errors," Wiley, New York, 1940.
3. Fry, T. C.: "Probability and Its Engineering Uses," Van Nostrand, Princeton, N.J., 1928.
4. "Handbook of Chemistry and Physics," Chemical Rubber Publishing Co., Cleveland (revised periodically).
5. Rutherford, E., H. Geiger, and H. Bateman: The Probability Variations in the Distribution of Alpha Particles, *Phil. Mag.*, vol. 20, pp. 698–707, 1910.
6. Rutherford, E., J. Chadwick, and C. D. Ellis: "Radiations from Radioactive Substances," Cambridge, New York, 1930.
7. Rasetti, F.: "Elements of Nuclear Physics," Prentice-Hall, Englewood Cliffs, N.J., 1936.
8. Strong, J.: "Procedures in Experimental Physics," Prentice-Hall, Englewood Cliffs, N.J., 1938.
9. Rainwater, L. J., and C. S. Wu: Applications of Probability Theory to Nuclear Particle Detection, *Nucleonics*, vol. 1, no. 2, pp. 60–69, October, 1947.
10. Evans, R. D.: "The Atomic Nucleus," McGraw-Hill, New York, 1955.
11. Friedlander, G., and J. W. Kennedy: "Nuclear and Radiochemistry," Wiley, New York, 1955.
12. Wilks, S. S.: "Elementary Statistical Analysis," Princeton University Press, Princeton, N.J., 1948.
13. Jarrett, A. A.: Statistical Methods Used in the Measurement of Radioactivity (Some Useful Graphs), *U.S. Atomic Energy Comm. Rept.* AECU-262 (Mon P-126), June 17, 1946.
14. Loevinger, R., and M. Berman: Efficiency Criteria in Radioactivity Counting, *Nucleonics*, vol. 9, no. 1, pp. 26–39, 1951.
15. Outteridge, K. D.: The Statistics of the Adjustment and Comparison of Counters, United Kingdom Atomic Energy Authority Report AERE 1/M 32, 1954.
16. Thomas, A.: How to Compare Counters, *Nucleonics*, vol. 6, no. 2, pp. 50–53, 1950.
17. Libby, W. F.: "Radiocarbon Dating," 2d ed., University of Chicago Press, Chicago, 1955.
18. Bousquet, A. G.: Counting Rate Meters versus Scalers, *Nucleonics*, vol. 4, no. 2, pp. 67–76, February, 1949.
19. Calvin, M., C. Heidelberger, J. C. Reid, B. M. Tolbert, and P. F. Yankwich: "Isotopic Carbon," Wiley, New York, 1949.

4

The Practice of Radiological Safety

Although the potential hazard of radiation has been known since the early work with radioactive materials, formal radiological safety (or health physics) groups did not develop on a large scale until the Manhattan Engineering Project in 1943. Considerable information has been developed to indicate the potential biological effects of radiation. Information gained at Hiroshima, at Los Alamos, and from animal studies has given a clear picture of the effects of massive, acute doses of radiation on human and animal life. Of considerably more concern to laboratory workers, however, are the potential effects of chronic low-level exposure to ionizing radiation. Data have indicated that this hazard lies in the possibility of increasing the incidence of leukemia, cancer, and cataracts and of decreasing the life span and also the possibility of genetically affecting one's offspring.

Although such potentiality must be considered, not only by workers in the radioactivity field but also by the general public, a proper approach would be to determine what levels of radiation are significant and what methods can be used to limit the exposure of any individual to an insignificant level. The report of the Research Council of the National Academy of Science (1) gives a thorough survey of these problems and includes recommendations for the general population. In the United States the Atomic Energy Commission has fundamental responsibility for those workers in the radiation field who are associated with its laboratories or who use materials from its plants. The Commission has made great efforts to determine the nature and extent of radiation hazard. Acceptable levels of radiation have been determined, and laboratory workers are made responsible for their activities in accordance with these recommendations. It should be emphasized that all radiation exposure should be kept at a minimum, since permissible levels of radiation exposure are always somewhat arbitrary.

The factors which determine the potential radiation hazard for biological damage can be grouped as follows:

1. Total dose—this is significant both for occupational problems and for the general populace. The summary report of the NRC-NAS committee gives valuable information on the problems associated with a determination of this value.
2. The relative biological effectiveness of the various types of radiation.
3. The energy of the radiation.
4. The biological tissue involved.
5. The dose rate.
6. The area or volume of the body exposed.
7. The radiation external or internal to the body.

The necessity of precautions for radiation work is the same as for other types of scientific work except that the radiation is not directly detected by the sense organs of the body. This means that a constant program of monitoring is necessary in the vicinity of large sources. If the monitoring instrument indicates that the dosage rate is too high, one or more of the three primary parameters must be modified, as follows:

1. *Shielding.* A thickness of an appropriate material should be added between the source and the worker.
2. *Distance.* An increase in distance between the source and the worker diminishes the radiation intensity. The radiation intensity from an extended or wide-area source varies (approximately) inversely as the first power of the distance, whereas the inverse-square law holds for a point source.
3. *Time.* No part of the body should remain in a radiation field any longer than necessary. The total dose is proportional to the time spent in the field.

Internal exposures are those in which radioactive material has entered the body by ingestion, by inhalation, or through the skin. The internal hazard from radioactive materials in the body is dependent on several factors. The hazard is greater in the following situations:

1. When the radioactive element is retained for a long time in the body.
2. When the element concentrates in a single body organ.
3. When the radioactivity has a high specific activity.
4. When the energy of the radiation is high.
5. When the relative biological effectiveness of the radiation is high.
6. When the radiological half-life is intermediate.

In the consideration of the half-life, short-lived materials decay so rapidly that no great amount of radiation damage may be observed, whereas long-lived materials have such low specific activity that it is difficult to concentrate sufficient material in the organ. The materials with half-lives of months to several years have the greatest potential hazard. To avoid internal exposure it is necessary to keep all radioactive materials away from the mouth, to control radioactivity in water and air supplies, and to check all factors continuously. These factors are considered in more detail later in this chapter, but two points really summarize the requirements for radiological safety:

1. The best protection against internal exposure is good housekeeping.
2. The best protection against external exposure is good instrumentation which is kept in operating condition at all times and which is used.

4-1. The Maximum Permissible Exposure to Radiation

It was pointed out in Chap. 1 that the potential hazard of work with radiation has to do with the energy transferred to a biological system. This effect is probably of most importance in ionizing collisions; so the units of radiation dosage, the rad and the roentgen, were defined in Chap. 1 in these terms. Although the general definitions apply to any system in which the energy transfer is of importance, the problems of radiological safety are concerned with the prevention of these effects in humans. Consequently, a number of special problems have been studied in connection with the problems of dose, dose rate, and the irradiated-organ volume.

One of these problems has to do not only with the different kinds of radiation, but also with the differences in radiosensitivity of various organs of the body. For this reason a term has come into use relating these various factors. This term is the relative biological effectiveness, abbreviated RBE, and is used to compare the effectiveness of an absorbed dose of radiation delivered in different ways. As pointed out in the Report of the International Commission on Radiological Units and Measurements in Handbook 62 (2), it signifies that m rads delivered by a particular radiation procedure produces a biological response identical with that produced by m(RBE) rads delivered by a different procedure.

The statement that "the RBE of alpha radiation relative to gamma radiation is 10" indicates that alpha radiation produces a particular biological response in the same degree as 10 times the number of rads of gamma radiation. The Handbook goes on to point out that the concept of RBE has a limited usefulness because the biological effectiveness of any radiation depends on many factors, such as the absorbed dose rate, the oxygen tension, the pH, the temperature, and the type of biological effect. As a result, another concept has come into use which may be more useful in future calculations. This is the linear energy transfer, abbreviated LET, which measures the rate at which the energy is used up in the system along its path length. Table 4-1 gives values for the RBE and LET for several types of radiation. This is a modification of the table given in the Radiological Health Handbook (3).

TABLE 4-1
RBE AND LET VALUES FOR RADIATION OF DIFFERENT SPECIFIC IONIZATIONS

Type of radiation	Average specific ionization, (ion pairs/μ water)	RBE	Average LET to water, kev/μ
1. X-rays and electrons (also in certain cases heavy particles)	100 or less	1	3.5 or less
2. Heavy ionizing particles (alpha, proton, neutron, recoil atoms)	100–200	1–2	3.5–7.0
	200–650	2–5	7.0–23
	650–1,500	5–10	23–53
	1,500–5,000	10–20	53–175

The RBE dose is equal numerically to the product of the dose in rads and an arbitrarily selected RBE value with respect to a particular type of electromagnetic radiation. The standard usually taken is X or gamma radiation having a LET in water of 3 kev/μ delivered at a rate of about 10 rads/min.

The unit of RBE dose is the rem, which was originally an abbreviation for roentgen equivalent, man (or mammal), and is a measure of equivalent damage. It is also defined somewhat arbitrarily on the basis of generally agreed values of the RBE. The rem is therefore used only with respect to calculations involved in radiation protection; for example, one could say that "the permissible weekly whole-body RBE dose is 0.3 rem regardless of the type of radiation to which a person is exposed."

Several publications (4–7) discuss the limiting values for maximum permissible exposures. A number of other papers describing the problems encountered in the determination of these values are listed in the supplementary references to this chapter. Also included in the supplementary references is the listing of the National Bureau of Standards Handbooks which have been issued in this field. Several of these are cited separately in the text. A summary of the values for occupational exposure to maximum permissible radiation levels for various types of ionizing radiations which have been recommended by the National Committee on Radiation Protection and the International Commission of Radiological Protection in the 1958 revision of Handbook 59 is given in Table 4-2.

It is generally considered that these rates can be averaged safely for periods of a few months at a time, but it is generally considered a better practice to limit the exposure of persons to a factor of 10 less than these

TABLE 4-2

MAXIMUM PERMISSIBLE EXPOSURE FOR VARIOUS TYPES OF IONIZING RADIATIONS (OCCUPATIONAL LEVELS)

Type of radiation	RBE (11)	Basic exposure, mrads/week*	
		1958	Recommended 1959†
X and gamma rays	1	300	100
Beta rays and electrons	1	300	100
Thermal neutrons	2.5	120	40
Fast neutrons	10	30	10
Alpha particles	10	30	10
Protons	10	30	10
Heavy ions	20	15	5

* Basic exposure rate permissible to gonads, eyes, and blood-forming organs of persons of age 18 or over.

† Revised Handbook 59 and ICRP Handbook.

values if a long period of time is involved. The revised Handbook 59 also gives other limitations for long periods of exposure by requiring that the dose accumulated over a period of years be restricted to a value given by $5(N - 18)$ rem, in which N is the worker's age. Exposures to persons under age 18 and other nonradiation workers are limited to one-tenth of the permissible occupational exposure.

It is recommended in the Handbook that the rates are to be applied on a weekly basis, although the International Commission's publication permits the exposure interval to be increased to 13 weeks if the accumulated dose in this period does not exceed 3 rem. The requirements further state that the 13-week interval may begin at the time of high exposure. If a high exposure is received in the thirteenth week of a given period of satisfactory exposure, the exposure during the following 12 weeks must then be proportionally reduced.

Handbook 59 also permits receipt of *emergency exposures* of up to 25 rem once in a lifetime. This exposure may be made over a period of 1 month, and this is assumed to have no bearing on the weekly permissible exposure status of the worker. Permissible emergency exposures of the hands, forearms, feet, and ankles may be as high as 125 rem on the same basis.

It is quite evident that one of the main emergency possibilities would be in the event of nuclear warfare resulting in high radioactive contamination. A number of these problems have been discussed by Gray and Martens (8). As a result of these limitations and allowances a typical set of instructions to rescue teams involved in operations in contaminated areas might be the following:

1. A single exposure of 25 rem may be permitted.
2. If it is necessary to save life or if it is essential to the national defense, exposures of 100 rem may be taken in a single day, 150 rem may be taken in a single week, or 300 rem may be taken in a single month.
3. Do not take any exposure, particularly high exposure, which is unnecessary, and in so far as practical, limit high exposure to males who do not intend to beget children. Unnecessary exposure of pregnant women should be avoided.

It might be noted that at higher radiation exposures it might be expected that the worker would show signs of radiation sickness such as nausea and drowsiness, but it is not expected that the limits set above would seriously incapacitate the person involved.

The problem of internal dosage limits is considerably more complicated even than that of external dosimetry, because there are usually many factors of uncertainty such as the physical or chemical form of the radioactive material, the method of entry into the body, the deposition and retention pattern of the material, and the relative radiosensitivity of the various organs. In 1953 the Subcommittee on Internal Dose of the National Committee on Radiation Protection prepared Handbook 52 (9), which gives the maximum permissible body burden q and the maximum permissible concentration MPC in air and water. The 1959 revision of the Handbook contains data for 227 radioisotopes, giving information on radioisotopes in the gastrointestinal tract and other critical body organs along with information on whole-body effects.

In order to make calculations on the internal dose received by the body by ingestion or the inhalation of radioactive material, one of the important factors is the fraction of the material which deposits in the critical body organ, which is the organ receiving the isotope resulting in the greatest damage to the body. The maximum permissible concentrations correspond to the concentration in water and air that will result in a total body burden q after a person has been exposed continuously to the contaminated water and air for a certain period of time. The MPC is then given by the following equation:

$$\text{MPC} = \frac{aqf_0}{Tf[1 - \exp(-0.693t/T)]} \tag{4-1}$$

in which MPC is the number of microcuries per cubic centimeter of air or water that results in the total body burden q. This body burden is defined as the number of microcuries in the total body required to deliver a dose rate of 0.3 rem/week to the critical organ. The values of the constant a are indicated below. The fraction f_0 is the fraction of the radioisotope remaining in the critical organ compared with that in the total body, and f is the fraction of the radioisotope taken into the body that arrives in the critical organ. The period of time over which the exposure is considered is denoted by t, with T being the effective half-life of the radioisotope in the critical organ. The effective half-life is related to the radiological half-life T_{rad} and the biological half-life T_{biol} by the following equation:

$$T = \frac{T_{biol}T_{rad}}{T_{biol} + T_{rad}} \tag{4-2}$$

If the effective half-life is given in days, the constant a is 3.5×10^{-8} and 3.11×10^{-4} for air and water respectively.

The maximum permissible body burden can be calculated using Eq. (4-3) as follows:

$$q = \frac{5.6 \times 10^{-5} mW}{f_0 \Sigma E(\mathrm{RBE})N} \tag{4-3}$$

in which m is the mass of the critical organ in grams, W is the permissible limit in rads per week, E is the effective energy of the radiation in Mev per disintegration, RBE is that for the radiation as given in Table 4-2, and N a nonuniform distribution factor. This is given as 5 for alpha particles or electrons from all radionuclides for which bone is the critical body organ with the exception of P^{32} and Ra^{226}. The factor N is taken as 1 for all tissues other than bone.

A full description of the assumptions and limitations of these equations is given in Handbook 52 (9) and its 1959 revision. A number of papers of interest in this area are referred to by Morgan (10). An excellent summary of a number of factors of importance to radiological safety is also given in his chapter in the Handbook of Nuclear Instruments and Techniques (11).

A detailed treatment of the biological effects of radiation is not within the scope of this book, but attention should be called to the great amount of work which has been done in order to establish the effects of overexposure to radiation. It should also be emphasized that, although the radiation problems are of considerable popular interest, they do not represent an entirely new hazard. It is important that a balanced point of view be maintained with respect to the relative hazards of various levels of radiation exposure and also the relative hazards of radiation exposure as compared with other types of agents which can lead to

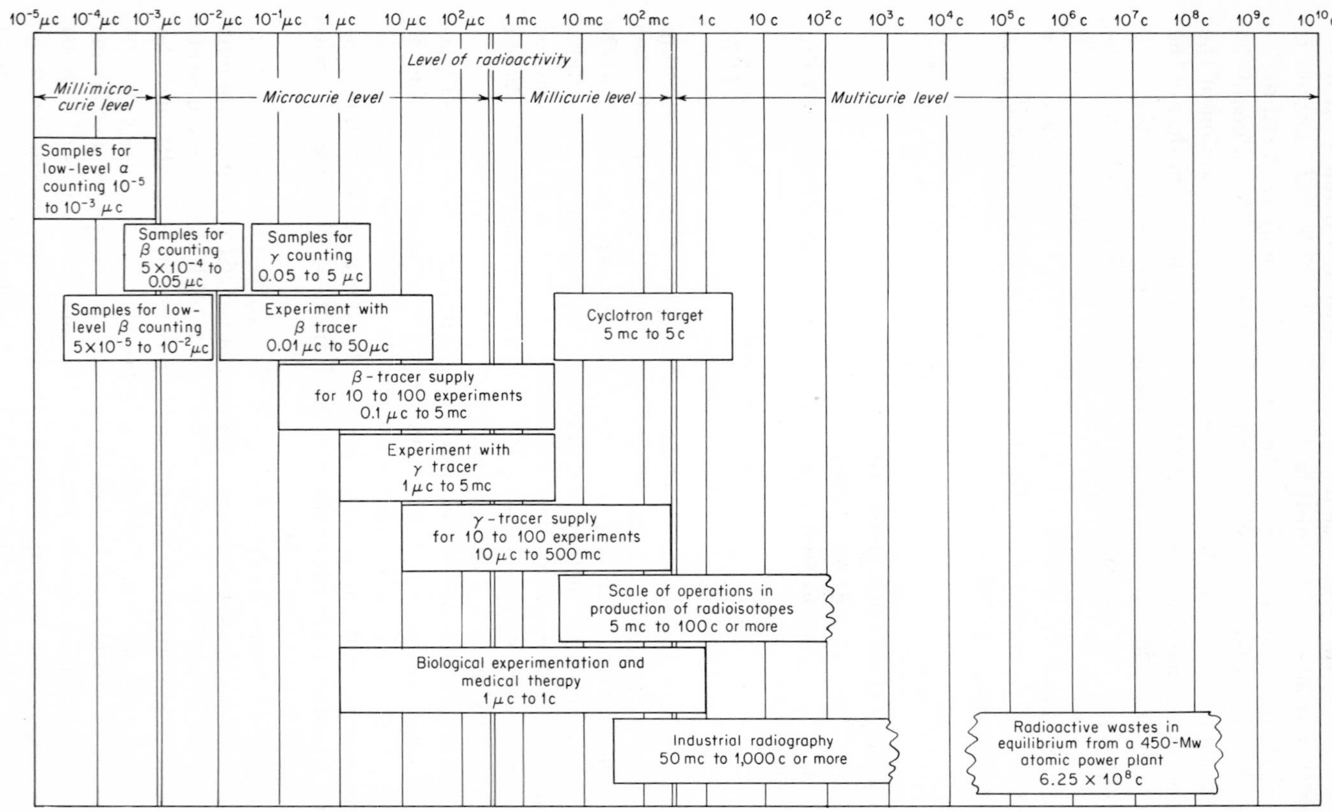

FIG. 4-1. Levels of radioactivity required for radioisotope work. [*From Morgan* (10).]

biological and genetic damage. There is no question as to the potential ill effects of overexposure to radiation in both somatic and genetic areas, but this should lead only to an increased awareness and respect for the radiation problems and to the necessity of minimizing the potential hazard while taking advantage of the tremendous potential for progress which is inherent in their use. A comprehensive summary of the status of a number of these problems has been given in the Report of the Committee on Pathological Effects of Atomic Radiation which has been published by the National Academy of Sciences and the National Research Council (1) and in a report on the effects of atomic radiation published by the United Nations (12). A number of papers and books having to do with the general problems of biological effects are given in the supplementary references.

4-2. Levels of Radioisotope Operations

Although the exposure limitations discussed above apply to all work with radioactive materials, the operational problems of limiting the exposure to these values vary considerably with the level of radioactive material being used in a particular laboratory. Levy (13) classified the problems of laboratory design and manipulations under three headings: microcurie-level laboratories in which amounts of activity ranging from 10^{-3} μc to 0.5 mc were handled, millicurie-level laboratories with activities ranging from 0.5 mc to 0.5 curie, and a multicurie-level laboratory handling all activities greater than 0.5 curie. Morgan (11) has suggested the addition of a millimicrocurie-level or "cold" laboratory which it is essential to keep clear of all extraneous radioactivity. Levy's chart, with some modifications made by Morgan showing the approximate amount of radioactivity encountered in various types of problems, is given in Fig. 4-1. The type of facility which is required for various operations can be determined by reference to the chart. Bizzell (14) has described the types of facilities needed for these levels of laboratories.

Although it is possible to classify laboratory facilities as to the level of activity to be employed in them, it should be pointed out that there are also differences in the requirements for working with various radioisotopes depending on the half-life, the types of radiation, and the other factors relative to their internal dose concentrations. The Subcommittee on Safe Handling of Radioisotopes of the National Committee on Radiation Protection has given, in Handbook 42 (15), a tentative list of isotopes classified according to their radiotoxicity. This listing of relative hazard is given in Table 4-3 together with an approximate indication of the relative amounts which may be handled in the various types of facilities. It is suggested that the designations "cold" (or ultralow

TABLE 4-3

RELATIVE INTERNAL HAZARD OF VARIOUS β- AND γ-EMITTING ISOTOPES

Radiotoxicity group	Activity limits		
	Low	Intermediate	High
Slight hazard Na^{24}, K^{42}, Cu^{64}, Mn^{52}, As^{76}, As^{77}, Kr^{85}, Hg^{197}	Up to 1 mc	1–10 mc	Above 10 mc
Moderately dangerous H^3, C^{14}, Na^{22}, S^{35}, Cl^{36}, Mn^{54}, Fe^{59}, Co^{60}, Sr^{89}, Nb^{95}, Ru^{103}, P^{32}, Te^{127}, Te^{129}, I^{131}, Cs^{137}, Ba^{140}, La^{140}, Ce^{141}, Pr^{143}, Nd^{147}, Au^{198}, Au^{199}, Hg^{203}	Up to 0.1 mc	0.1–1 mc	Above 1 mc
Very dangerous Ca^{45}, Fe^{55}, Sr^{90}, Y^{91}, Zr^{95}, Ce^{144}, Pm^{147}, Bi^{210}	Up to 0.01 mc	0.01–0.1 mc	Above 0.1 mc

level), low level, intermediate level, and high level be applied to these facilities instead of the curie designations because of the variation in potential hazard from the different types of radioisotopes. The Handbook points out that these activity limits do not indicate clear-cut distinctions. Any quantity near a limit should be considered a borderline case.

Some of the salient points to be considered in planning for laboratory facilities at the various levels will be enumerated in the following sections (11):

1. Millimicrocurie-level or "cold" laboratories
   a. No biological radiation hazards.
   b. Chief problems are to maintain low background and negligible contamination from radioactive materials.
   c. Counting chambers must be constructed of low-background materials.
   d. Special protective clothing may be required or entrance denied to all but authorized persons to eliminate possible contamination.
2. Microcurie or low-level laboratories (low-toxicity groups)
   a. Sources should be handled with gloves for alpha and soft-beta emitters or with tongs for hard-beta and gamma-emitting sources.
   b. No work should be permitted with open wounds, and caution should be exercised to avoid puncture wounds with contaminated objects.

c. Pipetting by mouth should be prohibited, and glass blowing should not permit inhalation of possible contaminated air.

d. Work may be done over blotting or absorbent paper in trays in conventional chemical hoods if no possible air turbulence brings the material back into the working area.

e. Essentially no shielding is required at this level since the glass or container is usually adequate.

f. Ordinary drains may be used if no more than 0.5 mc is disposed of daily providing adequate water (not less than 50 gal for 0.5 mc) is used for dilution.

g. Levels of 0.5 mc may be disposed of by incineration in some cases if the stack is high enough or far enough removed so that it does not contaminate laboratories and other populated areas.

h. Counting rooms are usually designed at this level. Either close shielding around the counting chambers may be used or a wall of 1 to 2 ft of concrete may be constructed to lower the background.

i. All persons working at this and higher levels should have personnel monitoring meters (pocket chambers and/or film badges) and should have a survey meter available for the location of contamination. Not necessary for low-energy beta work.

j. Survey equipment should also be furnished at this and all higher levels to permit the worker to determine the permissible working time and the level of contamination of the working spaces.

3. Millicurie or intermediate-level laboratories

a. Absorbent paper and trays should be used and the work done in specially designed hoods or glove boxes (see Figs. 4-2 and 4-3).

b. The so-called radiochemical hood (Fig. 4-2) is designed with "picture-frame" baffles around the hood opening which permit much smoother air flow at low hood air velocities. They also have the utilities and service controls outside the hood itself and are frequently larger from front to rear to permit a wall of shielding in front with adequate work space behind.

c. Some operations require that filters be used on the hood or glove-box exhaust.

d. The inner surfaces of the hood or glove box should be of stainless steel or should be covered with a strippable plastic to permit easy decontamination.

e. Protective clothing should be required, and consideration should be given to laundering it within the laboratory area.

f. No food should be brought into the laboratories, and no smoking should be permitted.

g. Radioactive wastes should not be placed in drains until the minimum concentrations of the National Committee on Radiation Protection can be obtained (see item 2*f*).

h. General shielding is required which may consist of lead or iron bricks. The hoods and work tables should be designed to support the required amount of shielding.

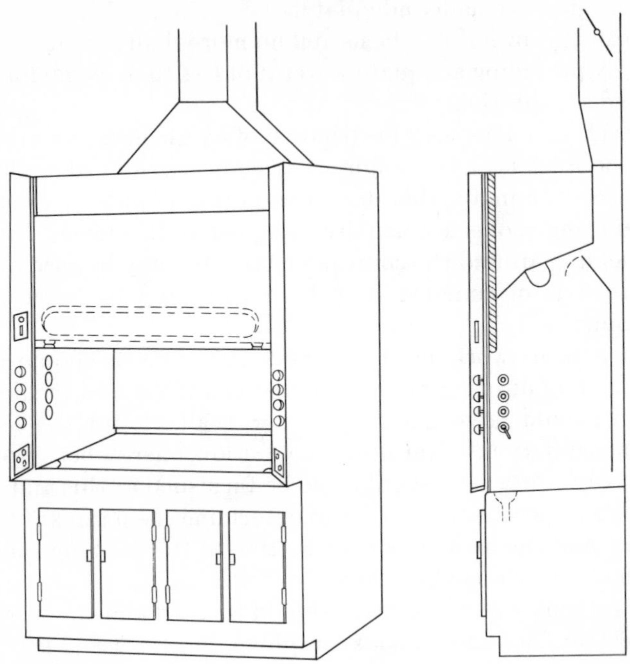

FIG. 4-2. Radiochemical fume hood. (*From C. L. Comar, "Radioisotopes in Biology and Agriculture," McGraw-Hill, New York,* 1955.)

i. Remote-control devices are required. These may include long tongs, remote pipetters, or mechanically operated manipulation devices.

j. Holdup tanks, underground storage, and properly designed waste-disposal facilities are usually required.

4. Multicurie or high-level laboratories

a. Operations are usually done in thick-walled cells or caves controlled either by mechanical "hands" or by vacuum-compressed air systems for transfer of materials.

b. The cells are exhausted through filters into suitable stacks.

c. Liquid waste is carried into specially designed tanks or other disposal systems.

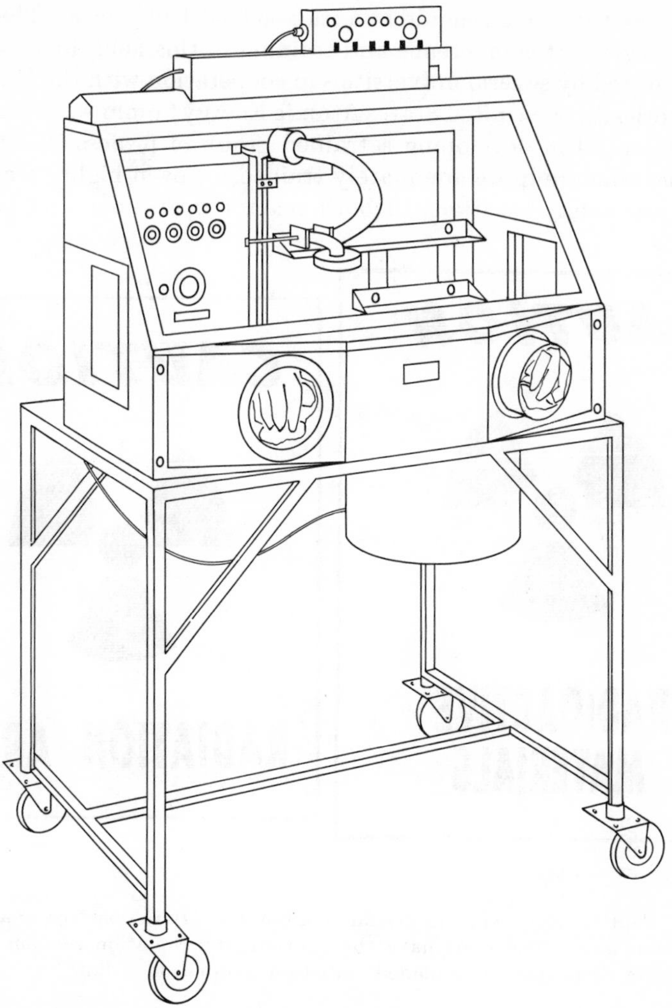

FIG. 4-3. Typical glove box. (*Courtesy Allied Nucleonics Co.*)

It is the responsibility of each person working with radioactive isotopes to make certain that the proper techniques and precautions are being utilized as required by the particular problem at hand. However, an institution usually has an isotope committee to exercise general supervision of the radioisotope work. In addition, institutions with a number of laboratory groups working with radioisotopes usually find it desirable to make one individual responsible for the over-all radiation safety program. Wherever possible, in organizations having many laboratories, this person should be a trained health physicist. There are varying degrees of competence and training in this field, but the program operated by several universities in cooperation with the National Laboratories for the United States Atomic Energy Commission has been quite successful in developing a trained group of professional health physicists who are quite adequately trained for even highly technical radiological safety positions in both reactor operations and isotope programs.

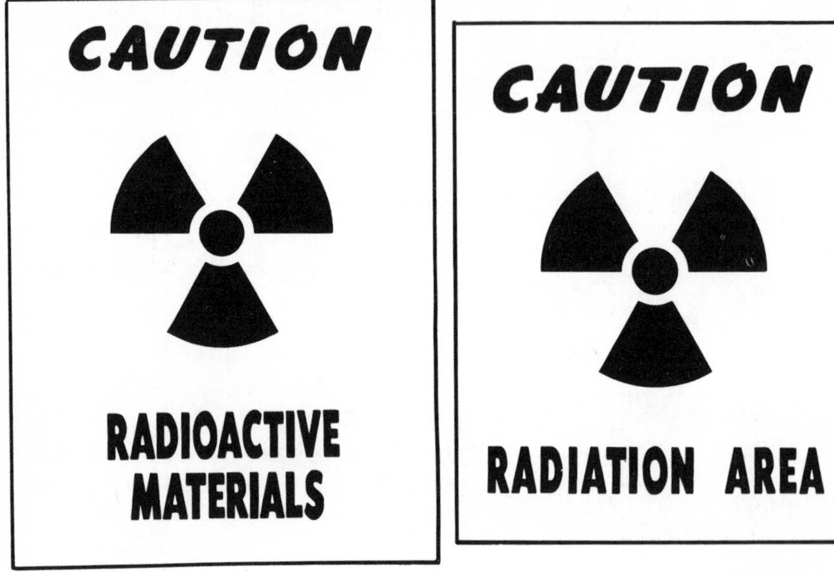

(*a*) (*b*)

Fig. 4-4. Caution sign with radiation symbol for (*a*) radioactive materials, (*b*) radiation level. The signs have the conventional radiation caution colors, i.e., magenta or purple three-bladed radiation symbol on yellow background.

Whether it be possible or necessary to employ full-time professional health-physics personnel, there are a number of responsibilities which must be accepted by someone in the organization. These have been outlined by Morgan. Someone must be responsible for determining that:

1. The buildings and hoods are of appropriate design and properly located for work with radioisotopes.
2. The proper techniques are used for safe handling of the materials.
3. Persons working with radioactive material have adequate training and understanding of the radiation-protection rules and of the maximum permissible levels of radiation exposure, and know how to use and

interpret properly the readings of the radiation-protection meters furnished to them.

4. The surface contamination and air activity in the laboratory and in the area surrounding the laboratory remain at an acceptable level; the waste solids are properly buried or incinerated; and high-level radioactive wastes are properly packaged and are turned over to qualified and authorized agencies for disposal.

5. All the radiation-protection instruments that are needed are available in proper operating condition and are maintained in proper calibration.

6. Complete and up-to-date records are kept on all personnel exposures and on all levels of air and water activity in the area about the plant. Radiation warning signs must be posted where applicable (Fig. 4-4).

7. Continuously recording instruments, shields, decontamination facilities, etc., are provided where needed.

4-3. Radiation-protection Instrumentation

Several references have been made above to the need for proper instrumentation to determine the radiation and contamination levels that exist in the laboratory. In addition, each person working in intermediate- or high-radiation fields is required to have proper personnel monitoring equipment on his person in order to maintain records of the radiation to which he has been exposed.

Any laboratory in which radioisotope work is carried on needs to have two types of portable survey meters. The principles of these instruments have been described in Chap. 2. One of these instruments is a very sensitive instrument to determine the presence of relatively low levels of radiation either from a working area or from contamination. The other instrument required is a very reliable device which is relatively energy-independent and which maintains its calibration over long periods of time. The first of these is usually a portable G-M counter, and the second is more often a portable ionization chamber utilizing a vacuum-tube electrometer. The Landsverk or Lauritsen fiber electroscopes also exhibit very high reliability and are used for long-term calibrations. It is quite possible that portable scintillation counters will become standard instruments for these purposes in the near future.

The instruments required for personnel monitoring are usually film meters, pocket ionization chambers, or pocket dosimeters of either the quartz-fiber or chemical type. In many intermediate- and high-level laboratories, each person is required to wear both a pocket ionization chamber or similar instrument and a film meter. The chief advantage of the film meter is that it can serve as a permanent record of the cumulative exposure over a period of time. It is assumed that such a permanent record has an adequate legal status for administrative purposes. Likewise, film meters under proper conditions can indicate the exposure to mixtures of beta, X, and gamma radiation.

Many factors are involved in the proper control and interpretation of film-badge readings, such as the uniformity of the development procedure, the calibration and comparisons made with a standard film exposure, and the time and temperature of the photographic development. Interpretation is particularly difficult when the meter has been subjected to mixed radiations.

Pocket ionization chambers are used to give rough estimates of the amount of exposure which the individual has received. They have had several objectionable features, such as their insensitivity to beta radiation, the mechanical difficulties when jarred or dropped, and their sensitivity to humidity changes. Considerable development work has been done on these devices, and great improvement has been noted in recent years.

The portable quartz-fiber electroscope or dosimeter indicates the amount of radiation to which the individual has been exposed at any given time, by a direct reading of the indicator on the scale. These instruments do not need to be discharged to be read and are used mostly in high-radiation fields where it is important not to exceed the upper limit of permissible exposure.

These instruments are not usually expected to attain high precision or accuracy but are used primarily to indicate the general level of the radiation and of the exposure received, although it is possible to obtain good results if proper care is taken in the calibration and the measurement. In general, one might expect accuracy to be of the order of 15 to 25 per cent in a given reading with either a portable survey meter or a typical personnel monitoring device. This is usually sufficient for the purposes for which they are employed. The calibration of these instruments is described in Chap. 7 along with calibration experiments.

4-4. Problems of Decontamination and Waste Disposal

Two basic references of particular interest are NBS Handbook 42, referred to earlier, entitled Safe Handling of Radioisotopes, and Handbook 48 (16), entitled Control and Removal of Radioactive Contamination in Laboratories. Other booklets in the series are important, but a number of recommendations in these two have direct bearing on common laboratory problems of decontamination and waste disposal and are therefore included here. In Handbook 42, the philosophy is stated:

Contamination of the person or of laboratory areas and equipment is a problem of fundamental importance to everyone working with radioactive isotopes. Constant vigilance to prevent contamination or to contain its spread must be maintained by every user. Personnel should be thoroughly informed concerning local safety measures and should always be fully aware of all safety devices and recommended emergency procedures before beginning work.

The National Committee recommends the establishment of an Isotopes Committee, as mentioned above, in each institution where work with radioactive isotopes is carried on. The responsibility of this committee is "the surveillance of all activities involving the handling and use of radioisotopes."

The problem of contamination of the hands or other parts of the body depends on all the isotope characteristics, such as half-life, radiation energy, and biological deposition characteristics. Care should always be taken to avoid any type of contamination of any part of the body. However, contamination may be found on the body, the clothing, or laboratory tools and glassware appearing in other parts of the laboratory after an accident or accidental transfer of material.

The maximum contamination permitted on any surface of the body or laboratory material is outlined in Handbook 48 as follows: The maximum permissible exposure due to spot contamination (Table 4-3: group I, slight hazard, and group II, moderately dangerous) is 1 mrep/hr average as measured in a small volume of air (in a thin layer) above any 2 in.^{2} of the body (or other surface). If a gamma-emitting radioisotope is the contaminant on the surface, this corresponds approximately to a reading of about 1,000 cpm when a Geiger-Müller counter (with a flat plate area of 2 in.^{2}) is placed as close as possible to the contaminated area. A thin-walled Geiger-Müller counter may be used to measure low-energy beta-emitting contaminants such as C^{14} or S^{35}. In case of contamination by radioisotopes of group III (very dangerous), the measurable radiation at the surface should be reduced to as near background as possible while the maximum permissible level of contamination is 0.1 mrep/hr (less than 100 cpm). It is important for each worker to ascertain from proper sources the group in which lies the radioactive isotope of interest. As mentioned above, the "mrep/hr" unit is no longer used, but the number of counts per minute above the surface is essentially the same. If contamination above the levels indicated is observed, the following procedures for decontamination may be used.

Decontamination of the Skin. Thorough washing with soap and water is the best general method for decontamination of hands and other parts of the body (as well as many other surfaces). Recommended procedures include washing for not less than 2 min or more than 3 min by the clock, with a mild pure soap and a good lather, paying particular attention to the outer edges of the hands, around the fingernails, and between the fingers. If this procedure is not effective after three or four trials, as indicated by monitoring the area, scrub the hands with a soft brush using a heavy lather. At least three washes including rinses should be made within 8 min, of which at least 6 min should be devoted to scrubbing. Only light pressure should be applied—not sufficient to bend the brush bristles out of shape or to scratch or erode the skin. Lanolin or hand cream may be applied afterward to prevent chapping.

If these procedures are not adequate, chemical decontamination may be used. There are two processes in general use. One successful method for heavy contamination is to spread a liberal portion of freshly prepared titanium dioxide paste over affected areas. Work the paste over the skin for at least 2 min. Rinse with warm water and wash thoroughly. The paste should be prepared by mixing precipitated titanium dioxide with a small amount of lanolin, which should never be permitted to dry.

For very heavy contamination, mix equal volumes of a saturated solution of potassium permanganate and 0.2 *N* sulfuric acid. Pour this over the wet hands, rubbing the entire surface and using a hand brush for not more than 2 min. (The time limit should be adhered to closely in order not to remove skin.) Rinse with warm water and apply a freshly prepared 5 per cent solution of sodium acid sulfite in the same manner as above, using a hand brush and tepid water for not more than 2 min. Wash with soap and water and rinse thoroughly.

A hand-decontamination kit should be maintained in each washroom associated with laboratories where work is done with radioisotopes. Extreme precautions must be taken to avoid cuts or puncture wounds. This is especially true when working with isotopes of groups II and III and with all radioactive isotopes at intermediate or high levels. If a wound occurs, wash the affected part immediately with large volumes of running water. Light tourniquet action to stop venous return may be desirable to stimulate bleeding, but the arterial flow should not be restricted. More detailed emergency procedures are given below.

Decontamination of Clothing. Garments in each of the following classifications should be laundered following the indicated procedure:

Class 1. Less than 1,000 cpm for groups I and II and less than 100 cpm for group III. Release for ordinary laundering.

Class 2. Up to 10,000 cpm. Two hot rinses, hot solution of 3 per cent citric acid wash, hot rinse, hot suds, hot rinse, hot 1.5 per cent citric acid wash, three hot rinses, cold rinse, starch if desired. Monitor and repeat if necessary.

Class 3. More than 10,000 cpm. Laundering procedures are the same as for class 2 but should be performed separately from less contaminated clothes. Monitor and rewash all garments that do not fall in class 1.

Rubber gloves and other rubber goods decontaminate readily. They should first be washed with suds and hot water. If this is not effective, they should be washed in dilute nitric acid, followed by a wash with scouring powder and a thorough rinse in running water. Dry on paper towels, which should be promptly discarded in the dry active-waste can.

Decontamination of Laboratory Surfaces and Glassware. Tools and other equipment should be placed in nonporous metal trays or pans that are located away from the working space. Line such trays or pans with absorbent disposable paper, which should be changed frequently. Auxiliary containers, blotters, and covers should always be used where danger of spills and contamination of person or equipment is possible at all levels of activity. Contaminated equipment or other material should be isolated in designated areas in the laboratory or storage place and should not be replaced in the common stock area where it could be used in a nonradioactive area. Temporary labeling of such equipment is desirable, and monitoring of such equipment following their use should be a routine procedure.

Decontamination practices for equipment fall into two broad classifications: corrosive and noncorrosive. It is desirable to use a noncorrosive method, although many times this is not effective and then the surface of the material must be removed. General procedures are given in Table 4-4, which is based on information in the Radiological Health Handbook (3).

Since many laboratory areas are renovated from already existing facilities, some special problems of decontamination are frequently found with respect to the selection of working surfaces. Such problems are specifically considered in designing a new laboratory, but in remodeling or continuing its use it is helpful to have some information about the selection of laboratory construction materials. Listed below are the recommendations taken from Handbook 48 for materials which may be used in renovating existing laboratory space:

1. Wood—not recommended because of its high porosity.
2. Concrete—not recommended because of high porosity, although painting with strippable plastic will help. Strippable paint cannot be used on floors or work surfaces.
3. Soapstone—not recommended because of high porosity.
4. Porcelain—not recommended for permanent installation. Suitable for pans and trays if used with absorbent paper.

TABLE 4-4

USEFUL DECONTAMINATION METHODS FOR LABORATORY SURFACES

Surface	Method	Advantages	Disadvantages
Paint	Water	Most practical for gross decontamination	Protection needed from spray; runoff must be controlled
	Detergents	Most commonly available	Mild action
	Complexing solvents	Holds contamination in solution	Requires 5 to 30 min; little penetration; little value on weathered surfaces
	Organic solvents	Quick dissolving action useful on vertical or overhead surfaces	Toxic and flammable; requires ventilation and fire precautions
	Caustics	Minimum contact with surface; high decontamination factor	Applicable only on horizontal surfaces; not to be used on Al or Mg
	Abrasion (wet)	Complete removal of surface; feasible for large-scale operations	Too harsh for many surfaces
Glassware	Detergent	Readily available	Efficiency depends on nature of contaminant
	Reagents, (e.g., mineral acids, trisodium phosphate)	Nature of contaminant determines choice of reagent	Single reagent not suitable for all contaminants; repeated small quantities more efficient than large quantities
Metal	Water	Most practical method of gross decontamination	Same as for painted surfaces
	Detergents	Removal of oil or grease films	Same as for painted surfaces
	Organic solvents	Stripping off grease	Same as for painted surfaces
	Complexing agents	Holds contamination in solution	Best for horizontal surface; limited value for porous surfaces
	Inorganic acids	Fast, complete decontamination	Good ventilation required; possibility of excessive corrosion, toxicity
	Acid mixtures	Action of weak acid reduces contamination on unweathered surfaces	Same as for inorganic acids
	Abrasion (wet)	Same as for paint	Control of powdered contaminant; too harsh for many surfaces
Concrete and brick	Abrasion (vacuum blasting)	Same as for wet abrasion although less effective	Same as for wet abrasion
Wood	Planing	Complete removal; minimum dust hazard	May impair utility

5. Tile (ceramic)—acceptable for floors if tightly laid and well sealed.

6. Asphalt tile—recommended. Easy to replace and flows into cracks. Should be kept heavily waxed.

7. Rubber tile—recommended. Easy to replace. Should be heavily waxed.

8. Linoleum—acceptable if laid in large sheets. Difficult to replace in small sections. Should be heavily waxed.

9. Polished stabilized stainless steel (e.g., AISI type 304, 316, or 347)—recommended but costly for large installations. Easily etched by HCl fumes. Recommended for work trays to be used inside hoods.

10. Plain rolled stainless steel—not recommended, since steel entraps particles in microscopic pores.

11. Plate glass—recommended, but there is danger of cracking.

12. Tempered glass—recommended for table tops and other work surfaces. Should be cut to size before tempering.

13. Strippable plastics—recommended for use in covering work surfaces where there is light wear. Low porosity. Danger of attack by organic solvents.

14. Paint, varnish, lacquers—not recommended except for walls. Tygon acceptable.

15. Tempered Masonite and Masonite die stock—recommended for use in covering work surfaces. May be laid in large sheets, but cracks and edges must be well sealed.

16. Vinyl floor coverings and vinyl plastics tile—recommended; very resistant to ordinary laboratory chemicals and wears exceptionally well. Cracks should be well sealed. Danger of solution by some organic solvents.

Disposal of Contaminated Wastes. One of the most important unsolved problems confronting nuclear workers at the present time is that of the disposal of the large quantities of radioactive waste products which are formed in the projected large-scale nuclear power industry. It is probable that power reactors collectively will create thousands of curies per day of waste which must be disposed of in some satisfactory manner. By such standards the disposal problems of a typical radioisotope laboratory are small but they are important and can become quite difficult ones to solve in certain cases. For short-lived isotopes there is essentially no problem since the usual rule of thumb requires their storage for 10 half-lives, after which they may be treated as inactive samples or solutions. Actually, 10 half-lives still leave a residuum of about 0.1 per cent of the activity, and in laboratories using quite large amounts of radioactivity this is not a sufficient decay factor to be adequate.

Two general policies are usually advocated for waste disposal. One of these is that of permitting maximum dilution, the other that of bringing about maximum concentration. In the maximum dilution procedures, the assumption is made that the dilution brings about such a minimum concentration that the potential hazard is negligible. This dilution might be water, earth, or air, but it must be pointed out that there is always the possibility that some systems or organism such as algae may reconcentrate the material to a potentially hazardous level. The procedure of maximum concentration requires a safe area in which the active material can be kept for a long period compared with its half-life. For fission-product mixtures and other isotopes such as C^{14}, this means that permanent title to the area must be vested in an institution which can retain control. In practice, organizations that may be able to do this are governmental agencies.

There are several procedures and handbooks referring to waste disposal of specific isotopes such as C^{14}, P^{32}, and I^{131}. These are included in the list of Handbooks in the supplementary references to this chapter. Likewise, Handbook 42 gives several general statements of disposal of contaminated materials. These are outlined below:

1. *Absorbent papers, wipes, etc.* Waterproof disposable containers to hold the discarded bench paper and wiping papers should be provided at each laboratory station. Regular collections of these disposal vessels should be made. The eventual disposal of such items is determined by the half-life and toxicity level of the isotopes involved. With short half-lives, retention of the materials in a controlled area until their residual activity is insignificant is a preferred method. With long-lived isotopes the laboratory management is committed to a prevention of contamination of the public domain.

2. *Active solutions.* The disposal of active solutions to the public sewers can be considered safe only when the possible subsequent chemical, physical, and biological concentrations still leave the materials at safe strengths. Disposal to water systems should include consideration of the accumulation of activity in soil, mud, and algae. Excreta from isotope-injected animals or patients and liquors from equipment or clothing decontamination may require attention as active solutions.

3. *Tools and equipment.* Tools and other miscellaneous equipment used in handling radioisotopes should be regarded as contaminated and should not be released for other work until proved otherwise. Extensive publications are available on the problems of waste disposal, and the investigator is referred to the papers on this subject listed in the supplementary references at the end of the chapter, as well as the survey by Morgan (10).

Disposal services are available from AEC-licensed organizations.

4-5. Typical Rules for the Operation of an Intermediate-level University-type Radioisotope Laboratory

These regulations apply to all persons who work with or in an area containing radioactive materials in this laboratory. Specifically, this includes those persons who are:

Enrolled in a nuclear-chemistry laboratory course, or
Conducting research as undergraduate or graduate students, or
Temporarily utilizing (after proper authorization from the person in charge of the laboratory) the facilities of this laboratory.

General

1. Before starting work with radioactive materials each person shall make known any previous work with radioactive materials or radiation sources and any exposure over the maximum permissible dose.
2. Topcoats, hats, and other personal belongings including books (other than those required for work) should not be brought into the laboratory, where they may become contaminated.
3. Eating, drinking, smoking, and application of cosmetics in the laboratory (including the locker room and the counting room) are forbidden.
4. High standards of cleanliness and good housekeeping should be maintained throughout the laboratory.
5. Protective clothing (e.g., laboratory coat) should be worn in the laboratory but not taken into the counting room.
6. Rubber gloves should not be taken into the counting room.
7. Pipetting liquids of any type by mouth or the performance of any similar operation by mouth suction is forbidden.
8. Before the laboratory is left, the hands shall be washed and then checked with a suitable survey meter. Contamination remaining after a thorough washing should be reported to the instructor.
9. If, in the course of work, personal contamination is suspected, a survey with a suitable instrument shall be made immediately, to be followed by the required cleansing. Routine precautionary surveys should be made at frequent intervals.

Safe Handling

10. It is required (17) that the total gamma irradiation of any part of the body should not exceed 300 mrem/week. (This limit is subject to being revised downward.)
11. Pocket ionization chambers or dosimeters should be worn when any work is conducted in an area where the radiation level is greater

than 5 mrem/hr at 1 in. from the source, as shown by a suitable survey meter.

12. Survey meters must be used to check the dosage level for various steps in experiments with radioactive materials.

13. Approved warning signs (17) must be properly displayed in all areas where there is a radiation hazard. This is essential for the protection of *everyone* who might have cause to enter the laboratory and would, therefore, include not only other students and staff, but also the janitor, watchman, firemen, etc.

14. All containers containing radioactive materials, including sealed sources and standard sources, should be labeled with radiation warning tape. The isotope, amount, and date should be indicated.

15. Radioactive material, including portable sources, should be stored in the special area provided, and there should be sufficient shielding to reduce the radiation level below 5 mr/hr at the surface of the shield.

16. Operations with loose radioactive materials, evaporation of radioactive liquids, handling of radioactive gases, and any process which could lead to the creation of airborne activity, e.g., release of spray from radioactive liquid, must be conducted in a hood or in a glove box if the latter offers greater protection.

17. As a guide to the use of rubber gloves it is helpful to remember that the safest policy is to adopt the use of aseptic techniques in handling radioactive materials. This does not imply that rubber gloves must be worn routinely, but when there is a strong possibility of hand contamination they should be worn as, for example, in the use of a separatory funnel.

18. A person with breaks in the skin of the hands must wear rubber gloves and should consult his instructor or adviser before starting work.

Radioactive Waste—Storage and Disposal

19. Liquid waste should be stored separately from solid waste.

20. For each radioisotope the wastes should be stored separately or mixed according to the half-lives; e.g., carbon-14 waste should not be mixed with phosphorus-32 waste.

21. Radioactive waste should be stored in containers which are labeled as to content, date, and radiation level. The containers should be tightly sealed and should not constitute a spillage or dust hazard. The containers should be stored in accordance with item 15.

22. Waste reading above background should not be poured into the drain or into the normal refuse cans.

23. Waste containing short-lived radioisotopes may be disposed of as ordinary waste after examination with an appropriate radiation

detector shows the level of radioactivity to be not greater than background.

24. The mode of disposal of waste containing long-lived radioisotopes depends upon the physical form of the waste and the chemical properties as well as the half-life (radioactive and biological) of the material. In some cases disposal by ordinary means is possible after suitable volume and/or isotopic dilution, i.e., addition of solvent and/or a stable isotope or isotopes of the same element in an appropriate chemical form. Several commercial organizations have been licensed to accept and dispose of radioactive wastes.

Contamination

25. Any contamination of the body or clothing must be reported to the instructor or adviser *at once.*

26. Accidental contamination of apparatus, e.g., tongs, bench tops, hoods, floor, etc., must be reported, and the apparatus must be clearly marked as to the radioisotope, the area contaminated (sometimes conveniently encircled with wax marking pencil), and survey-meter reading.

27. Certain general procedures are effective for removing contamination. These involve the use of acids, complexing agents, abrasives, etc. The selection of a detailed procedure depends upon the chemical properties of the element to be removed, and therefore certain reagents which form insoluble compounds with the element must be avoided.

28. Contaminated glassware, such as centrifuge tubes and pipettes, should be treated first with an appropriate solubilizing agent. This is followed by a wash with tap water and finally distilled water. A survey meter should be used to determine the effectiveness of the decontamination operation. If the extent of contamination to be removed is of the order of 1 μc, the portion of washings containing the bulk of this activity should be stored. *Under no circumstances* should contaminated glassware or other apparatus be returned to the storage areas used for clean apparatus.

4-6. Emergency Precautions

It is evident that good housekeeping and attention to the details outlined above are mandatory in work with radioisotopes. However, there are two emergency situations which do occur in laboratories, and it is necessary to consider the procedures to follow in these possibilities beforehand. These are the accidental injury with an object contaminated by radioactive material and spills of radioactive solutions. Naturally, the specific emergency procedures to be followed in these cases differ with varying circumstances, but recommended general procedures should be publicized in advance of any such emergency. The following procedures are slightly modified from those in use at the Oak Ridge National Laboratory and may be adapted to the workers in any particular laboratory:

1. Procedure in dealing with wounds in which there is a break in the skin that may result in introducing contamination into the body
   a. Place the wound under large volumes of running water immediately, i.e., within 15 sec following the accident. Spread the edges of the wound if possible to permit complete flushing action. While the wound is being flushed with water, rub it gently with a wet cotton gauze using liquid soap if necessary to remove dirt and grease from the wound. This should be followed by step *b*(1) or (2).
   b. (1) If the wound is contaminated with the "very hazardous" materials and if it is located on the body where a tourniquet can be applied, and if medical aid is close at hand, apply a tourniquet and rush the person to medical aid. It is desirable to stop venous flow but not to restrict arterial flow. Proceed with step *c* below.
   (2) If medical aid is not available in 15 min or if the wound is contaminated with the moderately dangerous or slightly hazardous radioisotopes, apply the tourniquet if it can be applied so as to stop only the venous flow (otherwise omit the tourniquet entirely), and continue washing for at least 5 min. If the wound is on the finger, a milking action can be used effectively to increase the bleeding and to retard the venous flow of blood. Save the object causing the wound for examination to estimate the extent of the hazard. Proceed with step *c*.
   c. Report to the medical department as soon as possible after 5 or 10 min of washing. The wound should be tested with probe counters; if there is residual radioactive contamination, the physician will débride the wound and forward the excised tissue to the health-physics laboratory for radiochemical analysis.
2. Procedure in case of spill of radioactive material
   a. Try to estimate the hazard caused by the spill, and evacuate persons from the areas. Require those remaining in the area (including yourself) to wear appropriate clothes and other protective devices as required.
   b. Prevent spread of activity by
   (1) Cutting off room-ventilation fans.
   (2) Applying absorbents such as paper, sand, etc., to the contaminated area.

(3) Roping off or barricading contaminated area and placarding with signs bearing the conventional radiation-danger symbol and pertinent hazard information (see Fig. 4-4).
(4) Closing windows and doors.

c. Sound alarm and summon help as needed.
d. Permit only authorized newcomers to enter the contaminated area, and then only after proper clothing is used.
e. Permit no one to leave the contaminated zone until he is checked for radioactive contamination and decontaminated in an appropriate manner if necessary.
f. Consider protection for those performing cleanup work.
(1) Provide masks or other protective devices if necessary.
(2) Provide expendable protective clothing.
(3) Erect shielding or limit the working time if necessary.
(4) Have all persons engaged in cleanup operations go to a contamination checking station after each operation.
(5) Use suitable instruments to monitor and estimate the exposure of each person engaged in the cleanup.

g. In cleaning up the spill, do not spread contamination.
h. If material involved in the spill is short-lived, it may be better to seal off the affected area and leave for considerable period of decay.
i. Either dispose of or decontaminate materials involved in the contaminated area of the radioactive material.
j. Keep proper records on all spills and how decontamination was effected.
k. Refer to the literature for a discussion of decontamination procedures applied to specific cases.
l. Many spills of radioactive material can be avoided or the consequences minimized by the proper design of laboratories and equipment. Obviously the best policy with respect to spills is to avoid having them by providing adequate equipment and conducting training programs.

One other useful precautionary measure is utilized in many laboratories. This is to arrange a working agreement between the fire department and the persons responsible for radiation protection. The fire department should know in which building work is done with radioisotopes in quantities greater than microcurie amounts. In some laboratories a distinctive marker is placed on doors of rooms in which millicurie amounts of activity are used. The telephone number of the person responsible for the area may be included on the marker should it be necessary to reach him in case of fire or explosion.

Experiment 4-1
The Decontamination of Surfaces

Isotopes which may be used in this experiment include anything which might be vaporized or spilled. It is suggested that the following four isotopes be used, because they represent materials that are in common use at the present time and are materials which are usually handled by technicians:

Na^{24}	I^{131}
Fe^{59}	P^{32}

Apparatus and Materials

Portable detection apparatus (preferably one of the G-M tube type)
Sections of a flat portion of each of the following materials:

Glass	Stainless steel
Unglazed brick	Unpainted wood
Painted wood	Glazed brick or tile
Asphalt tile	Linoleum
Sheet iron	Plastic
Plate with strippable coating	

Jar of cleaning solution (sulfuric-dichromate mixture)
Jar of detergent solution
Samples of various cleansers such as Versene and Radiac wash
4 oz of appropriate radioactive solutions
Four pipettes (one for each radioactive substance)
Heat lamp

Procedure

The procedure may be made as elaborate as desired, and several series of tests may be made on each type of material. A sample of radioactive substance having about 20,000 cpm in a regular counter is dried on a piece of the material under test. If the piece is large enough, each of the four isotopes may be evaporated on a corner of the same piece and thus be subjected to the same decontamination treatment. A reading is made on each spot with the portable detection instrument and is recorded as the initial activity. The first decontamination procedure for each piece might be treatment by water. After an initial washing with water (the amount of radioactivity being sufficiently low, it may be washed down the drain with a large quantity of water), the samples are again dried and measured. Readings are recorded after the first water wash. The same samples are then washed a second time with water, dried, and remeasured after the second water wash.

If readings are significantly below the initial reading, i.e., if significant decontamination took place with water, another sample of radioactivity should be placed on the surface, dried, and measured. For the next step a detergent should be used. The activity after one or two washes with detergent should be recorded and compared with readings before the detergent was applied.

The activity should be brought to a high level again, dried, and measured. The surface should then be treated with the usual sulfuric acid–dichromate cleaning solution and the results recorded.

After the other measurements have been made, record a background measurement. Even if this is small compared with initial readings, it should be recorded since the contamination may drop essentially to background. Hence this value should be used in the calculation of the decontamination factor.

Analysis of Data

The decontamination factor for each material, for each isotope, and for each treatment should be calculated by determining the ratio of activity before the treatment to the activity afterward. (Sometimes the factor is defined in the inverse way.) Tabulate the various factors and determine the proper order of usefulness for each isotope of the various materials that might be used for construction purposes.

Experiment 4-2
Radiation Shielding

Radioisotopes which are useful in this experiment include any of the large number of isotopes which are purchased in large quantities (millicurie amounts or greater). Of particular interest might be the following:

P^{32}	Na^{24}
Fe^{59}	I^{131}
Co^{60}	Au^{198}

Apparatus and Materials

Portable detection apparatus (preferably both G-M units and ionization chamber units)
G-M counter apparatus
Sheet of Lucite plastic or glass (¼ in. thick)
Several sheets of lead or steel (assorted thicknesses such as ½, 1, and 2 in. thick)
Sheet of photographic film or photographic paper wrapped in black paper

Procedure

Beta-ray Shielding. To demonstrate the shielding of beta radiation one may use a bottle of P^{32} or other beta-ray-emitting substance. The source is first monitored to determine to what distance a safe approach can be made. This may be demonstrated also by bringing the bottle into the vicinity of a counter using a pair of laboratory tongs. Very few counts per minute will be measured through the wall of the bottle. If the top of the bottle is then removed and the counter held over the open mouth of the bottle, the counter will "jam" at some distance away when a large amount of radioactivity is present.

More quantitative information may be obtained by opening such a bottle and determining the cone of the radiation above the bottle's mouth. It can be readily seen that radiation levels are high in this region, so that care should be taken when procuring samples from the bottle. Shielding may then be demonstrated by interposing a sheet of Lucite or glass between the open bottle mouth and the monitoring instrument. It is observed that Lucite or glass is a satisfactory shielding material for work with beta-ray-emitting isotopes.

Bremsstrahlung. In spite of the fact that few counts are observed through the wall of a bottle containing large amounts of P^{32}, another illuminating experiment can be performed by wrapping a piece of film or photographic paper (protected from light by black paper) around the bottle and leaving it overnight or longer depending on the amount of activity in the bottle. On development of the film or paper, distinct blackening is observed because of the bremsstrahlung.

Gamma Radiation. In shielding from gamma radiation, it is desirable in general laboratory use to obtain empirical practical values of the radiation hazard for a number of different isotopes. This information should be routinely obtained on receiving the first lot of each kind of gamma-emitting shipment. Two measurements should be made on a source of radioactivity in which the approximate quantity of radioactivity is known. A measurement is made with the ionization-chamber device at some arbitrary distance, and the number of milliroentgens per hour per millicurie at that distance is determined as a rough guide to future shipments. This measurement should be made at a distance at which intensity readings are fairly high for the highest-activity shipments expected. With the sample and detector in the same position, a sheet of metal (lead or steel) is inserted between them. A reading is taken, and a second or thicker sheet of metal is inserted and another measurement made. Several measurements may be made by placing together several such sheets.

Analysis of Data

The cone of radiation from a beta-ray source is important, both because of the fact that it has rather definite boundaries and also because of the fact that relatively little information has been available for calculations of beta radiation dosages. However, a considerable amount of work is described in Hine and Brownell (4). Readings for beta radiation are not correctly given in milliroentgens per hour but should be given in mrem per hour or rads per hour.

The blackening of the photographic film near the sample of the pure-β-emitting substance is caused by the bremsstrahlung produced in the shielding material. One word of warning should be given. The calibration of the film by conventional methods (Expt. 7-6) does not give proper results for most bremsstrahlung measurements, since the X-ray film is hypersensitive and energy-dependent for radiation of around 100 kev. A factor-of-10 difference may be observed between ionization measurements made on bremsstrahlung by photographic methods and those made by use of an ionization chamber.

The rough data from the gamma-ray absorption curve may be plotted on semilogarithmic paper, and the half-thickness (usually in inches of whatever shielding is being used) then determined. This is an empirical factor that can be used to good advantage for any given isotope in subsequent shielding problems. This value should not be expected to agree closely with the values obtained by more precise methods. (See Chaps. 6 and 7.)

Experiment 4-3

The Determination of Isoexposure Distances (Isodose Lines)

Isotopes used for this procedure may be of any kind of substance emitting high levels of energetic gamma rays. Fairly high specific activity should be obtained in order to make the sources small in volume and area. Convenient sources might be prepared from any of the following isotopes:

Sb^{124}	Ir^{192}	Ra^{226}
Co^{60}	Ta^{182}	

Apparatus and Materials

Portable detection equipment (at least one should previously be calibrated)

Three to five samples (or more if available) of gamma-ray-emitting radioactive materials (should be of the order of 50 mc each and should be sealed to avoid loss of material)

Linear graph or polar-coordinate paper

Measuring tape (50 ft preferable, although approximate results may be obtained by stepping off distances rather than measuring them)

Barriers of various building materials may be included to demonstrate scattering effects

Procedure

Instruments should first be intercalibrated at 10 and 20 mr/hr, so that the reading corresponding to these radiation intensities is known for each instrument.

Sources emitting gamma radiation should be located in a random pattern over an area large enough to contain a number of points at which radiation reaches a certain predetermined level. To do this it is usually convenient to mark off a grid system on the field and proceed down the grid lines with the meter until a point is reached at which the meter reads approximately 10 mr/hr. Measure or estimate this position on the grid and proceed to a point which reads about 20 mr/hr. Survey the entire area by following the grid lines, and record the coordinates of all points reading 10 and 20 mr/hr (or any other reading of interest).

Analysis of Data

A sheet of graph paper is first marked off to scale corresponding to the grid system in the "contaminated" field. The 10 mr/hr readings are then located on the graph by a point corresponding to the location of the field, and lines are drawn connecting all these points in the manner of a contour map. Points having 20 mr/hr readings are then located on the graph and connected by lines in a similar manner. These lines should then serve to obtain an approximate location of all the active spots and may be used to estimate the level of activity at any other point in the field. From this procedure the resultant estimation of the length of time a worker could remain in that location and not receive more than the maximum permissible dose can be determined.

Recommendations of the National Committee on Radiation Protection

The following Handbooks contain recommendations of the National Committee on Radiation Protection. They are issued by the National Bureau of Standards and are available from the Superintendent of Documents, Government Printing Office, Washington 25, D.C., at the prices indicated.

No. 42, Safe Handling of Radioactive Isotopes, 20 cents

No. 47, Recommendations of the International Commission on Radiological Protection and of the International Commission on Radiological Units 1950, 20 cents (superseded by Handbook 62)

No. 48, Control and Removal of Radioactive Contamination in Laboratories, 15 cents

No. 49, Recommendations for Waste Disposal of Phosphorus-32 and Iodine-131 for Medical Uses, 15 cents
No. 50, X-ray Protection Design, 20 cents
No. 51, Radiological Monitoring Methods and Instruments, 15 cents
No. 52, Maximum Permissible Amounts of Radioisotopes in the Human Body and Maximum Permissible Concentrations in Air and Water (reissued 1959 as Handbook 69), 20 cents
No. 53, Recommendations for the Disposal of Carbon-14 Wastes, 15 cents
No. 54, Protection against Radiation from Radium, Cobalt-60, and Cesium-137, 25 cents
No. 55, Protection against Betatron-Synchrotron Radiations up to 100 Million Electron Volts, 25 cents
No. 56, Safe Handling of Cadavers Containing Radioactive Isotopes, 15 cents
No. 57, Photographic Dosimetry of X- and Gamma Rays, 15 cents
No. 58, Radioactive-waste Disposal in the Ocean, 20 cents
No. 59, Permissible Dose from External Sources of Ionizing Radiation (revised 1958), 30 cents
No. 60, X-ray Protection, 20 cents
No. 61, Regulation of Radiation Exposure by Legislative Means, 25 cents
No. 62, Report of the International Commission on Radiological Units and Measurements, 40 cents
No. 69, Handbook 52, reissued 1959, 35 cents

Cited References

1. Report of the Committee on Pathological Effects of Atomic Radiation, National Academy of Sciences–National Research Council, Publication 452, Washington, 1956.
2. Report of the International Commission on Radiological Units and Measurements, *Natl. Bur. Standards Handbook* 62 (supersedes Handbook 47), 1957.
3. Kinsman, Simon, et al. (comp. and ed.): "Radiological Health Handbook," U.S. Department of Health, Education, and Welfare, Robert A. Taft Sanitary Engineering Center, Cincinnati, Ohio, 1957.
4. Hine, G. J., and G. L. Brownell: "Radiation Dosimetry," Academic Press, New York, 1956.
5. United States National Committee on Radiation Protection: "Permissible Dose from External Sources of Ionizing Radiation: Recommendations," Washington, 1954 (*Natl. Bur. Standards Handbook* 59, with Apr. 15, 1958, insert).
6. Morgan, K. Z.: Recent Changes in Maximum Permissible Exposure Values, *A.M.A. Arch. Ind. Health*, vol. 16, pp. 357–362, 1957.
7. "Recommendations of the International Commission on Radiological Protection," Pergamon, New York, 1959.
8. Gray, D. E., and J. H. Martens: "Radiation Monitoring in Atomic Defense," Van Nostrand, Princeton, N.J., 1951.
9. United States National Committee on Radiation Protection: "Maximum Permissible Concentrations in Air and Water," rev., Washington, 1959 (*Natl. Bur. Standards Handbook* 69).
10. Morgan, K. Z.: Maximum Permissible Internal Dose of Radionuclides: Recent Changes in Values, *Nuclear Science and Eng.*, vol. 1, pp. 477–500, 1956.
11. Morgan, K. Z.: Techniques in Personnel Monitoring and Radiation Surveying,

in A. H. Snell (ed.), "Handbook of Nuclear Instruments and Techniques," National Research Council, Washington (in press).

12. "Report of United Nations Scientific Committee on the Effects of Atomic Radiation," United Nations General Assembly, New York, 1958.
13. Levy, H. A.: Some Aspects of the Design of Radiochemical Laboratories, *Chem. Eng. News*, Dec. 10, 1946, pp. 3168–3173.
14. Bizzell, O. M.: Equipment for Radioisotope Laboratories, *U.S. Atomic Energy Comm. Rept.* AECU-2875, 1954.
15. United States National Committee on Radiation Protection: "Safe Handling of Radioactive Isotopes," Washington, 1949 (*Natl. Bur. Standards Handbook* 42).
16. United States National Committee on Radiation Protection: "Control and Removal of Radioactive Contamination in Laboratories," Washington, 1951 (*Natl. Bur. Standards Handbook* 48).
17. Standards for Protection against Radiation, pt. 20, chap. I, title 10, *Federal Register*, vol. 22, no. 19, Jan. 29, 1957, and amendments.

Supplementary References

General References

Blizard, E. P.: Nuclear Radiation Shielding, *Ann. Rev. Nuclear Sci.*, vol. 5, pp. 73–98, 1955.

Cantril, S. T., and H. M. Parker: The Tolerance Dose, *U.S. Atomic Energy Comm. Rept.* MDDC-110, 1945.

Glasstone, S. (ed.): "The Effects of Nuclear Weapons," Government Printing Office, Washington, 1957.

Health Physics Insurance Seminar, *U.S. Atomic Energy Comm. Rept.* TID-388, 1951.

Morgan, K. Z.: Health Physics, in Harold Etherington (ed.), "Nuclear Engineering Handbook," McGraw-Hill, New York, 1958.

Robertson, J. K.: "Radiology Physics: An Introductory Course for Medical or Premedical Students and for All Radiologists," 2d ed., Van Nostrand, Princeton, N.J., 1948.

Rockwell, T. (ed.): "Reactor Shielding Design Manual," McGraw-Hill, New York, 1956.

Sproull, W. T.: "X-rays in Practice," McGraw-Hill, New York, 1946.

Weyl, C., S. R. Warren, Jr., and D. B. O'Neill: "Radiologic Physics," 2d ed., Charles C Thomas, Springfield, Ill., 1951.

Biological Effects of Radiation and Dosimetry

Blomfield, G. W., and F. W. Spiers: Dose Measurement in Beta-ray Therapy, *Brit. J. Radiol.*, vol. 19, pp. 349–356, September, 1946.

Bloom, W. (ed.): "Histopathology of Irradiation from External and Internal Sources," McGraw-Hill, New York, 1948.

Bush, F.: The Integral Dose Received from a Uniformly Distributed Radioactive Isotope, *Brit. J. Radiol.*, vol. 22, pp. 96–105, January, 1949.

Dobson, R. L., and J. H. Lawrence: Physiological Effects of Radiant Energy, *Ann. Rev. Physiol.*, vol. 10, pp. 479–500, 1948.

Failla, G.: Some Aspects of the Biological Action of Ionizing Radiations, *Am. J. Roentgenol. Radium Therapy Nuclear Med.*, vol. 44, pp. 649–664, November, 1940.

Hemplemann, L. H., H. Lisco, and J. G. Hoffman: The Acute Radiation Syndrome: A Study of Nine Cases and a Review of the Problem, *Ann. Internal Med.*, vol. 36, no. 2, pt. I, February, 1952.

Hollaender, A.: "Radiation Biology," vol. I, "High Energy Radiation," pts. I and II, McGraw-Hill, New York, 1954.

———: "Radiation Biology," vol. II, "Ultraviolet and Related Radiations," McGraw-Hill, New York, 1955.

Howland, J. W., and S. L. Warren: The Effects of Irradiation from the Atomic Bomb on the Japanese, *U.S. Atomic Energy Comm. Rept.* MDDC-1301, 1947.

Jacobson, L. O., E. K. Marks, and E. Lorenz: The Hematological Effects of Ionizing Radiations, *Radiology*, vol. 52, pp. 371–395, March, 1949.

Lea, D. E.: "Actions of Radiations on Living Cells," Cambridge, New York, 1946.

MacComb, W. S., and E. H. Quimby: Rate of Recovery of Human Skin from the Effects of Hard or Soft Roentgen Rays or Gamma Rays, *Radiology*, vol. 27, pp. 196–207, August, 1936.

Marinelli, L. D., E. H. Quimby, and G. J. Hine: Dosage Determination with Radioactive Isotopes. I, Fundamental Dosage Formulae, *Nucleonics*, vol. 2, no. 4, pp. 56–66, April, 1948; II, Biological Considerations and Practical Applications, vol. 2, no. 5, pp. 44–49, May, 1948.

Nickson, J. J. (ed.): "Symposium on Radiobiology: The Basic Aspects of Radiation Effects, Oberlin College, June 14–18, 1950," Wiley, New York, 1952.

Oddie, T. H.: Dosage from Radioisotopes Uniformly Distributed within a Sphere, *Brit. J. Radiol.*, vol. 24, pp. 333–336, June, 1951.

Price, C. H. G.: Observations upon the Lymphopenia of X-ray Irradiation, *Brit. J. Radiol.*, vol. 21, pp. 481–493, October, 1948.

Rossi, H. H., and R. H. Ellis, Jr.: Calculations for Distributed Sources of Beta Radiation, *Am. J. Roentgenol. Radiation Therapy Nuclear Med.*, vol. 67, pp. 980–988, June, 1952.

Spear, F. G.: "Radiations and Living Cells," Wiley, New York, 1953.

Spiers, F. W.: Effective Atomic Number and Energy Absorption in Tissues, *Brit. J. Radiol.*, vol. 19, pp. 52–63, February, 1946.

———: The Influence of Energy Absorption and Electron Range on Dosage in Irradiated Bone, *Brit. J. Radiol.*, vol. 22, pp. 521–533, September, 1949.

Warren, S., et al.: Effects of Radiation on Normal Tissues, *A.M.A. Arch. Pathol.*, vol. 34, pp. 443–450, 562–608, 749–787, 917–931, 1070–1084, 1942; vol. 35, pp. 121–139, 304–353, 1943.

Zirkle, R. E. (ed.): "Effects of External Beta Radiation," McGraw-Hill, New York, 1951.

Decontamination and Waste Disposal

Hammond, R. P.: Decontamination of Radioactive Waste Air, *U.S. Atomic Energy Comm. Rept.* AECD-2711, declassified 1949.

"Laboratory Design for Handling Radioactive Materials, Sponsored by the American Institute of Architects and the Atomic Energy Commission, November 27 and 28, 1951," Building Research Advisory Board Research Conference Report 3, National Research Council, Washington, 1952.

Rodger, W. A., and P. Fineman: A Complete Waste-disposal System for a Radiochemical Laboratory, *Nucleonics*, vol. 9, no. 6, pp. 51–61, December, 1951.

Sanitary Engineering Conference, Baltimore, Md., Apr. 15–16, 1954, *U.S. Atomic Energy Comm. Rept.* WASH-275, 1955.

Shannon, R. L.: Radioactive Waste Disposal: A Bibliography of Unclassified Literature, *U.S. Atomic Energy Comm. Rept.* TID-375, 1950.

Straub, C. P., W. J. Lacy, and R. J. Morton: Methods of Decontamination of Low-level Radioactive Liquid Wastes, *Proc. Intern. Conf. Peaceful Uses Atomic Energy, Geneva, 1955*, vol. 9, pp. 24–27, United Nations, New York, 1956.

———, R. J. Morton, and O. R. Placak: Studies on the Removal of Radioactive Contaminants from Water, *J. Am. Water Works Assoc.*, vol. 43, pp. 773–792, October, 1951.

Symposium on Radioactive Wastes, *Ind. Eng. Chem.*, vol. 43, pp. 1499–1544, July, 1951.

Vorees, H. E., T. F. Davis, and T. N. Hubbard, Jr.: Radioactive Waste Processing and Disposal: A Bibliography of Selected Report Literature, *U.S. Atomic Energy Comm. Rept.* TID-3311, 1958.

Waste Disposal Symposium, *Nucleonics*, vol. 4, no. 3, pp. 9–23, March, 1949.

Western, F.: Problems of Radioactive Waste Disposal, *Nucleonics*, vol. 3, no. 2, pp. 43–49, August, 1948.

5

The Preparation of Radioactive Sources

5-1. Choice of Source

Selection of a method of radioactivity measurement or assay involves the choice of a radiation detector and the choice of a counting source. These are not independent choices. Usually, the type of source, i.e., solid, liquid, or gaseous, is chosen first and then a detector is chosen. Furthermore, for a given type of source and a given radionuclide there may be a variety of acceptable chemical forms to choose from. Source preparation is an important part of any assay procedure, especially when high precision is desired as in absolute counting, calibration of detectors, and comparison of samples for which small differences in activity are important.

Briefly, the following factors must be taken into account in selecting a method of assay and, therefore, selecting a source:

1. Nature (type and energy) of radiation emitted by the radionuclide or radionuclides in the material
2. Range of quantity of radionuclide available for preparation of counting source
3. Range of concentration of radionuclide in counting source
4. Magnitude of acceptable counting error
5. Number of samples to be assayed
6. Ease of source preparation

There may still be a choice of assay methods which are comparable except when examined on the basis of additional (beyond factors 5 and 6) economic considerations. Thus the final choice might be based on:

1. Flexibility of the method, i.e., relative usefulness as a general method for the needs of the laboratory
2. Cost of the radiation-detection system and necessary auxiliary apparatus as for combustion and gas transfer

Even after all the above factors have been considered, a definite choice may not be easy nor can it be said that there is necessarily one "best" method for each assay problem. The personal preference of the researcher has a variable but strong influence on the final choice. All these decisions relative to assay methods are part of the larger topic of experiment design which is discussed in Sec. 10-2.

In a sense, labeling of materials with radioisotopes is allied to source preparation. Except for activation, isotope exchange, and recoil labeling, conventional chemical reactions are used. There are numerous references to procedures and techniques for labeling compounds, particularly for tritium and C^{14}. It is felt that the subject is beyond the scope of this book, but a few supplementary references including bibliographies have been listed at the end of the chapter.

5-2. Solid Sources

Solid sources are satisfactory for many radionuclides and can often be used with the simplest type of radiation-detection equipment. The preparation of solid sources involves three steps, namely (1) preparing, i.e., labeling, etc., the source mount or backing or support; (2) depositing or plating the radioactive material; and (3) covering the deposit or sealing the source. The more common methods of deposition are (1) evaporation of a solution containing the radioactive material in a nonvolatile form dissolved in a volatile solvent, (2) mounting as a dry powder, (3) mounting and drying a precipitate initially collected as a slurry or as a cake on a filter plate, and (4) electrodeposition from a solution.

Among the factors to be considered in the preparation of a solid source are the area, uniformity of thickness, and chemical stability of the deposit. For many kinds of work the exact area of the deposit is not important if it is within limits imposed by the type of radiation detector used. For maximum precision in comparative measurements, however, suitable measures must be taken to ensure that all deposits are as nearly as possible the same in shape (most commonly circular) and area.

The extent to which self-absorption of beta radiation occurs in a source depends on the thickness of the source and the atomic number of the material forming the deposit as well as on the energy of the radiation. Although self-absorption is a more serious problem for low-energy beta emitters, all beta emitters show self-absorption to some extent because of the low-energy beta rays present in beta-ray spectra. Uncertainties in self-absorption and self-scattering effects can be minimized by making the source uniform in thickness.

During the past fifty years there have been numerous publications dealing with techniques for solid-source preparation for hundreds of radionuclides. The techniques are quite general, and only a few references will be cited in this section to illustrate certain points. It is suggested that the reader consult the supplementary references and Refs. 1 to 8 for further information on specific radionuclides.

Mounting Materials. Some of the more commonly used source-mounting materials are listed in Table 5-1, together with comments on

TABLE 5-1

RESISTANCE OF BACKING MATERIALS TO CHEMICAL ATTACK

Material	*Comment*
Aluminum	Attacked by acids and strong caustic, e.g., NaOH
Cellophane tape	Attacked by organic solvents, concentrated H_2SO_4; useful for dispersed powder sources
Copper	Attacked by nitric acid; useful for electrodeposition
Filter paper	Attacked by strong acid and strong caustic
Formvar, Zapon	Attacked by organic solvents; useful for extremely thin backing (Chap. 6, Refs. 10, 11)
Glass	Attacked by strong caustic, e.g., NaOH, and by HF
Lusteroid	Attacked by strong caustic; useful for HF
Nickel-plated steel	Attacked by concentrated acid
Platinum	Attacked by aqua regia; useful for electrodeposition and ignition
Polyethylene	Relatively inert; useful for HF
Polystyrene	Attacked by organic solvents
Porcelain	Attacked by strong caustic, e.g., NaOH, and by HF
Stainless steel	Attacked by HCl, HF
Teflon	Relatively inert; useful for HF

their resistance to chemical attack. The more popular materials, e.g., copper, glass, porcelain, and steel, are commercially available in one or more forms, such as flat or cupped planchets of various sizes and as fritted filter plates. The choice of backing material is influenced by other factors, such as resistance to heat, backscattering coefficient, and cost. Filter paper and other organic materials are sensitive to heat and must be heated cautiously. This is true for organic material in the form of a thin film. Distortion and even thermal decomposition may occur at temperatures well below 100°C.

For very-low-level counting, attention must be given to contamination of the backing by naturally occurring radioactive impurities. Glass and porcelain generally contain enough potassium so that the beta-ray emission rate associated with K^{40} may be from a fraction to several per minute. For gamma counting, and particularly for alpha counting, contamination of metal backing material by radium and its daughters can become a serious problem. Comparisons of the natural radioactivity contamination of metals have been made by Bearden (9) and McDaniel, Schaefer, and Colehour (10).

Methods for Labeling Sources. Sources should be labeled *before* deposition of radioactive material. Metal and even glass backing can be readily labeled by writing on the underside with a "vibratool." For cupped planchets it is more convenient to place the identification on the side. Ordinary ink or glass-marking ink may be used for some surfaces such as porcelain. If a wax pencil is used, it should be remembered that the wax may melt and flow if the source is heated and the wax label may be accidentally removed when the source is handled. Wax pencil—and to a somewhat lesser extent ordinary ink—is not satisfactory with respect to permanence.

It is important that radioactive sources (solid, liquid, or gaseous) be clearly and permanently labeled, not only for the usual reasons of providing identification for a particular sample of material, but also because of the possible health hazard associated with some radionuclides and because of the need to know what the radioactive material is for the purpose of disposal. It is frequently helpful to store samples of a given radionuclide together so that the hazard and disposal problems can be evaluated if the label becomes illegible. Metallic or glass filter frits should not be labeled in the porous area.

Usually the following identifying information should be given:

1. Nature of the radioactive material, e.g., P^{32}
2. Date
3. Code number for identifying the particular source
4. Initials of person preparing the source

Storage containers for sources should be labeled with the standard radioactivity warning symbol (Fig. 4-4).

Deposition or Plating Methods. *Evaporation of Liquids.* Simple evaporation of liquid solutions to form a solid residue containing the material to be counted is a convenient method for many materials, especially since an aliquoting process may be required to provide the proper source strength. In general, the strength of counting sources is sufficiently low so that micropipettes may be used readily with only moderate shielding, if any.

Simple micro transfer pipettes of the type illustrated in Fig. 5-1 are available from many standard laboratory supply houses in a variety of sizes from 1 to 500 λ ($1\ \lambda = 10^{-3}$ ml). They are commonly calibrated by means of mercury, and the specified volume then refers to the volume of liquid contained rather than that delivered. To obtain the entire contents of the pipette it is necessary to rinse the pipette with the solvent involved. Rinsing consists in repeatedly drawing fresh solvent in amounts less than the capacity of the pipette into the pipette as far as the calibration mark and then transferring the liquid to the initial aliquot. Small droplets of solvent for this purpose can be placed in advance around the periphery of the source planchet or on a separate planchet.

Micropipettes can be obtained calibrated in terms of the volume delivered, but the amount delivered varies with the properties of the liquid pipetted. Self-filling (by capillary action), self-adjusting, dilution, and graduated micropipettes are also available.

The simplest pipette control consists of a glass syringe which is connected to the pipette by means of a piece of rubber or Tygon tubing (Fig. 5-1). The sliding plunger should be lubricated with a thin film of a grease which does not soften as the syringe is held in the hand and allow

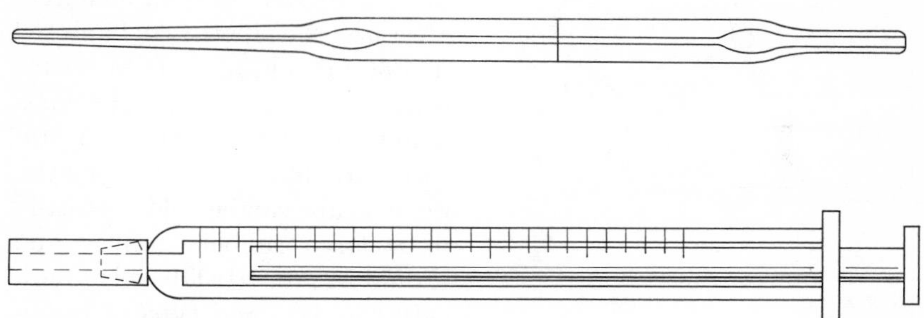

FIG. 5-1. Micropipette and control.

the plunger to fall by gravity. Microsyringes with a threaded plunger inside the sliding plunger are also available. Care should be taken to avoid pulling solutions of radioactive material into the pipette control.

The use of a micropipette for the preparation of a counting source is illustrated in Fig. 5-2. The subsequent step of evaporating the solvent is best carried out in a hood. The following points should be kept in mind in connection with the use of micropipettes: (1) A micropipette containing radioactive material should be handled with care because of the possible radiation hazard. (2) The outside of a pipette is a source of contamination, and if the pipette is placed on the bench top after use, it should be placed on a piece of disposable tissue which can be removed to a waste storage container. (3) When air is forced from the tip of a micropipette through a deposited droplet, the bubbles can spread contamination in the vicinity as they break through the surface of the droplet.

Pipettes—micro or macro—should be decontaminated as soon as possible. Various devices for holding micropipettes while they are being cleaned and dried are commercially available. A simple device of use in decontaminating micropipettes consists of a small, glass funnel with a narrow stem (sufficiently narrow to support the pipettes) mounted in a rubber stopper fitted in the neck of a suction flask. While the pipette is supported vertically in the funnel, decontaminating agents appropriate for the chemical substance to be removed are applied to the pipette with a dropper. Chromic acid and hydrochloric acid are suitable for many cases. The pipette is finally rinsed with distilled water and dried by suction. After decontamination, the pipettes should be checked for radioactivity with a suitable counter, e.g., a laboratory monitor with thin-window Geiger tube.

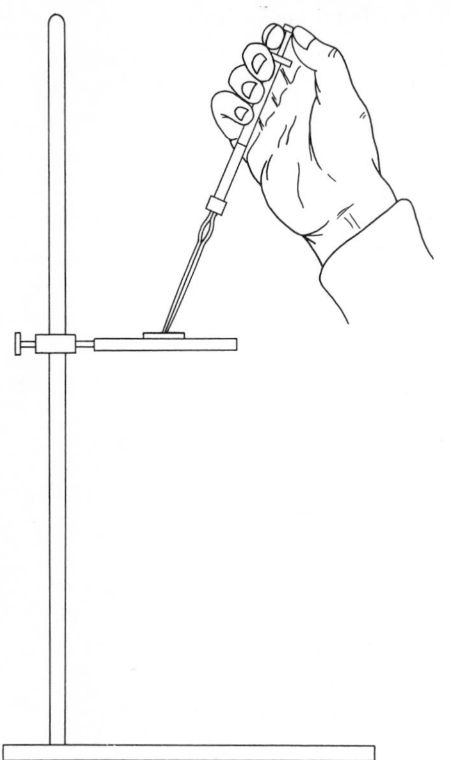

FIG. 5-2. Use of a micropipette for source preparation.

If it is not feasible to decontaminate a micropipette immediately after use, the pipette can be stored in a 50-ml conical centrifuge tube containing a small piece of disposable tissue at the bottom to protect the delicate tip of the pipette. Such a tube can be held vertically in a large rubber stopper and should be properly labeled to indicate the date and type of radioactive material.

Standard Mohr and serological pipettes subdivided to 1 λ and 10 λ are also useful for source preparation and general aliquoting of radioactive materials.

Several techniques may be used to define the area of a source in addition to the use of planchets with raised concentric rings on the bottom. One consists in placing a confining barrier around the desired area of the planchet by applying a substance such as a hydrocarbon wax, a silicone wax, or a cement not wetted by the liquid to be evaporated. In the case of aqueous solutions a wax ring formed by marking on the surface with a wax pencil is helpful (but not foolproof) in keeping a droplet of liquid from spreading to the edge of the mount. An unbroken ring is obtained more readily if the mount is warmed before the wax is applied. Melting of the wax during evaporation and final drying of the deposit can be minimized by use of a suitable high-melting wax.

A second technique for defining the deposit area is to prepare the surface of the mount by depositing first a material such as insulin in such a way as to have it, when dry, define the area desired for the deposit of radioactive material. Aqueous solution will tend to remain on the treated area during the drying step provided the quantity of aqueous solution applied is not excessive.

For very thin sources, the problem of obtaining uniform thickness by evaporation of a solvent is one of preventing the activity from being concentrated in a few islands or aggregates scattered over the area represented by the source as a whole. Simple evaporation of a volatile solvent to leave a nonvolatile residue will generally produce an uneven deposit consisting of rings or ridges or other localized amounts of solid. This is illustrated by the paired sources shown in Fig. 2-19. Unsatisfactory deposits may result from the precipitation of solute during the whole evaporation step as the solution becomes more concentrated. Because precipitates generally tend to deposit preferentially on particles previously deposited rather than on uncovered surface, the deposit consists of aggregates if it is built up slowly during the evaporation. To minimize this effect it is desirable to select a solvent providing a high solubility of the material to be deposited.

Among the techniques for improving the uniformity of the deposit are (1) the addition of a wetting agent (although such a substance may cause trouble in retaining the desired area of deposit), (2) rotation of the mount (although this probably does not prevent growth of small particles), (3) freeze drying or removal of the solvent by sublimation under vacuum, and (4) addition of appropriate reagents to cause precipitation before evaporation. Sample rotators are commercially available, or they may be readily constructed from a few common pieces of equipment. In general there should be some provision for varying the rotational speed for optimum effect for each type of source material.

Uniform area and thickness can often be obtained by evaporating a liquid sample on a piece of absorbent material placed in the bottom of a cupped planchet. Examples of such absorbent material are lens tissue and filter paper.

When liquid to be dried contains excess acid or base, it is usually better if the acid or base can be easily volatilized along with the solvent. Thus HCl is more easily removed than H_2SO_4; whereas NH_4OH is volatilized easily at a moderate temperature, NaOH is nonvolatile. If a volatile acid or base is present, it should not be neutralized prior to removal of the solvent because of the resulting salt residue. If, for some reason such as danger of loss of radioactive material, it is necessary to neutralize an acid or base, it is worth remembering that some of the ammonium salts, e.g., NH_4Cl, can be removed by sublimation if the source can be heated hot enough.

Chemical instability of the source deposit can give rise to measurement problems, particularly with low-energy beta emitters. For example, if the deposit contains a substance which reacts with carbon dioxide or is hygroscopic or deliquescent, it will absorb moisture or CO_2 (11–13) from the atmosphere at room temperature with resultant change in counting rate. In such cases the source deposit must be either converted to another chemical material or hermetically sealed under reproducible conditions. For some cases salts can be converted to more stable basic salts by reacting a residue from evaporation with ammonia vapor dispensed from a polyethylene wash bottle containing cotton soaked in concentrated ammonium hydroxide.

Mounting Dry Powder. Frequently it is not convenient to dissolve or slurry a sample of powdered solid material whose radioactivity is to be measured. A few examples are powdered minerals, ash, and dried soil. In most cases the powder is simply weighed into a cupped planchet of suitable diameter and depth and distributed evenly by compressing the solid or tapping the planchet to pack the particles.

Since the observed activity for a radioactive material in powder form depends upon the bulk density (14) and the roughness (15) of the surface of the source, some workers (16) pelletize powder samples to improve the uniformity. The pelleting die must be cleaned carefully, of course, to prevent spread of contamination from one sample to another.

Because of the danger of disturbing the deposit or even spilling part of it either inside or outside the counter, loose powder sources should usually be treated with a binder such as a dilute solution of collodion or a cement. The solution, e.g., 0.5 per cent collodion in acetone or ether-ethanol mixture, is cautiously placed on the powder by means of a medicine dropper. In addition it may be advisable to seal a thin metal or plastic foil over the source to prevent loss of powder during handling.

Source mounts for fairly thin sources of powders can be made simply by cementing a flat metal ring (about 0.015 in. thick) to the top side of a labeled flat metal planchet having the same outside diameter. The rings can be prepared from commercially available flat planchets and might, for example, have a 1-in. outside diameter and a ¾-in. inside diameter. A graded series of deeper planchets for self-absorption studies, etc., can be prepared by cementing several rings together to form a laminated mount. (See Expts. 5-1 and 8-8.)

Mounting Solids in Slurry Samples. There are occasions when it is convenient to transfer small amounts of precipitate to a source mount and merely evaporate the solvent. Such might be the case for a precipitate which has been washed free of excess precipitant and is collected in a centrifuge tube so that the excess solvent can be decanted or pipetted off.

Transfer of 0.1 ml or less to a flat planchet and 1 ml or so to a cupped planchet can be achieved by means of a slurry transfer pipette. The latter consists of a medicine dropper with the end tapered and elongated (but *not* drawn to a fine capillary) to provide sufficient length for the pipette to reach the bottom of the precipitation vessel, e.g., centrifuge tube. Transfer of a precipitate by pouring and subsequent washing with a jet of water is not satisfactory because of the excessive volumes of water involved. Instead, the precipitate is slurried with the minimum solvent required to provide a slurry dilute enough to be readily pulled into and discharged from the slurry pipette. When quantitative transfer is necessary, the centrifuge tube or other vessel is rinsed out repeatedly with 1 or 2 drops of wash water, using the pipette to loosen particles and wash them to the bottom of the vessel. The difficulty of recovering the precipitate from the inside of the pipette varies with the material being transferred. If the process of forcing wash liquid in and out of the pipette is not adequate, it may be necessary to remove the rubber bulb and clean the inside with a capillary pipette introduced through the top. Sometimes the precipitate inside the pipette is best dissolved and reprecipitated in the centrifuge tube. In extreme cases, it may be necessary to clean the pipette more than once in this way until the amount retained by the pipette is negligible.

In the course of transferring the precipitate with the pipette and during the subsequent evaporation and additional transfer (if the planchet will not hold all the liquid at one time), it is in order to take the precautions mentioned in the previous sections to ensure an even layer of uniform size particles. Cohn and Lind (17) recommend the use of surface-active agents to minimize the retention of slurried solid on the walls of a cupped planchet. Dried slurry samples may not require any added binder, but the source should be covered (unless absorption losses are prohibitive) to prevent spillage.

Techniques have been described for collecting the solid from a slurry by centrifugation (7). Comar (18) has used a device in which a removable cupped planchet serves as the bottom of a centrifuge "tube." Extreme care must be taken to obtain a tight seal between the cupped planchet and the cylinder.

Filtration. For routine work involving precipitates such as barium carbonate and calcium oxalate, filtration of a precipitate on a combination filter and source mount is a popular method. With proper technique the area and thickness of samples can be controlled within narrow limits. The reproducibility which can be attained is often necessary for work involving the comparison of a large number of samples for which self-absorption corrections must be made, e.g., C^{14}-labeled $BaCO_3$.

The requirements of a good filtration apparatus are as follows:

1. The filter medium (paper, frit) should serve as the source mount so that the solid does not have to be transferred.

2. The area and centering of the deposit should be well defined and reproducible.

3. The apparatus should not leak because of the possible loss of material and spread of contamination.

4. The filter medium with active material should be readily removable without disturbing the layer of solid and with a minimum of manipulation.

5. The filter should retain the precipitate with a minimum of loss into the filtrate.

6. The filter should give an even layer of solid.

7. The apparatus should be readily decontaminated.

8. The apparatus should not be attacked by common reagents.

9. The interior design should permit washing the precipitate off the wall onto the filter.

The following are a few notes relative to the use of filtration units:

1. The applied pressure difference (obtained with a water aspirator or mechanical pump) should be adjustable by bleeding or bypassing, so that the proper filtration rate can be obtained for each substance filtered.

2. As an aid to obtaining uniform-thickness sources prepared by filtration, a simple manometer or mechanical vacuum gauge can be used to help adjust filtration conditions.

3. There should be means for admitting air gently when filtration is complete.

Many designs for filtration devices have been described in the literature (7, 8, 18–29), and several are available commercially. Bronner and Jernberg (28) have devised a centrifugal filtration assembly for simultaneous filtration and separation of a precipitate from the supernate. Two filtration devices are illustrated in Fig. 5-3*a* and *b*. The filter device represented in Fig. 5-3*b* has been used rather extensively in a laboratory course by one of the authors. It permits mounting a solid by filtration on filter paper inside a commercially available cupped planchet. Such a source mount is prepared by perforating the bottom of a stainless-steel cupped planchet with a No. 50 drill, providing about 30 holes about $\frac{3}{32}$ in. apart on centers. The planchets can be reused indefinitely. They may be labeled on the side by means of number punches. In use, the planchet containing a piece of filter paper, e.g., Whatman 42 (slightly undersize to provide for swelling when wet), is placed over a hole in a rubber stopper which is fitted in a suction flask. The hole, cut somewhat smaller than the diameter of the planchet, is tapered to about half the depth of the stopper, and connects with a smaller hole at the bottom through which a piece of glass tubing is inserted to serve as a stem of the filter funnel. For ease of decontamination of the stopper, the glass tube should not project into the upper hole.

In operation, the cupped planchet is pulled down against the stopper when suction is applied and is simply lifted off after the suction is released. Any liquid on the bottom of the planchet should be removed with disposable tissue. After the filter paper is dried with or without

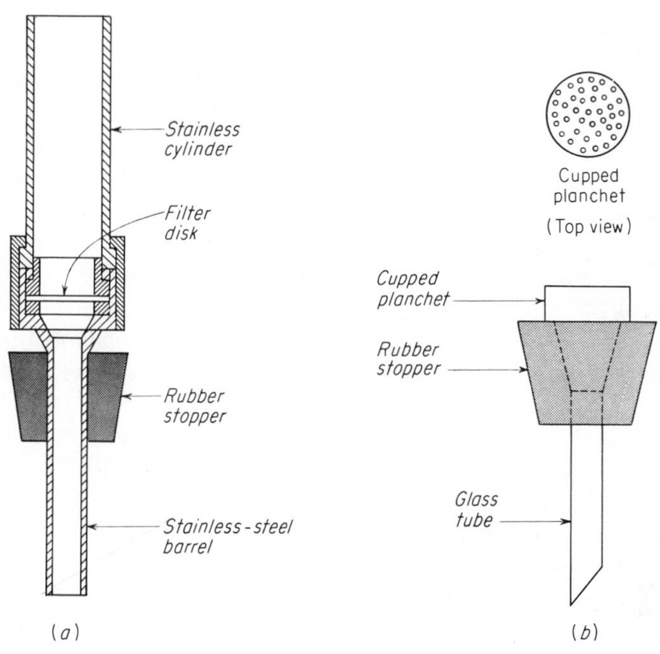

FIG. 5-3. (a) Typical filtration unit for radioactive samples; (b) filtration device.

suction, it is left in the cup for counting. One advantage of this type of filtration device is that the filter paper does not have to be disturbed since it is already on a support.

Whatever filter device is used, care must be taken to avoid cracking the cake during the filtration and drying operations. The following are useful in minimizing the cracking of filtered mats:

1. Slow filtration
2. Addition of a dilute solution of binder such as collodion just before drying
3. Slow drying with suction applied either with or without a heat lamp over the filter unit

When filter-paper circles are used, there are a number of problems in supporting the paper in the counter and keeping the paper flat. When the paper has to be transferred to a suitable backing before measurement, it is commonly held on a flat planchet and kept from curling while being stored or counted by means of a cement or a retaining ring. When cement is used, it should not be allowed to soak up into the cake unless it is also intended to be a binder for the solid. As an aid in holding the dried paper in place, an expandable open metal ring made from heavy aluminum foil can be inserted so as to press against the edge of the paper and the inner wall of the planchet. Usually, if the paper is dried slowly at room temperature with suction until thoroughly dry, it is sufficiently air-equilibrated to remain flat. A paper filter which has been overheated may not remain flat as it cools and absorbs moisture from the air.

When the weight of filtered solid is to be determined, the filter paper should be pretreated with all the wash solutions used in the source preparation and dried in the same way before the initial weight is obtained.

Electrodeposition. For certain elements it is convenient to prepare solid sources by electrodeposition on a conducting surface. Usually the substance is electrodeposited in elemental form, e.g., bismuth, cobalt, copper, gold, iron, nickel, and polonium, but electrodeposition of an oxide is also used for some elements, e.g., actinium, lead, plutonium, and uranium. Cathodic deposition of a hydrous oxide (or hydroxide) involves reduction of the hydrogen-ion concentration at the cathode, with a corresponding increase in hydroxyl-ion concentration, without maintaining a balance of hydrogen ions in solution by equivalent anodic oxidation of water.

The electrodeposition method has the advantage of making possible the preparation of thin films of uniform thickness. This is important for radionuclides which decay by electron capture, low-energy electron emission, or alpha emission, since the emitted radiation is relatively nonpenetrating. Furthermore, in the case of a substance which deposits in elemental form, a source of maximum specific activity can be obtained.

Several designs of electrodeposition cells have been described in the literature (31–39), and cells can be obtained commercially. A typical cell (Fig. 5-4) consists of a base with an electrical contact; a removable cylinder (commonly glass) which constitutes the cell wall; an electrode consisting of a flat circular counting plate or planchet made of a material such as copper, gold, nickel, platinum, silver, or stainless steel; a gasket for making a tight seal between the bottom of the cylinder and the electrode; and a clamping device. The planchet must be thoroughly cleaned before use. Cleaning may consist in immersing the planchet in an acid, e.g., dilute nitric acid for copper, or heating the planchet to a high temperature. Oxide deposits on platinum, for example, are commonly ignited to dehydrate the oxide. Decontamination of ignited noble-metal planchets may be difficult because of diffusion of the activity into the metal.

The separate rotating electrode may consist merely of a platinum wire wrapped as a spiral around a glass tube. The wire is sealed through the tube at the bottom, and passes up through the tube to make electrical contact with the stirring device. Conventional sources of d-c potential are used.

Procedures for obtaining good-quality adherent deposits are somewhat empirical. Optimum conditions for each of the following must be determined in devising a satisfactory procedure:

1. Applied potential
2. Current density
3. Shape and size of the rotating electrode
4. Distance between electrodes
5. Agitation of the solution
6. Speed of rotation of rotating electrode
7. Temperature
8. Concentration of reagents, including complexing agents

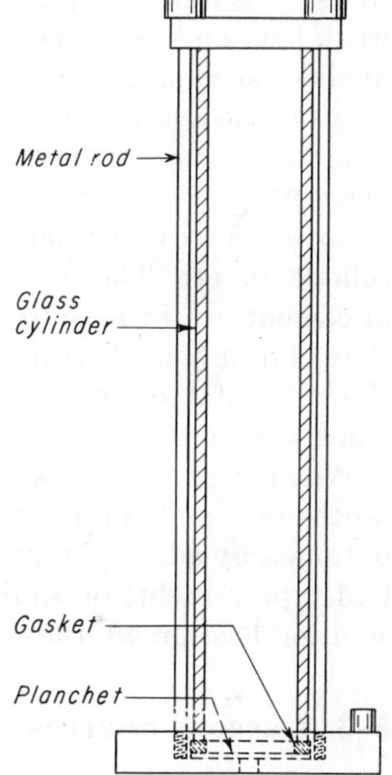

FIG. 5-4. Electrodeposition cell.

In general, isotopic carrier is added before electrodeposition if such is not already present in the sample. Haissinsky (40) and Rogers and Byrne (41) have discussed the process of electrodeposition of substances at tracer concentration.

For some elements, e.g., bismuth, lead, or polonium, a source can be prepared by the related process of chemical displacement with a more active element (Hevesy and Paneth, chap. 22).

Other Methods. Various special techniques have been devised for the preparation of very thin sources of radioactive material. Hufford and Scott (42) have summarized many of the techniques. Examples of methods described in individual publications are preparation by vacuum evaporation (43), cathode sputtering (44), and electrostatic spraying of a solution (45).

Covering Materials for Solid Sources. There are several reasons for covering sources. By covering and sealing a source, loss of radioactive material and associated contamination of the laboratory, counting room, and counting equipment are minimized. Sometimes a source is purposely covered to absorb weak radiation as well as to limit the detected radiation to a known amount of high-energy radiation (see Expt. 5-1). A cover may also be used to seal a source hermetically or protect a thin deposit against scratches.

There are, on the other hand, radionuclides whose radiation is so nonpenetrating that attenuation of the radiation in a cover is prohibitive to its measurement. Such is the case for alpha emitters in general, for weak beta emitters such as H^3, C^{14}, S^{35}, Ca^{45}, and Ni^{63}, and for radionuclides such as Zn^{65} which emit conversion electrons or X radiation. In any case a cover will absorb some of the radiation, and for certain kinds of measurements it may be necessary to make corrections for such absorption.

Covers may be prepared from thin foils of aluminum, polystyrene, cellophane, etc. They are readily attached by a rubber or celluloid type of cement, or if the source and cover will withstand the temperature, they can be joined with a sealing wax. Foils in the range of density thickness of 2 to 4 mg/cm^2 are available and are generally satisfactory when there are no special requirements for the cover.

When the cover thickness must be limited to a few micrograms or tenths of a milligram per square centimeter, a protective film can be obtained by adding dropwise a very dilute solution of collodion, celluloid-type cement, or similar material to the cold source. After the solution has spread, the solvent is cautiously evaporated.

5-3. Gaseous Sources

Radioactivity measurements for the radioisotopes of certain chemical elements, e.g., noble gases, necessarily involve gaseous sources. Techniques for the assay of radon have been described in many publications (46–52). Krypton and xenon have received special attention because of their production in nuclear fission (53, books 2 and 3). Gaseous sources may be used on occasion for counting the radioisotopes of other elements such as O^{19} (29 sec), N^{16} (7.3 sec), and Ar^{41} (1.83 hr), which are produced when air is irradiated with neutrons as in an air-cooled nuclear reactor.

For tritium, C^{14}, and S^{35}, which are generally encountered in solid or liquid compounds, it is often advantageous to convert the solid or liquid to a gaseous compound, or to elemental form in the case of tritium. The interest in gaseous sources for these three radionuclides stems from the problem of measuring the weak beta radiation which they emit. The maximum beta-ray energies are 0.0176, 0.155, and 0.167 Mev for tritium, C^{14}, and S^{35} respectively. Serious or even prohibitive loss in sensitivity and detection efficiency can arise from self-absorption of the weak beta radiation in solid sources and absorption in a detector window. The latter can be eliminated by placing the solid source inside a windowless Geiger or proportional detector. For material having a relatively high specific activity this technique is often adequate. It has even been used for tritium (54–57) with counting efficiencies of 0.2 to 2.5 per cent.

In order to reduce self-absorption losses, counters have been designed to permit a gas such as $C^{14}O_2$ or $S^{35}O_2$ to be confined in an external chamber adjacent to the window of a thin-window Geiger tube (58–60). Sulfur 35 has also been assayed as H_2S and SO_2 in gas mixtures by means of a probe-type scintillation crystal (61). These various types of counters can be used for stationary or flowing gas samples. For a given radioactive gas the self-absorption correction factor is a function of the gas pressure.

Both self-absorption and window absorption can be eliminated by making the radioactive material part of the detector itself. Thus, the material in the form of a gas can be placed in a gas counter, or in the form of a solid or a liquid it can be dissolved or suspended in a liquid-scintillating solution. The latter method is described in Sec. 5-4. It is through the development of assay methods which eliminate self-absorption that the great potential of tritium can be realized.

In principle, gas counters, e.g., ionization chambers, proportional counters, or Geiger counters, should be capable of high detection efficiency. They differ, however, with respect to (1) sensitivity, which depends upon the background rate, (2) type of gaseous source and, therefore, ease of source preparation, and (3) associated electronic apparatus. Among those workers who favor gas counting of weak beta emitters there is strong support to be found for each type of counter. As a generality, source preparation for all three types of gas counters involves two steps, namely (1) production and purification of a sample of radioactive gas and (2) transfer of the sample to the counter. Vacuum techniques are involved. References 7 and 62 to 64 are but a few of the many sources of information on vacuum techniques. With respect to gas-assay methods and techniques the texts of Calvin et al. (7) and Glascock (62) are excellent sources of information for C^{14} and for C^{14} and tritium respectively.

Carbon 14. The most commonly used gaseous source for C^{14} is carbon dioxide, although acetylene is also used. The C^{14}-labeled CO_2 may be produced by combustion of labeled organic compounds or by evolution from a labeled carbonate. Standard wet- and dry-combustion techniques used in the analysis of organic compounds have been modified for use with radioactive materials. In some procedures provision is made for both chemical and activity analysis.

The chemical behavior of labeled compounds is the same as that for unlabeled compounds except for the isotope effect. The latter can be a source of error in assay methods. Thus Armstrong and coworkers (65) observed that isotope fractionation, i.e., variation in the C^{14} content of the product CO_2, occurs during oxidation reactions. As a general precaution for either type of combustion it is important to oxidize the entire sample to CO_2 and mix the resulting CO_2. Mixing is particularly important if the entire sample of CO_2 is not transferred to the counter.

Combustion methods have been used to produce CO_2 for the preparation of solid sources, e.g., $BaCO_3$, as well as sources for gas counting. In the references for combustion techniques cited below, the CO_2 may not have been used for gas assay. In principle, however, the CO_2 obtained by any combustion process can be used for gas assay if the oxidation apparatus is attached to a suitable vacuum line for purifying the CO_2, i.e., removing water and other chemical contaminants which could arise from nitrogen- or sulfur-containing compounds, and filling the counter.

Most wet-combustion methods are based on the method of Van Slyke and Folch (66). Details of variations in apparatus and procedure are given in several publications (7, 8, 26, 62, 67–75). Briefly, the method consists in mixing the sample and a liquid oxidizing solution such as a mixture of iodic, chromic, sulfuric, and phosphoric acids in a glass reaction vessel connected to a suitable device for utilization of the CO_2. Oxidation takes a few minutes, and the apparatus is fairly simple when only C^{14} is to be determined. For gas counting, the CO_2 may be absorbed in an alkaline hydrazine solution and then, after transfer to a suitable apparatus, reliberated to fill a counter (26, 75, 76), or it may be separated from noncondensable gases by vacuum-line techniques and transferred directly to a counter as generated. Wet-oxidation methods using alkaline potassium permanganate (77) and persulfate for water-soluble compounds (78) have also been used.

Dry-combustion methods for C^{14}-labeled compounds have been described by many workers (27, 62, 79–83). The labeled sample is oxidized slowly in a furnace through which a stream of purified oxygen flows. Quartz or fused-silica combustion tubes are often used since the furnace temperature is in the range of 550 to 800°C. In the attached vacuum line, water is collected first in a dry-ice-cooled trap, which is followed by a liquid-nitrogen-cooled trap for the CO_2. Excess oxygen is pumped off while the oxidation products are frozen. The quantity of CO_2 can be measured prior to transfer to the counter by means of a manometric system consisting of a manometer and flasks having known volumes.

Double-liquid manometers have been devised for low-pressure measurements (27,83). Since oxides of nitrogen interfere with the operation of a counter and introduce errors in gas volume measurements, they must be removed when nitrogenous material is oxidized. Commonly this is done by reduction of the oxides of nitrogen to noncondensable nitrogen with metallic copper (27). Christman, Stuber, and Bothner-By (83) have shown that nitrogen dioxide can be removed effectively also by passing the combustion products over manganese dioxide. Dry combustion takes about 30 min to 1 hr. A major part of this time is required to bring the furnace temperature to its maximum value.

When CO_2 is generated by evolution from $BaCO_3$, a nonvolatile acid such as perchloric, phosphoric, or sulfuric acid is used (67, 75, 77, 84–87). Some workers prefer perchloric acid because the barium perchlorate formed is soluble. Metathesis of barium carbonate with lead chloride has also been used (84, 88) to produce CO_2.

TABLE 5-2

REFERENCES TO TECHNIQUES FOR FILLING GAS COUNTERS WITH C^{14}-LABELED GASES

Counter	*Reference*
Ion chamber	7, 62, 87, 96, 97
Proportional counter	26, 27, 71, 72, 75, 81, 85, 93, 98*
G-M counter	67, 84, 86, 99, 100

* Continuous flow.

Since acetylene, C_2H_2, contains twice as many carbon atoms as CO_2 per mole, it has been used (89, 90) in preference to CO_2 for the measurement of natural radiocarbon. Acetylene can be prepared from the CO_2 obtained by combustion of organic material. The method of Arrol and Glascock (91), for example, involves the reaction of CO_2 with an active metal such as barium to form a carbide which is subsequently reacted with water to yield acetylene.

References to filling techniques for the three types of counters are given in Table 5-2. Ion chambers of the Borkowski type (92) having a volume of 100 to 250 ml are commonly filled to a total pressure of CO_2 in the range of 50 cm to 1 atm. They are generally used with a vibrating-reed electrometer. Ion chambers have a sensitivity of about 100 dps of C^{14} and will accept a relatively large sample, e.g., on the order of 10 mmoles of CO_2. The latter is about twenty times the amount of carbon which can be handled conveniently as a solid source of $BaCO_3$. Stress currents resulting from mechanical stress of the center-rod insulator can be a source of error in ion-chamber measurements. Brownell and

Lockhart (87) recommend allowing an ion chamber to rest for a half-hour or more between filling and ion-current measurement to allow for the decay of stress currents produced in the course of evacuating and filling the chamber. Ion chambers may exhibit memory effects, i.e., C^{14} contamination of the inside surface. Contamination can be minimized by proper treatment of the inside surface. It is usually less of a problem for ion chambers than for other types of counters.

Proportional counters are fast and will handle samples of high specific activity. The Bernstein and Ballentine (85) proportional tube is illustrated in Fig. 5-5. Such a tube, which may also be used for S^{35} and tritium, is filled by transferring the CO_2 sample through the vacuum line to the evacuated tube while it is immersed in liquid nitrogen. A counter containing only CO_2 can be operated in the proportional (93) or limited proportional region (81). Some workers prefer to add a conventional proportional-counter filling gas such as methane (85) or P-10 (10 per cent methane, 90 per cent argon) (76). Because of the low energy of the C^{14} beta radiation, more than the usual electronic amplification is needed before the pulses are acceptable for a scaler. Information has been published on memory effects (71) and errors (94) for proportional counting of C^{14}.

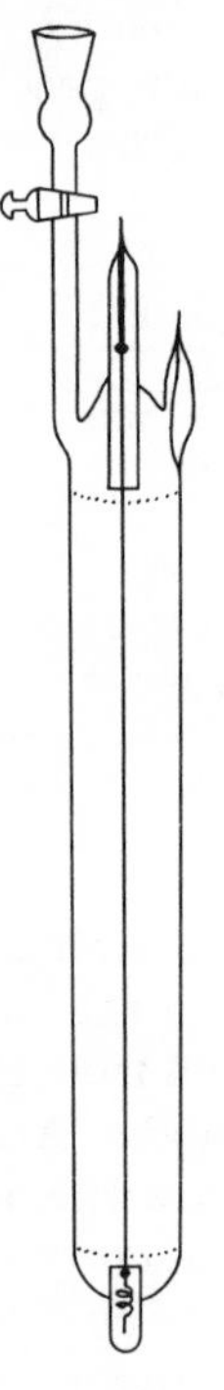

FIG. 5-5. Proportional tube for gas-phase counting. [*From Bernstein and Ballentine* (85).]

Geiger tubes require the simplest electronic circuitry for pulse counting. They are very sensitive to impurities, however, and are relatively slow. Memory effects have been observed (84). Pure carbon dioxide is not a satisfactory gas filling for a Geiger tube (95). A charge-transfer gas such as carbon disulfide is added to a pressure of about 2 cm of mercury, i.e., about 10 per cent of the CO_2 pressure. External quenching is required for CO_2-CS_2 filled counters.

Tritium. Gas assay of tritium-labeled organic material usually involves combustion to produce tritium water. The latter is separated from the products of combustion by vacuum-line condensation in a dry-ice-cooled trap. As for C^{14} assay, the dry combustion methods are based on standard methods used for analysis of organic compounds. References 56, 79, 83, and 101 to 103 deal with combustion procedures for tritium.

Exchange of tritium with ordinary hydrogen can occur in the course of assaying a sample, i.e., during combustion, transfer of source material to the counter, and measurement of the activity. Exchange is less likely for tritium-labeled hydrocarbons than for water or hydrogen.

Although water obtained by combustion can be introduced into a Geiger counter as water vapor (104–107), it is usually converted to hydrogen or a hydrocarbon, or a mixture of hydrogen and hydrocarbon. Only small amounts of water are acceptable for a Geiger counter. Furthermore, exchange with hydroxyl hydrogen on the glass surface of the counter leads to contamination (104–107), although Cameron (106) reports relatively little contamination.

TABLE 5-3

REFERENCES TO TECHNIQUES FOR FILLING GAS COUNTERS WITH TRITIUM-LABELED GASES

	Hydrogen	Water	Methane	Other
Ion chamber	62, 79, 108, 110, 118			103*
Proportional counter	85		56, 113–115	98†
Geiger counter	109, 111, 112, 119, 120	104–107		62,‡ 117,‡ 121,§ 116¶

* Hydrogen and methane.
† Mixture of labeled hydrocarbons.
‡ Butane.
§ Methanol.
¶ Acetylene.

Tritium in the form of hydrogen may be assayed in an ion chamber, proportional counter, or Geiger counter. Contamination is usually least serious for a metallic ion chamber (108). Tritium hydrogen can be produced by the reaction of tritium water with active metals such as calcium (109), lithium aluminum hydride (79), magnesium amalgam (108, 110), sodium (111), and zinc (54, 112).

As a hydrocarbon source, tritium methane can be produced by the reaction of water with a Grignard reagent such as CH_3MgI (113, 114) or aluminum carbide, Al_4C_3 (56, 115). Similarly, the calcium carbide–water reaction has been used (116) to produce tritium acetylene, and the reaction of C_4H_9MgBr with water has been used (62, 117) to produce tritium butane. Direct conversion of an organic substance to a mixture of methane and hydrogen by fusion with zinc and nickelic oxide has been employed by Wilzbach, Kaplan, and Brown (103).

As for C^{14}, all reactions used for source preparation, i.e., combustion or conversion to a gas, must be carried to completion in order to avoid isotope fractionation (116).

References to counter-filling methods for gas assay of tritium are listed in Table 5-3.

5-4. Liquid Sources

General. There are certain cases in which it is convenient to measure the radioactivity of a material in the liquid state. Thus (1) it may be difficult and time-consuming to convert the material to a solid or a gas; (2) a liquid source may be advantageous when sensitivity or large sample size is important; and (3) it may be relatively easy to recover the source material unchanged.

Liquid sources can be counted with the following types of detectors (see Chap. 2):

1. Dipping Geiger counter—a glass-wall counter which dips into the liquid (122–124). Decontamination can be an objectionable feature (125).
2. Jacketed or annulus-type Geiger counter (126–128) or crystal scintillator (129).
3. End-window or cylindrical Geiger counter with sample in a dish below (124, 130–133). Freedman and Hume (125) covered the liquid with a film of lacquer.
4. Internal-sample gas-flow counter. The radioactive material is contained in a dish which is placed inside the counter (57). A relatively nonvolatile solvent such as formamide may be used (77, 134–137).
5. End-window Geiger tube or flat scintillation crystal with an attached flat coil of plastic tubing or a cylindrical Geiger tube wrapped with plastic tubing. Such an arrangement can be used for continuous-flow measurements (138, 139).
6. Cylindrical Geiger tube surrounded by an annulus-type (Marinelli) beaker (132).
7. "Texas"-well type of Geiger counter with a ring of vertical anodes surrounding the source (132).
8. Crystal scintillation counter: well type, end-on type, and dip type (133, 140–142).
9. High-pressure ionization chamber with sample in a test tube (92, 132).
10. Liquid-scintillation counter—discussed separately below.

Except for the liquid-scintillation counter and possibly the internal-source counter, absorption losses for liquid sources are too large to make them useful for low-energy beta emitters. Well-type scintillation counters are very convenient for gamma emitters or high-energy beta emitters. The sample is placed in a test tube (or first in a screw-cap vial and then a test tube) which is positioned in the shielded well. Samples having a volume of 2 to 100 ml can be counted depending upon the size of the crystal.

For a given quantity of a radionuclide in solution and a given detector, the observed counting rate will depend on the over-all composition of the solution. Chiang and Willard (143) studied the effects of a change of solution composition for Geiger counters. They observed that the specific counting rate may increase (for gamma emitters) or decrease (for beta emitters) when the density of the solution is increased. The rate of change was found to depend on the atomic number of the elements in the salts used to increase the density. Other investigators (144, 145) have also studied the effect of changes in solution composition on the counting rate for Geiger counters.

Sources for Liquid-scintillation Counting. Internal-sample liquid-scintillation counting is a method of assay in which self-absorption and window absorption of nuclear radiation are eliminated by dissolving or suspending the sample in a scintillating liquid. The method is particularly advantageous for weak beta emitters, and it is often the method of choice for C^{14} and tritium. It is very valuable for low-level counting since it is capable of high sensitivity and provides high efficiency for large samples (146). Applications to the assay of tritium and C^{14}, especially in biological materials, are rapidly increasing (141, 147–149). The method is, of course, useful also for higher-energy beta emitters and alpha emitters (150, 151).

Since the radioactive sample becomes a component of the final scintillating liquid, its properties must be considered in selecting a liquid system. In a sense, the various components of the scintillating liquid become part of the source. It is appropriate, then, to consider in some detail the various properties of, and techniques for the use of, scintillating liquids.

In scintillation counting of beta emitters, the lower the energy of the beta rays, the fewer the photons emitted by the scintillator per disintegration, and therefore the fewer the photoelectrons produced in the photomultiplier. Thermionic-emission background arising within the photomultiplier becomes more troublesome than for alpha, gamma, or high-energy beta scintillation counting. It is common to reduce the thermionic background by:

1. Careful selection of photomultipliers with the best signal-to-noise ratio.
2. Use of two photomultipliers operated in coincidence (152–155), particularly for tritium counting, although this is becoming less important as photomultipliers are improved (156–158).
3. Pulse-height discrimination, which permits rejection of both the

relatively weak noise pulses and the very large pulses arising from cosmic rays or gamma-ray background.

4. Refrigeration of the photomultipliers and scintillating source. Refrigeration leading to temperatures in the range of 5 to $-10°C$ is more important for tritium than for C^{14} or S^{35}. With improved photomultipliers refrigeration is less of a requirement when two tubes are used in coincidence.

In addition to the radioactive sample the scintillating solution consists of the following:

1. A bulk solvent which absorbs most of the energy of the beta rays and transfers the energy efficiently to a solute which acts as the primary scintillator. Alkyl benzenes such as toluene, xylene, triethylbenzene, or ethylbenzene are suitable solvents (150, 159, 160). Toluene is a popular solvent. The double-solvent system dioxane and naphthalene (50 g naphthalene/liter) is also used (150, 160), particularly for toluene-insoluble radioactive samples, but its high freezing point (12°C) limits the refrigeration temperature.

2. A soluble scintillator such as *p*-terphenyl or 2,5-diphenyloxazole (PPO). The latter is the more soluble in toluene and is easier to keep in solution at a low temperature. A typical concentration is 4 g/liter.

3. A solute, also a scintillator, which shifts the spectrum emitted by the primary scintillator to longer wavelengths. The secondary solute absorbs the light emitted by the primary scintillator and reemits it a somewhat longer wavelength nearer to that needed for optimum operation of the photomultiplier. Hayes, Ott, and Kerr (161) recommend 1, 4-di-[2-(5-phenyloxazolyl)]-benzene (POPOP) and 2,5-di(4-biphenylyl)-oxazole (BBO) as wavelength shifters. Also of interest are 1,6-diphenyl-1,3,5-hexatriene and 2-(1-naphthyl)-5-phenyloxazole. Depending upon the temperature and, therefore, the solubility, a concentration of about 0.05 to 0.1 g/liter is usually adequate.

4. A diluent, which may be added if the radioactive sample does not dissolve readily in the preferred bulk solvent. Diluents, which favorably alter the solvent character of the solution but also decrease the counting efficiency, include hydrocarbons, ethers, and alcohols (160).

One of the advantages claimed for liquid-scintillation counting is the ease of preparation of the radioactive sample. In the simplest case an aliquot of material to be assayed is simply added to a glass bottle containing a suitable volume of stock scintillating solution and, after mixing of the contents, the bottle is placed in a cell holder which is optically coupled to the photomultiplier or photomultipliers.

Experience has shown (150, 160, 162) that, as for any method, successful application requires that consideration be given to certain details such as the following.

Properties of the Radioactive Sample. The radioactive sample may be a solid or liquid which can be dissolved in the bulk solvent or bulk solvent plus diluent to form a homogeneous system, or it can be an insoluble finely divided solid which can be suspended in the scintillating liquid. For toluene-insoluble tritium water, absolute ethanol can be added as a solubilizing diluent. Hayes and Gould (148) suggest adding absolute ethanol to the tritium water sample to make 90 to 95 per cent ethanol, an aliquot of which is then added to the scintillating solution to give the desired final volume. As an example, 30 ml of final solution contained in a Pyrex weighing bottle (45 by 65 mm) might consist of 0.01 ml of water, 0.19 ml of absolute ethanol, and 29.8 ml of scintillating solution. The permissible amount of water is limited by the adverse effect water has on the counting efficiency. Ziegler, Chleck, and Brinkerhoff (163) optimize the water content when ethanol is used by plotting the product of the water volume and the counting efficiency as a function of the water volume in the scintillating solution. The dioxane-naphthalene mixture is a better solvent for water and has a greater sensitivity for the same total counting volume. Adsorption on the glass source container can be a problem for water samples at low concentrations.

The sample should not be a strong quenching agent, i.e., a substance which interferes with emission of light by the scintillator. Examples (150, 162, 164) of strong quenching agents are nitro and iodo compounds, mercaptans, phenols, amines, aldehydes, and ketones. Furthermore, the sample should not be a colored substance which absorbs the light emitted by the scintillator. These two criteria can seriously limit the size of sample which can be used. Phosphorescence caused by the sample can cause high counting rates. Herberg (165) has observed such an effect for proteins. On occasion thermal adaptation of the source has been found necessary in order to lower the background presumably caused by thermoluminescence. When tritium-labeled material causes interference it can usually be converted to water by the combustion methods used for gas assay methods.

Okita and coworkers (166) have devised a rapid method for direct assay of tritium in urine involving the removal of colored substances and quenching substances by adsorption on activated charcoal. Using 2.0 ml of decolorized urine, 0.1 ml of distilled water, 20.0 ml of absolute ethanol, 28.0 ml of toluene, and 100 mg of *p*-diphenyloxazole contained in a 50- by 600-mm weighing bottle, they were able to detect as little as 0.08 μc of tritium per liter of urine.

Helf and White (167) have used a liquid-scintillation method for directly assaying carbon 14 in labeled organic nitrocompounds (explosives), thereby eliminating the need for combustion. Such compounds absorb ultraviolet light emitted by the scintillator, but addition of a wavelength shifter partially restores the counting efficiency. The authors suggest neglecting the absorption effect in comparative measurements by counting the same concentration of a given labeled material for all measurements or correcting for the absorption by first determining the dependence of counting rate on concentration for the material involved. Helf and coworkers (168) have also used liquid-scintillation counting for assay of sulfate impurity in cellulose nitrate.

Passmann, Radin, and Cooper (169) devised a method for the determination of C^{14} in the form of CO_2 by dissolving the CO_2 in a toluene-methanol scintillator solution. The CO_2 is first dissolved in a high-molecular-weight quaternary ammonium hydroxide by diffusion within a closed flask. No vacuum equipment is needed. The authors claim that samples as large as 5 mmoles of carbon can be handled by this method.

One obvious way to overcome the problem of low solubility of an organic substance in the scintillating solution is to prepare a soluble derivative. Hayes and coworkers (170), however, have prepared suspensions of microsized particles of a variety of insoluble materials including C^{14}-containing tissues. For the latter there is obviously a considerable saving in time for sample preparation as compared with oxidative methods. Samples are recoverable by filtration. To reduce errors from settling of the solid, the mixture can be shaken between counts or the counting rate can be extrapolated to zero time for a series of counts obtained for an undisturbed sample. Settling effects can be minimized in suspension scintillation counting by addition of a thixotropic agent such as aluminum stearate (171) or thixcin (172) to form a scintillating gel. Counting efficiency is not impaired by high concentration of optically dense suspended white material, but colored material will decrease the efficiency by light absorption (170). Self-absorption of the weak beta rays is not a problem for C^{14}-labeled solids, but it does prohibit the use of suspended tritium-labeled material.

Ease of sample preparation cannot be claimed as an advantage of the liquid-scintillation counting method for radiocarbon dating. Except for liquid samples (155) it is generally necessary to burn the sample and convert the $C^{14}O_2$ to a soluble organic compound. If converted to toluene, the sample (normally large) can serve as the bulk solvent.

Multiple-labeled compounds, e.g., labeled with tritium and C^{14} or with tritium, C^{14}, and P^{32}, can be assayed for the different radionuclides if the beta-ray energies are sufficiently different. Thus, since the output of the scintillator is essentially proportional to the beta-ray energy, the radiation from two radionuclides such as tritium and C^{14} can be distinguished by various suitable adjustments of the electronic equipment, i.e., variation in high voltage applied to the photomultiplier, amplifier gain, or discriminator control (162, 173).

Sample Size. For assay of material of relatively high specific activity the sample size should be kept small in order to minimize the lowering of the detection efficiency by dilution and quenching and to minimize the total volume and background. Hayes (150) reports backgrounds of 75 to 100 cpm for tritium and 30 to 60 cpm for all other radionuclides for liquid volumes of 25 ml and 2 in. of lead shielding. Background increases, of course, when the high voltage applied to the photomultiplier is increased to obtain greater sensitivity.

On the other hand, for assay of material having a low specific activity the sample should be as large as possible except as limited by lowering of the counting efficiency. The counting efficiency can be determined by the use of an internal homogeneous standard as described in Chap. 7.

Purity of Solvent and Phosphor. Solvents must be of the highest purity to be free of quenchers. Even dissolved oxygen can act as a quencher. Methods of removing dissolved oxygen by flushing with nitrogen (174) or argon (175) or by ultrasonic degassing (163, 176) have been devised. When a large volume of solvent is required or when the sample activity is very low, it is advantageous to use a solvent of petrochemical origin in order to avoid the natural C^{14} background.

The organic compounds used as phosphors should be the special "scintillation grades." They should not be exposed to ultraviolet light, and stock scintillation solutions are best stored dark and cold.

Source Container. It is common practice to place the source, i.e., scintillating liquid and sample, in a glass bottle. Weighing bottles (30 to 60 ml) have lost popularity in favor of the less expensive, nonleaking medicine vials with polyethylene caps (160, 167, 170). For example, Kimble Opticlear 5- or 10-dram vials are convenient. Variations in wall thickness and in position of the vial in the shielded cell holder are usually not critical. Colored glass should obviously be avoided, and thin glass is an advantage with respect to lower K^{40} background counts.

Phosphorescence of the glass vials following exposure to ultraviolet light, i.e., sunlight or light from fluorescent lights, can produce a high false counting rate which may require minutes to hours to decay.

Experiment 5-1
Preparation of a Long-lived Beta Reference Source

A long-lived source of radioactivity is commonly used to check the day-to-day performance of nuclear radiation-detection equipment. For beta-ray detectors a source may be prepared conveniently from U_3O_8, which satisfies the requirements of providing a long-lived radioactive substance and of being chemically stable. Some of the other radioactive materials which may be used for the preparation of reference beta sources are Sr^{90}-Y^{90}, RaD-E-F, Tl^{204}, and C^{14}. Beta-gamma sources may be prepared from Co^{60}, Cs^{137}, and sealed Ra^{226}.

The useful beta radiation emitted by U_3O_8 is that associated with UX_2, which is produced as follows:

$$_{92}U^{238}(U_I) \xrightarrow[4.49 \times 10^9 \text{ years}]{\alpha} {}_{90}Th^{234}\ (UX_1) \xrightarrow[24.10 \text{ days}]{\beta^-}$$

$$_{91}\underset{(0.63\%\ IT)}{Pa^{234}\ (UX_2)}\ 99.3\% \xrightarrow[1.175 \text{ min}]{\beta^-} {}_{92}U^{234}\ (U_{II}) \xrightarrow[2.48 \times 10^5 \text{ years}]{\alpha} {}_{90}Th^{230}, \text{ etc.}$$

In purified natural uranium (99.28 per cent U^{238}, 0.713 per cent U^{235}, 0.0058 per cent U^{234}) and its compounds, the uranium series in effect ends with U^{234} because of its long life and that of its alpha-emitting daughter 8.0×10^4 year Th^{230} (Io). In uranium minerals, of course, the remaining alpha- and beta-emitting members of the series, which terminates in Pb^{206}, are also present. A similar condition holds for the actinium series starting with U^{235} and terminating in effect as a source of beta radiation with Th^{231} (UY).

The weak beta radiation (0.191 Mev, 65 per cent; 0.100 Mev, 35 per cent) emitted by Th^{234} is absorbed partially in the solid oxide and partially in any covering material. If, as in the source preparation described below, a cover having a thickness of about 35 mg/cm^2 is placed over the oxide, the beta radiation detected will be that from UX_2. (Consider the similar situation for RaD-E-F beta sources.) If the sample of purified uranium oxide is old, i.e., 240 days or more, the UX_1 and UX_2 will be in secular equilibrium with the parent U^{238} and will then have a disintegration rate calculable for a known quantity of uranium. U_3O_8 is also used to prepare alpha sources* (see Expt. 5-2).

Apparatus and Materials

Analytical balance
U_3O_8 (c.p. grade or better)
Flat metal (e.g., copper, stainless steel) planchet 1 in. in diameter
Flat metal ring, conveniently made from 1-in. planchet, 3/4 in. ID, approximately 0.015 in. thick
Aluminum foil, 1-in. circle, about 35 mg/cm^2 (about 0.005 in. thick)
Tweezers
Dilute solution of collodion or a cement in an appropriate solvent
Cement (e.g., celluloid type)
Spatula
Heat lamp

* B. C. Carsen, C. W. Reed, L. Curtis, and L. Baurmash, Low-rate Alpha Scintillation Counter, *Nucleonics*, vol. 5, no. 4, pp. 55–59, 1949.

Procedure

Cement a ring (centered) on the top side of a labeled planchet. When the cement is dry, the resulting source mount is weighed to the nearest 1/10 mg on an analytical balance.

Add about 80 mg of U_3O_8 to the weighed source mount, and determine the exact weight of oxide added. (**Caution:** Avoid spilling any U_3O_8 and keep in mind that whatever is used in handling the U_3O_8 will be a potential source of contamination.) This quantity of U_3O_8 should provide a beta counting rate of about 5,000 cpm for a thin-end-window G-M tube with a counting yield of about 10 per cent. Distribute the U_3O_8 as a relatively uniform layer by gently tapping the mount on the edge.

Cautiously add enough collodion solution with a dropper to wet completely the oxide layer without greatly disturbing the uniformity of the layer. Dry the sample slowly under a heat lamp.

Cement an aluminum cover on the source using a minimum of cement on the ring without disturbing the U_3O_8 (see Fig. 5-6).

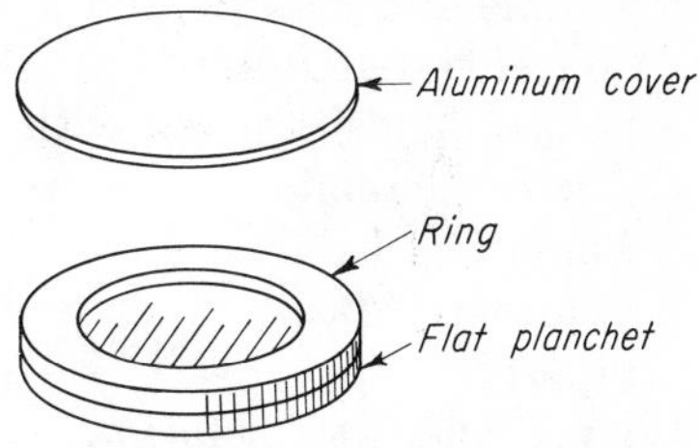

FIG. 5-6. Source mounts for powder sources (Expt. 5-1).

Since this source will be counted many times, it should be marked on top to facilitate orientation or positioning in the source holder.

In general, the same counting period—that corresponding to a total of at least 10,000 counts—should be used whenever the activity of the U_3O_8 reference source is measured.

Analysis of Data

1. Calculate the weight of U_3O_8 required to provide a beta counting rate of 5,000 cpm at 10 per cent counting yield.

2. Prepare a graph showing the counting rate of the reference source as a function of time. Keep this plot up to date so that any operational difficulties for the G-M counters may be detected at once.

3. For use of this source in geometry determinations, see Expt. 7-2.

4. Under proper conditions the reference source may be used to normalize data collected over an extended period of time. When changes are made in the counting equipment, the reference source cannot generally be used without absorption corrections to normalize data for radionuclides emitting radiation of a different type or of very different energy from that emitted by the reference source because of the energy dependence of absorption in the counter window.

5. For use of this source in a study of statistical fluctuations in nuclear-particle counting, see Expt. 3-3.

Experiment 5-2

Preparation of Samples for Alpha-ray Measurements

Uranium is one of the few alpha-emitting elements which is readily available for practical purposes. The procedure for electrodeposition of uranium oxide in this experiment follows closely one described by Lilly.* An alternative procedure has been described by Hull.†

Apparatus and Materials

- Alpha-detection apparatus
- Sample of U_3O_8 (about 100 mg)
- Concentrated HNO_3
- Electrodeposition cell with platinum disk as cathode and platinum wire as anode
- Analytical balance
- Volumetric flask
- Pipette
- 1 per cent NaF solution
- Stirring motor
- Battery or other d-c source
- Rheostat
- Muffle furnace

Procedure

The procedure outlined here is sufficient to obtain qualitative separation of the uranium for counting purposes. If the method is used for quantitative separation and assay of uranium, the original reference should be consulted.

The sample, which should consist of nearly pure U_3O_8, is weighed and dissolved in as little concentrated nitric acid as possible—not to exceed 15 drops. If the sample dissolves completely, the solution is transferred to a volumetric flask and made up to volume. If it does not dissolve, the sample may be made up to volume and centrifuged to remove the insoluble material, which usually is mostly silica.

The volumetric flask and pipette sizes should be chosen so that approximately 0.5 mg of uranium is in the plating aliquot. This amount is pipetted into the electrodeposition cell, keeping the volume down to

* R. C. Lilly, A Non-gravimetric Method for the Determination of Uranium on Platinum Disks, *U.S. Atomic Energy Comm. Rept.* MDDC-430, 1947.

† D. E. Hull and B. Cohen, The Counting Method of Isotopic Analysis of Uranium, *U.S. Atomic Energy Comm. Rept.* MDDC-387, 1947.

about 10 ml. Add 2 ml of 1 per cent sodium fluoride and adjust the stirrer so that it is about 1/4 in. above the surface of the disk. Adjust the current to about 50 ma. Add an additional 1 ml of 1 per cent sodium fluoride after 1 hr. After about 1 1/2 hr plating, the sample may be removed, dried, and ignited to a black color in the muffle furnace. The sample may then be measured in a suitable alpha counter.

Analysis of Data

A sample made by this procedure is a satisfactory operational standard for alpha counters, although it has no particular advantage over a sample prepared from an equilibrium mixture of RaD-E-F. The above procedure could be used as a rapid proximate assay for uranium in ores, although if more than an estimate is desired, the original references and procedures should be used. This practice does give the thin deposit which is of paramount importance in measuring alpha radiation.

Experiment 5-3

Preparation of Liquid Samples for Comparative Measurement of High-energy Beta and Gamma Radiation

Beta emitters dissolved in water or a relatively nonvolatile organic solvent can often be counted rather simply with a Geiger counter. The method has been used for high-energy beta emitters. Because of absorption losses, relatively strong sources are needed.

If a gamma-ray scintillation counter is not available, gamma emitters may also be counted with a Geiger counter while contained in a liquid. Absorption losses are generally less serious in this case.

The following are a few radioisotopes for which radioactivity measurement can be made with a glass-wall tube and for which liquid sources can be used:

Na^{22}	Fe^{59}†	As^{76}	Au^{198}†
Na^{24}	Co^{60}†	$Ru\text{-}Rh^{106}$	Hg^{203}†
P^{32}	Cu^{64}†	I^{131}†	
K^{42}	Zn^{65}†	La^{140}	

† Primarily dependent on gamma-ray measurement.

Apparatus and Materials

Detection apparatus

Geiger-counter apparatus with glass-wall counter tube, dipping tube, or jacketed tube; or

Ionization chamber which can be placed near surface of liquid or which may be brought into the vicinity of a source which is emitting gamma radiation

One large (3-in.) petri dish
One Lucite holder for centrifuge cup
One swinging beaker shelf on a ring stand
Source of appropriate radioactive material

Procedure

The procedure depends somewhat on the type of equipment which is available, although the sample preparation is essentially the same in any case. The actual preparation consists in making up the various samples in which it is desired to compare the activity in the same volume of liquid and in placing the known volume of liquid in the petri dish when the glass-wall tube is used or in the centrifuge cup when the dipping counter is employed. The detector may be mounted in several ways, one of the most convenient being to clamp it directly onto a ring stand. The samples may be placed on the table, but it is desirable that the tube be placed somewhat higher for ease and operation, so that a swinging beaker shelf can be used to good advantage. One typical setup for the glass-wall tube and petri dish is shown in Fig. 5-7.

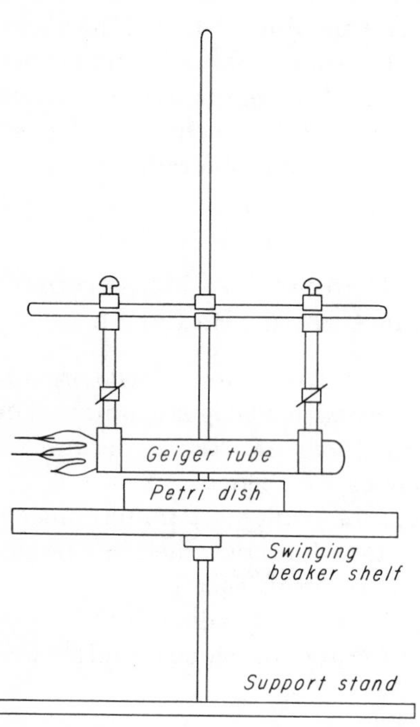

FIG. 5-7. Arrangement for counting liquids in open dish (Expt. 5-3).

Perform a series of measurements with the same amount of radioactivity in the petri dish, but successively increase the volume of water in the dish. Essentially the same procedure may be followed with the dipping counter to determine the optimum volume of sample to be used.

Analysis of Data

As in other cases of relative measurement, the important factor here is reproducibility. The conditions of measurement, including the isotope, type of liquid, position, and other factors, must be closely reproduced if the measurements are to have significance. These methods may frequently be used to good advantage in the work with biological materials (Expt. 10-3), since the dry ashing of such materials frequently involves a long and unsatisfactory process of sample preparation. It must be remembered that the measurements one obtains by these methods give only the specific activity directly (cpm per milliliter) and not total activity. Reasonably good total-activity measurements may be obtained by making appropriate calculations.

Experiment 5-4
Preparation of Samples in the Gaseous State for Measurement

The apparatus and procedure are intended primarily for measurement of the radioactivity of C^{14}-labeled CO_2 in an ion chamber, but with relatively little modification they can be used for CO_2 with other types of detectors and for S^{35}-labeled gases.

Apparatus and Materials

Vacuum train and pump (see Fig. 5-8). This may be attached to CO_2 generation unit, combustion train, or any other type of gas-generation system. All are best located in a hood.
Ionization chamber or gas counter.
Tank of nitrogen (with reducing valve).
Sample of radioactive $BaCO_3$ (or other suitable material for gas generation). Amount depends upon the specific activity of the carbonate and the volume of the detector.
Concentrated H_3PO_4.
Dry ice.
Acetone.
Liquid nitrogen.
Two dewar flasks.

Procedure

The ion chamber (or counter) is evacuated while the gas sample system (combustion furnace or gas generator followed by purification traps) is isolated by means of a stopcock. If the carbon dioxide generation system illustrated in Fig. 5-8 is used, the C^{14}-labeled carbonate (as solid or an aqueous solution) is placed in the flask and phosphoric acid is placed in the funnel. A dewar flask containing a mixture of dry ice and acetone is placed around the first trap, which is used to remove water vapor from the gas stream.

The proper stopcocks are opened to permit a stream of nitrogen gas to flow gently from the inlet at the generator through both traps to the outlet to the atmosphere (in hood). After the second trap and remainder of the manifold have been swept out with dry nitrogen from the first trap, a dewar flask containing liquid nitrogen is placed around the second trap, which is used to collect the labeled CO_2.

A few drops of phosphoric acid are added to the carbonate cautiously, and then the two-way stopcock is turned to allow the nitrogen carrier gas to transfer the carbon dioxide to the liquid-nitrogen trap. The process is repeated until all the carbonate sample has been converted to CO_2 and the latter transferred to the second trap.

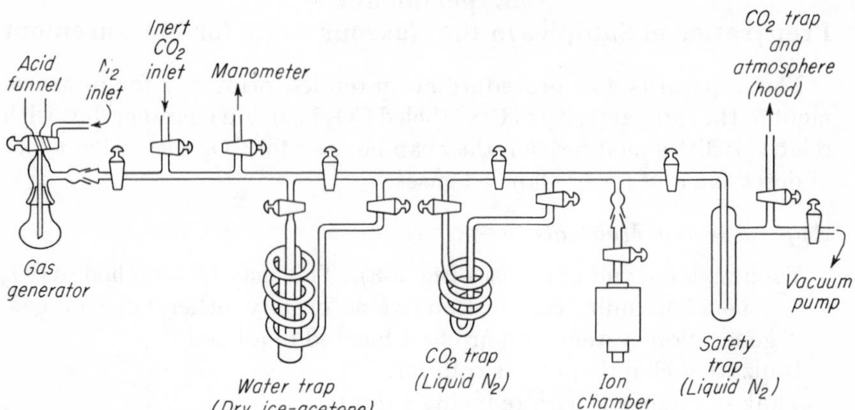

FIG. 5-8. Apparatus for filling ion chamber or gas counter with $C^{14}O_2$ (Expt. 5-4). [*Modified form of apparatus of Bernstein and Ballentine* (85).]

With the bypass stopcock and the outlet stopcock on the first trap closed, the second trap (including all three stopcocks) and manifold connecting it with the ion chamber are evacuated. The second trap is then closed, and with the bypass stopcock open, the remainder of the system is evacuated with the stopcocks to the generator, inert CO_2 inlet, and manometer closed.

The bypass stopcock on the second trap is closed, the stopcock on the manifold side of the trap leading to the vacuum pump is closed, and then the stopcock on the detector and that on the outlet side of the second trap are opened. The liquid nitrogen is removed from the trap, thereby permitting the carbon dioxide to vaporize as the trap becomes warm.

Inert CO_2 (or a counter gas such as methane) is allowed to enter the manifold and first trap (bypass stopcock closed) until a suitable pressure (greater than that of the labeled CO_2 in the detector but somewhat less than the desired final pressure) is indicated on the manometer. The inert CO_2 is allowed to pass through the first trap into the detector by way of the second trap until sufficient inert CO_2 is admitted from the gas cylinder to provide adequate gas pressure for the particular detector. The addition should be conducted rapidly and in such a manner as to

(1) sweep all the labeled CO_2 into the detector and (2) minimize back-diffusion of the labeled CO_2. The stopcock to the detector is closed, and the manifold is evacuated or flushed to the atmosphere (hood) through a soda lime tube or a barium or sodium hydroxide bubble tower. Air is admitted to the manifold, and the ion chamber is removed for radioactivity measurement.

If time permits, the gaseous-source method may be compared with the solid-source method by counting a suitable solid source prepared from the same labeled material.

Several variations of the apparatus illustrated in Fig. 5-8 are described in the literature. For example, calibrated flasks and calibrated connecting manifolds are required for quantitative measurements when only a known fraction of the labeled CO_2 is transferred to the detector. Furthermore, the gas may be counted in a proportional or Geiger tube using a suitable additive filling gas. CO_2, for example, may be flushed out of the generating system into the counting tube with inert CO_2 or with the additive gas, or it may be condensed in the tube by immersing the tube in liquid nitrogen.

In many cases it is desirable to utilize the gas in some other experiment or to recover the material for some other purpose. All this may be done by reintroducing the liquid nitrogen around the second trap and allowing the gas from the ionization chamber or counting tube to be cooled down in this portion. This should solidify all the carbon dioxide in a few minutes and separate it again from other gases. This gas may then be passed through a bubble tower or a precipitation tower for recovery or for disposal.

(**Caution:** It is usually better to precipitate or absorb radioactive carbon dioxide in a solution than to allow it to be vented to the atmosphere even in a hood. It should never be vented into the laboratory atmosphere.)

Cited References

1. Gordon, C. L.: Nucleonics, *Anal. Chem.*, vol. 21, pp. 96–101, 1949.
2. Kohman, T. P.: Measurement Techniques of Applied Radiochemistry, *Anal. Chem.*, vol. 21, pp. 352–364, 1949.
3. Gordon, C. L.: Nucleonics, *Anal. Chem.*, vol. 23, pp. 81–86, 1951.
4. Gordon, C. L.: Nucleonics, *Anal. Chem.*, vol. 26, pp. 176–181, 1954.
5. Meinke, W. W.: Nucleonics, *Anal. Chem.*, vol. 28, pp. 736–756, 1956.
6. Meinke, W. W.: Nucleonics, *Anal. Chem.*, vol. 30, pp. 686–728, 1958.
7. Calvin, M., C. Heidelberger, J. C. Reid, B. M. Tolbert, and P. F. Yankwich: "Isotopic Carbon," Wiley, New York, 1949.
8. Comar, C. L.: "Radioisotopes in Biology and Agriculture," McGraw-Hill, New York, 1955.
9. Bearden, J. A.: Radioactive Contamination of Ionization Chamber Materials, *Rev. Sci. Instr.*, vol. 4, pp. 271–275, 1933.

10. McDaniel, E. W., H. J. Schaefer, and J. K. Colehour: Dual Proportional Counter of Low-level Measurements of Alpha Activity of Biological Materials, *Rev. Sci. Instr.*, vol. 27, pp. 864–868, 1956.
11. Armstrong, W. D., and J. Schubert: Exchange of Carbon Dioxide between Barium Carbonate and the Atmosphere, *Science*, vol. 106, pp. 403–404, 1947.
12. Yankwich, P. E.: Loss of Radioactivity from Barium Carbonate Samples, *Science*, vol. 107, pp. 681–683, 1948.
13. Samos, G.: Some Observations on Exchange of CO_2 between $BaCO_3$ and CO_2 Gas, *Science*, vol. 110, pp. 663–665, 1949.
14. Faul, H., and G. R. Sullivan: Density Correction in Beta-ray Assaying of Rock and Mineral Samples, *Nucleonics*, vol. 4, no. 1, pp. 53–56, 1949.
15. Libby, W. F.: Simple Absolute Measurement Technique for Beta Radioactivity, *Anal. Chem.*, vol. 29, pp. 1566–1570, 1957.
16. Burr, W. W., Jr., and J. A. Marcia: Preparation of Pressed Samples for Counting Carbon-14-labeled Compounds, *Anal. Chem.*, vol. 27, p. 571, 1955.
17. Cohn, A., and R. M. Lind: An Improved Procedure for Plating Uniform $BaCO_3$ Precipitates, *Intern. J. Radiation and Isotopes*, vol. 3, pp. 44–45, 1958.
18. Comar, C. L., S. L. Hansard, S. L. Hood, M. P. Plumlee, and B. F. Barrentine: Use of Calcium-45 in Biological Studies, *Nucleonics*, vol. 8, no. 3, pp. 19–31, 1951.
19. Henriques, F. C., Jr., G. B. Kistiakowsky, C. Margnetti, and W. G. Schneider: Radioactive Studies: Analytical Procedure for Measurement of Long-lived Radioactive Sulfur, S^{35}, with a Lauritsen Electroscope and Comparison of Electroscope with Special Geiger Counter, *Ind. Eng. Chem., Anal. Ed.*, vol. 18, pp. 349–353, 1946.
20. Abers, E. L.: An Inexpensive Filter-cup for Collecting and Counting Active Precipitates, *Nucleonics*, vol. 3, no. 4, pp. 43–44, 1948.
21. Armstrong, W. D., and J. Schubert: Determination of Radioactive Carbon in Solid Samples, *Anal. Chem.*, vol. 20, pp. 270–271, 1948.
22. Roberts, J. D., W. Bennett, E. W. Holroyd, and C. H. Fugitt: Measurement of Carbon 14, *Anal. Chem.*, vol. 20, pp. 904–905, 1948.
23. Hutchens, T. T., C. K. Claycomb, W. J. Cathey, and J. T. Van Bruggen: Techniques in the Use of C^{14} as a Tracer. 2, Preparation of $BaCO_3$ Plates by Centrifugation, *Nucleonics*, vol. 7, no. 3, pp. 41–44, 1950.
24. Schweitzer, G. K., and B. R. Stein: Measuring Solid Samples of Low-energy Beta Emitters, *Nucleonics*, vol. 7, no. 3, pp. 65–72, 1950.
25. Migicovsky, B. B., and W. A. Evans: Filtration and Mounting Device for Ca^{45} Measurement, *Nucleonics*, vol. 9, no. 3, pp. 77–78, 1951.
26. Van Slyke, D. D., R. Steele, and J. Plazin: Determination of Total Carbon and Its Radioactivity, *J. Biol. Chem.*, vol. 192, pp. 769–805, 1951.
27. Anderson, R. C., Y. Delabarre, and A. A. Bothner-By: Chemical Analysis and Isotopic Assay of Organic Compounds, *Anal. Chem.*, vol. 24, pp. 1298–1303, 1952.
28. Bronner, F., and N. A. Jernberg: Simple Centrifugal Filtration Assembly for Preparation of Solid Samples for Radioassay, *Anal. Chem.*, vol. 29, p. 462, 1957.
29. Schweitzer, G. K., and J. S. Eldridge: Reproducibility of Radioactive Sample Preparation Techniques, *Anal. Chim. Acta*, vol. 16, pp. 189–193, 1957.
30. Barker, F. B., and L. L. Thatcher: Modified Determination of Radium in Water, *Anal. Chem.*, vol. 29, pp. 1573–1575, 1957.

31. Ross, J. F., and M. A. Chapin: The Electrolytic Separation of Radioactive Iron from the Blood, *Rev. Sci. Instr.*, vol. 13, pp. 77–80, 1942.
32. Peacock, W. C., R. D. Evans, J. W. Irvine, Jr., W. M. Good, A. F. Kip, S. Weiss, and J. G. Gibson: The Use of Two Radioactive Isotopes of Iron in Tracer Studies of Erythrocytes, *J. Clin. Invest.*, vol. 25, pp. 605–615, 1946.
33. Miller, H. W., and R. J. Brouns: Quantitative Electrodeposition of Plutonium, *Anal. Chem.*, vol. 24, pp. 536–538, 1952.
34. Theurer, K., and T. R. Sweet: Determination of Small Amounts of Zinc in Aluminum Alloys, *Anal. Chem.*, vol. 25, pp. 119–121, 1953.
35. Wilson, C. R., and A. Langer: Electrodeposition of Uranium Oxide on Aluminum, *Nucleonics*, vol. 11, no. 8, p. 48, 1953.
36. Van Cleve, A., and F. D. McDonough: Electroplating Technique for Tl^{204}, *Nucleonics*, vol. 12, no. 12, p. 53, 1954.
37. Moore, F. L., and G. W. Smith: Electrodeposition of Plutonium, *Nucleonics*, vol. 13, no. 4, pp. 66–69, 1955.
38. Maletskos, C. J., and J. W. Irvine, Jr.: Quantitative Electrodeposition of Radiocobalt, Zinc, and Iron, *Nucleonics*, vol. 14, no. 4, pp. 84–93, 1956.
39. Salyer, D., and T. R. Sweet: Determination of Cobalt by Anodic Electrodeposition, *Anal. Chem.*, vol. 28, pp. 61–63, 1956.
40. Haissinsky, M.: "Electrochimie des substances radioactives et des solutions extrêmement diluées," Hermann, Paris, 1946.
41. Rogers, L. B., and J. T. Byrne: Critical Interpretation of Electrodeposition Studies Involving Traces of Elements, *J. Electrochem. Soc.*, vol. 98, pp. 457–463, 1951.
42. Hufford, D. L., and B. F. Scott: Techniques for the Preparation of Thin Films of Radioactive Material, Paper 16.1 in "The Transuranic Elements," McGraw-Hill, New York, 1949.
43. Sherwin, C. W.: Vacuum Evaporation of Radioactive Materials, *Rev. Sci. Instr.*, vol. 22, pp. 339–341, 1951.
44. Novakov, T., and M. Mladjenovic: Preparation of Thin Beta-ray Sources by Cathode Sputtering, *Rev. Sci. Instr.*, vol. 27, pp. 415–416, 1956.
45. Carswell, D. J., and J. Milsted: New Method for the Preparation of Thin Films of Radioactive Material, *J. Nuclear Energy*, vol. 4, pp. 51–54, 1957.
46. Evans, R. D.: Apparatus for the Determination of Minute Quantities of Radium, Radon, and Thoron in Solids, Liquids and Gases, *Rev. Sci. Instr.*, vol. 6, pp. 99–112, 1935.
47. Curtiss, L. F., and F. J. Davis: A Counting Method for the Determination of Small Amounts of Radium and of Radon, *J. Research Natl. Bur. Standards*, vol. 31, pp. 181–195, 1943.
48. Fineman, P., et al.: An Emanation Method for Radium Analysis, Paper 16.7 in "The Transuranic Elements," McGraw-Hill, New York, 1949.
49. Rodden, C. J.: Determination of Naturally Occurring Radioactive Elements, *Anal. Chem.*, vol. 21, pp. 327–335, 1949.
50. Hursh, J. B., and A. A. Gates: Body Radium Content of Individuals with No Known Occupational Exposure, *Nucleonics*, vol. 7, no. 1, pp. 46–59, 1950.
51. Rodden, C. J.: "Analytical Chemistry of the Manhattan Project," pp. 368–371, McGraw-Hill, New York, 1950.
52. Hursh, J. B.: Measurement of Breath Radon by Charcoal Adsorption, *Nucleonics*, vol. 12, no. 1, pp. 62–65, 1954.
53. Coryell, C. D., and N. Sugarman: "Radiochemical Studies: The Fission Products," 3 books, McGraw-Hill, New York, 1951.

54. Eidinoff, M. L., and J. E. Knoll: The Measurement of Radioactive Hydrogen in Solid Samples—Comparison with Gas Counting, *Science*, vol. 112, pp. 250–251, 1950.
55. Jenkins, W. A.: Estimating the Tritium Content of Tritiated Water, *Anal. Chem.*, vol. 25, pp. 1477–1480, 1953.
56. Banks, T. E., J. C. Crawhall, and D. G. Smyth: Some Techniques in the Assay of Tritium, *Biochem. J.*, vol. 64, pp. 411–416, 1956.
57. Jackson, F. L., and H. W. Lampe: Direct Counting of Tritium-tagged Solid and Liquid Samples, *Anal. Chem.*, vol. 28, pp. 1735–1737, 1956.
58. Kummer, J. T.: Counter Design for Gaseous Weak Beta Emitters, *Nucleonics*, vol. 3, no. 1, pp. 27–28, 1948.
59. Bonner, F., and J. Turkevitch: Study of the Carbon Dioxide–Carbon Reaction Using C^{14} as a Tracer, *J. Am. Chem. Soc.*, vol. 73, pp. 561–564, 1951.
60. Norris, T. H.: A Gas-sample Counting Method for Soft β-emitters, *J. Am. Chem. Soc.*, vol. 74, pp. 2396–2398, 1952.
61. Mai, K. L., and A. U. Babb: Scintillation Counter for Vapor-phase Analysis, *Nucleonics*, vol. 13, no. 2, pp. 52–54, 1955.
62. Glascock, R. F.: "Isotopic Gas Analysis for Biochemists," Academic Press, New York, 1954.
63. Strong, J.: "Procedures in Experimental Physics," Prentice-Hall, Englewood Cliffs, N.J., 1943.
64. Guthrie, A., and R. K. Wakerling: "Vacuum Equipment and Techniques," McGraw-Hill, New York, 1949.
65. Armstrong, W. D., L. Singer, S. H. Zbarsky, and B. Dunshee: Errors of Combustion Compounds for C^{14} Analysis, *Science*, vol. 112, pp. 531–533, 1950.
66. Van Slyke, D. D., and J. Folch: Manometric Carbon Determination, *J. Biol. Chem.*, vol. 136, pp. 509–541, 1940.
67. Skipper, H. E., C. E. Bryan, L. White, Jr., and O. S. Hutchison: Techniques for In Vivo Tracer Studies with Radioactive Carbon, *J. Biol. Chem.*, vol. 173, no. 1, pp. 371–381, 1948.
68. Lindenbaum, A., J. Schubert, and W. D. Armstrong: Rapid Wet Combustion Method for Carbon Determination, *Anal. Chem.*, vol. 20, pp. 1120–1121, 1948.
69. Hutchens, T. T., C. K. Claycomb, W. J. Cathey, and J. T. Van Bruggen: Techniques in the Use of C^{14} as a Tracer. 1, Apparatus and Technique for Wet Combustion of Non-volatile Samples, *Nucleonics*, vol. 7, no. 3, pp. 38–41, 1950.
70. Van Slyke, D. D., J. Plazin, and J. R. Weisiger: Reagents for the Van Slyke–Folch Wet Carbon Combustion, *J. Biol. Chem.*, vol. 191, pp. 299–304, 1951.
71. Buchanan, D. L., and A. Nakao: A Method for Simultaneous Determination of Carbon-14 and Total Carbon, *J. Am. Chem. Soc.*, vol. 74, pp. 2389–2395, 1952.
72. Weisburger, J. H., E. K. Weisburger, and H. P. Morris: An Improved Carbon-14 Wet Combustion Technique, *J. Am. Chem. Soc.*, vol. 74, pp. 2399–2400, 1952.
73. Baker, N., H. Feinberg, and R. Hill: Analytical Procedures Using a Combined Combustion-Diffusion Vessel. Simple Wet-combustion Method Suitable for Routine Carbon-14 Analysis, *Anal. Chem.*, vol. 26, pp. 1504–1506, 1954.

74. Van Slyke, D. D.: Wet Carbon Combustion and Some of Its Applications, *Anal. Chem.*, vol. 26, pp. 1706–1712, 1954.
75. Simpson, L.: A Simplified Procedure for Proportional Counting of C^{14}-labeled Carbon Dioxide, *Int. J. Applied Radiation and Isotopes*, vol. 3, pp. 172–175, 1958.
76. Sinex, F. M., J. Plazin, D. Clareus, W. Bernstein, D. D. Van Slyke, and R. Chase: Determination of Total Carbon and Its Radioactivity. II, Reduction of Required Voltage and Other Modifications, *J. Biol. Chem.*, vol. 213, pp. 673–680, 1955.
77. Moyer, J. D., and H. S. Isbell: Preparation and Analysis of Carbon-14-labeled Cyanide, *Anal. Chem.*, vol. 29, pp. 393–396, 1957.
78. Katz, J., S. Abraham, and N. Baker: Analytical Procedures Using a Combined Combustion-Diffusion Vessel. Improved Method for Combustion of Organic Compounds in Aqueous Solution, *Anal. Chem.*, vol. 26, pp. 1503–1504, 1954.
79. Biggs, M. W., D. Kritchevsky, and M. R. Kirk: Assay of Samples Doubly Labeled with Radioactive Hydrogen and Carbon, *Anal. Chem.*, vol. 24, pp. 223–224, 1952.
80. Kirsten, W.: Recent Developments in Quantitative Organic Microanalysis, *Anal. Chem.*, vol. 25, pp. 74–86, 1953.
81. Bradley, J. E. S., R. C. Holloway, and A. S. McFarlane: Assay of C^{14} in the Gas Phase as Carbon Dioxide, *Biochem. J.*, vol. 57, pp. 192–195, 1954.
82. Christman, D. R., N. E. Day, P. R. Hansell, and R. C. Anderson: Improvements in Isotopic Carbon Assay and Chemical Analysis of Organic Compounds by Dry Combustion, *Anal. Chem.*, vol. 27, pp. 1935–1939, 1955.
83. Christman, D. R., J. E. Stuber, and A. A. Bothner-By: Dry Combustion and Volumetric Determination of Isotopic Carbon and Hydrogen in Organic Compounds, *Anal. Chem.*, vol. 28, pp. 1345–1347, 1956.
84. Engelkemeir, A. G., W. H. Hamill, M. G. Inghram, and W. F. Libby: The Half-life of Radiocarbon (C^{14}), *Phys. Rev.*, vol. 75, pp. 1825–1833, 1949.
85. Bernstein, W., and R. Ballentine: Gas Phase Counting of Low Energy Beta-emitters, *Rev. Sci. Instr.*, vol. 21, pp. 158–162, 1950.
86. Eidinoff, M. L.: Measurement of Radiocarbon as Carbon Dioxide inside Geiger-Müller Counters, *Anal. Chem.*, vol. 22, pp. 529–534, 1950.
87. Brownell, G. L., and H. S. Lockhart: CO_2 Ion-chamber Techniques for Radiocarbon Measurement, *Nucleonics*, vol. 10, no. 2, pp. 26–32, 1952.
88. Zwiebel, N., J. Turkevich, and W. W. Miller: Preparation of Radioactive CO_2 from $BaCO_3$, *J. Am. Chem. Soc.*, vol. 71, pp. 376–377, 1949.
89. Barker, H.: Radiocarbon Dating: Large-scale Preparation of Acetylene from Organic Material, *Nature*, vol. 172, pp. 631–632, 1953.
90. Crathorn, A. R.: Use of an Acetylene-filled Counter for Natural Radiocarbon, *Nature*, vol. 172, pp. 632–633, 1953.
91. Arrol, W. J., and R. F. Glascock: The Conversion of Carbon Dioxide into Acetylene on the Scale of 2–20 Micromoles, *J. Chem. Soc.*, 1948, pp. 1534–1537.
92. Borkowski, C. J.: Instruments for Measuring Radioactivity, *Anal. Chem.*, vol. 21, pp. 348–352, 1949.
93. Freedman, A. J., and E. C. Anderson: Low-level Counting Techniques, *Nucleonics*, vol. 10, no. 8, pp. 57–59, 1952.
94. Christman, D. R., and A. P. Wolf: Inherent Errors and Lower Limit of Activity Detection in Gas-phase Proportional Counting of Carbon-14, *Anal. Chem.*, vol. 27, pp. 1939–1941, 1955.

95. Brown, S. C., and W. W. Miller: Carbon Dioxide Filled Geiger-Müller Counters, *Rev. Sci. Instr.*, vol. 18, pp. 496–500, 1947.
96. Henriques, F. C., Jr., and C. Margnetti: Analytical Method for Determination of Long-life C^{14}, *Ind. Eng. Chem., Anal. Ed.*, vol. 18, pp. 417–419, 1946.
97. Janney, C. D., and B. J. Moyer: Routine Use of Ionization Chamber Method for C^{14} Assay, *Rev. Sci. Instr.*, vol. 19, pp. 667–674, 1948.
98. Wolfgang, R., and F. S. Rowland: Radioassay by Gas Chromatography of Tritium- and Carbon-14-labeled Compounds, *Anal. Chem.*, vol. 30, pp. 903–906, 1958.
99. Miller, W. W.: High Efficiency Counting of Long-lived Radioactive Carbon as CO_2, *Science*, vol. 105, pp. 123–125, 1947.
100. Eidinoff, M. L.: Measurement of Radiocarbon as CO_2 in Geiger-Müller Counters, *Science*, vol. 108, pp. 535–536, 1948.
101. Verly, W. G., J. R. Rachele, V. D. Vigneaud, M. L. Eidinoff, and J. E. Kroll: A Test of Tritium as a Labeling Device in a Biological Study, *J. Am. Chem. Soc.*, vol. 74, pp. 5941–5943, 1952.
102. Payne, P. R., I. G. Campbell, and D. F. White: The Combustion of Tritium-labelled Organic Compounds, *Biochem. J.*, vol. 50, pp. 500–502, 1952.
103. Wilzbach, K. E., L. Kaplan, and W. G. Brown: The Preparation of Gas for Assay of Tritium in Organic Compounds, *Science*, vol. 118, pp. 522–523, 1953.
104. Pace, N., L. Kline, H. K. Schachman, and M. Harfenist: Studies on Body Composition. IV, Use of Radioactive Hydrogen for Measurement in Vivo of Total Body Water, *J. Biol. Chem.*, vol. 168, pp. 459–469, 1947.
105. Butler, E. B.: Counting Tritiated Water at High Humidities in the Geiger Region, *Nature*, vol. 176, pp. 1262–1264, 1955.
106. Cameron, J. F.: Measurement of Tritium in Water Samples, *Nature*, vol. 176, p. 1264, 1955.
107. Drever, R. W. P., and A. Moljk: Measurement of Tritium as Water Vapor, *Rev. Sci. Instr.*, vol. 27, pp. 650–651, 1956.
108. Swain, C. G., V. P. Kreiter, and W. A. Sheppard: Procedure for Routine Assay of Tritium in Water, *Anal. Chem.*, vol. 27, pp. 1157–1159, 1955.
109. Henly, J. W., and L. C. Schwendiman: Hydrogen Counter for Analysis of Dilute Tritium Oxide, *Radiation Research*, vol. 4, pp. 278–285, 1956.
110. Henriques, F. C., Jr., and C. Margnetti: Analytical Procedure for Measurement of Radioactive Hydrogen (Tritium), *Ind. Eng. Chem., Anal. Ed.*, vol. 18, pp. 420–422, 1946.
111. Guin, S., and A. M. Delluva: The Biological Synthesis of Radioactive Adrenalin from Phenylalanine, *J. Biol. Chem.*, vol. 170, pp. 545–550, 1947.
112. Grosse, A. V., W. M. Johnston, R. L. Wolfgang, and W. F. Libby: Tritium in Nature, *Science*, vol. 113, pp. 1–2, 1951.
113. Robinson, C. V.: A Methane Proportional Counting Method for the Assay of Tritium, *Rev. Sci. Instr.*, vol. 22, pp. 353–355, 1951.
114. Robinson, C. V.: Improved Methane Proportional Counting Method for Tritium Assay, *Nucleonics*, vol. 13, no. 11, pp. 90–91, 1955.
115. White, D. F., I. G. Campbell, and P. R. Payne: Estimation of Radioactive Hydrogen (Tritium), *Nature*, vol. 166, pp. 628–630, 1950.
116. Wing, J., and W. H. Johnston: Method for Counting Tritium in Tritiated Water, *Science*, vol. 121, pp. 674–675, 1955.
117. Glascock, R. F.: Estimation of Tritium and Some Preliminary Experiments in Its Use as a Label for Water, *Nucleonics*, vol. 9, no. 5, pp. 28–34, 1951.

118. Wilzbach, K. E., A. R. Van Dyken, and L. Kaplan: Determination of Tritium by Ion Current Measurement, *Anal. Chem.*, vol. 26, pp. 880–883, 1954.
119. Brown, R. M., and W. E. Grummitt: The Determination of Tritium in Natural Waters, *Can. J. Chem.*, vol. 34, pp. 220–226, 1956.
120. Eidinoff, M. L.: The Quantitative Measurement of Tritium: Hydrogen-Alcohol-Argon Mixtures, *J. Am. Chem. Soc.*, vol. 69, pp. 2504–2507, 1947.
121. Bradley, J. E. S., and D. J. Bush: A Simple Method for the Assay of Tritium in Water Samples, *Intern. J. Appl. Radiation and Isotopes*, vol. 1, pp. 233–234, 1956.
122. Bale, W. F., F. L. Haven, and M. L. Le Fevre: Apparatus for the Rapid Determination of β-ray Activity in Solutions, *Rev. Sci. Instr.*, vol. 10, p. 193, 1939.
123. Solomon, A. K., and H. D. Estes: The Measurement of Radioactivity in Solution, *Rev. Sci. Instr.*, vol. 19, pp. 47–50, 1948.
124. Comar, C. L.: Radioisotopes in Nutritional Trace Element Studies. I, *Nucleonics*, vol. 3, no. 3, pp. 32–45, 1948.
125. Freedman, A. J., and D. N. Hume: A Precision Method of Counting Radioactive Liquid Samples, *Science*, vol. 112, pp. 461–463, 1950.
126. Olson, A. R., W. F. Libby, F. A. Long, and R. S. Halford: An Improvement on the Quantitative Determination of Radioactivity, *J. Am. Chem. Soc.*, vol. 58, pp. 1313–1314, 1936.
127. Rose, G., and E. W. Emery: Effects of Solution Composition in a G-M Counter for Liquid Samples, *Nucleonics*, vol. 9, no. 1, pp. 5–12, 1951.
128. Loosemore, W. R.: Monitoring of Water for Fission-product Contamination, *Nucleonics*, vol. 11, no. 10, pp. 36–40, 1953.
129. Haigh, C. P.: Gamma-ray Scintillation Counting for Weak Radioactive Solutions, *Nucleonics*, vol. 12, no. 1, pp. 34–39, 1954.
130. Bale, W. F., and J. F. Bonner, Jr.: Determination of Radioactivity, in A. Weissberger (ed.), "Physical Methods of Organic Chemistry," 2d ed., vol. I, pt. II, Interscience, New York, 1949.
131. Goddu, R. F., and L. B. Rogers: Counting of Radioactivity in Liquid Samples, *Science*, vol. 114, pp. 99–100, 1951.
132. Bruner, H. D., and J. D. Perkinson: A Comparison of Iodine-131 Counting Methods, *Nucleonics*, vol. 10, no. 10, pp. 57–61, 1952.
133. Tabern, D. L., and T. N. Lahr: A Simplified Method for Determining Radioisotopes in Tissues, *Science*, vol. 119, pp. 739–740, 1954.
134. Schwebel, A., H. S. Isbell, and J. V. Karabinos: A Rapid Method for the Measurement of Carbon-14 in Formamide Solution, *Science*, vol. 113, pp. 465–466, 1951.
135. Seliger, H. H., and A. Schwebel: Standardization of Beta-emitting Nuclides, *Nucleonics*, vol. 12, no. 7, pp. 54–63, 1954.
136. Schwebel, A., H. S. Isbell, and J. D. Moyer: Determination of Carbon-14 in Solutions of C^{14}-labeled Materials by Means of a Proportional Counter, *J. Research Natl. Bur. Standards*, vol. 53, pp. 221–224, 1954.
137. Pearce, E. M., F. De Venuto, W. M. Fitch, H. E. Firschein, and U. Westphal: Rapid Determination of Radiocarbon in Animal Tissues, *Anal. Chem.*, vol. 28, pp. 1762–1765, 1956.
138. Ketelle, B. H., and G. E. Boyd: The Exchange Adsorption of Ions from Aqueous Solutions by Organic Zeolites. IV, The Separation of the Yttrium Group Rare Earths, *J. Am. Chem. Soc.*, vol. 69, pp. 2800–2812, 1947.

139. Sear, H.: A Method for Presenting Liquid Samples to the Flat Surface of a Scintillation Crystal, *Nucleonics*, vol. 11, no. 4, pp. 52–53, 1953.
140. Loevinger, R., and S. Feitelberg: Using Bremsstrahlung Detection by a Scintillator for Simplified Beta Counting, *Nucleonics*, vol. 13, no. 4, pp. 43–45, 1955.
141. Wagner, C. D., and V. P. Guinn: For Low Specific Activity: Use Scintillation Counting, *Nucleonics*, vol. 13, no. 10, pp. 56–59, 1955.
142. Hine, G. J., and A. Miller: Large Plastic Well Makes Efficient Gamma Counter, *Nucleonics*, vol. 14, no. 10, p. 78, 1956.
143. Chiang, R. S., and J. E. Willard: Effect of Density and Average Atomic Number of the Medium on the Counting Yield of Beta and Gamma Radiation in a Solution-type Geiger Counter, *Science*, vol. 112, pp. 81–84, 1950.
144. Barnes, R. B., and D. J. Salley: Analysis for Potassium by Its Natural Radioactivity, *Ind. Eng. Chem.*, *Anal. Ed.*, vol. 15, pp. 4–7, 1943.
145. Lavik, P. S., H. Harrington, and G. W. Buckaloo: Improved G-M Counter for Liquid Samples, *Nucleonics*, vol. 9, no. 6, pp. 68–70, 1951.
146. Anderson, E. C., and F. N. Hayes: Recent Advances in Low Level Counting Techniques, *Ann. Rev. Nuclear Sci.*, vol. 6, pp. 303–316, 1956.
147. Farmer, E. C., and I. A. Berstein: Determination of Specific Activities of Tritium-labeled Compounds with Liquid Scintillators, *Science*, vol. 117, pp. 279–280, 1953.
148. Hayes, F. N., and R. G. Gould: Liquid Scintillation Counting of Tritium-labeled Water and Organic Compounds, *Science*, vol. 117, pp. 480–482, 1953.
149. Hayes, F. N., E. C. Anderson, and W. H. Langham: The Role of Liquid Scintillators in Nuclear Medicine, *Proc. Intern. Conf. Peaceful Uses Atomic Energy, Geneva, 1955*, vol. 14, pp. 182–187, United Nations, New York, 1956.
150. Hayes, F. N.: Liquid Scintillators: Attributes and Applications, *Intern. J. Appl. Radiation and Isotopes*, vol. 1, pp. 46–56, 1956.
151. Basson, J. K.: Absolute Alpha Counting of Astatine-211, *Anal. Chem.*, vol. 28, pp. 1472–1474, 1956.
152. Raben, M. S., and N. Bloembergen: Determination of Radioactivity by Solution in a Liquid Scintillator, *Science*, vol. 114, pp. 363–364, 1951.
153. Audric, B. N., and J. V. F. Long: Measurement of Low Energy β-emitters by Liquid Scintillation Counting, *Research (London)*, vol. 5, pp. 46–47, 1952.
154. Hiebert, R. D., and R. J. Watts: Fast-coincidence Circuit for H^3 and C^{14} Measurements, *Nucleonics*, vol. 11, no. 12, pp. 38–41, 1953.
155. Arnold, J. R.: Scintillation Counting of Natural Radiocarbon. I, The Counting Method, *Science*, vol. 119, pp. 155–157, 1954.
156. Weinberger, A. J., J. B. Davidson, and G. A. Ropp: Liquid Scintillation Counter for Carbon-14 Employing Automatic Sample Alternation, *Anal. Chem.*, vol. 28, pp. 110–112, 1956.
157. Seaman, W.: Simple Liquid Scintillation Counter for Chemical Analysis with Radioactive Tracers, *Anal. Chem.*, vol. 29, pp. 1570–1573, 1957.
158. Hodgson, T. S., B. E. Gordon, and M. E. Ackerman: Single-channel Counter for Carbon-14 and Tritium, *Nucleonics*, vol. 16, no. 7, pp. 89–94, 1958.
159. Hayes, F. N., B. S. Rogers, and P. C. Sanders: Importance of Solvent in Liquid Scintillators, *Nucleonics*, vol. 13, no. 1, pp. 46–48, 1955.
160. Davidson, J. D., and P. Feigelson: Practical Aspects of Internal-sample Liquid-scintillation Counting, *Intern. J. Appl. Radiation and Isotopes*, vol. 2, pp. 1–18, 1957.

161. Hayes, F. N., D. G. Ott, and V. N. Kerr: Pulse-height Comparison of Secondary Solutes, *Nucleonics*, vol. 14, no. 1, pp. 42–45, 1956.
162. Guinn, V. P.: private communication (Shell Development Company, Emeryville, Calif.).
163. Ziegler, C. A., D. J. Chleck, and J. Brinkerhoff: Radioassay of Low Specific Activity Tritiated Water by Improved Liquid Scintillation Techniques, *Anal. Chem.*, vol. 29, pp. 1774–1776, 1957.
164. Kerr, V. N., F. N. Hayes, and D. G. Ott: Liquid Scintillators. III, The Quenching of Liquid Scintillator Solutions by Organic Compounds, *Intern. J. Appl. Radiation and Isotopes*, vol. 1, pp. 284–288, 1957.
165. Herberg, R. J.: Phosphorescence in Liquid Scintillation Counting of Proteins, *Science*, vol. 128, pp. 199–200, 1958.
166. Okita, G. T., J. Spratt, and G. V. Leroy: Liquid-scintillation Counting for Assay of Tritium in Urine, *Nucleonics*, vol. 14, no. 3, pp. 76–79, 1956.
167. Helf, S., and C. White: Liquid Scintillation Counting of Carbon-14 Labeled Organic Nitrocompounds, *Anal. Chem.*, vol. 29, pp. 13–16, 1957.
168. Helf, S., T. C. Castorina, C. G. White, and R. J. Graybush: Radioassay of Tagged Sulfate Impurity in Cellulose Nitrate, *Anal. Chem.*, vol. 28, pp. 1465–1468, 1956.
169. Passmann, J. M., N. S. Radin, and J. A. D. Cooper: Liquid Scintillation Technique for Measuring Carbon-14-dioxide Activity, *Anal. Chem.*, vol. 28, pp. 484–486, 1956.
170. Hayes, F. N., B. S. Rogers, and W. Langham: Counting Suspensions in Liquid Scintillators, *Nucleonics*, vol. 14, no. 3, pp. 48–51, 1956.
171. Funt, B. L.: Scintillating Gels, *Nucleonics*, vol. 14, no. 8, pp. 83–84, 1956.
172. White, C. G., and S. Helf: Suspension Counting in Scintillating Gels, *Nucleonics*, vol. 14, no. 10, pp. 46–48, 1956.
173. Okita, G. T., J. J. Kabara, F. Richardson, and G. V. Leroy: Assaying Compounds Containing H^3 and C^{14}, *Nucleonics*, vol. 15, no. 6, pp. 111–114, 1957.
174. Pringle, R. W., L. D. Black, B. L. Funt, and S. Sobering: A New Quenching Effect in Liquid Scintillators, *Phys. Rev.*, vol. 92, pp. 1582–1583, 1953.
175. Ott, D. G., F. N. Hayes, J. E. Hammel, and J. F. Kephart: Argon Treatment of Liquid Scintillators to Eliminate Oxygen Quenching, *Nucleonics*, vol. 13, no. 5, p. 62, 1955.
176. Chleck, D. J., and C. A. Ziegler: Ultrasonic Degassing of Liquid Scintillators, *Rev. Sci. Instr.*, vol. 28, pp. 466–467, 1957.

Supplementary References

Radioisotope Labeling

Ahrens, R. W., M. C. Sauer, and J. E. Willard: Hydrogen Labeling of Hydrocarbons Using Ionizing Radiation, *J. Am. Chem. Soc.*, vol. 79, pp. 3285–3286, 1957.

Atomic Energy Supplement, *J. Am. Chem. Soc.*, vol. 74, pp. 2389–2445, 1952.

Brown, L. M., A. S. Friedman, and C. W. Beckett: Bibliography of Research on Deuterium and Tritium Compounds, 1945 to 1952, *Natl. Bur. Standards Circ.* 562, January, 1956.

Brown, W. G., L. Kaplan, A. R. Van Dyken, and K. E. Wilzbach: Tritium as a Tool for Industrial and Chemical Research, *Proc. Intern. Conf. Peaceful Uses*

Atomic Energy, Geneva, 1955, vol. 15, pp. 16–23, United Nations, New York, 1956.

Crompton, C. E., and N. H. Woodruff: Chemical Syntheses of Radioisotope-labelled Compounds, *Nucleonics*, vol. 7, no. 3, pp. 49–65, 1950; vol. 7, no. 4, pp. 44–61, 1950.

Gordus, A. A., M. C. Sauer, Jr., and J. E. Willard: Evidence on Mechanisms of Halogen and Tritium Recoil Labelling Reactions, *J. Am. Chem. Soc.*, vol. 79, pp. 3284–3285, 1957.

Johnson, V. R., L. M. Brown, and A. S. Friedman: Bibliography of Research on Deuterium and Tritium Compounds 1953 and 1954, *Natl. Bur. Standards Circ.* 562, supplement 1, July, 1957.

Labeled-compound Suppliers, *Nucleonics*, vol. 13, no. 12, pp. 80–84, 1955.

Lemmon, R. M.: Radiation Decomposition of Carbon-14-labeled Compounds, *Nucleonics*, vol. 11, no. 10, pp. 44–45, 1953.

Miller, W. W., and T. D. Price: Research with Carbon-14, *Nucleonics*, vol. 1, no. 3, pp. 4–22, 1947; vol. 1, no. 4, pp. 11–21, 1947.

Rowland, F. S., and R. W. Wolfgang: Tritium-recoil Labeling of Organic Compounds, *Nucleonics*, vol. 14, no. 8, pp. 58–61, 1956.

Sayed, M. F. A. E., and R. Wolfgang: Chemical Reaction of Recoil Tritium with Gaseous Alkanes, *J. Am. Chem. Soc.*, vol. 79, p. 3286, 1957.

Schrodt, A. G., and W. F. Libby: Direct Production of Radioactive Aliphatic Hydrocarbons by Pile Irradiation, *J. Am. Chem. Soc.*, vol. 76, p. 3100, 1954.

Tolbert, B. M., N. Garden, and P. T. Adams: Special Equipment for C^{14} Work, *Nucleonics*, vol. 11, no. 3, pp. 56–58, 1953.

——— and D. Kritchevsky: Synthesis of Labeled Organic Compounds, *U.S. Atomic Energy Comm. Rept.* UCRL-1866, July, 1952.

Tritium Tracing—A Rediscovery, *Nucleonics*, vol. 16, no. 3, pp. 62–67, 1958.

Wolf, A. P., and R. C. Anderson: Radioactive Anthracene-C^{14} and Acridine-C^{14} from the Neutron Irradiation of Acridine, *J. Am. Chem. Soc.*, vol. 77, pp. 1608–1612, 1955.

Wolfgang, R., F. S. Rowland, and C. Nigel Turton: Production of Radioactive Organic Compounds with Recoil Tritons, *Science*, vol. 121, pp. 715–717, 1955.

Woodruff, N. H., and E. E. Fowler: Biological Syntheses of Radioisotope-labeled Compounds, *Nucleonics*, vol. 7, no. 2, pp. 26–41, 1950.

General

Aronoff, S.: "Techniques of Radiobiochemistry," Iowa State College Press, Ames, Iowa, 1956.

Bleuler, E., and G. J. Goldsmith: "Experimental Nucleonics," Rinehart, New York, 1952.

Cook, G. B., and J. F. Duncan: "Modern Radiochemical Practice," Oxford, New York, 1952.

Faires, R. A., and B. H. Parks: "Radioisotope Laboratory Techniques," Pitman, London, 1958.

Friedlander, G., and J. W. Kennedy: "Nuclear and Radiochemistry," chap. 10, Wiley, New York, 1955.

Hevesy, G.: "Radioactive Indicators," Interscience, New York, 1948.

——— and F. A. Paneth: "A Manual of Radioactivity," Oxford, New York, 1938.

Kamen, M. D.: "Radioactive Tracers in Biology," 3d ed., Academic Press, New York, 1957.

Libby, W. F.: "Radiocarbon Dating," 2d ed., University of Chicago Press, Chicago, 1955.

Reynolds, M. B.: Techniques for Counting Radiokrypton, *Nucleonics*, vol. 13, no. 5, pp. 54–56, 1955.

Schweitzer, G. K., and I. B. Whitney: "Radioactive Tracer Techniques," Van Nostrand, Princeton, N.J., 1949.

Siri, W. E.: "Isotopic Tracers and Nuclear Radiations," McGraw-Hill, New York, 1949.

Wahl, A. C., and N. A. Bonner: "Radioactivity Applied to Chemistry," Wiley, New York, 1951.

Yagoda, H.: "Radioactive Measurements with Nuclear Emulsions," Wiley, New York, 1949.

6

The Laboratory Characterization of Radiation

Of specific interest to the radioisotope research worker are the manipulations and techniques that are commonly used in the counting room. Since the problems met in the laboratory are those of the measurement or characterization of the radiation and shielding from it, the primary factors to be considered are those involving absorption and scattering of radiation. Much general information regarding radiation measurement is contained in Chap. 2, but the purpose of this chapter is to describe specific techniques involved in common laboratory practice. These techniques usually involve the determination of the energies of the radiation, their scattering and absorption characteristics, and the determination of the shielding required for safe work with them.

6-1. Absorption Curves

A standard technique in many laboratories in characterizing radiation is that of plotting an absorption, or attenuation, curve. Such curves are actually "transmission" curves, but the term "absorption" is quite commonly used. If an alpha or beta radioactive source is placed in a position near a detector and a thin foil of any suitable material is placed between the sample and the detector, a certain fraction of the rays will be stopped by the foil. If this foil is replaced by a thicker one, a larger fraction of the radiation will be stopped. By continuing this process with successively thicker foils, a point is finally reached beyond which no appreciable change is noted. Such a leveling off may be caused by reaching the natural background or the background of gamma radiation from the source which is not attenuated by the thin foil. In taking measurements with thick filters, difficulties are frequently encountered because of the poor statistical reliability of the measurements. Generally speaking, absorption-curve data are not precise, but valuable information can be obtained from them about the nature of the radiation from the source. They are frequently used to determine the experimental "range" for alpha and beta radiation which may be considered loosely as the thickness of filter required to stop all the radiation. Precise definitions of the terms vary for the two kinds of radiation. In practice, experimental-range values are related to the calculation of energies.

Absorption curves can be taken with either integrating or resolving detectors. The intensity of the radiation (or data proportional to the intensity) is plotted as the ordinate of the curve, with the thickness as the abscissa. Since the curve resembles an exponential curve, the usual practice is to plot the logarithm of the counting rate or rate of drift rather than the intensity values themselves. If the data are plotted on semilogarithmic paper, a straight line is frequently obtained over the major portion of the curve. There is no theoretical reason for the exponential appearance of an alpha or beta absorption curve, since their shape is determined by a compensation of several factors such as the wide angle from which the particles may be scattered into the detector, the varying path lengths of the radiation particles in the foil, and, in the case of beta radiation, the shape of the beta-ray spectrum. Many of the earlier workers expressed their data in terms of a relative absorption factor, or "stopping power." Likewise, the range of various radiations was formerly expressed as centimeters of air.

It has been known for some time that, to a first approximation, the stopping power of different materials for alpha and beta radiation is nearly independent of the atomic number and is a function only of the mass interposed in the path of the radiation. This is strictly valid only for the direct ionization processes inasmuch as other types of interactions, such as scattering phenomena, occur relatively infrequently as compared with the ionization effects. If the above assumption is made, the following relationship holds:

$$F = d \times x \tag{6-1}$$

where F = absorption factor
x = thickness of filter
d = density of filter

In typical units

$$F = \frac{\text{mg}}{\text{cm}^3} \times \text{cm} = \frac{\text{mg}}{\text{cm}^2} \tag{6-2}$$

The attenuation or absorption factor is thus proportional to the mass of the absorbing material in the path of the radiation and not to the atomic number of the material. Equal values in "mg/cm²" units, then, give equal absorption. Although many workers use terms such as "surface density" for the designation of mg/cm², the term "density thickness" has been in use in our laboratories for several years and describes the concept more adequately. An additional advantage of this term is that it may be shortened to "thickness" in common usage when no ambiguity is caused. The use of mg/cm² is particularly convenient when compensation for the absorption of various types of material, such as counter windows, air, and source covers, is being made. The term density thickness is also used to describe the thickness of the solid in a counting sample and in some laboratories to describe the thickness of a support on which a source is mounted. In practice, the density thickness may be determined either by measuring the actual thickness of the material and multiplying by its known density or more often by weighing a sample of known area. Since aluminum foils can be obtained conveniently, they are commonly used for experimental measurements of absorption. Common sets of filters may include foils from 1.7 mg/cm² density thickness (0.00025 in. thick) to 3,400 mg/cm².

In making absorption measurements, the filters are interposed one at a time until the counting rate or other measure of intensity (the apparent activity) drops to the background radiation or until the apparent activity becomes constant. If the apparent activity becomes constant significantly above the background, it may indicate that gamma radiation is being emitted from the source. Investigation of gamma-radiation characteristics with aluminum filters is usually not satisfactory; hence lead absorbers are more frequently employed.

Alpha-ray Curves. As described above, an absorption curve of alpha radiation falls off rapidly unless the radiation is well collimated. Alpha-ray curves may be plotted on semilogarithmic or linear paper. Linear plots permit the determination of the range from the intercept on the abscissa. Other techniques such as absorption by a gas are used for the determination of alpha-ray ranges and are usually more reliable than those using solid filters.

Beta-ray Absorption Curves. The data for beta-ray absorption curves are usually plotted as the logarithm of the apparent activity against the density thickness in milligrams per square centimeter. Such a curve is shown in Fig. 6-1*a*. A distinction is sometimes necessary between a curve plotted with "added absorption" and one plotted with "total absorption." The "added-absorption" curve is plotted by using the apparent activity with no aluminum or other filter present, without making corrections for absorption by the air, detector window, or other absorbing media. These corrections may be negligible for "hard" or energetic radiation but may be of considerable importance for "soft" radiation. For example, about half the radiations from C^{14} are absorbed by the window of a tube with about 3 mg/cm² density thickness.

The "total-absorption" curve includes the absorption by the sample covering, by the air between the source and detector, and by the detector window. Obviously, except for the sample covering, these factors are not involved if the sample is placed in a windowless counter. To evaluate these effects an aluminum absorption curve is plotted as described above (Fig. 6-1*b*). The density thicknesses of the window (as given by the manufacturer) and the cover are included by extending the

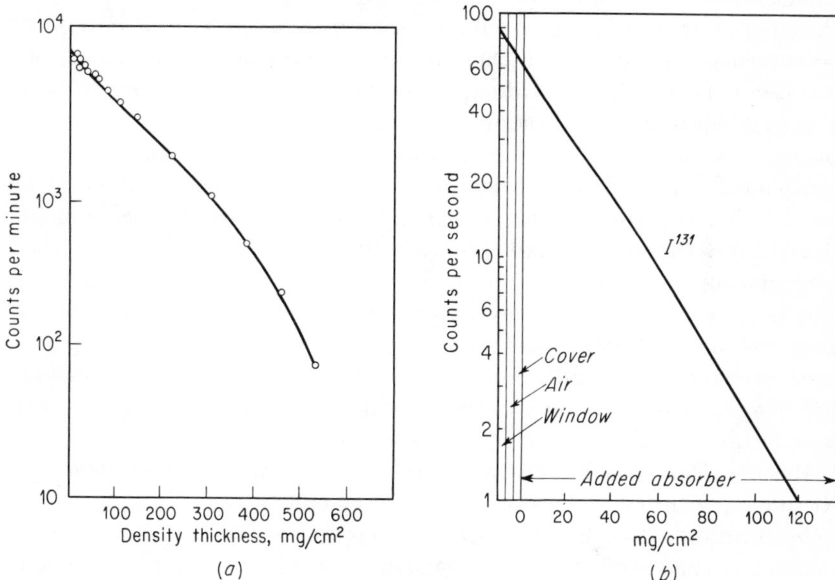

Fig. 6-1. (*a*) Beta-ray absorption in aluminum for pure-beta-emitting source. (*b*) First portion of aluminum absorption curve for I^{131}, showing the method of correction for absorption of air, counter window, and sample covering.

scale to the left from the zero thickness, or the point of no added absorber. The density thickness of the air is determined from the known density of air. The value is 1.295 mg/cm³ for dry air at STP and approximates 1.2 mg/cm²/cm path length for usual laboratory conditions. In plotting the curve the density-thickness values for the air, the sample cover, and the detector window are plotted and the curve is extrapolated with a straight line to the zero total-absorption point. Since some samples emit an inordinately high proportion of low-energy electrons, the extrapolation should usually be made from the portion of the curve between 5 and 15 mg/cm² added absorber.

Absorption curves are also used in the determination of the ratios of the apparent activity for different energy radiations at different positions relative to the detector. The ratio of the two apparent activities may vary by several per cent if one compares the gross counting rates. If extrapolated corrections are made as described above, the ratios are found to be constant for the various sources at the different positions.

For the careful measurement of radiation, one must consider the position of the absorber in relation to the sample and the detector. Zumwalt (1) has shown that, in the use of large rectangular lead filters with end-window counters, the counting rate may be changed by 20 to 30 per cent by placing the filter directly over the sample in a given geometrical arrangement rather than by placing the filter close to the counter tube window. Wide-angle scattering is considerably greater when the filter is near the source. It is a generally accepted practice to place the absorber as close to the window of the detector as possible, the sample being placed at any distance which gives a convenient counting rate. When possible, initial counting rates should be of the order of 100 to 200 times the background rate without filters. This permits satisfactory measurements to be made without using excessive counting time. The background count should be subtracted from all data before plotting, although for precise work a background count should be made with each absorber since radiation reaching the detector from the housing may vary. This is usually necessary only for thick absorbers or when contamination of the absorber is suspected.

Resolution of Absorption Curves. In many cases, semilogarithmic absorption curves (and also decay curves) are obtained which exhibit an inflection point indicating the presence of two or more components in the curve. Such complex curves can be resolved by subtracting one component of the curve from the total curve, thus obtaining simple curves which may be considered independently. Although the technique is generally applicable to curves on semilogarithmic paper, it is particularly important in the case of radioactive absorption and decay curves. Resolution into these components is frequently essential for the interpretation of the data. The same type of curve subtraction can be used to resolve absorption curves having two beta components if the energy values differ sufficiently.

A typical curve is shown in Fig. 6-2. This curve shows the presence of two components, of which one is rather easily absorbed by the aluminum filter (segment XY or components $A + B$) and the other shows little attenuation by the filters (segment YZ or component B). Component A is characteristic of a beta- (or alpha-) ray curve, and B is characteristic of gamma radiation. In the first portion of the curve, the contribution of component B is nearly constant with increasing thickness of filter but not entirely so. The second portion of the curve represents the gamma radiation after all the beta radiation has been absorbed.

This segment may be extrapolated back to the zero absorption point Z'. The contribution of component B at any thickness can be determined from the extrapolated curve. The counting rate at any point on the extrapolated gamma curve may then be subtracted from the total-activity curve, and the difference plotted. This difference curve (segment $X'Y'$ in Fig. 6-2) represents the behavior of pure component A, or

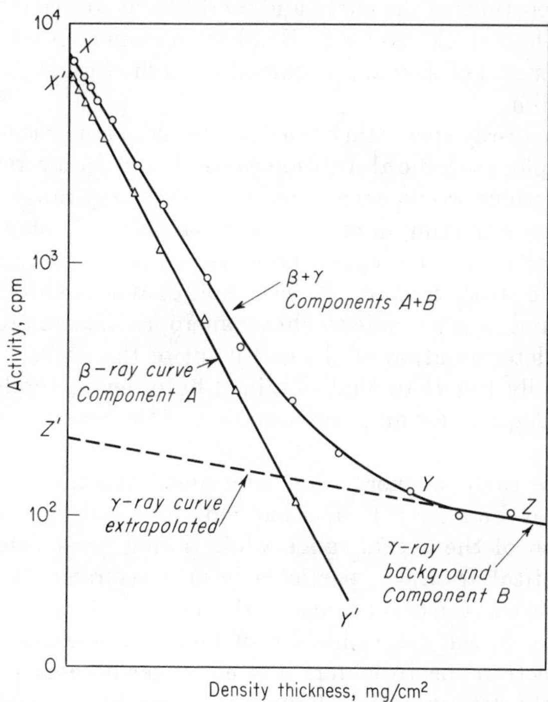

FIG. 6-2. Beta- and gamma-ray absorption curve, showing the method of resolving the two components.

the absorption curve of the beta radiation alone. This portion of the curve may be expanded in scale and replotted for greater accuracy if desired.

In principle, it is possible to resolve several components, including more than one group of beta rays, by this method. In practice, it is difficult to resolve the components unless the slopes differ by a factor of 2 or more in cases in which comparable amounts of the two components are present. There is correspondingly less accuracy when there is a disparity in the relative contributions of the components.

Determination of Beta-ray Maximum Energy from Absorption Measurements. Although the precise determination of beta-ray energy requires the use of a beta-ray spectrometer, it is frequently desirable to determine approximate values for the maximum beta-ray energy, and for this purpose one may use the absorption curve. For measurements of high beta-ray energy one can determine a "half-thickness" from the curve even though the absorption characteristics are not strictly exponential. The half-thickness value obtained varies for different portions of the curve and for different source mounts. For example, the half-thickness for RaE radiation mounted on a brass plate is about 75 per cent of the value obtained when the RaE is mounted on a thin plastic film.

Since the beta-ray spectrum has a definite end point at the maximum energy, a semilogarithmic absorption curve should drop vertically at its termination, which would correspond to the beta-ray range, i.e., thickness to stop the maximum-energy beta particles. It should also be remembered that the intercept of the curve on the abscissa has no meaning on a semilogarithmic plot. If the sample does not exhibit a gamma-ray background, it is possible to obtain an approximation to the range by a visual determination of the end point of the curve. The visual range is usually less than that obtained by other methods, but it is frequently adequate for an approximation of the maximum radiation energy.

One of the early workers who determined the ranges of various radiations was Feather (2). His methods involved the very careful determination of the actual range while taking great care to attain proper statistical accuracy, particularly in measurements made near the range. He was the first to suggest the use of a reference standard of known energy in the determination of unknown energies. With the advent of electron spectrometers it is no longer necessary to use this method for the determination of energy values, but various modifications of Feather's techniques are useful in obtaining an approximation of the beta-ray maximum energy.

By relating Feather's range values with more recently determined spectrometric values for the maximum energy, the following expression gives the range-energy relationship for the relatively few spectra which Feather examined:

$$R = 0.543E_{\text{max}} - 0.160 \tag{6-3}$$

in which the range R is expressed in grams per square centimeter and the maximum beta-ray energy E_{max} is given in Mev. This relationship holds for maximum beta-ray energies between 0.8 and 2.3 Mev.

More recently, Glendenin (3) has applied the Feather comparison technique in a simplified form and has compared the ranges and energies for a larger number of radionuclides. He also extended the values to include energies between 0.3 Mev and about 3.6 Mev. The Glendenin expressions for the range-energy relationships are as follows:

$$R = 0.542E_{\text{max}} - 0.133 \qquad \text{for } E_{\text{max}} \text{ greater than 0.8 Mev} \tag{6-4}$$

and

$$R = 0.407E_{\text{max}}^{1.38} \qquad \text{for } E_{\text{max}} \text{ between 0.15 and 0.8 Mev} \tag{6-5}$$

The units are the same as given above. The Glendenin relationships are plotted in Fig. 6-3 and are satisfactory to quite low energies.

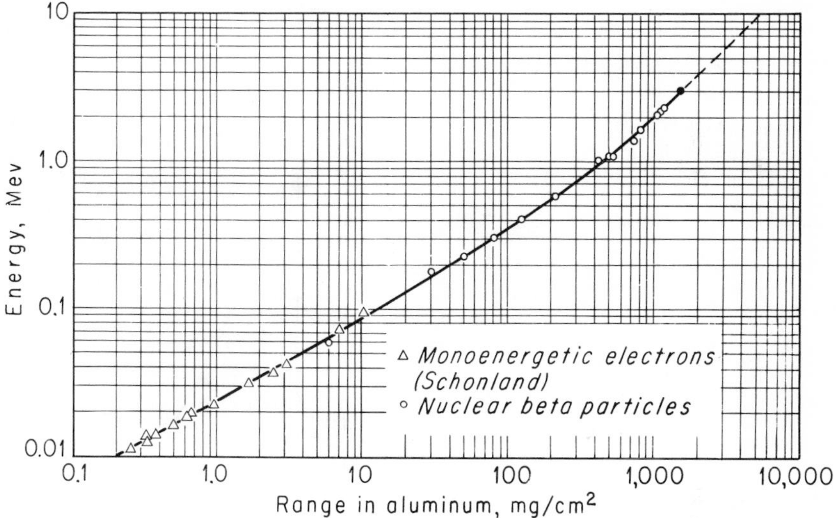

FIG. 6-3. Range of electrons of various energies in aluminum. [*From Glendenin* (3).]

The basis of the Glendenin modification of the Feather-method range determination is the assumption that the shapes of beta-ray spectra are the same. This is clearly not valid for curves of different "forbiddenness" but is frequently satisfactory for routine laboratory work. If one plots a curve of known range and energy and compares the shape with a curve of unknown range, it is possible to obtain adequate information about the predicted range without actually determining the end point. Suitable standards of known characteristics are RaE, with an E_{max} of 1.17 Mev and a range of 508 mg/cm^2, or UX_2, which has an E_{max} of 2.32 Mev and a range of 1,105 mg/cm^2. Some laboratories use P^{32}, with a maximum energy of 1.71 Mev and a range of 760 mg/cm^2, although its half-life is only 14.22 days. There are several methods in common use to make the curve comparisons and to determine the Feather range.

One of these methods is to determine the fraction by which the apparent activity of the standard curve decreases in a given fraction of the range. That is, if one uses RaE, with 508 mg/cm² as a standard, one can determine the fraction which would be transmitted by a filter of 50.8 mg/cm² density thickness. Since 50.8 mg/cm² is not an easily

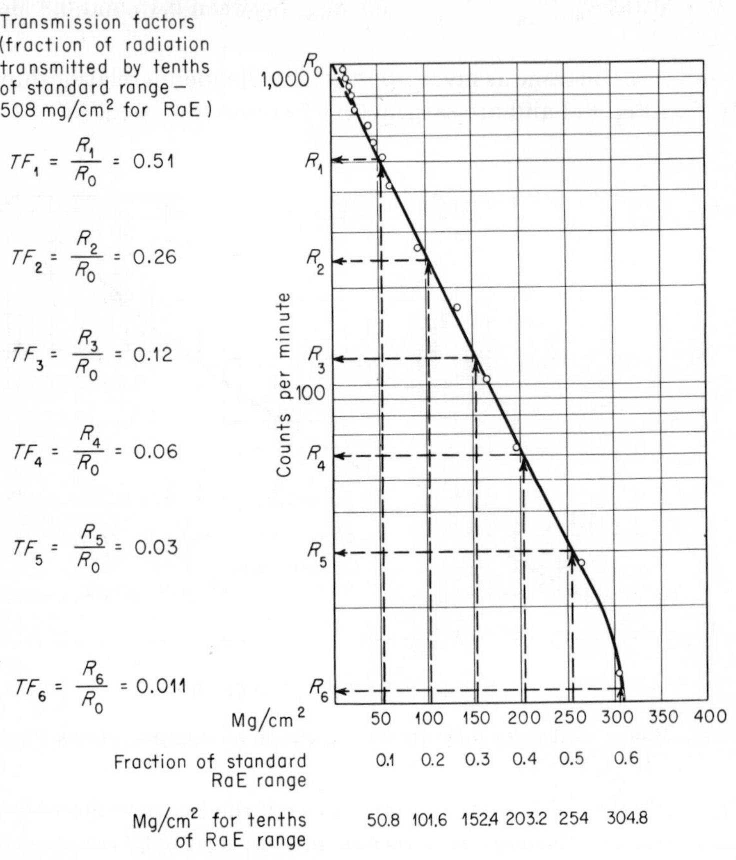

FIG. 6-4. Determination of transmission factors for absorption curve of known range (RaE range, 508 mg/cm²).

obtainable thickness of aluminum, the interpolated value can be read from the aluminum absorption curve as shown in Fig. 6-4. Depending on the geometrical arrangement of the source, filter, and detector, the fraction transmitted by this filter may be between 0.46 and 0.52. This fraction transmitted may then be called the first-tenth transmission factor. Similarly, other transmission factors may be determined from the standard curve for successive tenths of the range. Typical values are given in Table 6-1. The transmission factors are determined on the portion of the curve for which data are available. This might typically represent six or seven tenths of the range.

If a curve of unknown range is then plotted, it follows that this curve would likewise be characterized by the same transmission factors if the shapes of the two curves were the same. If the transmission factors have been previously determined, the initial counting rate may be multiplied by the transmission factors for each fraction, e.g., one-tenth.

TABLE 6-1

EXAMPLES OF TRANSMISSION FACTORS FOR RaE IN ALUMINUM

Fraction of known range, f	Mg/cm^2	Fraction transmitted (transmission factor), TF
0.1	50.8	0.51
0.2	101.6	0.26
0.3	152.4	0.12
0.4	203.2	0.06
0.5	254	0.03
0.6	304.8	0.01

TABLE 6-2

DETERMINATION OF RANGE OF RADIATION OF UNKNOWN ENERGY

Fraction f	Transmission factor TF (from Table 6-1)	Cpm	Fractional range R_f, mg/cm^2	Calculated range R_f/f, mg/cm^2
0.1	0.51	3,060	30	300
0.2	0.26	1,560	58	290
0.3	0.12	720	85	285
0.4	0.06	360	112	280
0.5	0.03	180	137	275
0.6	0.01	60	165	275

One can then determine from the unknown curve the thickness which would permit this proportion of the radiation to be transmitted. This thickness then represents one-tenth of the unknown range. For example, data might be obtained from an absorption curve of unknown energy (Fig. 6-5) which had an apparent activity R_0 of 6,000 cpm with no added absorber.

From inspection of Table 6-2, it can be seen that an average predicted range could be obtained from the values corresponding to the various tenths. However, frequently, as in the above example, the range decreases at higher fractions of the range and a more suitable method for determining the Feather range is to plot the calculated ranges against their corresponding fractions, as in Fig. 6-6. The curve is extrapolated to the tenth fraction, giving 270 mg/cm² as the Feather range for this curve. This range value may then be introduced into the

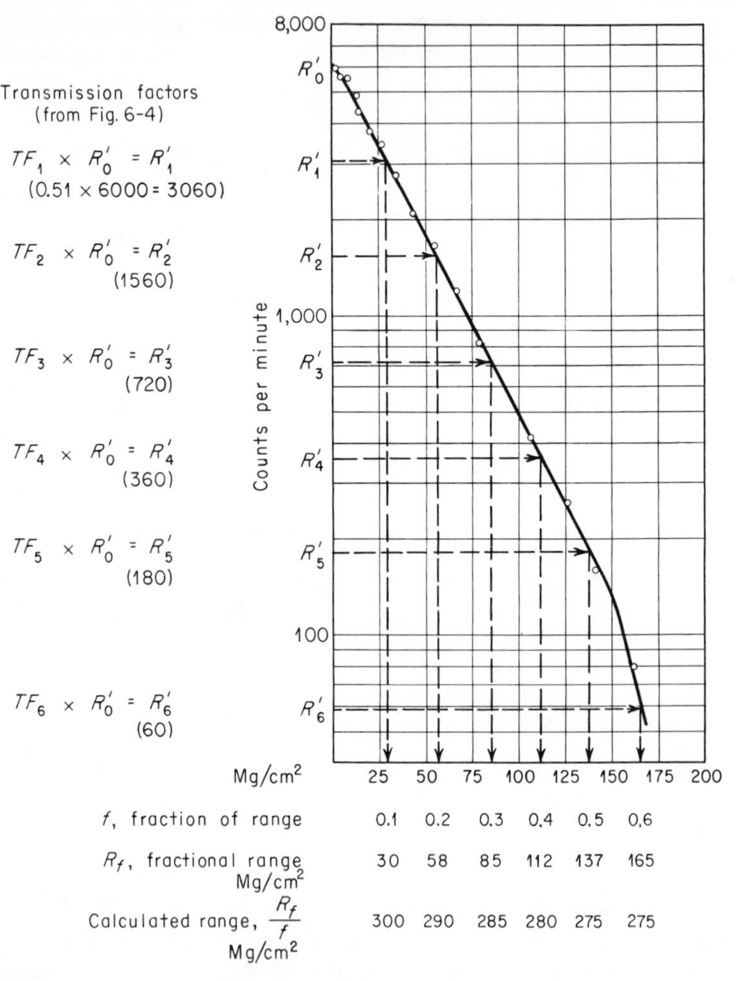

Fig. 6-5. Determination of range values predicted by various transmission factors.

Feather or Glendenin expressions, or the plot in Fig. 6-3, to determine the maximum energy (0.68 Mev in this case) of the curve of unknown energy. If the calculated range values increase during the first few fractions, one should examine the original beta-ray curve to determine if there is a lower-energy component which should be resolved.

Glendenin's original technique for obtaining Feather ranges was by use of a Feather template or analyzer. This method is quite satisfactory, although separate templates must be made for each type of graph paper, whereas the transmission factors may be applied directly to any semi-logarithmic beta-ray curve. The Feather method, using either the transmission factor or template method, might be expected to give values within 10 to 15 per cent of the accepted energy, or considerably better with care and experience. For composite beta-ray curves separate determinations should be made of each beta-ray range after the curves have been resolved into their individual components. In each case, any gamma radiation present should be subtracted before the Feather analysis is attempted.

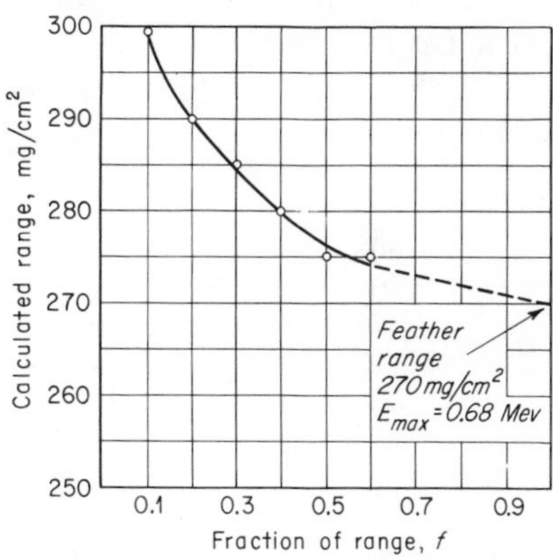

FIG. 6-6. Determination of Feather range from values derived for various fractions of range as determined by the Feather transmission-factor method.

One of the interesting more recent techniques for the determination of beta-ray maximum energies from absorption curves is one developed by Harley and Hallden (4). In this method the usual semilogarithmic absorption curves are prepared. However, instead of attempting to extrapolate in some manner to determine the end point of the curve, the slope of the curve is calculated. Likewise, the slope of a standard reference curve such as the curve for P^{32} or RaE is calculated. To a reasonable approximation the ratio of these slopes should be a measure of the relative maximum energy. Consequently, a calibration curve is prepared by plotting the logarithm of the ratio of the slopes against the logarithm of the maximum energy for various beta-ray emitters. Adequate energy determinations are possible using this method, although some anomalous results are noted by the authors. It is claimed that the technique has special advantages for certain cases, and it should be examined by an investigator interested in these problems.

An additional method for determining the range energy from an absorption curve was devised by Bleuler and Zunti (5) and is described by Segrè (6). This method is somewhat similar to the method of transmission factors described above in that it requires determinations from the absorption curve of the absorber thicknesses d_n required to reduce the counting rate by 2^n, where $n = 1, 2, 3, \ldots$. Bleuler and Zunti have published graphs that give the E_{max} as a function of each of the d_n values. This method requires a rather laborious interpolation of E_n values from the curves of $d_n = f(E_n, Z)$. Usually eight or nine points must be calculated before a satisfactory calculation is possible. There is a theoretical basis for the relationship between the nuclear-charge effect and the spectral shape, and it is possible to attain good accuracy by this method.

An interesting comparison of the above three methods and the half-thickness method (Sec. 6-4), which is a straightforward determination of the half-thickness for the radiation and its comparison with a standard or the use of an empirical relationship, is given by Duncan and Thomas (7). Table 6-3 gives some of the results of their experimental comparison of the methods.

TABLE 6-3

COMPARISON OF METHODS FOR DETERMINING MAXIMUM β-RAY ENERGIES

Method	Activity required	Approx error, %	Time involved	Use	Number of observations
Feather (template)	5,000–50,000	2–4	Fairly rapid after template constructed	When accuracy is required and high activity is available	6–10 accurately determined
Bleuler and Zunti	5,000	1–2	Slow	Most generally useful when accuracy is required	Only part of curve for 3% accuracy, but may reach 1% if 9⁄10 of curve is used
Half-thickness	Down to 200	5	Very rapid	Only when quick and rough value is required	Several observations in the first few half-thicknesses
Harley and Hallden	Can be used down to 500–1,000	5, with 2,000 cpm	Rapid	When quick estimate is required or low activity is available	4–5 observations

From Duncan and Thomas (7) the results given in the table demonstrate that fairly high accuracy is obtainable with these methods when great care is taken. However, it is evident that the determination of a precise energy value cannot be obtained by absorption methods but must be performed on a beta-ray spectrometer. For rapid laboratory work, the time involved in making the measurements and the calculations must be balanced against the accuracy required for the problem at hand.

It should be noted that in all the absorption measurements the position of the source relative to the detector and absorber is quite critical. The simplest technique is usually to make certain that the reference source and the unknown source are measured in the same relative position and that the filters are also used in the same manner in both cases. In the template method described above, the usual practice is to make a series of templates for various shelf positions. For example, one template may be prepared for "sample in second shelf, absorber in first shelf" or "sample in fourth shelf, absorber in first shelf," and so forth. It is usually considered better to place the absorber as close to the detector as possible to avoid scattering difficulties. An excellent review of the problems of determining ranges and energies by absorption methods has been prepared by Katz and Penfold (8).

6-2. Scattering of Beta Radiation

It is probable that most of the investigators in tracer laboratories make use of comparative measurements in which variations in sample mounting and positioning are controlled as much as possible. It is of some importance, however, to understand the nature of the sample-preparation variables. One of these factors is the scattering of beta radiation from the source mounting and counting chamber. There are three interrelated parameters which are most prominent in a consideration of reflection or backscattering from the source mount. These factors are the thickness and atomic number of the mounting materials and the energy of the radiation. These factors have been investigated by Zumwalt (1), Yaffe and Justus (9), and Burtt (10) with comparable results.

The investigation of the effect of the thickness of the backing material can be carried out by mounting sources on varying thicknesses of material. The counting rates with backing are then compared with the counting rates of the sample with "no" backing. The "no"-backing condition can be approximated by mounting the sample on a very thin plastic film by techniques such as those described by Fry and Overman (11). The percentage increases in counting rate with backing over measurements made with no backing are plotted against the density thickness of the backing or supporting material. Figure 6-7 shows the "build-up" of counting rate from varying thicknesses of aluminum backing.

These experiments show that a "saturation" value in the increase is reached at about 0.2 of the Feather range. This means that no further increase in counting rate is observed with an increase in backing thickness. This is called the infinite thickness for that radiation. Further, the infinite thickness is approximately independent of the atomic number of the backing material. This is to say that the infinite thickness in milligrams per square centimeter for a given radiation is approximately the same for all backing materials.

Although the thickness of backing which produces the saturation value for the counting rate is independent of the atomic number, the magnitude of the increase is quite dependent on it. For example, the infinite thickness for RaE beta radiation is about 90 mg/cm² for both polystyrene and platinum. The increase in counting rate between a thin backing and a backing with this density thickness is about 15 per cent with polystyrene, as compared with an increase of about 60 per cent in the case of a platinum support. A typical example of a curve showing the

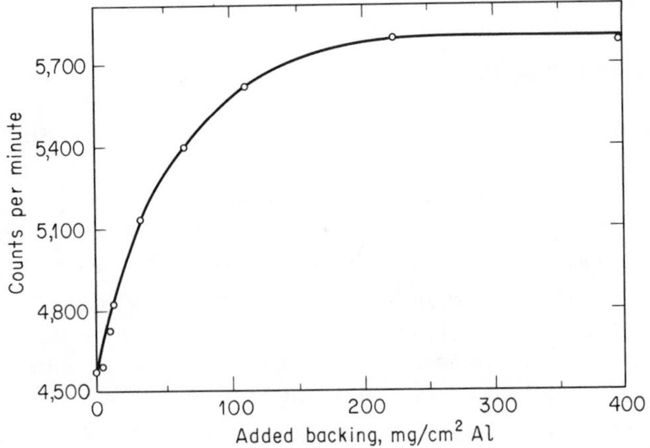

FIG. 6-7. Aluminum build-up curve; backscattering of P^{32} beta radiation.

increase in counting rate, i.e., the "build-up" as a function of the atomic number of the backing material, is shown in Fig. 6-8. (See Expt. 6-2.)

The relationship of the backscattering effect and the energy of the radiation to the type of backing material is somewhat more complex. It has been shown that there is a marked difference in backscattering effect with different radiation energies in the usual end-window counting arrangement. Typical results are shown in Fig. 6-9. For example, Co^{60}, which has a 0.3-Mev maximum energy, mounted on an infinite thickness of platinum, has about 35 per cent increase over the negligible backing measurement, whereas a P^{32} source having a 1.71-Mev maximum energy shows about 75 per cent increase under the same conditions.

These experiments were performed by taking gross measurements without compensation for the absorption effects of the counter window, the source cover, or the air between the source and window. These conditions correspond to the usual practice of making comparative or relative measurements. However, scattering corrections are more important when experiments are being conducted to determine the absolute amount of radioactivity in the sample. It is found that the

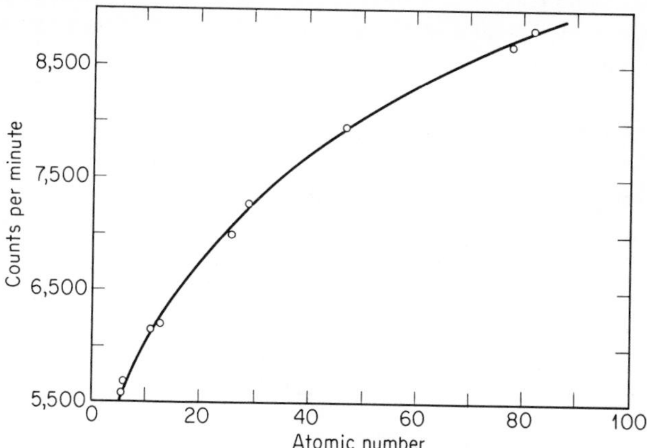

FIG. 6-8. Backscattering of P^{32} beta radiation as a function of atomic number of backing.

magnitude of the backscattering increase does change in these cases because of window, sample cover, and air absorption effects. If the absorption curve is extrapolated to compensate for the losses in these

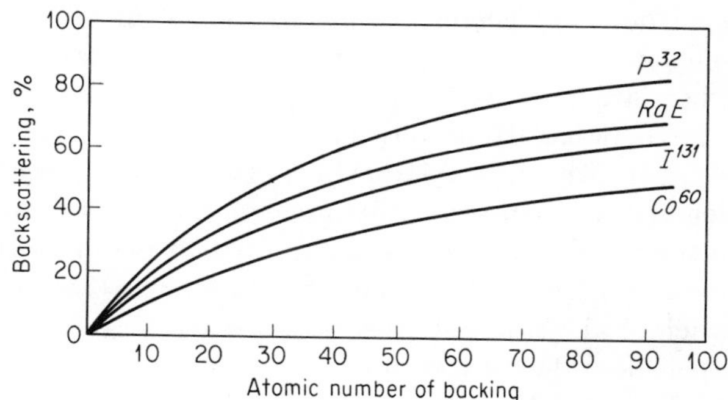

FIG. 6-9. Saturation backscattering as per cent of forward radiation for beta emitters of different energy. Air and window absorption corrections have not been applied. [*From Zumwalt* (1).]

absorbing materials, it is found that the magnitude of the backscattering effect is independent of the beta-ray energy for a given backing material. A plot of the backscattered increase at the point of zero total absorber for various materials is shown in Fig. 6-10. The difference in the effect in the two cases results from the fact that the backscattering radiation is strongly degraded in energy. Consequently, the radiation which has very low energy initially is selectively absorbed by the air and the window. The fraction of backscattered particles is considered to be approximately the same for all energies.

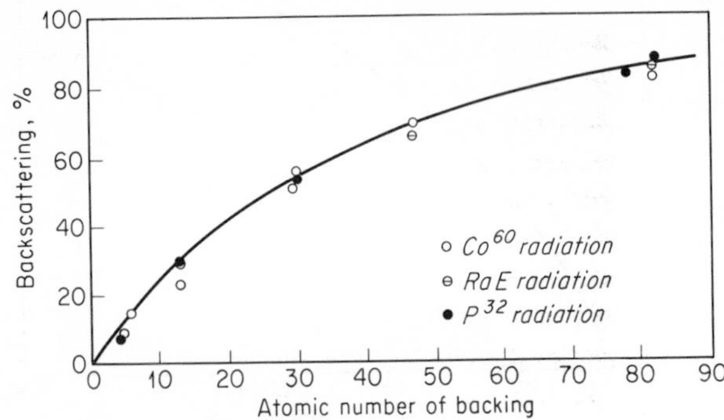

FIG. 6-10. Saturation backscattering as per cent of forward radiation for beta emitters of different energy. Air and window absorption corrections have been applied. [*From Zumwalt* (1).]

6-3. Self-absorption of Beta Radiation

It was pointed out earlier that beta radiation is characterized by having a specific range corresponding to its maximum energy. This range can be determined by the use of external absorbers as described. Such absorbers are quite useful in making corrections for air, window, and cover corrections. However, it can be seen that material in the sample itself may also be quite important in the absorption of the radiation, particularly for samples emitting beta rays of low energy. Extensive treatment of the practical techniques of dealing with absorption problems are given by Calvin et al. (12), Comar (13), Kamen (14), and Yankwich et al. (15). Self-absorption may come into play in two types of experimental circumstances.

If standard sample thicknesses can be obtained and routine comparative measurements carried out with this thickness of source, there is no problem with respect to such self-absorption. However, in many cases, several samples must be prepared which differ in the total weight of the sample, even if the concentration or specific activity of the material is the same for all samples. In other experiments, it may be possible to obtain the same amount of source material for each of several samples, but the material may be from different parts of the chemical or biological system and consequently have differing specific activity.

Compensation must be made for the amount of radiation lost in the sample itself in either case.*

One of the simplest ways of compensating for differences in self-absorption in various samples is by the use of empirical calibration curves. In both experimental situations mentioned above, these curves are prepared by making measurements on a set of samples having known density thickness. In the first case, if the series of samples is prepared having a constant specific activity, the apparent activity measured increases with increasing sample weight, as shown in Fig. 6-11*a*. The dashed line indicates the amount of activity which should be detected if no self-absorption were observed. The solid curve shows the actual apparent activity measured. The amount of self-absorption is shown by the difference between the dashed and solid curves. The thickness of the sample is increased to a point corresponding to the range of the beta particles of maximum energy. When this range is reached (it is effectively observed at about 0.75 of the Feather range), the detector measures the radiation arising only in the top layer of the source, which then appears to be "infinitely" thick. No increase in apparent activity is observed with increasing sample thickness, although the solid angle or "geometry" may vary in extreme cases, which might cause variation in measured activity. If samples are prepared and measured at infinite

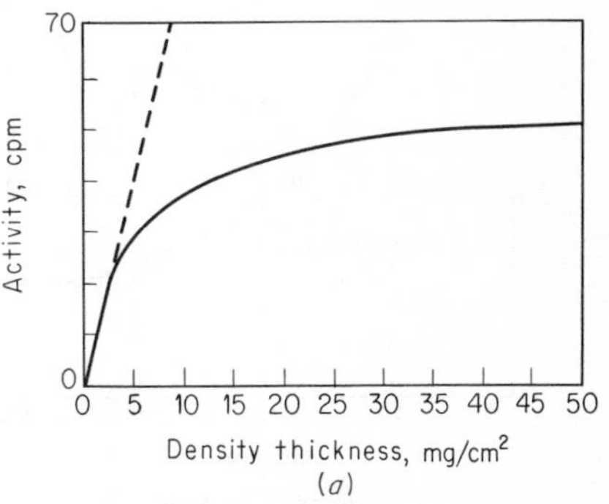

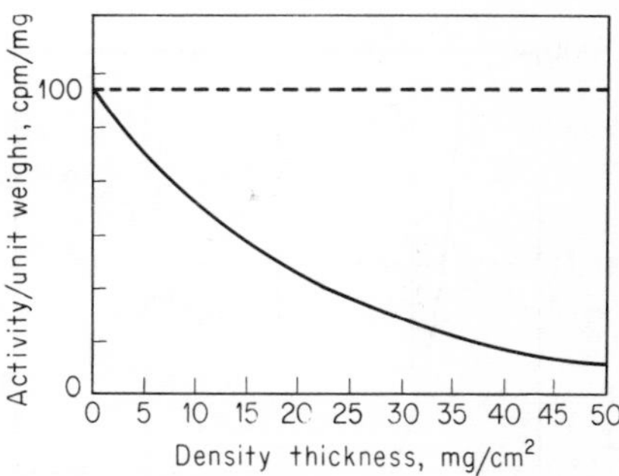

FIG. 6-11. Self-absorption curves taken with samples of (*a*) constant specific activity and (*b*) constant total activity.

* One interesting way of eliminating the need for such compensation has been used for samples of biological tissue containing low-energy beta emitters. Because of the difficulty in sample preparation and the variability in solid content of aqueous solutions, urine, blood plasma, and other fluids, a 1-in. disk of filter paper was used as the sample holder. A few drops of fluid were placed on the paper, which was then air-dried and measured at the "infinite" sample thickness. In this case, the sample absorption was negligible in comparison with the absorption of the filter paper. It is evident that this technique is not suitable unless large amounts of radioactivity are available for the samples.

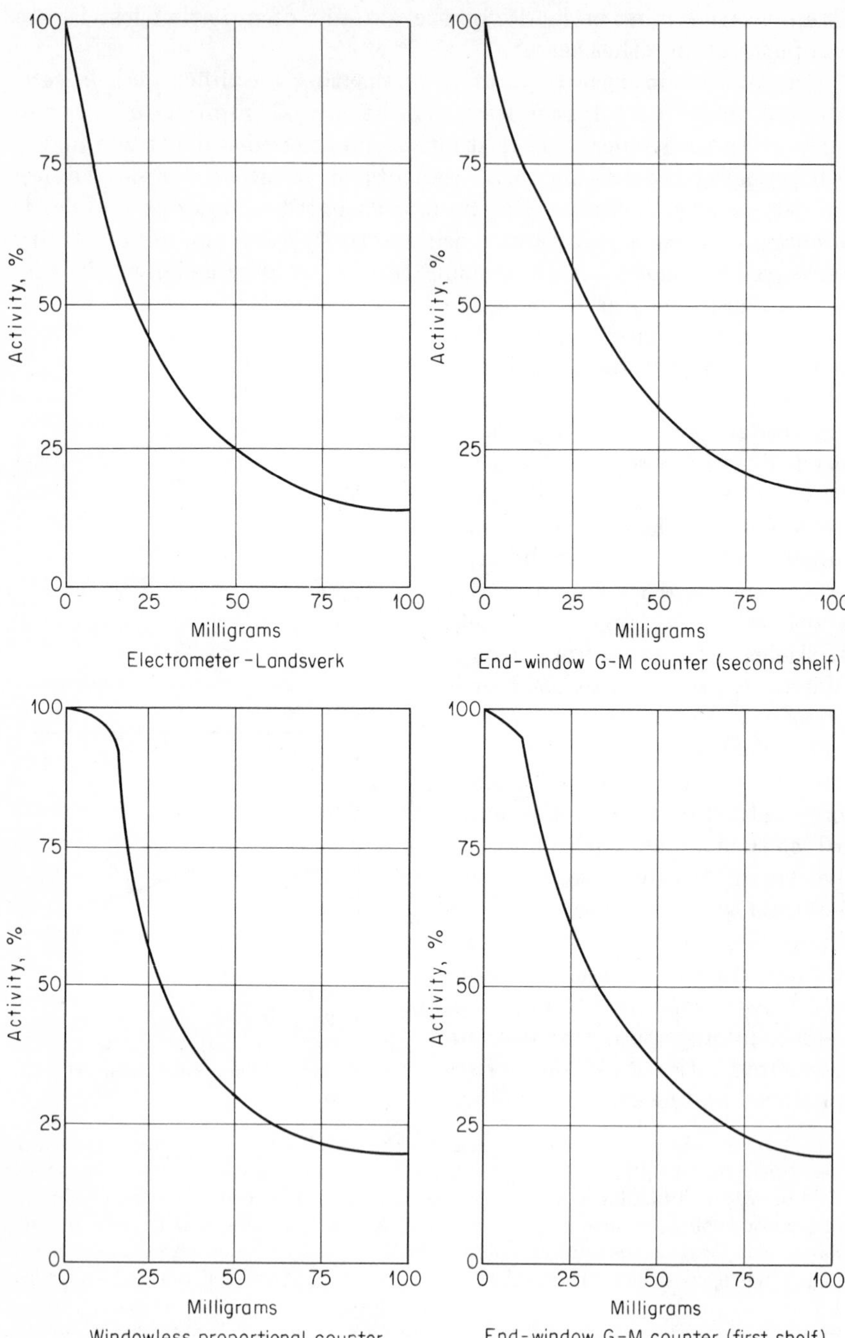

FIG. 6-12. $BaCO_3$ self-absorption curves (per cent of maximum specific activity).

thickness, the "saturation value" of the apparent activity is then proportional to the specific activity of the sample.

In the second type of experiment, a series of samples are prepared having a constant total activity in the sample but the series of samples are successively more diluted by inert material. In this case, instead of observing a constant total activity in each sample, the apparent activity decreases with increasing sample thickness, as shown in Fig. 6-11*b*. Since the samples become continuously more dilute, no infinite-thickness point is reached and the samples continue to decrease in apparent activity until the dilution corresponds to the background of the detector. A curve like Fig. 6-11*b* can be plotted directly from the data for Fig. 6-11*a* (14).

Both Fig. 6-11*a* and *b* are useful working curves for various types of experiments. Figure 6-11*a* is primarily useful for the determination of the infinite-thickness value for the radiation. If this infinite thickness is known, many experiments can be performed quite satisfactorily by making certain that the samples have this minimum thickness. This type of curve is usually less useful in working with samples that are not infinitely thick, so that it is usually better to use a curve such as Fig. 6-11*b* when working with samples thinner than infinite.

It would seem apparent that the best way of using Fig. 6-11*b* would be to express all values in terms of apparent activity at zero thickness. In some laboratories standardized curves are drawn showing the per cent of maximum specific activity as a function of thickness in order to simplify the calculation of correction factors for various samples. Unfortunately, the shape of the curve in the neighborhood of zero sample thickness is not known and varies with the position of the sample with respect to the detector and with the different types of detectors in use. Part of the variation near zero thickness is caused by the "self-scattering" of the radiation by the sample. Some of the radiation is deflected into the detector by the material in the sample. Consequently, it is extremely difficult to get precise information on the total or absolute amount of activity in a sample if self-absorption is important. Several such curves for various counting conditions are shown in Fig. 6-12.

It is apparent that the use of a "standardized curve" might be misleading unless adequate reproducibility of counting conditions is attained. The method for data treatment in many laboratories is to normalize the data about any convenient point in the experimentally obtained portion of the curve and express the apparent activity of other samples as percentages of this value. Thus, some of the correction factors would be greater and some less than 100 per cent, but it would not be necessary to extrapolate the curve to a zero thickness point.

Although most laboratory situations can be handled quite satisfactorily either by standardizing on a sample-preparation method and source or by the use of the calibration curves described above, there have been a number of attempts to work out analytical expressions for the self-absorption factors. Among the papers evaluating these factors are those by Libby (16), Aten (17), Schweitzer and Stein (18), and Gora and Hickey (19). All these workers express self-absorption factors as semiempirical absorption coefficients. The general treatment used assumes an exponential decrease in activity of the form

$$\frac{R}{R_\infty} = 1 - e^{-\mu x} \tag{6-6}$$

where R = measured activity
R_∞ = "true" activity at infinite thickness
μ = effective self-absorption coefficient (a function of range)
x = thickness of sample

If R_0 is the true activity of the samples and if it remains constant, this equation transforms to

$$\frac{R}{R_0} = \frac{1 - e^{-\mu x}}{\mu x} \tag{6-7}$$

Several of the above authors describe techniques for the determination of the self-absorption coefficient either from the self-absorption data or by use of an external absorber which are quite useful in many cases, although many laboratory workers prefer to use the experimental working curves described above. (See Expt. 6-3.)

6-4. Determination of Gamma-ray Energy

In principle, information about gamma-ray energies can be determined by absorption methods in the same manner as for beta radiation, although precise determination of the energy can be made only with a spectrometer. The availability of scintillation spectrometers, fortunately, is increasing rapidly, so that many laboratories no longer attempt to make gamma-ray absorption measurements.

The general methods of making absorption measurements are the same as outlined above for alpha rays or beta rays, although the usual filters are lead rather than aluminum since the gamma radiation is much more penetrating. The description was given above of the methods for resolving the components of absorption curves. One of the somewhat troublesome aspects of gamma-ray measurements with filters is that the gamma radiation ejects secondary electrons from the filter and in some cases the filter acts more like a "radiator" of electrons than like a filter.

One of the most important factors in the determination of even approximate energy values by absorption measurements is the relative positions of the source, filter, and detector because of the scattering of the radiation. Johnston and Willard (20) have investigated the effects of these factors. Two extreme cases might be visualized to show the effect of the scattered photons in such measurements. In one arrangement, the source, filter, and detector are spaced a great distance apart. This means that any interaction of the gamma-ray photon with the filter will remove the photon from the beam so that it is not measured by the detector. An experiment performed with this arrangement would then give the total absorption coefficient for all types of interactions for that particular energy and absorbing material. This arrangement is described as "good" geometry and is the method used for determining most of the absorption coefficients in the literature.

Unfortunately, many laboratory experiments, using standard counting arrangements and lead filters, do not correspond to this "good" geometry. Likewise, shielding arrangements, using extended or large-area sources, do not conform to this geometry, so that for many practical experiments one is not justified in using published absorption coefficients if they are determined under "good" geometrical conditions. For an extreme case, it is possible to calculate the absorption coefficient, if all the Compton photons were scattered into the detector, by subtracting the Compton scattering coefficient from the total absorption coefficient. Such a calculated curve would correspond to the "worst" geometry.

Usual laboratory experiments involve geometry arrangements intermediate between these two extremes; so properly neither data can be used. This means that one procedure would be to determine a calibration curve using samples of known energy in a particular laboratory arrangement. Variations can be demonstrated quite easily by measuring a source with a thick lead filter in one position and then merely inverting the filter in the same shelf position. Twenty to thirty per cent variation in counting rate is not unusual between the measurements made with the filter in the two positions.

It is common in usual laboratory practice to use half-thickness units rather than absorption coefficients. The half-thickness is calculated from the relation

$$X_{1/2} = \frac{0.693}{\mu} \tag{6-8}$$

in which $X_{1/2}$ is the half-thickness and μ is the absorption coefficient. Curves showing the half-thickness values for various energy radiations in aluminum and lead are shown in Figs. 6-13 and 6-14. The curves A

and B in these figures show the extremes for "good" and "bad" geometry. As noted above, with usual laboratory conditions intermediate between these extremes it is not possible to determine precise energy values for gamma radiation under such conditions from either curve. The practical problems of using half-thickness and absorption-coefficient values in the solution of shielding problems are discussed by Morgan (21).

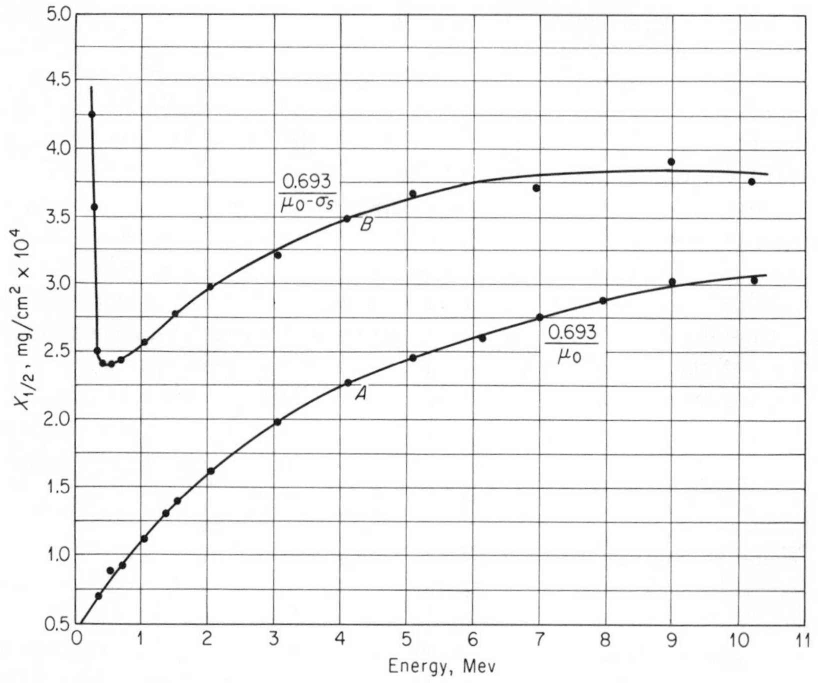

FIG. 6-13. Half-thickness for gamma radiation in aluminum. (*Calculated by R. G. Fluharty.*)

Although the half-thickness values are quite important for shielding calculations when the energy of the gamma radiation is known, it was pointed out in the paragraph above that absorption curves and the measured half-thickness values are not appropriate for the determination of precise gamma-ray energies. For this, the usual type of spectrometer employed is the scintillation spectrometer, which was described in Chap. 2. The use of the spectrometer for energy determination was mentioned in that chapter, but it is of some interest to consider this in more detail.

The gamma spectrometer consists of a scintillation crystal (usually thallium-activated sodium iodide), phototube, linear amplifier, differential pulse-height analyzer, and a counting-rate meter or scaler. Frequently automatic-recording strip-chart potentiometers are also used for ease of recording data. The instrument registers the rate of gamma interactions with the crystal which may be plotted against the pulse-height analyzer setting. This setting is proportional to the quantity of energy lost to the scintillation crystal by the incoming photon. The

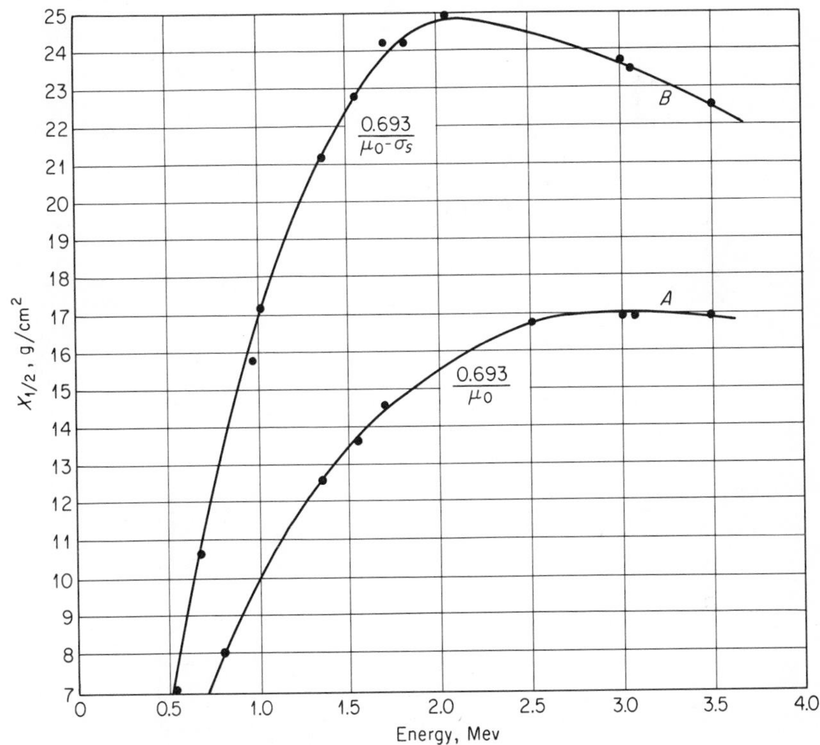

FIG. 6-14. Half-thickness for gamma radiation in lead. (*Calculated by R. G. Fluharty.*)

photopeak is found on this plot at the setting proportional to the energy of the photon. This maximum may serve to identify the nuclide emitting the gamma radiation in the sample.

As described in Chap. 1, gamma radiation interacts with matter by several processes. In the photoelectric interaction, electrons recoil in the scintillator crystal with an energy equal to that of the incident photon. This produces a maximum in the pulse-height curve which is called the photoelectric peak. In the Compton interaction, recoil electrons are produced at an energy less than the gamma-ray photon, depending on the angle of its scatter. This appears in the pulse-height

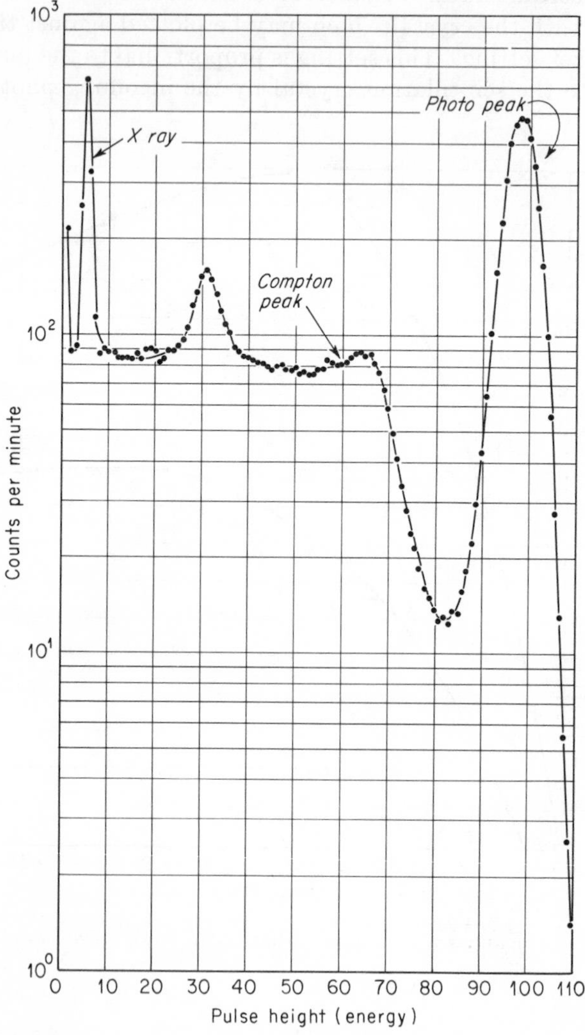

FIG. 6-15. Spectrum of Cs^{137} gamma radiation obtained with a scintillation spectrometer.

plot as a continuous distribution (usually with an indefinite maximum) ranging downward, i.e., toward low energy from the photoelectric peak. If the energy of the incident gamma ray is high, a pair-production peak may appear 1.02 Mev below the photoelectric maximum. The energy of the gamma ray usually must be 3 to 4 Mev before this is observed. A typical spectrum for Cs^{137} is shown in Fig. 6-15. This illustrates the high resolution obtainable for the photopeak and also shows the nature of the Compton continuum. The increase in apparent activity at very low energy is caused by the "noise" of the instrument.

The spectrometer may be calibrated for energy determination using any of a number of gamma-ray photopeaks from nuclides like Cs^{137} (0.663 Mev), I^{131} (0.364 Mev), Au^{198} (0.400 Mev), Cr^{51} (0.32 Mev), and Zn^{65} (1.12 Mev). As described in Expt. 6-5, the calibration may be done by setting a known energy peak at an arbitrarily determined setting on the pulse-height dial. For example, the counting rate corresponding to the 1.12-Mev photopeak from Zn^{65} may be set at a given setting such as 700 on the pulse-height dial on a typical instrument. It is important to have this setting at such a value that the range of the dial may be used for other energies. If the calibration setting is too low, the spectrum will be compressed unduly, whereas if it is chosen too high, it will not be possible to determine the positions of high-energy gamma rays. The pulse-height values are then determined for the region of the Zn^{65} peak. A sample emitting lower-energy gamma radiation, e.g., Cr^{51}, is then measured, and the pulse-height values determined in the region of its photopeak. The pulse-height values corresponding to other energies may likewise be determined, and a calibration curve is prepared by plotting the pulse-height values corresponding to the known energies against these energy values. At this particular instrument setting (voltage, slit width, and pulse height) the pulse height is then proportional to the energy. An unknown energy may be determined by measuring its pulse-height maximum and reading the appropriate value of the energy from the curve. Such a curve of pulse height vs. energy calibration is shown in Fig. 6-16.

Although these instruments are relatively new, a number of types are commercially available. They have found their way into a wide variety of applications. For example, Connally and LeBouef (22) have been able to develop it into a very useful quantitative analytical tool by calibrating the area under the photopeak for samples of known concentration. They point out that the instrument has wide usefulness in activation analysis, wear and corrosion studies of alloys, the investigation of chromatographic separations using tracers, and the studies of systems containing several radioisotopes. The device is potentially useful in any system in which it is desired to detect and measure radiation. It has found wide acceptance in clinical studies in which it is desired to make quantitative comparisons of the strengths of various sources (e.g., comparing a standard sample with the iodine uptake in the thyroid gland) where scattering effects need to be eliminated. Measurements are made by setting the instrument to register counts only in the photopeak region, since these correspond to unscattered radiation.

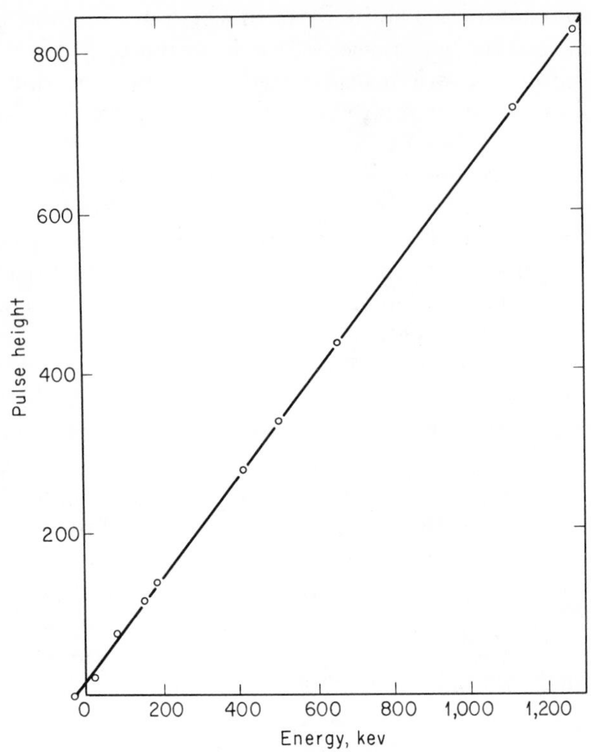

Fig. 6-16. Response curve for NaI crystal in gamma-ray spectrometer. (*From F. Bernstein, Nucleonics, vol.* 14, *no.* 4, *p.* 47, 1956.)

Experiment 6-1

Determination of Maximum Energy for Beta Radiation by Absorption Measurements in Aluminum

This experiment gives an opportunity to obtain aluminum absorption data for several radionuclides, prepare absorption curves, and analyze the data to obtain values for maximum beta-ray energies.

Apparatus and Materials

Beta counter with thin-window detector equipped for making aluminum absorption measurements

Set of aluminum absorbers (ranges from about 1 to about 3,500 mg/cm^2)

Sources of beta emitters or materials for preparation of source

A reference source or source of known range is required and also a radionuclide of "unknown" energy; suggested radionuclides are P^{32}, Bi^{210} (RaE), Co^{60}, C^{14}, S^{35}, Na^{24}, UX_2, and possibly mixtures

Procedure

As pointed out in the text, the most satisfactory simple methods for determining beta-ray energies are relative ones. Measurements should be obtained for the reference source at sample and absorber shelf positions identical with those for the "unknown" sources, since the shape of the absorption curves will depend, to some extent, on the counting arrangement.

Each available sample should be counted with no absorber and then with absorbers of various thicknesses until the counting rate is decreased to background or to a counting rate for background plus photons (X rays, bremsstrahlen, or gamma rays). Absorption of all radiation above natural background should be confirmed by a second, thicker absorber. For samples emitting photons, a sufficient number of absorption measurements should be taken to establish the slope of the photon absorption curve.

Analysis of Data

Plot each absorption curve on a separate piece of semilogarithmic graph paper having the appropriate number of cycles. In locating the origin, allow for extrapolation of the curve to the left, a distance corresponding to the total absorption in the source cover, air, and detector window.

Prepare a table of transmission or intensity-reduction factors TF for tenths of the range for the reference radionuclide (RaE or P^{32}) as described in the text. Using this table for the Feather method, find the ranges for the beta radiations of the other sources. Determine the E_{max} values corresponding to the ranges and compare with accepted values.

Estimate the E_{max} values also by graphical extrapolation of absorption curves and comparison of slopes of log-log plots of transmission curves.

Experiment 6-2
A Study of the Backscattering of Beta Rays

The dependence of backscattering on thickness and on atomic number can be illustrated easily for a given beta emitter. Comparison of the results with those for other beta emitters having different energy is discussed in the text of this chapter. Energy dependence is not a factor when comparison is made by the extrapolation method. In this experiment, backscattering factors are obtained for P^{32} or a similar energetic beta-ray-emitting radionuclide.

Apparatus and Materials

Beta-ray detector suitable for aluminum absorption measurements
Set of aluminum absorbers
Carrier-free solution of P^{32} or similar radionuclide
Micropipette and syringe
Materials for preparation of thin source backing—cast film or thin-sheet polystyrene; rubber cement or cellophane tape
Source holder designed so that various backing materials can be placed under the source
Backing materials

1. Aluminum foils in various thicknesses (preferably to provide at least 10 points between 3 and 200 mg/cm^2 and 3 or 4 points between 200 and 400 mg/cm^2)
2. Infinite thicknesses of elemental materials covering a wide range of atomic number: C (graphite), Cu, Ag, Pt, Pb, also of glàss, steel, and polystyrene
3. Polystyrene film about 5 mg/cm^2 (four or five pieces)

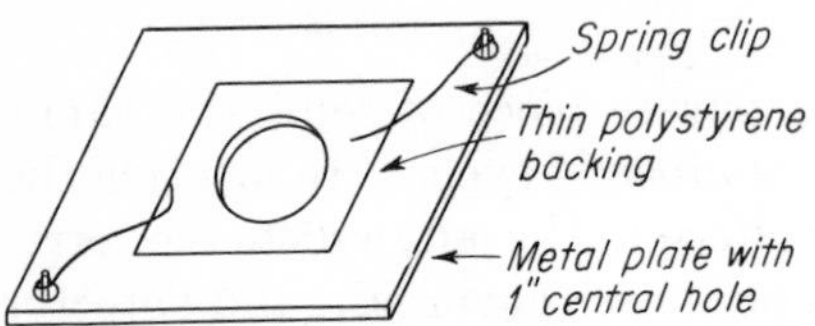

FIG. 6-17. Source holder for backscattering measurements (bottom view).

Procedure

Prepare the source mount using a holder as shown in Fig. 6-17.

Remove spring clips by loosening and withdrawing the mounting screws. Fasten a piece of thin (not over 1.5 mg/cm^2) polystyrene sheet to the bottom surface of the plate or card using cellophane tape or rubber cement as follows:

1. Apply rubber cement to the card covering an area as large as the piece of polystyrene.
2. Allow the cement to dry.
3. Cement on the piece of polystyrene, stretching it tight to remove any wrinkles in the region of the 1-in. opening.

Place the plate, with polystyrene film underneath, on a hard, smooth (uncontaminated) surface and make two concentric wax rings (as large in diameter as possible) on the upper surface of the polystyrene with a glass-marking pencil. As described in Chap. 5 on preparation of sources, these wax rings are used to confine the droplet of liquid to be dried on the polystyrene.

Using a suitable micropipette, transfer a portion of the P^{32} solution to the center of the top side of the mount which has been positioned under a heat lamp. If more than 100 λ is required, it is preferable to add the excess in subsequent aliquots to avoid contamination of the metal card, which will result if the droplet overflows the confining rings. The sample should be dried slowly with the heat lamp—at a distance far enough away to avoid softening the polystyrene. Use ammonia vapor to neutralize the last trace of acid when the deposit appears to be dry.

When the source has been thoroughly dried, cement a second piece of thin polystyrene as a cover on the top of the card over the 1-in. hole. If the thickness of the thin polystyrene backing is not known, it should be measured (weight and area) from a large enough piece of the same material to give an accurate value.

When adding backing material, care should be taken to avoid disturbing the thin backing supporting the activity, since a slight displacement of the P^{32} will change the counting yield.

Fasten the spring clips to the metal card and determine the effect of backing as follows:

1. Measure the counting rate of the source with no added backing, and then with at least one, two, three, and four pieces of 4.8 mg/cm^2 polystyrene. Allow time for the collection of 40,000 or more counts per point.
2. Measure the counting rate for various thicknesses of aluminum foil up to at least 400 mg/cm^2 (for P^{32}).
3. Measure the counting rate for saturation backing of carbon, glass, polystyrene, steel, copper, silver, platinum, and lead.
4. Obtain an aluminum absorption curve for the source without added backing and with saturation lead backing.

Analysis of Data and Report

Plot the "build-up" curve (counts per minute vs. added backing) for polystyrene and extrapolate back through the thickness of the permanent polystyrene backing to obtain a counting rate $\text{cpm}_{0,\,\text{extrap}}$ for the P^{32} without any backing.

Plot the "build-up" curve for aluminum and show where saturation thickness is effectively reached.

Calculate the backscattering factor f_B, where

$$f_B = \frac{\text{cpm}_{\text{satn backing}}}{\text{cpm}_{0,\,\text{extrap}}}$$

for each saturation backing. Plot both f_B and the per cent increase in counts per minute against atomic number of the backing. (For Pyrex glass the effective atomic number is 10.48, although this experiment permits the determination of the effective atomic number of materials for which it is not known.)

Plot the two aluminum absorption curves on the same piece of semilogarithmic paper. Also plot the difference curve. Discuss the significance of the difference between the two absorption curves.

Experiment 6-3
A Study of the Self-absorption of Beta Radiation

The constant-specific-activity and the external-absorber methods are used to evaluate beta-ray self-absorption corrections in this experiment.

Apparatus and Materials

Radiation-detection equipment, including a thin-window G-M tube or proportional tube or corresponding windowless flow-type detector
Sample of weak-beta emitters (S^{35} is used in procedure described below, but C^{14} or Ca^{45} could also be used)
Filtration device and source-preparation materials
Heat lamp
Aluminum absorbers
Graduated pipettes: 1 and 10 ml
Solution of barium chloride (0.2 to 0.5 *M*)
Labeled H_2SO_4 solution (0.110 *M*) having a counting rate of about 5,000 cpm at 10 per cent counting yield for $BaSO_4$ prepared therefrom (having a density thickness of 50 mg/cm^2)
Analytical balance
Hot water bath
Centrifuge tubes: 15 and 40 ml
Stirring rods

Procedure

Prepare eight samples in accordance with the schedule given in Table 6-4.

Add the labeled H_2SO_4 and H_2O to the centrifuge tube, heat nearly to boiling in a hot water bath, and precipitate $BaSO_4$ by adding $BaCl_2$ dropwise while stirring the liquid in a centrifuge tube. Allow the precipitate to settle, and test for complete precipitation. After several minutes of additional heating to coarsen the $BaSO_4$ precipitate, filter on previously weighed filter mounts. Attempt to obtain an even layer of solid in the filter. Wash out the excess $BaCl_2$ with a few drops of H_2O. Dry the precipitate carefully without curling the paper. (Care must be taken to avoid loosening any of the radioactive solid which would spread contamination in the counter. This may be avoided to some extent if samples are treated with a very dilute solution of collodion or other adhesive after the drying operation.) Reweigh and count the sources.

Count all samples under identical conditions for periods of time to give an acceptable σ_R (Chap. 3).

TABLE 6-4

THE PREPARATION OF $BaSO_4$ SAMPLES FOR SELF-ABSORPTION MEASUREMENTS

Nominal weight of $BaSO_4$, mg	Nominal thickness,* mg/cm^2	Vol of H_2SO_4 solution,† ml	Vol of H_2O, ml	Vol of $BaCl_2$ solution,‡ ml	Size of centrifuge tube, ml
2.5	0.5	0.1	5	1	15
5.0	1	0.2	5	1	15
10	2	0.4	5	1	15
25	5	1.0	10	2	40
50	10	2.0	10	2	40
125	25	5.0	10	5	40
175	35	7.0	10	10	40
250	50	10.0	10	10	40

* For a filter area of 5 cm^2.
† For 0.110 M H_2SO_4.
‡ Volume for $BaCl_2$ solution containing 22 mg Ba/ml.

For one of the higher-counting-rate samples, make aluminum absorption measurements and plot a complete absorption curve. If it is not feasible to obtain the absorption curve, measure the counting rate through a single aluminum absorber of thickness such that the measurements with and without absorber differ by a factor of about 2 (17).

Analysis of Data

From the known area of the $BaSO_4$ layer and the weight, calculate the thickness of each sample in milligrams per square centimeter.

Plot (1) the total activity in counts per minute against thickness and (2) the specific activity in counts per minute per milligram vs. thickness.

Examine the specific-activity plot for evidence of self-scattering for very thin samples. Extrapolate the curve to zero thickness and find the specific activity. Compare this value with the specific activity at zero thickness obtained from the initial slope of the total-activity plot.

Calculate the self-absorption correction factor:

$$f_S = \frac{\text{specific activity for finite thickness}}{\text{specific activity for (extrapolated) zero thickness}}$$

for each thickness, and plot the values as a function of thickness.

From external-absorber data, calculate μ for the S^{35} beta rays in aluminum, assuming that the absorption curve is initially approximately exponential. Assuming μ to be the same for $BaSO_4$, calculate the self-absorption correction factors over the same range as covered by the eight samples. Compare results and evaluate the limitations, advantages, and disadvantages of the external-absorber method.

If only a single absorber measurement is available, it should be used to calculate μ and to estimate the self-absorption factor.

Experiment 6-4
Determination of Approximate Gamma-ray Energies by Absorption in Lead

The purpose of this experiment is to illustrate the determination of gamma-ray energy from a measurement of a half-thickness in lead. This method is moderately satisfactory for obtaining the gamma-ray energy when a single gamma is emitted, or for obtaining the average energy when more than one gamma is emitted, or the energy of a gamma ray which greatly predominates over a variety of low-intensity photons. The effect of the geometrical arrangement of counter to scaler to absorber on the relationship between half-thickness and E_γ should be considered. Precise energy values should be determined with a gamma-ray spectrometer.

Apparatus and Materials

Radiation detector suitable for detection of gamma rays and for use of lead absorbers
Set of lead absorbers (from about 300 to about 30,000 mg/cm^2)
Prepared source of gamma radiation, e.g., Co^{60}, I^{131}, Na^{24}, Zn^{65}, or materials for such preparation

Procedure

When a source is to be prepared for measurement with a Geiger or proportional counter, prepare it at a level such that a reasonable counting rate can be obtained for the gamma rays after absorption of beta radiation.

Determine the gamma-ray counting rate for samples with each absorber interposed between the source and the detector.

Measure the background counting rate without the sample, but with a lead absorber in place. Repeat for a range of absorbers if time permits.

Analysis of Data

Examine the background measurements made with the absorbers and establish the proper background value to use for each absorption measurement, taking into account possible natural radioactivity of the lead and possible shielding of the counter by thick lead absorbers.

Correct the absorption measurements for background and plot the data on semilog graph paper. If a straight line is obtained, find the half-thickness of the radiation in lead from the slope of the line. If a curved line is obtained, resolve it into straight lines and determine the corresponding half-thickness for each component.

From a suitable graph (e.g., Fig. 6-14) of half-thickness vs. E_γ, determine the probable photon energy. If various gamma emitters of known energy are available covering a suitable range of energy, a plot for E_γ vs. $X_{1/2}$ can be obtained for the counting equipment actually used.

Report $X_{1/2}$ and μ for lead and the approximate E_γ.

Experiment 6-5
Gamma-radiation Measurements with a Scintillation Spectrometer

One recent development in the routine measurement of gamma radiation is the commercial availability of scintillation spectrometers. A number of types of single- or multiple-channel differential analyzers are available, like the so-called "medical" spectrometer designed by instrument designers at the Oak Ridge National Laboratory and commercially available from several companies. This experiment was developed by L. K. Akers of the Oak Ridge Institute of Nuclear Studies.

Apparatus and Materials

Scintillation spectrometer (medical or other single-channel analyzer) equipped with suitable scintillation detector, photomultiplier, and other accessories
Holder for radioactive source (mounted several centimeters from crystal)
Holder for small petri dish
One 10-cm petri dish
Holder for beaker of water behind source mount
One 500-ml beaker

Source of Cr^{51}, Zn^{65}, or other suitable gamma-ray emitters of known energy

A source of "unknown" gamma-ray energy

Procedure

Scattering of Radiation. Consult operating instructions for the particular spectrometer being used. Most instruments have a high voltage control, a linear amplifier gain control, and a pulse-height selector dial, in addition to a means for indicating the counting rate. They may also have a single-channel width-selector control. Instructions included here correspond to those for a medical spectrometer. A study of the operating manual will indicate the appropriate settings corresponding to those suggested. The suggested channel width for this experiment is 50 on a typical instrument. Using a sample of Cr^{51}, calibrate the pulse height by varying the high voltage and linear amplifier to the point that the 0.32-Mev photoelectron peak of the Cr^{51} falls at approximately 500 on the pulse-height dial. Place a source of Cr^{51} at a convenient (½ in.) distance above the scintillation crystal, and obtain the spectrum of the source by determining the counting rate at various pulse-height selector settings.

Place a small petri dish full of water between the source and the crystal, and again obtain the Cr^{51} spectrum. With the petri dish removed, place a beaker of water on top of the source (for backscattering of the radiation) and obtain another spectrum. Plot the spectra for the three cases on a single semilogarithmic sheet, with the counting rate on the log scale and the pulse-height reading on the linear scale.

Pulse Height vs. Energy Calibration. The spectrometer is set up as in the previous section except that it is calibrated with the Zn^{65} photoelectric peak (1.12 Mev) adjusted to approximately 700 on the pulse-height dial. Leave high voltage and amplifier gain fixed for the remainder of the experiment.

Obtain the pulse-height spectrum of Zn^{65} for the region of the photopeak only. Determine a similar spectrum for Cr^{51} (without recalibrating) in the photopeak region only. From the Zn^{65} and Cr^{51} data plot the pulse height, i.e., the reading on the pulse-height dial at the maximum counting, vs. the peak energy on linear paper. Draw a straight line through the two points determined for the energy of the Cr^{51} and the Zn^{65} photoelectric peak energies. Energies of the Cr^{51} and Zn^{65} are 0.32 and 1.12 Mev respectively.

Next obtain the γ spectrum of the source of "unknown" energy. Obtain "unknown" γ energies from the curve of pulse height vs. energy by determining the energy that corresponds to the maximum in the spectrum.

Cited References

1. Zumwalt, L. R.: Absolute Beta Counting Using End-window Geiger-Mueller Counters and Experimental Data on Beta-particle Scattering Effects, *U.S. Atomic Energy Comm. Rept.* AECU-567, 1949.
2. Feather, N.: Absorption Method of Investigating Primary Beta-particles from Radioactive Substances, *Proc. Cambridge Phil. Soc.*, vol. 34, pp. 599–611, October, 1938.
3. Glendenin, L. E.: Determination of the Energy of Beta Particles and Photons by Absorption, *Nucleonics*, vol. 2, no. 1, pp. 12–32, January, 1948.
4. Harley, J. H., and N. Hallden: Analyzing Beta Absorption Graphically to Identify Emitters, *Nucleonics*, vol. 13, pp. 32–35, January, 1955.
5. Bleuler, E., and W. Zunti: Zur Absorptionsmethode der Bestimmung von β und γ Energien, *Helv. Phys. Acta*, vol. 19, pp. 375–398, 1946.
6. Segrè, E. (ed.): "Experimental Nuclear Physics," vols. I and II, Wiley, New York, 1953.
7. Duncan, J. F., and F. G. Thomas: Three Beta-absorption Methods—How Do They Compare? *Nucleonics*, vol. 15, no. 10, pp. 82–85, October, 1957.
8. Katz, L., and A. S. Penfold: Range-Energy Relations for Electrons and the Determination of Beta-ray End-point Energies by Absorption, *Revs. Modern Phys.*, vol. 24, pp. 28–44, January, 1952.
9. Yaffe, L., and K. M. Justus: Back-scattering of Electrons into Geiger-Müller Counters, *J. Chem. Soc.*, 1949, suppl. 2, pp. S341–S351.
10. Burtt, B. P.: Absolute Beta Counting, *Nucleonics*, vol. 5, no. 2, pp. 28–43, August, 1949.
11. Fry, L. M., and R. T. Overman: The Preparation of Very Thin Plastic Films, *U.S. Atomic Energy Comm. Rept.* AECD-1800, 1948.
12. Calvin, M., C. Heidelberger, J. C. Reid, B. M. Tolbert, and P. F. Yankwich: "Isotopic Carbon: Techniques in Its Measurement and Chemical Manipulation," Wiley, New York, 1949.
13. Comar, C. L.: "Radioisotopes in Biology and Agriculture: Principles and Practice," McGraw-Hill, New York, 1955.
14. Kamen, M. D.: "Isotopic Tracers in Biology: An Introduction to Tracer Methodology," 3d ed., Academic Press, New York, 1957.
15. Yankwich, P. F., T. H. Norris, and J. Huston: Correcting for the Absorption of Weak β-particles in Thick Samples. General Method for use in Tracer Work, *Anal. Chem.*, vol. 19, pp. 439–441, 1947.
16. Libby, W. F.: Measurement of Radioactive Tracers, Particularly C^{14}, S^{35}, T, and Other Longer-lived Low-energy Activities, *Anal. Chem.*, vol. 19, pp. 2–6, January, 1947.
17. Aten, A. H. W., Jr.: Corrections for Beta-particle Self-absorption, *Nucleonics*, vol. 6, no. 1, pp. 68–74, January, 1950.
18. Schweitzer, G. K., and B. R. Stein: Measuring Solid Samples of Low-energy Beta Emitters, *Nucleonics*, vol. 7, no. 3, pp. 65–72, September, 1950.
19. Gora, E. K., and F. C. Hickey: Self-absorption Correction in $Carbon^{14}$ Counting, *Anal. Chem.*, vol. 26, pp. 1158–1161, 1954.
20. Johnston, F., and J. E. Willard: Effect of Absorber Position on Counting Rate of Collimated and Uncollimated Beta and Gamma Radiation, *Science*, vol. 109, pp. 11–12, 1949.
21. Morgan, G. W.: Some Practical Considerations in Radiation Shielding, U.S. Atomic Energy Commission, Isotopes Division Circular B-4, Oak Ridge, Tenn., 1948.

22. Connally, R. E., and M. B. Leboeuf: Analysis of Radionuclide Mixtures Using a Gamma-Beta Scintillation Spectrometer, *Anal. Chem.*, vol. 25, pp. 1095–1100, 1953.

Supplementary References

Armstrong, W. D., and J. Schubert: Determination of Radioactive Carbon in Solid Samples, *Anal. Chem.*, vol. 20, pp. 270–271, March, 1948.

Brownell, G. L.: Interaction of Phosphorus-32 Beta Rays with Matter, *Nucleonics*, vol. 10, no. 6, pp. 30–35, June, 1952.

Henriques, F. C., Jr., and C. Margnetti: Radioactive Studies, *Ind. Eng. Chem., Anal. Ed.*, vol. 18, pp. 476–478, June, 1946.

Kohman, T. P.: Measurement Techniques of Applied Radiochemistry, *Anal. Chem.*, vol. 21, pp. 352–364, 1949.

Larson, F. C., A. R. Maass, C. V. Robinson, and E. S. Gordon: Self-absorption of Sulfur-35 Radiation in Barium Sulfate, *Anal. Chem.*, vol. 21, pp. 1206–1207, 1949.

Marinelli, L. D., R. F. Brinckerhoff, and G. J. Hine: Average Energy of Beta-rays Emitted by Radioactive Isotopes, *Revs. Modern Phys.*, vol. 19, pp. 25–28, January, 1947.

Rosenblum, S.: Recent Progress in Alpha-ray Spectroscopy, *Nucleonics*, vol. 4, no. 3, pp. 38–42, March, 1949.

Schonland, B. F. J.: The Passage of Cathode Rays through Matter, *Proc. Roy. Soc.* (*London*), vol. 104A, pp. 235–247, 1923.

Wick, A. N., H. M. Barnet, and N. Ackerman: Self-absorption Curves of Carbon-14 Labeled Barium Carbonate, Glucose, and Fatty Acids, *Anal. Chem.*, vol. 21, pp. 1511–1513, 1949.

Yaffee, L., and K. M. Justus: Erratum: A Rapid Method for the Determination of the Maximum Energies of β-emitters with Simple Spectra, *Phys. Rev.*, vol. 74, p. 850, Oct. 15, 1948.

Yankwich, P. E., and J. W. Weigl: The Relation of Backscattering to Self-absorption in Routine Beta-ray Measurements, *Science*, vol. 107, pp. 651–653, June 18, 1948.

7

Standardization of Radioactive Sources and Calibration of Radiation Detectors

Although most radioactivity work involves relative or comparative measurements for a series of samples, it is sometimes desirable to know the actual amount of radioactive material present. To cite but three examples, a knowledge of the actual amount is needed in the evaluation of target yields, in the estimation of the health hazard of contaminated food or drinking water, and in the use of radioisotopes for medical purposes.

The quantity of a radionuclide present in a source can be expressed as a weight, a number of atoms, or a disintegration rate. For the very-long-lived radionuclides it is often convenient to specify the weight, particularly if the chemical properties rather than the radioactivity is of interest. Usually the important information is the rate at which the source emits radiation and, in some cases, the related rate at which the source transfers energy to the surroundings. The process of determining the disintegration rate of a source is commonly referred to as the standardization of the source. The term "absolute counting" is frequently used when the measurement technique is such that the disintegration rate can be readily obtained from the observed counting rate.

The disintegration rate, which depends on the characteristic disintegration constant as well as the number of atoms of the radionuclide, is expressed in terms of curies or submultiples thereof, and the radiation dosage received by the surroundings may be expressed in terms of roentgens, rads, etc., and their submultiples. These units have been defined in Chap. 1. As discussed in Chap. 4, the radiation dose which the surroundings receive from a source depends on the type and energy of the radiation emitted and on the nature of the surroundings as well as the amount of radioactive material.

By virtue of their design and operation, certain radiation detectors are suitable for standardizing radioactive sources. Most of the detectors and counting systems used for routine work, however, must be calibrated by means of a standard source.

7-1. Standardization of Radioactive Sources

It is convenient to classify radioactive standards and the methods of standardization as primary or secondary in accordance with common practice for other types of standards. A primary method is one by which the disintegration rate of a source can be determined with equipment which does not require calibration with a standard source of radioactive material. It follows that a secondary method is one which involves equipment that has been previously calibrated. Secondary standards are standardized by comparison with primary standards, such as those prepared by the National Bureau of Standards. The Subcommittee on Standards of Radioactivity of the International Commission on Radiological Units and Measurements reported (1) in 1956: "The accuracy to be aimed at for primary radioactivity standards should be 1 percent. An accuracy of 2 percent is probably at present obtainable in some cases. To attain this objective, frequent intercomparisons between standardizing laboratories are desirable. The desirable accuracy for secondary standards is 3 percent, but for most medical purposes an accuracy of 5 percent is sufficient."

The term "reference source" is often used to describe a source which has been compared with a standard source of a different radionuclide. Long-lived reference sources are commonly used in conjunction with short-lived standards. Various long-lived simulated standards having radiation characteristics similar to those of a short-lived radionuclide have been devised (2, 3).

Summaries of the problems of standardization are given in several references (4–10). Some of the salient points are considered in this chapter.

In general it is not possible to standardize a sample accurately unless the decay scheme is known. The extent to which decay-scheme data are needed varies from one method to another. As a minimum it is necessary to know the types of transitions involved, e.g., β^-, β^+, EC, etc., and their percentage of the total decay process. Decay schemes are given in a number of nuclear-data tabulations (11–14).

Primary Methods. *$4\pi\beta$ Counting.* A 4π counter is one which completely surrounds the source. Under ideal conditions, all radiation emitted by the source enters the sensitive volume of the detector; 4π counting, especially with proportional or Geiger counters, is the method of choice at the present time for beta emitters. As an example, a National Bureau of Standards type (6) of $4\pi\beta$ proportional counter is illustrated in Fig. 7-1.

The method is applicable to beta emitters with beta radiation having an E_{max} greater than about 0.3 Mev. For beta-gamma emitters the gamma rays do not interfere, since pulses from cascade gamma rays are in coincidence with beta pulses and are not counted separately within

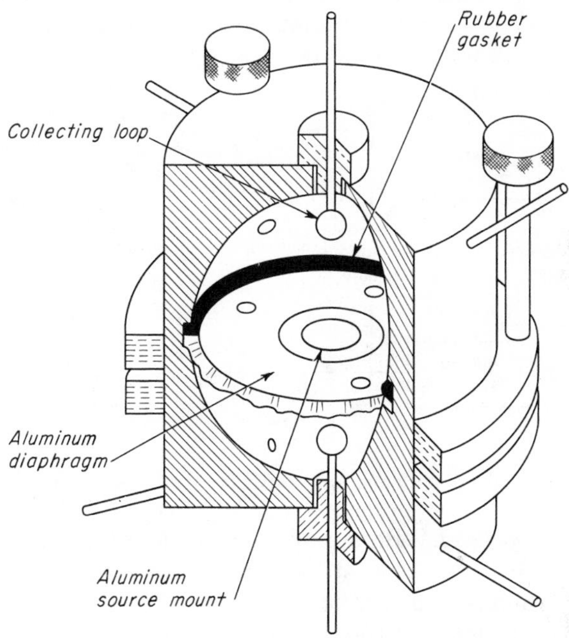

FIG. 7-1. Diagram of 4π beta counter used by the National Bureau of Standards. [*From Seliger and Schwebel* (6).]

the resolving time of the counter. In any case the counting rate is essentially equal to the disintegration rate. A knowledge is needed of the percentage of each of any additional types of transition which may occur without the emission of a negatron or a positron, e.g., EC or formation of metastable states.

Corrections must be made if the intrinsic efficiency of the counter for beta radiation (probability that a beta ray passing through the sensitive volume will interact to the extent needed to initiate a pulse) is less than 100 per cent and if absorption in the source mount and self-absorption in the source occur. An extensive study of this type of 4π counting has been made by Pate and Yaffe (15).

Crystal-scintillation counters can also be used for $4\pi\beta$ counting. A thin source of a beta emitter is placed between two beta-sensitive scintillating crystals, e.g., anthracene, which are optically coupled to separate photomultipliers. The technique is suitable for standardization of beta emitters with medium- or high-energy beta radiation, e.g., P^{32}, Sr^{90}-Y^{90}, I^{131}, Tl^{204} (16).

Another $4\pi\beta$ method is based on the use of a liquid-scintillation counter (17). The source is mounted between two very thin foils of cellulose acetate which are immersed in the liquid. Corrections are applied for absorption of beta radiation in the foils and for discrimination losses of weak pulses from low-energy beta rays.

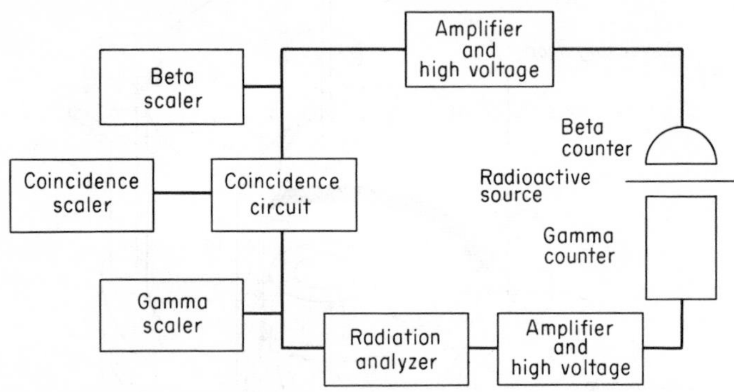

FIG. 7-2. Diagram of coincidence apparatus for standardization measurements.

Coincidence Counting. Beta-gamma coincidence counting is suitable for nuclides which have at least one beta and one gamma ray per disintegration. The method can be used only when the decay scheme is known, and it is more satisfactory for simple cases such as nuclides having a single beta and single gamma ray. The detection system is shown schematically in Fig. 7-2. The beta detector may be of any type, e.g., thin-window Geiger counter or a thin beta-sensitive crystal with photomultiplier. Its efficiency for detecting gamma rays should be low. The gamma detector may be either a high-efficiency Geiger counter or a scintillation detector. Pulses that occur simultaneously in both counters within a predetermined time (of the order of a microsecond or less apart) are counted by a coincidence circuit.

In this arrangement, the counting rate measured by the beta counter R_β is the product of the true disintegration rate A_0 and the efficiency of the beta counter ϵ_β. Likewise, the counting rate in the gamma counter R_γ is the product of the true disintegration A_0 and the gamma counter efficiency ϵ_γ. Thus

$$R_\beta = A_0\epsilon_\beta \tag{7-1}$$

$$R_\gamma = A_0\epsilon_\gamma \tag{7-2}$$

and the coincidence counting rate R_c is the true disintegration rate times the product of the two detector efficiencies:

$$R_c = A_0 \epsilon_\gamma \epsilon_\beta \tag{7-3}$$

Solving the three equations in terms of the known beta, gamma, and coincidence counting rates, the disintegration rate of the sample is given by

$$A_0 = \frac{R_\beta R_\gamma}{R_c} \tag{7-4}$$

This formulation does not include corrections for background, including gamma rays detected by the beta counter or random coincidence rates. Dunworth (18) and Mitchell (19) give details of these techniques.

This method can be accurate but is limited to a relatively few nuclides like Co^{60}, I^{131}, Na^{22}, and Au^{198}. It is not satisfactory for P^{32}, C^{14}, Tl^{204}, and other pure-beta emitters or for gamma emitters for which the decay scheme is not known.

Gamma-gamma coincidence counting using sodium iodide crystals has application in the standardization of nuclides such as Co^{60} and Na^{24} (9).

Gas Beta Counting. Beta emitters for which gaseous sources can be prepared can be standardized by the method of internal gas counting. Fortunately three important low-energy beta emitters, namely, tritium, C^{14}, and S^{35}, which cannot be standardized by the $4\pi\beta$ method are amenable to primary standardization by gas counting. Among the several possible gaseous forms are tritium, CO_2, and SO_2. The counters are the cylindrical type and are operated in the proportional or Geiger regions. External and self-absorption corrections are eliminated, but corrections must be made for end effects, which can be minimized by minimizing the gas volume beyond the sensitive volume of the counter. Within the sensitive volume the intrinsic efficiency is essentially 100 per cent. Several workers have used this method (20–22).

Weight and Isotopic Analysis. When the number of atoms N and the half-life of the radionuclide in a sample are known, the disintegration rate can be calculated from $A = \lambda N$, as discussed in Chap. 8. This method is suitable for long-lived radionuclides and has been used for naturally occurring radionuclides such as Ra^{226} since shortly after the discovery of radioactivity.

The atoms in a sample are counted indirectly by weighing the sample. Thus from the weight of a sample of a substance such as pure radium bromide the number of atoms of radium (Ra^{226}) can be calculated, i.e., the weight in grams divided by the molecular weight and multiplied by Avogadro's number. In the case of radium an early value of 3.7×10^{10}

for the radioactivity as alpha disintegrations per second of the radon in equilibrium with 1 g of radium was taken as the basis of the curie unit of radioactivity.

Primary RaD-E-F sources are prepared by the National Bureau of Standards by electrodeposition of a known amount of lead containing RaD which has been quantitatively extracted from pitchblende of known radium content (9). The lead is commonly deposited on 1-in.-diameter palladium-clad silver disks. The RaE and RaF daughters grow into secular equilibrium according to the following scheme:

$$\text{RaD }(\text{Pb}^{210}) \xrightarrow[\text{22 years}]{\text{weak beta}} \text{RaE }(\text{Bi}^{210}) \xrightarrow[\text{5.0 days}]{\text{1.17-Mev beta}} \text{RaF }(\text{Po}^{210}) \xrightarrow[\text{138.4 days}]{\text{5.3-Mev alpha}} \underset{\text{stable}}{\text{RaG }(\text{Pb}^{206})}$$

Such sources may be prepared for use as beta (RaE) or alpha (RaF) standards. When used as a beta standard it is usual practice to cover the sources with a thin (6 mg/cm^2) aluminum absorber to filter out the alpha radiation and the low-energy beta radiation from the RaD. The sample then effectively emits beta rays having an E_{max} of 1.17 Mev, but it decays with a half-life of the 22-year parent RaD.

The preparation of RaD-E-F standard sources by evaporation of RaD-E-F solution has been described by Novey (23). Zumwalt (24), on the other hand, separated RaE from the equilibrium mixture and prepared a standard RaE source rather than an RaD-E-F source.

UX_1-UX_2 beta-ray standards can be prepared from a known weight of an aged sample of pure uranium metal or oxide, e.g., U_3O_8. For a sample in secular equilibrium the number of beta disintegrations per minute per milligram of contained uranium can be calculated from the relationship

$$\text{U}_\text{I}\ (\text{U}^{238}) \xrightarrow[4.51\times 10^{9}\text{ years}]{\text{alpha}} \text{UX}_1\ (\text{Th}^{234}) \xrightarrow[\text{24.10 days}]{\substack{\text{0.100 Mev, 35\%}\\ \text{0.191 Mev, 65\%}}} \text{UX}_2\ (\text{Pa}^{234}) \xrightarrow[\text{1.175 min}]{\substack{\text{0.58 Mev, 1\%}\\ \text{1.50 Mev, 9\%}\\ \text{2.31 Mev, 90\%}}} \text{U}_\text{II}\ (\text{U}^{234})$$

Normally the weak radiation from UX_1 is filtered out by absorption and only the radiation from the UX_2 is used. Zumwalt and Norris and Inghram (25) have described the preparation of UX_1-UX_2 standards which they used as sources of beta radiation from both UX_1 and UX_2. The simplest UX_2 standard consists of a thin layer of finely ground, pure, aged U_3O_8 (see Expt. 5-1). Corrections for self-absorption and for absorption in the cover are required. Because of the high energy of the UX_2 beta radiation these absorption losses are not appreciable.

Samples containing tritium or C^{14} can be standardized by weight together with a mass-spectrometric analysis to establish the atom per cent of radioisotope present (26).

Calorimetry. The energy emission of a sample of a pure-beta emitter can be measured calorimetrically (27, 28). If the average energy per disintegration is accurately known, the disintegration rate can be obtained. The method is suitable for alpha emitters and weak beta emitters, with tritium as a particular example.

Decay-product Yield. Since the decay rate is equal to the rate of decay-product formation, measurement of the latter rate can be used to standardize a sample. There are relatively few radionuclides for which this method is convenient. One example is tritium, which has the gaseous He^3 decay product (29).

Rate of Charge Loss. The rate of emission of beta rays from a source can be determined by measuring the charge loss from a source which is electrically insulated and is suspended in a vacuum (30, 31). An electrometer, e.g., Lindemann type, is used to measure the charge loss.

2π and Low-geometry Alpha Counting. Very thin alpha-emitting sources can be calibrated by means of 2π proportional-flow counters (9). Corrections for backscattering, e.g., the order of 4 per cent making $R = 0.52A$, and self-absorption must be taken into account (32, 33). Curtis and coworkers (33) and Glover and Hall (34) have used a low-geometry proportional counter having a known geometry calculated from the dimensions of the counter. Absolute alpha counting may also be achieved through the use of an alpha-scintillation counter employing a silver-activated zinc sulfide phosphor (34).

Ion-chamber Measurement of the Specific Gamma-ray Emission of Radium. As for X radiation the dose associated with a gamma emitter such as radium can be measured by means of a free-air ion chamber. The latter is a parallel-plate chamber having suitable dimensions and operated at a pressure of air such that saturation ionization occurs in the volume of air between the electrodes. Air pressure of the order of 10 atm is necessary to ensure proper measurement for gamma rays with a chamber of reasonable dimensions.

Cavity or thimble ion chambers are also used to measure the specific gamma-ray dose from radium. The wall of this device is made of a substance such as graphite having a mass absorption coefficient similar to that of air, since the ionization of the gas in the chamber is caused by electrons ejected from the wall as well as by electrons released directly in the gas volume. Details of the methods have been described in the reference text edited by Hine and Brownell (35).

A rather recent value of 8.26 ± 0.05 r/(mg)(hr) at 1 cm for the specific gamma-ray emission of radium enclosed in a 0.5-mm platinum capsule has been reported by Attix and Ritz (36).

Secondary Methods. Once primary standard sources of a radionuclide are available, secondary standards can be prepared by comparison with the primary standards using a suitable detector. The detector is thereby calibrated in terms of the particular radionuclide. In the simplest case, where the only variable in the comparison is the source strength, the obvious relationship between the activities and counting rates (or divisions per minute, etc., for integrating detectors) of two sources is

$$A_2 = A_1 \frac{R_2}{R_1} \tag{7-5}$$

where the rates are corrected for background and coincidence losses.

An observed counting rate R and the corresponding disintegration rate A can be related by the expression

$$R = YA \tag{7-6}$$

where Y is variously known as the counting yield, detection coefficient, or over-all counting efficiency. Calibration of a detector with a standard source consists in finding values of Y for the particular radionuclide for each possible arrangement of source and detector.

In most cases the techniques involved in the secondary methods are less difficult than those of the primary methods. Many of the detectors are those commonly used for routine radioactivity measurements. The need for calibration arises because one or more factors, such as the intrinsic efficiency, the effective geometry, or the window or wall absorption, are unknown.

Whenever a primary standard material is processed in some way prior to use for calibration, precautions must be taken to avoid isotopic fractionation. As pointed out in Chap. 5, such fractionation can lead to serious errors for tritium and carbon-14-labeled material.

7-2. Calibration of Detectors

General Considerations. It is of interest to examine the various factors which cause the difference between a measured source strength and the true strength of a source in disintegrations per second. For some detectors many factors are involved, whereas for others the value of Y is determined largely by one or two factors. Zumwalt (24) has given an expression resolving Y into a number of components for the case of a Geiger counter, which is one of the more difficult detectors to calibrate correctly. The following is a modification of Zumwalt's equation to cover detectors in general:

$$Y = Gf_W f_A f_B f_C f_H f_S f_E f_G f_I f_D \tag{7-7}$$

where G = geometry factor—fraction of total 4π solid angle subtended by source and detector; for a point source at a distance d from a circular window of radius r, $G = 0.50[1 - 1/(1 + r^2/d^2)^{1/2}]$; for extended disk sources an expression has been given by Burtt (37)

f_W = factor (≤ 1) for absorption of radiation from source in air and window or wall of detector

f_A = factor (≥ 1) for scattering of radiation into detector by air

f_B = factor (≥ 1) for backscattering of radiation by source backing

f_C = factor (≤ 1) for absorption of radiation by source cover or container or support (if radiation must pass through support to be counted)

f_H = factor (≥ 1) for scattering of radiation from detector housing, shield, etc.

f_S = factor ($\gtrless 1$) for self-absorption and self-scattering in source itself; for sources sufficiently thick for self-absorption to predominate, $f_S < 1$

f_E = factor (≤ 1) for intrinsic efficiency of detector for the particular radiation; for a resolving or pulse counter, it is the probability that a particle or photon will produce a detectable interaction in sensitive volume of detector (corrections for coincidence loss depend upon R and are applied to R, not f_E); for an ion chamber, recombination lowers the value of f_E

f_G = factor (≤ 1) for end effects, etc., within detector

f_I = factor (≤ 1) for interference with operation of detector, e.g., quenching or light absorption in a liquid scintillator arising from properties of source

f_D = factor (≤ 1) for fraction of disintegrations which result in emission of the particular radiation being counted; factor is evaluated from decay scheme; if short-lived daughters are present in source, "effective" f_D for source may exceed unity

No factor has been included for the calibration of associated electronic or mechanical equipment.

Except for G and f_I, these factors depend upon the type and energy of radiation. The factor f_S, for example, is extremely sensitive to source preparation for alpha emitters; less sensitive for beta emitters, but important for weak beta emitters; least sensitive for gamma emitters. Similarly the factor f_E for a given detector varies with the type and energy of the radiation interacting with the detector.

For the $4\pi\beta$ proportional-type counter used in primary standardization, all the factors except possibly f_S, f_C, and f_D are unity. In the case of internal gas beta counting with a proportional counter, all the factors are unity except for f_G. For an end-window Geiger counter, $f_E f_G$ is essentially unity for beta rays and a few of the other factors may be close to unity, depending upon the beta-ray energy and the properties of the source.

As used above, Y involves more than the calibration of the detector itself. It involves the characteristics of the detector, the geometrical relationship between the source and the detector, and certain properties of the source itself. To include all factors in a single efficiency factor is to calibrate an over-all counting procedure for a given radionuclide rather than a detector alone. In practice this is often done because the individual factors are not known.

Consider a given detector, a standard source S of a radionuclide, and a series of sources of the same radionuclide identical with the standard in every way except for the disintegration rates. The over-all counting efficiency Y_S as determined by the standard is the same as that for any source i in the series to be standardized. Then, $A_i = R_i/Y_S$. If the sources differ in any way so as to affect the source factors, that is, f_B, f_C, f_S, f_I, and G (if the source area is not a constant), R_i must be multiplied by a correction, or normalization, factor. Such a correction factor consists of the product of ratios of those factors which are not identical with those for the standard. If, for example, the sources differ with respect to backscattering and self-absorption, the modified expression for calculating the disintegration rate becomes

$$A_i = \frac{R_i}{Y_S} \frac{(f_B)_S}{(f_B)_i} \frac{(f_S)_S}{(f_S)_i} \tag{7-8}$$

In effect, the observed counting rate, after correction for background and coincidence losses, is adjusted to a value corresponding to the rate it would have as a standard source. Actually, it is not necessary to know the absolute values for each source factor in this case, since ratios are used. The effect can be expressed relative to the conditions for or properties of the standard source. For the case of a beta standard mounted on copper but used for other sources of the same radionuclide on glass, the backscattering correction factor can be obtained by comparing sources of equal strength prepared from equal aliquots of the source material and mounted on copper and on glass. Similarly, from a series of sources of different thicknesses a self-absorption correction factor can be calculated with $(f_S)_S$ for the thickness of the standard arbitrarily taken as unity for the purpose of calculating the correction factor.

If a long-lived reference source is compared with the standard source of a shorter-lived radionuclide, any changes in the efficiency of the detector itself can be discovered by periodic measurement of the activity of the reference source. At any time, a correction can be applied by multiplying Y by the ratio of the counting rate for the reference source at the given time to the rate at the time of comparison with the standard. Such an adjustment is based on the assumption that the detector factors which are involved change equally for any radionuclide. Large correction factors, therefore, cannot be used with confidence.

When a detector is calibrated with a standard source of one radionuclide for use in measuring disintegration rates of other radionuclides, the procedure for correcting the counting efficiency is the same as that described for variable sources of one radionuclide. Errors in the correction factors may be much larger, and many more correction factors may be required depending upon the lack of similarity of the radionuclides and sources.

As indicated previously, the counting efficiency as defined above is specific for a given radionuclide. If, then, a detector is calibrated with standard sources of different radionuclides, values of Y obtained may differ markedly. Such would be the case for the calibration of a thin-window Geiger counter with sources of C^{14}, Co^{60}, and P^{32} having different areas, backings, thicknesses, covers, etc. To relate these values and compare the standards requires either normalizing two values to the third by suitable correction factors or normalizing all three to a hypothetical standard point source with all source factors except G equal to unity. In order to use such a "universal" value of Y the counting rate for any source assayed must be corrected, through knowledge of the absolute values of the f factors, to a rate corresponding to the hypothetical source. In any case, whenever the detector is replaced or modified in any way, recalibration is necessary.

The calibration of a few specific detectors is discussed in the following section. Certain detectors, e.g., $2\pi\beta$ ion chamber or 4π ion chamber, are used routinely by the National Bureau of Standards for secondary standardization (6, 9). In any case, when the necessary standard is available, the most satisfactory way to calibrate a detector is to use a standard source of the same nuclide under identical measurement conditions.

Specific Detectors. *Ionization Chambers.* Integrating ion chambers for which ion current is measured cannot be used without calibration because there is no assurance that (1) all the radiation from the source is completely absorbed in the gas phase, i.e., that none reaches the wall or collecting electrode, (2) all ion pairs are produced in a region where they can be collected, and (3) no recombination of ions occurs. For alpha particles, limitations 1 and 2 can be minimized more readily than for beta particles, especially because of the continuous energy spectrum of the latter. For gamma rays exponential absorption makes the uncertainties more troublesome.

$2\pi\beta$ CHAMBER. A $2\pi\beta$ chamber of the type used by the National Bureau of Standards is illustrated in Fig. 7-3 (6). At the time of calibration with any primary standard, comparison is made with a long-lived RaD-E-F reference source.

CHAMBERS FOR INTERNAL GASEOUS SOURCES. When a gas such as tritium or C^{14} carbon dioxide is assayed in an ion chamber, calibration is required to take into account losses which cause the ion current to be less than the maximum. These losses are the absorption of radiation in the walls, center electrode, insulator, etc., of the chamber and the recombination of the ion pairs.

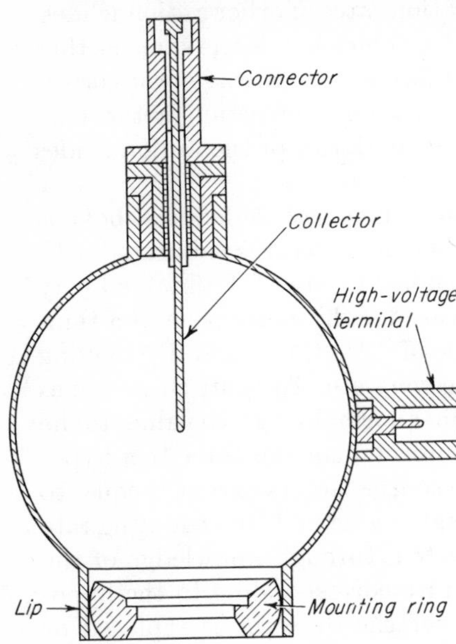

FIG. 7-3. Diagram of 2π beta ion chamber for standardization used by the National Bureau of Standards. [*From Seliger and Schwebel* (6).]

Primary standards of tritium, C^{14}, and S^{35} are available for conversion to the particular gaseous source desired.

$4\pi\gamma$ CHAMBER. Use of a $4\pi\gamma$ chamber is similar in principle to the use of a $4\pi\beta$ counter except that the shielding around the source is sufficient to stop the beta radiation. A chamber is shown in Fig. 7-4. A typical calibration procedure has been described by Jones and Overman (38). Some of these chambers have utilized argon under several atmospheres pressure to increase the gamma-detection efficiency, and a few have used sulfur hexafluoride as a filling material for the same reason.

Liquid sources with volumes in the range of 1 to 5 ml contained in glass ampoules or screw-cap vials can be compared with relatively low sensitivity to source positioning. Wide variations in sample volume may require self-absorption corrections.

The $4\pi\gamma$ ion chambers have been used to prepare secondary standards of Co^{60}, I^{131}, Au^{198}, Na^{22}, Na^{24}, Cs^{137}, and Hg^{203} (9).

ELECTROSCOPE. For a simple electroscope such as the Lauritsen type the calibration is commonly expressed in terms of units such as microcuries per scale division per minute for the source at a specified distance such as 1 m. The calibration applies to the linear-response region of the scale (see Expt. 2-1). Quartz-fiber electroscopes are most readily used for gamma-ray measurements, although thin walls permit the penetration of beta rays.

Geiger Counters or Proportional Counters. Calibration of a Geiger counter or a proportional counter for various shelf positions for a radionuclide for which a standard source is available is a relatively simple

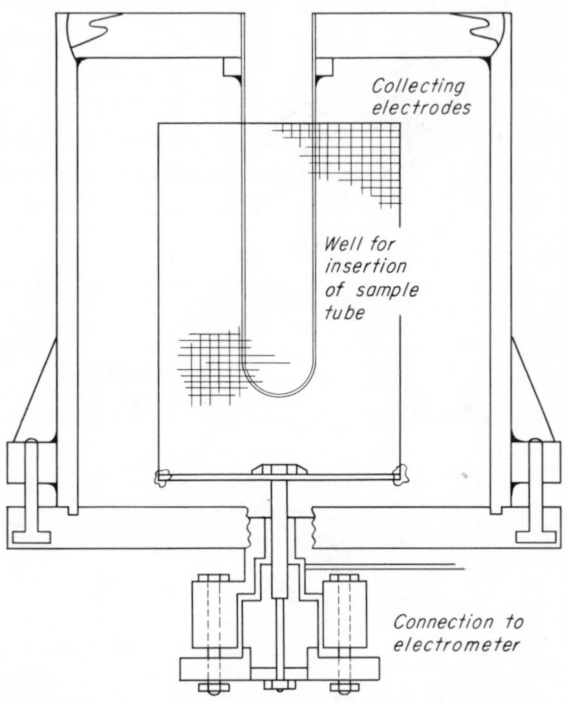

FIG. 7-4. Diagram of high-pressure 4π solid-angle gamma-ray ionization chamber. [*From Jones and Overman* (38).]

matter, as outlined above under General Considerations. The subject has been discussed in several reports, publications, and books (8, 10, 23, 24, 37, 39–41). There is a tendency, however, to calibrate a Geiger counter or a proportional counter with a standard of one radionuclide and then use the counter to find disintegration rates for all sorts of radionuclides except that used for the calibration. As mentioned previously, such practice requires the use of numerous correction factors and, in fact, it is surprising at times that a satisfactory value for a disintegration rate can be obtained after application of the necessary array of correction factors.

One typical case in which it is desirable to standardize a sample of radioactive material is in the measurement of a dose of radioactive iodine as required in many medical uses of radioactivity. The decay schemes of RaE and I^{131} are considerably different, as shown in Fig. 7-5. The techniques for correcting for absorption effects and backscattering were discussed in Chap. 6; so we may make approximate corrections for these effects by taking an absorption curve on each of the sources. If

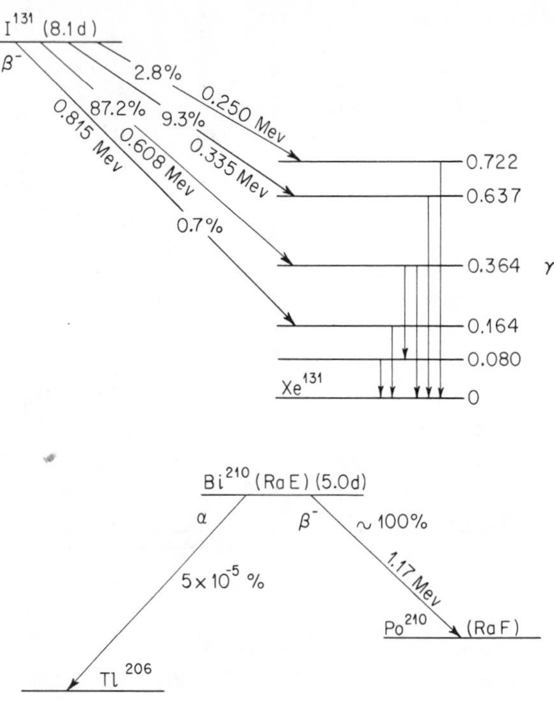

FIG. 7-5. Decay schemes for I^{131} and RaE. [*From Strominger, Hollander, and Seaborg* (13).]

both measurements are corrected to the value at zero total absorption, i.e., compensating for the air, window, and cover effects, the counting yield may be considered constant, so that direct comparison of their counting rates and disintegration rates may be made. It is apparent that fairly serious difficulties are involved in extrapolating both the RaD-E-F and I^{131} to zero total absorption, since both sources demonstrate a sharp inflection point in the first portion of the curves. The RaD-E-F curve exhibits both a high abundance of low-energy electrons from the RaD-E and usually shows a contribution from the alpha rays of the RaF daughter. The I^{131} curve exhibits the effect of the fairly large number of conversion electrons observed. A common practice in extrapolating these curves is to use as a basis the straight portion which is observed between about 5 and 15 mg/cm^2. This extrapolation was shown for I^{131} in Fig. 6-1. It is clear that both art and experience are required for successful use of this method, but it may be satisfactory to about 5 per cent accuracy. The calculations involved are described in Expt. 7-3.

A variety of standards, including the RaD-E-F standards mentioned in Sec. 7-1, can be obtained from the National Bureau of Standards and several nuclear-materials supply houses. Actually, the RaD-E-F sources are recommended only for use as long-lived reference sources in conjunction with calibration by means of a standard sample of the radionuclide of interest (9). In the example cited above, the preferable method would be to obtain a standard sample of I^{131} and compare it with an RaD-E-F source at the time of calibration with I^{131}.

The interpretation of counting data for beta-gamma emitters obtained with a thin-window Geiger or proportional counter is usually considered to be a straightforward matter. Thus, in the determination by absorption methods of E_{max} for the beta radiation of a beta-gamma emitter, the contribution from bremsstrahlung (42), annihilation radiation, and gamma radiation is subtracted graphically, as described in Chap. 6. Similarly, on the basis of absorption methods, any photon contribution is subtracted from the gross counting rate when a disintegration rate is determined by beta counting with a beta-calibrated end-window Geiger or proportional counter.

Actually, this simple subtraction procedure is not entirely correct. Gamma rays which enter the detector coincident with beta rays, within the resolving time of the detector, and cause ionization will not increase the counting rate beyond that attributable to the beta rays. When the beta rays are removed by means of an absorber, the pulse rate corresponding to the coincident beta-gamma pulses remains essentially constant, since the gamma-ray interaction still occurs. Only part of the photon counting rate, extrapolated back to zero absorber, should be subtracted from the total rate for no absorber. Further, when absorbers are used, the over-all gamma-ray response of a thin-window detector increases because the photons eject readily detected electrons from the absorber. The effect is accentuated when the absorbers are close to the detector window. For Co^{60}, for example, the build-up of secondary radiation can be recognized as a hump in the absorption curve. The over-all effect is an observed gamma contribution which is too high. When lead absorbers are used, a layer of low-Z material such as aluminum is sometimes placed between the absorber and the window to absorb the secondary electrons, although secondary electrons can be ejected from the aluminum to a lesser extent.

Since the intrinsic efficiency f_E is only about 0.01 for photons, depending upon the energy, as compared with essentially 1 for beta rays, the gamma-ray contribution measured by the absorber method in the case of beta rays having an $E_{\max}$ of at least 0.3 Mev is usually about 1 to 3 per cent. Thus for many purposes the above errors in the gamma background are second order and not serious. To take these errors into account quantitatively is not simple. Putnam (8) is one of the few authors who even mention them.

Scintillation Counters and Spectrometers. CRYSTAL TYPE. Scintillation counters (without pulse-height analyzer) are readily calibrated for a specific counting procedure by means of a standard source of the radionuclide of interest. The crystals may be NaI, with or without a well, or anthracene, for example.

For a gamma-ray scintillation spectrometer the problem is to relate some aspect of the spectrum to the disintegration rate of the source. The gamma-ray spectrum, i.e., counting rate as a function of pulse height or gamma-ray energy, for a radionuclide can be quite complex even though there may be but a single gamma ray emitted per disintegration (43–45). The complexity stems from the several types of gamma-ray interactions which can occur in a crystal of material such as NaI(Tl). Thus for high-energy gamma rays, i.e., well over 1 Mev, the spectrum can include, in addition to contributions from pair production, the Compton effect and the photoelectric effect for the incident radiation, contributions from annihilation photons, background, scattered radiation, and even summing effects for different photons interacting in coincidence. The Compton continuum, which commonly has a rather sharp edge in its high-energy side, appears on the low-energy side of the photopeak, as shown in Fig. 6-15. The pair peak appears at an energy 1.02 Mev below the photopeak and is superimposed on the Compton continuum.

Absorption of photons in NaI by the photoelectric effect, which predominates for photons having an energy less than 0.2 Mev, produces a sharp peak having a shape corresponding to that for a normal error distribution about the mean. The position of the photopeak in terms of pulse height or energy corresponds to the value E_γ, since the photon transfers all its energy to the crystal in the photoelectric effect. This peak is also known as the full-energy peak, since any sequence of interactions, e.g., multiple Compton processes, which results in absorption of the full photon energy within the resolving time of the phosphor will contribute to the peak if the pulse height per Mev is essentially independent of energy, as in the case of NaI. If some of the energy escapes from the crystal, the resulting pulse is not included under the peak. This can happen if a photoelectron produced on the surface of the crystal escapes. For low-energy incident photons in the range of 0.032 to about 0.1 Mev, some of the iodine X rays produced following the photoelectric effect can escape, causing the loss of 28 kev from the full energy and producing thereby a second small "escape" peak 28 kev lower in energy than the full-energy peak (45).

It is the full-energy peak which is used for measurement of disintegration rates as well as identification of radionuclides. The width at half-height of the peak is a measure of the resolution of the spectrometer. The half-width is proportional to $E_\gamma^{1/2}$, where the proportionality constant is characteristic of the detector. Commonly, energy resolution is expressed as the per cent of E_γ which the half-width represents. The per cent resolution varies inversely, then, as $E_\gamma^{1/2}$ and may be about 40 per cent at 20 kev, about 7 per cent at 661 kev, and about 6 per cent at 1.28 Mev.

In Eq. (7-6), R now corresponds to the counts per minute or second under the full-energy peak and is proportional to the area under the peak (corrected for background, Compton overlap, etc.). The counting yield Y includes contributions from the geometry factor G; factors such as f_S and f_C for very weak photons; f_E, which is the energy-dependent crystal efficiency; and f_D, if only a fraction of the disintegrations result in emission of the given photon.

Methods in use for determining the area under the full-energy peak are not unique for gamma-ray spectrometry. They include (1) measurement with a polar planimeter, (2) cutting out the peak shape on paper of uniform thickness (weight per unit area) and constant moisture content and weighing on an analytical balance, (3) counting squares, (4) automatic integration with a device attached to the recorder, and (5) calculation as the product of the peak height and half-width. Since the areas obtained by these methods do not agree exactly, the method chosen for routine use should be used for the calibration. The peak-height half-width method is the simplest, but the calculated area may be a few per cent less than that measured with a planimeter. Connally and Leboeuf (46) apply a correction factor for the effect of spectrometer slit width on the half-width, in addition to a normalizing factor of 1.07, to the calculated area. Other deviations from the ideal peak shape are not taken into account in the simple calculation. As an approximation for comparing counting rates for sources of a given radionuclide, the area, for constant resolution, may be taken as proportional to the peak height.

When the spectrometer is used to determine disintegration rates for radionuclides for which standard sources are available (as listed in Ref.

9), the counting yield at the full-energy peak can be obtained for each radionuclide for fixed measurement conditions without evaluation of all the component factors individually. By selecting radionuclides to provide a range of E_γ, e.g., Au^{198}, Cs^{137}, Zn^{65}, and Na^{22}, the counting yield can be evaluated as a function of E_γ, and from a plot the counting yield can be obtained for radionuclides for which standard sources are not available. This method has been used by Connally and Leboeuf (46) for the analysis of mixtures of gamma emitters.

Lazar, Davis, and Bell (47) have described a method for determining disintegration rates without the use of standard sources. It may be argued that the method qualifies as a primary one. In this method the ratio of the area under the full-energy peak to the area under the total spectrum is measured under conditions of minimum scattering for radionuclides emitting only one or two gamma rays per disintegration. This ratio is also known as the photofraction. The total efficiency $\epsilon_t(E)$ of the NaI crystal for all interaction processes is calculated from a knowledge of the total absorption coefficient (45), the diameter and thickness of the crystal, and the distance between the external source (assumed to be a point source) and the crystal surface. The peak efficiency $\epsilon_p(E)$, i.e., the probability that an incident gamma ray having energy E will cause a pulse that will fall in the full-energy peak, is then given by the product of the total efficiency and the ratio of the peak area to the total area. Curves obtained by Lazar and coworkers (47) relating peak efficiency and photon energy for NaI crystals are shown in Fig. 7-6.

Calculated values of the total efficiency and photofraction for various sizes of NaI crystals (not the well type) and for various distances between the source and the crystal have been reported in several publications (45, 48–50). Experimentally determined photofractions are generally preferred, since the calculated values are somewhat high.

The other factors needed to calculate a disintegration rate from an area and peak efficiency are the source geometry G and f_D. For the purposes of calculating G, the angle ϕ for the case of a point source located above the center of a cylindrical crystal is defined as the angle between a perpendicular normal to the plane of the top surface of the crystal at its center and the line drawn from the source to the circumference at the top of the crystal. The geometry factor is then given by

$$G = \tfrac{1}{2}(1 - \cos \phi) \tag{7-9}$$

Then

$$A = \frac{R}{\epsilon_p G f_D} \tag{7-10}$$

where f_D would correspond to the percentage of disintegrations giving rise to the gamma radiation less the amount of radiation internally converted. The method has been compared with other methods such as $4\pi\beta$ counting and has been found to agree to within 5 per cent (47). Connally (51) has applied the method to mixtures of radionuclides.

In the case of a mixture of gamma emitters it is necessary, first of all, that the component full-energy peaks be resolved. Connally and Leboeuf (46) use the criterion that the energies of the principal gamma photons must differ by more than the half-width. Secondly, because

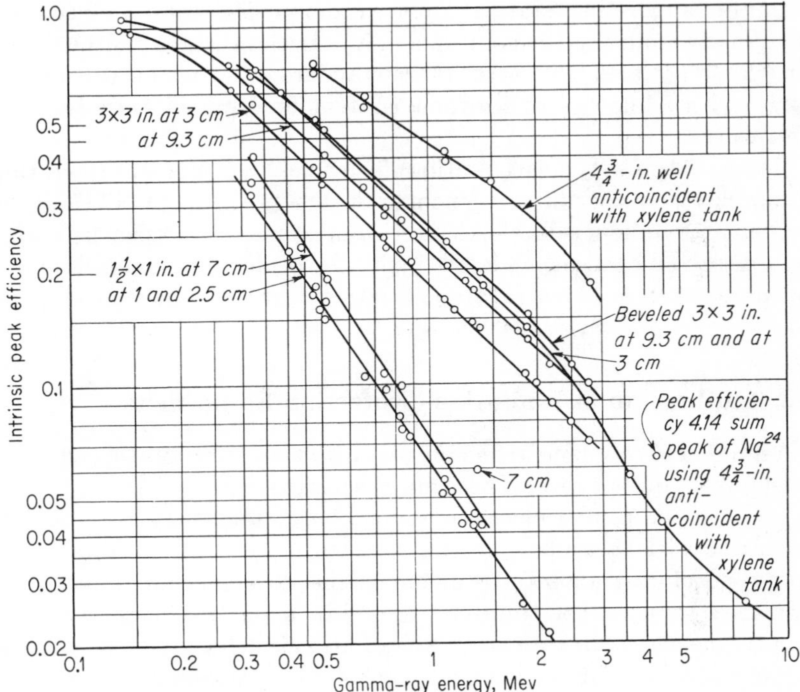

FIG. 7-6. Peak efficiency vs. energy for NaI crystals. [*From Lazar, Davis, and Bell* (47).]

the Compton continua and other minor peaks associated with the higher-energy photopeaks overlap the lower-energy photopeaks, it is necessary to subtract any overlap before obtaining the peak area. Connally and Leboeuf describe a procedure in which they record the characteristic spectrum of each component separately and normalize the individual spectral curves to a peak height of unity for the principal photopeak. The shapes of these normalized curves are then used to draw in the overlap region, starting at the high-energy end of the scan for the mixture, and the net peak areas are evaluated.

Peirson (52, 53) has described a two-crystal gamma-ray scintillation spectrometer in which the photopeaks are obtained alone. The pulses from an anthracene crystal which is primarily sensitive to the Compton effect are electronically subtracted from the Compton and photoelectric pulses from an NaI crystal.

LIQUID TYPE. A liquid-scintillation counter used for homogeneous sources (Chap. 5) can be calibrated rather simply by means of an internal standard (54, 55). It is possible to calibrate the counter for any particular sample by first counting the sample, adding a known small amount of an absolute standard of the radionuclide being assayed, and then finally counting the solution again. Tritium water and benzene-carboxylic-C^{14} acid are satisfactory standards (54) which can be obtained with a known radioisotopic content determined mass-spectrometrically.

Hayes (55) gives typical counting efficiencies for coincidence counting of samples with very little quenching of (1) 8 per cent for HTO, (2) 12 per cent for toluene-soluble tritium compounds, (3) 55 per cent with both dissolved and suspended C^{14} and S^{35}, (4) higher efficiencies with the more energetic betas, (5) almost 100 per cent for alpha emitters, and (6) 120 per cent for Cs^{137}-Ba^{137}.

7-3. Calibration of Radiation-protection Equipment

A number of problems are associated with the calibration of radiation detectors for dosage rate. These may be instrumental in nature, having to do with the proper electronic circuitry, or they may be problems associated with the radiations from a given source. An example of the first type of instrumental problem is the difference in information furnished by a Geiger counter and by an ionization chamber. The counter measures the rate at which radiation is being emitted, whereas the ionization chamber gives a measure of the total ionization produced by the radiation. This means that a counter may record events, the number of which is proportional to the disintegration rate, whereas the ionization chamber gives information which is more directly proportional to the potential damage to an organism. For this reason, radiation-protection devices should be calibrated in units of roentgens per hour or milliroentgens per hour rather than in counts per minute. Many commercial instruments include both units on the meter dial, but the equivalence thus indicated is valid only for the isotope with which the instrument is calibrated.

In principle, the calibration of these instruments consists in determining the reading of the instrument which corresponds to a given number of milliroentgens per hour for a standardized sample of a gamma emitter. There is no adequate calibration procedure which is valid for beta radiation, although a number of approximations have been made and film badges may give useful information on the beta-ray exposure. Several relationships are commonly used in the determination of the gamma-ray intensity from a given source which can be used in instrument calibrations. Several of these equations for calculating gamma-emitter dose in air have been summarized in the Radiological Health Handbook (56) as follows:

1. Exposure rate (from a point source)

$$I_\gamma = 0.156nE(10^5\mu_a) \tag{7-11}$$

where I_γ = mr/hr at 1 m/mc
n = number of gamma quanta per disintegration
E = energy of gamma quanta in Mev
μ_a = energy absorption coefficient for the gamma quanta in air (STP), cm^{-1}

2. Exposure rate (from point source of radium with 0.5-mm Pt filtration)

$$\text{mr/hr} = \frac{\text{no. of mg Ra}}{s^2} \tag{7-12}$$

where s = distance to source, yd, or

$$\text{mr/hr} = \frac{8{,}400(\text{no. of mg Ra})}{s^2} \tag{7-13}$$

where s = distance to source, cm.

3. Approximate exposure rate (from any gamma source)

$$\text{r/hr at 1 ft} = 6nCE \tag{7-14}$$

where C = number of curies
E = gamma-ray energy, Mev
n = number of gamma quanta per disintegration

4. Exposure rate (from any gamma source)

$$\text{mr/hr} = \frac{nI_\gamma}{s^2} \tag{7-15}$$

where n = number of millicuries
I_γ = mr/hr at 1 m/mc
s = distance, m

The I_γ values for a number of common isotopes calculated using Eq. (7-11) are shown in Table 7-1, which is likewise taken from the Radiological Health Handbook referred to above.

In practice, the procedures used for the calibration of both radiation-protection and personnel monitoring apparatus are essentially the same and involve placing the instrument or other measuring device (e.g., film badge, pocket chamber, or dosimeter) at a known distance from the standard source. If possible, the calibration should be performed (1) at a distance of at least 1 m to approximate point-source conditions and (2) at a location where scattering of radiation from solid objects will not be significant. It is frequently necessary to perform the calibration at several distances in order to determine values over several parts of the instrument range. This is usually necessary when the instrument has several range settings on it. In these cases, it is frequently desirable to

TABLE 7-1

CALCULATED GAMMA-RADIATION LEVELS FOR 1 C OF SOME RADIOISOTOPES

Isotope	I_γ at 1 yd, r/hr	I_γ at 1 m, r/hr	Isotope	I_γ at 1 yd, r/hr	I_γ at 1 m, r/hr
Na^{22}	1.51	1.26	Zn^{65}	0.36	0.30*
Na^{24}	2.31	1.93	I^{130}	1.48	1.23
Mn^{52}	2.30	1.92	I^{131}	0.276	0.231
Mn^{54}	0.54	0.45*	Cs^{137}	0.426	0.346
Fe^{59}	0.77	0.65	Ir^{192}	0.61	0.51
Co^{58}	0.67	0.56*	Au^{198}	0.297	0.248
Co^{60}	1.59	1.32	Ra^{226}	1.005†	0.84†
Cu^{64}	0.137	0.114			

* These isotopes have X-ray emission following electron capture, the intensity of which is negligible at 1 m but would not be negligible at distances of the order of 1 cm.

† With 0.5-mm Pt filtration. This figure is the commonly used one.

determine the calibration of one part of the instrument's range with the standardized source and to use other sources of different strengths for the other portions of the range. A secondary standardization of the sources is obtained by measuring them and the standard source in the same range of the instrument.

Experiment 7-1
Preparation of Primary RaE Standards

A method formerly used for preparing a primary beta standard is to separate RaE from an equilibrium mixture of RaD-E-F and to follow the decay of the RaE with a beta-ray counter. The consequent growth of the RaF alpha radiation is measured at various times with an alpha counter having known geometry. From the alpha radiation present at a given time, the original beta-ray activity of the RaE sample can be determined. If desired, a given position in respect to a counter may be calibrated as described in Expt. 7-2.

The radioisotope used in this experiment is an equilibrium mixture of RaD-E-F.

Apparatus and Materials

- One platinum disk
- One aluminum sample holder
- 0.5 *N* HCl (10 ml)
- Silver powder (0.1 g)
- One 60-ml separatory funnel
- Large waste beaker
- One wash bottle
- One 25-ml graduated cylinder
- One 1½-volt dry cell
- Assorted standard and micropipettes
- One heating lamp
- One pair forceps
- One stirring motor
- Platinum strip attached to stirring rod as anode
- One ring stand
- One split ring for separatory funnel
- One source of RaD-E-F mixture
- One stirring rod
- Two battery leads
- One ammeter
- One electrolysis cell

Procedure

Place 10 ml of 0.5 *N* HCl, the silver powder, and an appropriate amount of RaD-E-F solution in the separatory funnel. The funnel is shaken about 5 min in order to remove the RaF by the silver. The electrolytic cell is assembled using a platinum disk as the cathode and a platinum strip attached to the stirring rod on the motor as the anode. Transfer the RaD-E solution to the cell and apply a small potential.

After about an hour of electrolysis, remove the battery clips, lower the cell, and rinse the stirrer with distilled water. Pour the RaD solution into the "waste" beaker, wash the cell, and remove the platinum disk. Dry the disk carefully.

Measure the beta-ray activity with any suitable beta-ray counter and the alpha-ray activity on an alpha counter of known geometry. It is possible to calibrate a second beta-ray sample (one of long half-life) by making measurements at the same time and in the same position as the decaying RaE sample. Follow the activities daily and record the daily readings and the times for both measurements.

Analysis of Data

Using the value of 5.0 days for the half-life of RaE and 139.5 days for RaF and an assumed geometry factor of 0.51 for the alpha counter (parallel-plate counter in this case), and letting t be the time in days and

A_F the alpha activity at any given time, Zumwalt (24) found the true disintegration rate of RaE at time of initial separation* to be given by the following equation:

$$\text{dpm}_{\text{RaE}}\,(t = 0) = \frac{\dfrac{\text{cpm}_{\text{RaF}}}{0.5}\,(t = t)}{f\left(1 - \exp\dfrac{-t}{201.3}\right)(1 - f)\,\dfrac{5.0}{139.5 - 5.0}} \times \frac{1}{\exp\dfrac{-t}{201.3} - \exp\dfrac{-t}{7.22}}$$

An average of this initial activity, determined at various times from the various alpha-ray measurements, gives the value for the disintegration rate of RaE at the initial separation time. The disintegration rate of the RaE source at any other time t is given by this equation:

$$\text{dpm}_{\text{RaE}}\,(t = t) = \text{dpm}_{\text{RaE}}\,(t = 0)\left[f + (1 - f)\exp\frac{-t}{7.22}\right]$$

The form developed by Zumwalt, which includes the residue fraction f, is used here since it is expected that experimental conditions may cause this to be significant. As a first approximation for the preliminary data, the value of 0.1 may be used for this factor.

If the true value of the disintegration rate for the RaE sample is calculated, as indicated above after several time intervals, the secondary sample of RaD-E-F (or similar beta sample) may be calibrated in terms of disintegration rate by the following equation:

$$\text{dpm}_{\text{RaD-E-F}} = \frac{\text{dpm}_{\text{RaE}}}{R_{\text{RaE}}}\,R_{\text{RaD-E-F}}$$

in which R_{RaE} and $R_{\text{RaD-E-F}}$ are the counting rates and dpm_{RaE} and $\text{dpm}_{\text{RaD-E-F}}$ are the true disintegration rates of the primary and secondary standards respectively. If the actual disintegration rate for the secondary standard is determined in this manner, this source can be used as a secondary-standard sample by applying the proper decay corrections.

* It was found by Zumwalt that, if the current was too high, some RaD remained on the RaE disk, giving a measurable beta count after the RaE should have decayed. He defined the factor f as the ratio of beta counting rates taken after a long period of time (e.g., 40 days) to the counting rate at the initial time of separation. He indicates that it would usually have a value of less than 0.1.

Experiment 7-2
Calibration of Radiation-detection Equipment (General Procedures)

The part of the radiation-detection equipment to be calibrated consists of the detector and associated shielded assembly used in the accurate positioning of sources near the detector. The detector may be a Geiger tube, proportional tube, phosphor with photomultiplier tube, ionization chamber, etc. (See also Expts. 2-1, 2-4, and 2-5.)

One or more standard radioactive sources may be used. Calibration over a range of solid angle is often facilitated by the use of several standard sources of a given radionuclide which are identical except for source strength. In addition, when time permits, it is instructive to compare the calibration results obtained by the use of standard sources which differ with respect to radionuclide alone or radionuclide and such variables as area and thickness of active deposit, type of backing, and cover.

Apparatus and Materials

Radiation-detection equipment

Standard radioactive sources and/or standardized solution and materials for use in preparation of sources

Examples: (β) RaD-E-F, U_3O_8, Co^{60}, P^{32}, I^{131}, Au^{198}, Na^{24}, K^{42}; (γ) Co^{60}, radium, I^{131}

Certificate and any special instructions for use of each standard

Aluminum absorbers and possibly lead absorbers

Ruler (millimeter) of appropriate length

General Procedure

Before using a standard source establish the proper conditions, e.g., use of filter to absorb weak radiation, recommended by the supplier. Always handle standard sources with *extreme care* to avoid damaging them.

In preparing sources from a standardized solution of a radionuclide, use backing material (at least saturation thickness) and deposition methods suited to routine use for the particular radionuclide.

If, after calibration, the detection equipment is to be used in Expt. 8-8, a fixed position, e.g., a shelf very close to the detector, should be available.

Unless the necessary time is unreasonable for the sources available, allow sufficient time so that the standard deviation for each measurement of the apparent activity is not more than 1 per cent.

If a standard source being used to calibrate a detector for beta radiation has a detectable emission of gamma radiation, the contribution of the latter to the apparent activity should be ascertained by the use of lead absorbers and subtracted from the total. (Note that this is not necessary for the simple case of comparison of sources which are identical in every way except disintegration rate.)

Measure the distance from each fixed position to the sensitive region of the detector or detector window. The distance should be measured from the position where the radioactive deposit is located when the source is in position. **Caution:** Use extreme care when a thin-window detector is involved in order to avoid destruction of the detector.*

The three alternative procedures described below differ with respect to the type of calibration data obtained.

1. Using a standard source (or sources) of a given long-lived radionuclide, measure the apparent activity over the available range of solid angle for the detector. If more than one source is used to cover the range of solid angle, compare their apparent activities for at least one of the available fixed positions, e.g., shelf position.

2. Prepare a source (or sources) from a standardized solution of a relatively short-lived radionuclide, e.g., I^{131} or P^{32}. Measure the apparent activity of the source(s) at various fixed positions. In addition, measure the apparent activity for one or more reference† sources of a long-lived radionuclide.

3. Measure the apparent activity of one or more standard sources of at least two different radionuclides. At least one of these should be a long-lived source. If sources are prepared for the experiment from a standardized solution, prepare at least one on the same type of backing used for one of the other radionuclides.

Starting with very thin (5 mg/cm^2 or less) aluminum absorbers, measure the attenuation of the beta radiation from each of the different types of sources. Sufficient absorption data should be obtained to permit extrapolation of the absorption curves to zero total absorber.

Analysis of Data

Where applicable, correct the disintegration rates of the standards for radioactive decay after the date of certification.

Correct the apparent activity data for coincidence losses, background, and any gamma-ray contribution emitted from a beta standard.

* For uniformly manufactured tubes such as Geiger tubes, an old tube can be used to measure the distance from the window to a reference point on the tube such as a flange, which in turn can be used in the measurement of distances to source positions. Once the information is available for a given detector, it can be recorded and passed along to future users.

† In practice it is not necessary that the long-lived source be independently standardized, but it should be a durable reference source.

From the solid angles subtended by the detector and a point source at each fixed position, estimate the detection coefficient Y for each position, assuming it to be equal to G, the geometry factor. Correct these values, taking into account the finite dimensions of the sources used (see Ref. 37). Compare the results with those obtained by use of standard sources.

On the basis of the data obtained in procedure 1, calculate the detection coefficient for each fixed position for each standard source used. Tabulate the values as $Y \times 100$. Average the data when two or more sources of different strength were measured at a given position, and estimate errors in the results. Plot Y as a function of distance from the detector. Extrapolate the curve to zero distance.

Note that, although the set of calibration data is independent of source strength, it is specific for the given radionuclide, backing, area and thickness of deposit, and source cover. Therefore, a complete description of the source should accompany the data. Limitations on the use of the calibration results for other radionuclides and other source materials, etc., should be recognized.

Analysis of the data for the standard source(s) obtained in procedure 2 is the same as that described for procedure 1. The corresponding corrected apparent activity for the reference source for each position should be included in the tabulation. Any subsequent variation of detection coefficient such as might arise from uncertainty in setting the operating potential of the detector can be detected by checking the apparent activity of the reference source. The correction factor for Y is given by the ratio of the apparent activity at any given time to that observed when the reference source was compared with the standard source.

As mentioned in connection with the analysis of data for procedure 1, there are certain limitations on the usefulness of the calibration data. Consider also the limitations in usefulness of the long-lived reference source.

From the data obtained in procedure 3 calculate the detection coefficient for each fixed position for each standard source. For beta-ray standards, use the beta-ray absorption data to obtain an extrapolated (zero total absorber) apparent activity for each source, assuming as an approximation that one absorption curve can be used to determine the extrapolated apparent activity at any fixed position for a given radionuclide. Apply the appropriate backscattering factors (and any other known factors which differ for the sources) to the extrapolated apparent-activity values to normalize the data to unit factors. Recalculate the detection coefficients, which are now essentially equal to the geometry factors. Suggest reasons for any observed lack of agreement for these universal detection coefficients obtained with different sources. Obtain what appears to be the best average value for each fixed position, and plot the values as a function of distance.

Consider the limitations and requirements for use of the universal detection coefficients.

Experiment 7-3
The Use of Secondary Standards in the Calibration of an I^{131} Source

Most laboratories now purchase activity standards from commercial suppliers. These standards are calibrated and, when used properly, are suitable standards for most laboratory work. A bulletin usually accompanies the standards, giving the proper procedures for their use. Although the general procedures included here are for RaD-E-F standards, other calibrated sources are available.

Apparatus and Materials

Detection apparatus (preferably G-M counters)
RaD-E-F standard, such as NBS type, 500 dps (100- and 200-dps standards are also available)
Volumetric flasks, pipettes for dilution of samples
Two NBS silver disks faced with palladium (silver side may be used for noncorrosive solutions; the palladium side may be used for corrosive solutions or for electrodeposition)
Aluminum absorbers or filters
Semilogarithmic graph paper
French curve
Straightedge
Ethyl ether if disks are to be reused
HCl if disks are to be reused
NH_4OH if disks are to be reused
Abrasive if disks are to be reused
Diluting solution for I^{131}

Procedure

A typical shipment of I^{131} to be calibrated might contain 10 mc of I^{131} in approximately 1 ml of solution. If the specific activity is not known, trial dilutions are made. Before beginning work, determine the procedure to make proper dilutions such that your initial sample of the shipment is made with a 5-, 10-, or 20-λ pipette and the final source is made using a 50-λ volume. The final sample should contain approximately 5,000 cpm at an assumed counting yield of 7 per cent. This sample should then be suitable for measurement on the second shelf of the standard counting chamber.

Make the dilutions, which you have calculated to be correct, using the proper diluting medium, and prepare three identical samples by evaporation on the silver mounts provided. If the samples do not have at least 2,000 cpm on the second shelf, add enough of the radioactive material to bring the counting rate to approximately 5,000 cpm. Count each sample for a time long enough to give about 10,000 total counts. Average the three results and select the sample with a counting rate closest to the average of the three.

Make and plot absorption measurements on this sample with air and window corrections (see Chap. 6). This curve need not be extended to thick absorbers, but enough filters should be used in the series to reduce the counting rate to approximately 10 per cent of the original counting rate. Determine the counting rate at zero total absorber.

Using the calibrated RaD-E-F sample, which is also mounted on silver, determine the counting rate at zero total absorber for this sample at the same position used for the iodine sample. Make air, window, and cover corrections.

From the known disintegration rate of the RaD-E-F sample, calculate the counting yield Y for the particular shelf position. Determine the absolute disintegration rate for the iodine sample and calculate the specific activity (millicuries per milliliter) of the original solution.

Analysis of Data

When the absorption curves are plotted as described in Chap. 6 and the extrapolation is made through the air, cover, and window thicknesses, the corrected counting rate can be determined for both the standard and the I^{131} activity. The counting yield may be calculated for the given position from the known disintegration rate (the certificate value) of the standard A from the extrapolated counting rate for the sample by the following relation:

$$Y = \frac{R_{\text{RaD-E-F}}}{A_{\text{RaD-E-F}}}$$

The specific activity, in millicuries per millicurie, is then given by

$$A = \frac{R_{\text{I}}(\text{DF})}{Y \times 3.7 \times 10^7}$$

in which R_{I} is the extrapolated counting rate (cps) for the iodine source and DF is the dilution factor, which is calculated in the following manner:

$$\text{DF} = \frac{\text{volume of original solution}}{\text{aliquot of original taken}} \times \frac{\text{volume of final solution}}{\text{aliquot of final solution used}}$$

According to Chap. 6, if both samples are deposited on silver backing material and if the extrapolated counting rates are used, no correction for backscattering is necessary. If different backing materials are used, it is necessary to introduce the ratio of the backscattering effects into the calculation. These values may be determined from Fig. 6-10. The specific activity may also be corrected for decay by the use of the standard exponential term or by graphical methods, as outlined in Chap. 8.

Experiment 7-4
Determination of Disintegration Rates by Coincidence Measurements

Although many types of coincidence experiments are carried out by nuclear physicists, some routine measurements and calibrations may be performed by others interested in applied nuclear science. Any investigator who is considering doing a large amount of this type of work should examine the original literature. It is felt that, if a coincidence unit is available to the isotope worker, some experience may be obtained by using certain simple systems for study.

Although the method is applicable to many radioisotopes with known decay schemes, one simple choice would be to use a sample of Fe^{59}.

Apparatus and Materials

Coincidence detection apparatus (equipped with one beta detector and one gamma-ray detector).

One sample of appropriate radioactive substance. This should be active enough to give a counting rate of about 5,000 cpm in the beta counter and should be prepared on a thin mount to eliminate backscattering corrections. These factors can be introduced into the calculations if they cannot be eliminated experimentally.

Two aluminum or lead absorbers (should be at least 200 mg/cm^2 density thickness, for Fe^{59} sources, or otherwise thick enough to stop the beta radiation).

One standard source of gamma-emitting radioactive substance of known disintegration rate, e.g., a Co^{60} standard.

Procedure

The sample is placed in position between the two detectors. The aluminum absorber is placed close to the sensitive region of the gamma-ray counter, and a measurement is taken. The coincidence apparatus may be equipped with three scaling circuits so that beta counts, gamma counts, and coincidence counts may be recorded simultaneously. If this is not possible, separate counts must be made for each, using the appropriate detector and the scaler. The time for these separate counts should be the same. Measurements are taken for as long a period of time as possible in order to obtain statistical validity of the coincidence-count record. The beta counting rate, the gamma counting rate, and the coincidence counting rate are recorded.

The second absorber is then placed over the beta counter and another measurement made. This is to measure the gamma-gamma coincidence, which must be subtracted in the calculation of the beta-gamma coincidence measurement.

The random coincidence rate, which corresponds to the background measurement, may then be obtained by making another measurement on an active calibrated sample. The random rate is calculated from the known disintegration rate of the calibrated sample.

Analysis of Data

The results obtained will vary with the type of counters and the experimental arrangement of the apparatus. To show the order of magnitude of counts which one might expect, the following results would be reasonable figures for a given experiment:

	Counts per minute
Beta counting rate	5,000
Gamma counting rate	50 (or higher with scintillation detectors)
Coincidence counting rate	10

There are several methods of correction for the random coincidence rate in a given coincidence circuit. Possibly the simplest method is that indicated above in the measurement of the coincidence rate of a known sample, by using the difference between the known disintegration rate and the observed rate as the random rate for this particular arrangement from such data. Corrections might be the following:

	Counts per minute
Gamma-gamma coincidence rate	0.5
Random coincidence rate	0.5

By subtracting these corrections from the coincidence rate given above, it is possible to determine the disintegration rate of the Fe^{59} sample using Eq. (7-4).

It is seen from these figures that the length of time required for statistically valid measurements is rather long—particularly so for the correction factors. It is also noted that the random coincidence rate is directly proportional to the resolving time of the coincidence circuit. The rate given above corresponds to a circuit having a resolving time of

1 μsec, but it would not be unusual to find a circuit having 10 μsec. If resolving time were 10 μsec, the random rate would be 10 times higher, but the coincidence rate on the unknown sample would not increase. The length of time needed for the measurements in these various cases may be ascertained from Chap. 3.

For calculations involving radioisotopes with more complex decay schemes, texts such as Siegbahn* should be consulted.

Experiment 7-5

Calibration of Radiation-protection Equipment

Radiation-protection instruments should be calibrated periodically. The data obtained in this experiment will serve as one of the calibration checks for gamma radiation. Instrument readings are compared with known dosage rates in milliroentgens per hour at known distances from a standard source of radium.

Apparatus and Materials

Survey or monitoring instruments (for gamma radiations)
Standard radium† source—a 10-mg source is adequate although a 100-mg source may be useful
Meter stick or tape measure
Tongs for handling sources

Procedure

High-level radiation sources constitute a *radiation hazard* and should be used only under strict supervision. Do *not*, under any condition, attempt to pick up such a source with the fingers.

The source should be suspended so as to minimize scattering of gamma radiation from the source holder, walls, floor, beams, and metal furniture. For instruments which measure dosage rate (milliroentgens per hour or roentgens per hour), take readings at measured distances from the source, over as much of the range of the instrument as possible. Check readings for several, i.e., four to six, points for each scale.

For integrating instruments, such as dosimeters and other electroscopes, place the instruments at such distances that full-scale readings can be obtained in a reasonable time. Pocket chambers and dosimeters may be placed on the circumference of a circle having the source at its center. In any case, the method of mounting the detection device

* K. Siegbahn (ed.), "Beta- and Gamma-ray Spectroscopy," Interscience, New York, 1955.

† Other gamma sources such as Co^{60} are preferred by many workers since the potential hazard of leaking radon gas is eliminated.

should not lead to appreciable scattering of gamma radiation. For all instruments, the distance to the source should be measured from the center of the radiation-sensitive volume.

Analysis of Data

Calculate the dosage rates at appropriate distances from the standard source and tabulate the distance, observed instrument readings, and calculated dosage rates for each scale of each instrument. Plot the observed readings against the true or calculated value for all scales of a given instrument, using a single piece of linear graph paper of size suitable for mounting on the instrument. The use of colored inks helps to distinguish the data for different scales.

To facilitate dosage-rate calculations for various distances from a point source, the inverse-square factors may be obtained from a plot of intensity as a function of r^2 or $1/r^2$. As the distance between the source and the detector becomes small, i.e., less than 1 ft or more, the inverse-square law for a point source becomes an approximation because of the finite size of the source. Similarly, the dimensions of the radiation detector become an appreciable fraction of the distance of separation, so that the proper distance to use for dosage calculation becomes difficult to determine.

For the integrating instruments compare the calculated dosage (dosage rate and time of exposure) with the observed dosage and prepare a calibration report for each instrument. This may be represented graphically or as a table of percentage correction.

Experiment 7-6
Calibration of Personnel Monitoring Apparatus

Personnel monitoring devices are usually of two kinds—pocket ion chambers (or dosimeters) and film badges. It is possible to obtain film-badge service from several commercial sources, thereby rendering unnecessary badge calibration by the worker himself. However, the calibration of any of these instruments may be checked reasonably well if a radium source is available.

As in Expt. 7-5, it is desirable to use a calibrated radium source. However, if intercalibrations between various gamma-ray emitters are made, other standards may be substituted.

Apparatus and Materials

Dosimeters, pocket chambers, or film badges (dental X-ray film packets are satisfactory)
Photodensitometer for film badges

Developing materials for films (close control of time and temperature is essential)

Meter stick or measuring tape

Calibrated radium source (preferably at least 10 mg)

Procedure

The basic procedure for calibrating personnel monitoring devices is the same as for the calibration of meters in Expt. 7-5, except that only one scale is available on the personnel meters. Usually the radium source is suspended above the working surface, and the pocket meters or film badges are placed at some measured distance from it. The monitoring devices are left at this distance for a time interval sufficient to give a satisfactory reading on the device (usually above 50 to 100 mr total exposure). The exposure time may be calculated from the relationship among weight of radium, milliroentgens per hour, and distance given in the text [Eqs. (7-12) and (7-13)].

After the proper length of exposure, dosimeters may be read and checked with the calibration given by the manufacturer. If a difference is observed, a number of different total exposures should be measured and a curve determined for each instrument. A number of different exposures should be made with each new shipment of film to determine the ratio of total exposure of the film to the density of the blackening.

In using film badges, after one of the badges is calibrated by exposure to a standardized source for the required time length, the laboratory badges are developed simultaneously with the calibrated badge. If it is not possible to develop all of them at the same time, very careful control of the time and temperature of the developing solutions should be maintained. After the films are dried, photodensitometer readings for the calibrated and laboratory badges may be compared for the total dosage record.

Analysis of Data

Results are calculated from the known weight of radium, the length of time of exposure, and distances from a known point according to the equations in the text. In general, readings of less than 30 mr on any of these devices are not considered significant. Plot the working curves for the instruments (milliroentgens per hour vs. scale reading or milliroentgens per hour vs. film density).

Cited References

1. Report of the International Commission on Radiological Units and Measurements (ICRU), 1956, *Natl. Bur. Standards Handbook* 62, April, 1957.
2. Seliger, H. H.: The Applications of Standards of Radioactivity, *Intern. J. Appl. Radiation and Isotopes*, vol. 1, pp. 215–232, 1956.

3. Reynolds, S. A., and W. A. Brooksbank, Jr.: Tl^{204} as a Standard for Radioassays, *Nucleonics*, vol. 11, no. 11, pp. 46–47, 1953.
4. Conference on Absolute β Counting, *Prelim. Rept.* 8, Nuclear Science Series, National Research Council, October, 1950.
5. Perry, W. E.: Standardization of Radioactive Isotopes, *Natl. Phys. Lab. Rept.* (British), Department of Scientific and Industrial Research, 1953.
6. Seliger, H. H., and A. Schwebel: Standardization of Beta-emitting Nuclides, *Nucleonics*, vol. 12, no. 7, pp. 54–63, 1954.
7. Manov, G. G.: Standardization of Radioactive Sources, *Ann. Rev. Nuclear Sci.*, vol. 4, pp. 51–68, 1954.
8. Putnam, J. L.: Measurement of Disintegration Rate, in K. Siegbahn (ed.), "Beta- and Gamma-ray Spectroscopy," pp. 823–854, Interscience, New York, 1955.
9. Mann, W. B.: The Preparation and Maintenance of Standards of Radioactivity, *Intern. J. Appl. Radiation and Isotopes*, vol. 1, pp. 3–23, 1956.
10. Sinclair, W. K.: Standardization of X-ray Beams and Radioactive Isotopes, in G. J. Hine and G. L. Brownell (eds.), "Radiation Dosimetry," pp. 505–529, Academic Press, New York, 1956.
11. "Nuclear Data Sheets," National Academy of Sciences, National Research Council, Washington.
12. "New Nuclear Data," *U.S. Atomic Energy Comm., Nuclear Sci. Abstr.*, Technical Information Service.
13. Strominger, D., J. M. Hollander, and G. T. Seaborg: Table of Isotopes, *Revs. Modern Phys.*, vol. 30, pp. 585–904, 1958.
14. Strominger, D., and J. M. Hollander: Decay Schemes, *U.S. Atomic Energy Comm. Rept.* UCRL-8289, June, 1958.
15. Pate, B. D., and L. Yaffe: Disintegration-rate Determination by 4π Counting, *Can. J. Chem.*, vol. 33, pp. 610–632, 929–937, 1656–1668, 1955; vol. 34, pp. 265–274, 1956.
16. Smith, C. C., H. H. Seliger, and J. Steyn: Efficiency of 4π-crystal-scintillation Counting. 1, Experimental Technique and Results, *J. Research Natl. Bur. Standards*, vol. 57, pp. 251–255, 1956.
17. Belcher, H. H.: Scintillation Counters Using Liquid Media for Absolute Standardization and Radioactive Assay, *J. Sci. Instr.*, vol. 30, pp. 286–289, 1953.
18. Dunworth, J. V.: The Application of the Method of Coincidence Counting to Experiments in Nuclear Physics, *Rev. Sci. Instr.*, vol. 11, pp. 167–180, 1940.
19. Mitchell, A. C. G.: The Coincidence Method, in K. Siegbahn (ed.), "Beta- and Gamma-ray Spectroscopy," pp. 201–223, Interscience, New York, 1955.
20. Engelkemeir, A. G., and W. F. Libby: End and Wall Connections for Absolute Beta-counting in Gas Counters, *Rev. Sci. Instr.*, vol. 21, pp. 550–554, 1950.
21. Eidinoff, M. L.: Measurement of Specific Disintegration Rates by Internal Gas Counting, *Anal. Chem.*, vol. 23, pp. 632–635, 1951.
22. Bernstein, W., and R. Ballentine: Gas Phase Counting of Low Energy Beta-emitters, *Rev. Sci. Instr.*, vol. 21, pp. 158–162, 1950.
23. Novey, T. B.: RaDEF Standard Sources for Beta-disintegration Rate Determinations, *Rev. Sci. Instr.*, vol. 21, pp. 280–285, 1950.
24. Zumwalt, L. R.: Absolute Beta Counting Using End-window Geiger-Mueller Counters and Experimental Data on Beta-particle Scattering Effects, *U.S. Atomic Energy Comm. Rept.* AECU-567, March, 1950.
25. Norris, L. D., and M. G. Inghram: The Half-life of Carbon 14, *Phys. Rev.*, vol. 73, pp. 350–360, 1948.

26. Manov, G. G., and L. F. Curtiss: The Half-life of Carbon-14, *J. Research Natl. Bur. Standards*, vol. 46, pp. 328–333, 1951.
27. Zumwalt, L. R., C. V. Cannon, G. H. Jenks, W. C. Peacock, and L. M. Gunning: Comparison of the Determination of the Disintegration Rate of Radiophosphorus by Absolute Beta Counting and Calorimetric Measurement, *Science*, vol. 107, p. 47, 1948.
28. Bayly, J. G.: Calorimetric Measurement of the Disintegration Rate of a Phosphorus-32 Source, *Can. J. Research*, vol. 28A, pp. 520–529, 1950.
29. Jenks, G. H., F. H. Sweeton, and J. A. Ghormley: A Precise Determination of the Half-life and Average Energy of Tritium Decay, *Phys. Rev.*, vol. 80, pp. 990–995, 1950.
30. Rutherford, E., J. Chadwick, and C. D. Ellis: "Radiations from Radioactive Substances," p. 387, Cambridge, New York, 1930.
31. Clark, R. K.: Absolute Determination of the Emission Rate of Beta-rays, *Rev. Sci. Instr.*, vol. 21, pp. 753–759, 1950.
32. Kohman, T. P., D. P. Ames, and J. Sedlet: The Specific Activity of Radium, paper 22.60 in G. T. Seaborg, J. J. Katz, and W. M. Manning (eds.), "The Transuranium Elements," pt. II, McGraw-Hill, New York, 1949.
33. Curtis, M. L., J. W. Heyd, R. G. Olt, and J. F. Eichelberger: Absolute Alpha Counting, *Nucleonics*, vol. 13, no. 5, pp. 38–41, 1955.
34. Glover, K. M., and G. R. Hall: Precision Alpha-particle Counting, *Nature*, vol. 173, pp. 991–992, 1954.
35. Hine, G. J., and G. L. Brownell (eds.): "Radiation Dosimetry," Academic Press, New York, 1956.
36. Attix, F. H., and V. H. Ritz: A Determination of the Gamma-ray Emission of Radium, *J. Research Natl. Bur. Standards*, vol. 59, pp. 293–305, 1957.
37. Burtt, B. P.: Absolute Beta Counting, *Nucleonics*, vol. 5, no. 2, pp. 28–43, 1949.
38. Jones, J. W., and R. T. Overman: The Use and Calibration of a 100% Geometry Ion Chamber, *U.S. Atomic Energy Comm. Rept.* AECD-2367, 1948.
39. Gleason, G. I., J. D. Taylor, and D. L. Tabern: Absolute Beta Counting at Defined Geometries, *Nucleonics*, vol. 8, no. 5, pp. 12–21, 1951.
40. Siri, W. E.: "Isotopic Tracers and Nuclear Radiations," chap. 13, McGraw-Hill, New York, 1949.
41. Bleuler, E., and G. J. Goldsmith: "Experimental Nucleonics," pp. 80–88, Rinehart, New York, 1952.
42. Wyard, S. J.: Radioactive Source Corrections for Bremsstrahlung and Scatter, *Nucleonics*, vol. 13, no. 7, pp. 44–45, 1955.
43. Hofstadter, R., and J. A. McIntyre: The Measurement of Gamma-ray Energies with Single Crystals of NaI (Tl), *Phys. Rev.*, vol. 80, pp. 631–637, 1950.
44. Jordan, W. H.: Detection of Nuclear Particles, *Ann. Rev. Nuclear Sci.*, vol. 1, pp. 207–244, 1952.
45. Bell, P. R.: The Scintillation Method, in K. Siegbahn (ed.), "Beta- and Gamma-ray Spectroscopy," pp. 133–164, Interscience, New York, 1955.
46. Connally, R. E., and M. B. Leboeuf: Analysis of Radionuclide Mixtures, *Anal. Chem.*, vol. 25, pp. 1095–1100, 1953.
47. Lazar, N. H., R. C. Davis, and P. R. Bell: Peak Efficiency of NaI, *Nucleonics*, vol. 14, no. 4, p. 52, 1956.
48. Berger, M. J., and J. Doggett: Response Function of NaI (Tl) Scintillation Counters, *Rev. Sci. Instr.*, vol. 27, pp. 269–270, 1956.

49. Miller, W. F., J. Reynolds, and W. J. Snow: Efficiencies and Photofractions for Sodium-iodide Crystals, *Rev. Sci. Instr.*, vol. 28, pp. 717–719, 1957.
50. Stanford, A. L., Jr., and W. K. Rivers, Jr.: Efficiencies of Sodium Iodide Crystals, *Rev. Sci. Instr.*, vol. 29, pp. 406–410, 1958.
51. Connally, R. E.: Instrumental Methods of Gamma-ray Spectrometry, *Anal. Chem.*, vol. 28, pp. 1847–1853, 1956.
52. Peirson, D. H.: A Two-crystal Gamma-ray Scintillation Spectrometer, *Nature*, vol. 173, pp. 990–991, 1954.
53. Peirson, D. H.: The γ-ray Spectrum of Fission Products from Slow Neutron Irradiation of Uranium-235, *Brit. J. Appl. Phys.*, vol. 6, pp. 444–449, 1955.
54. Williams, D. L., F. N. Hayes, R. J. Kandel, and W. H. Rogers: Preparation of C^{14} Standard for Liquid Scintillation Counter, *Nucleonics*, vol. 14, no. 1, pp. 62–64, 1956.
55. Hayes, F. N.: Liquid Scintillators: Attributes and Applications, *Intern. J. Appl. Radiation and Isotopes*, vol. 1, pp. 46–56, 1956.
56. Kinsman, S. (ed.): "Radiological Health Handbook," Robert A. Taft Sanitary Engineering Center, Cincinnati, Ohio, 1957.

Supplementary References

Bayhurst, B. P., and R. J. Prestwood: A Method for Estimating Beta-counting Efficiencies, *Nucleonics*, vol. 17, no. 3, pp. 82–85, 1959.

Borkowski, C. J., and R. L. Clark: Gamma-ray Energy Resolution with NaI-Tl Scintillation Spectrometers, *Rev. Sci. Instr.*, vol. 24, pp. 1046–1050, 1953.

Caldwell, P. A., and J. D. Graves: Secondary-standard Co^{60} Sources Prepared by Electrodeposition, *Nucleonics*, vol. 13, no. 12, pp. 49–51, 1955.

Evans, R. D.: Radioactivity Units and Standards, *Nucleonics*, vol. 1, pp. 32–43, 1947.

Hofstadter, R., and J. A. McIntyre: Gamma-ray Spectroscopy with Crystals of NaI (Tl), *Nucleonics*, vol. 7, no. 3, pp. 33–37, 1950.

Hull, D. E., and G. H. Keirns: Calibrated Bench Used for Gamma Standardizing, *Nucleonics*, vol. 14, no. 8, pp. 95–96, 1956.

Jaffey, A. H.: Solid Angle Subtended by a Circular Aperture at Point and Spread Sources: Formulas and Some Tables, *Rev. Sci. Instr.*, vol. 25, pp. 349–354, 1954.

Loevinger, R., and S. Feitelberg: Using Bremsstrahlung Detection by a Scintillator for Simplified Beta Counting, *Nucleonics*, vol. 13, no. 4, pp. 42–45, 1955.

Loftus, T. P., W. B. Mann, L. F. Paolella, L. L. Stockmann, and W. J. Youden: Comparisons of National Radium Standards, *J. Research Natl. Bur. Standards*, vol. 58, pp. 169–174, 1957.

Mann, W. B.: Use of Callendar's "Radio-balance" for the Measurement of the Energy Emission from Radioactive Sources, *J. Research Natl. Bur. Standards*, vol. 52, pp. 177–184, 1954.

———: A Radiation Balance for the Microcalorimetric Comparison of Four National Radium Standards, *J. Research Natl. Bur. Standards*, vol. 53, pp. 277–281, 1954.

——— and H. H. Seliger: Efficiency of 4π Crystal-scintillation Counting. 2, Dead-time and Coincidence Connections, *J. Research Natl. Bur. Standards*, vol. 57, pp. 257–264, 1956.

——— and ———: Preparation, Maintenance, and Application of Standards of Radioactivity, *Natl. Bureau Standards Circ.* 594, June 11, 1958.

Pate, B. D., and L. Yaffe: A New Material and Techniques for the Fabrication and Measurement of Very Thin Films for Use in 4π-counting, *Can. J. Chem.*, vol. 33, pp. 15–23, 1955.

Scintillation Counter Symposium, *IRE Trans. on Nuclear Sci.*, vol. NS-3, no. 4, November, 1956.

Shapiro, P., and R. W. Higgs: NaI Summing Spectrometer, *Rev. Sci. Instr.*, vol. 28, pp. 939–941, 1957.

Upson, U. L., R. E. Connally, and M. B. Leboeuf: Analyzing for Low-energy Gamma Emitters in a Radionuclide Mixture, *Nucleonics*, vol. 13, no. 4, pp. 38–42, 1955.

Whyte, G. N.: Density Effect in X-ray Measurements, *Nucleonics*, vol. 12, no. 2, pp. 18–21, 1954.

8

The Rates of Radioactive Processes

8-1. Single Radionuclide

Basic Rate Equation. The disintegration of a radioactive substance is a typical first-order reaction. This can be shown experimentally or theoretically by assuming radioactive decay to be a random process and applying probability considerations.

Characteristic of first-order reactions, the fraction of atoms disintegrating in a given time interval will be constant. This may be represented by the equation

$$-\frac{dN/N}{dt} = \lambda \tag{8-1}$$

or

$$\frac{dN}{N} = -\lambda\, dt \tag{8-2}$$

or

$$\frac{dN}{dt} = -\lambda N \tag{8-3}$$

where N is the number (statistically, a large number) of atoms of a single radioactive substance present at time t and λ is the rate or disintegration constant. In general, λ is expressed in units of reciprocal seconds. For Na^{24}, for example, $\lambda = 1.30 \times 10^{-5}\ sec^{-1}$, or 1.30×10^{-3} per cent of the atoms disintegrate per second. The negative sign appears in the above equations since the number of atoms of the radioactive substance decreases with time. According to Eq. (8-3), we may also characterize the process by noting that the disintegration rate is proportional to the number of atoms present at a given instant.

Taking Eq. (8-2) as a convenient one for integration, we obtain

$$\int_{N_0}^{N} \frac{dN}{N} = -\lambda \int_0^t dt \tag{8-4}$$

The symbol N_0 is used to represent the number of atoms present initially at a reference time taken as zero. Integration of this equation in the standard form leads to

$$\ln \frac{N}{N_0} = -\lambda t \tag{8-5}$$

or

$$N = N_0 e^{-\lambda t} \tag{8-6}$$

Using common logarithms, Eq. (8-5) may be written as

$$\log N = \log N_0 - \frac{\lambda t}{2.303} \tag{8-7}$$

which is the equation for a straight line when log N is plotted as a function of time.

Counting Rate and Disintegration Rate. In practice one generally measures the counting rate of a sample rather than the number of atoms. The counting rate is proportional to the disintegration rate or absolute activity, which in turn is proportional to the number of atoms of the radionuclide present. The word "activity" is currently used rather loosely in a variety of ways. When it is important to distinguish between a disintegration rate and an experimentally determined counting rate, we shall use "absolute activity" or "true activity" interchangeably with the former, and "apparent activity," "measured activity," or "observed activity" as equivalent expressions for the latter. As is common practice, general descriptive phrases such as "Co^{60} activity" or "5.3-year activity" will be used occasionally. In fact, for most experiments involving radioactive materials, it is seldom necessary to know either the true disintegration rate or the number of atoms in a sample.

It is convenient at this point to rewrite, for use later, Eqs. (8-6) and (8-7) in terms of the absolute activity and the apparent activity. These two quantities may be related by the equation

$$R = YA \tag{8-8}$$

where R is the apparent activity, e.g., a measured counting rate, at a given time; A is the corresponding disintegration rate of the sample, e.g., disintegrations per unit time; and Y is the counting yield, a constant for a given measurement, as used by Kohman (1) and discussed in Chap. 7. In turn, A may be related to N, in accordance with Eq. (8-3), by the simple relationship

$$A = N\lambda \tag{8-9}$$

Equations (8-6) and (8-7) may now be expressed as

$$\frac{R}{R_0} = \frac{A}{A_0} = e^{-\lambda t} \tag{8-10}$$

and
$$\log \frac{R}{R_0} = \log \frac{A}{A_0} = -\frac{\lambda t}{2.303} \tag{8-11}$$

With λ in reciprocal seconds, the absolute activity is properly expressed as disintegrations per second (commonly abbreviated to dps). The unit of absolute activity in current usage is the curie, which was originally defined in terms of the radon in equilibrium with one gram of radium. By definition (2) the curie is now taken to be 3.700×10^{10} dps. For most tracer-level work the activity required is generally in the range of 10^{-6} to 10^{-3} curie, i.e., microcuries to millicuries, with less than a microcurie usually required for a measurement.

Counting rates are reported in various units in the literature, depending upon the custom of the laboratory, the type of counting and timing equipment, etc. Counts per minute (cpm), counts per second (cps), scale divisions per minute, etc., are common.

The Half-life. In the derivation and transformation of rate equations, it is customary and convenient to use λ as the characteristic time constant of the radionuclide. A second related constant, namely, the half-life, is used in most tables and charts of nuclear data. The concept of a half-life should be familiar to chemists from discussions of the half-time of first-order chemical reactions in elementary textbooks of physical chemistry. The half-life T of a radionuclide is the time required for the activity to decrease by 50 per cent. Thus, when t is equal to T,

$$\frac{R}{R_0} = \frac{A}{A_0} = \tfrac{1}{2} = e^{-\lambda T} \tag{8-12}$$

and
$$\lambda T = 0.693 \qquad \text{or} \qquad T = \frac{0.693}{\lambda} \tag{8-13}$$

Substituting for λ in Eq. (8-10), we obtain

$$\frac{R}{R_0} = \frac{A}{A_0} = e^{-0.693t/T} \tag{8-14}$$

or
$$\frac{R}{R_0} = \frac{A}{A_0} = (\tfrac{1}{2})^{t/T} \tag{8-15}$$

and Eq. (8-11) becomes

$$\log \frac{R}{R_0} = \log \frac{A}{A_0} = -\frac{0.301t}{T} \tag{8-16}$$

In these equations t and T are expressed in the same units of time, of course.

Since the disintegration rate of a sample decreases exponentially with time, a long time relative to one half-life is required for the activity to decrease to a negligible value. In practice, however, the activity of a sample is reduced by a factor of about 1,000 during a period of 10 half-lives since, by Eq. (8-15),

$$A = A_0(\tfrac{1}{2})^{10} = \frac{A_0}{1{,}024}$$

The Mean Life. A third characteristic constant for radionuclides is the mean life τ. To an observer, a particular atom in a sample of radioactive material may have a lifetime value between $t = 0$ and $t = \infty$. When observations are made for many atoms with all possible life periods, an average or mean value can be calculated. Thus at any time t the number of atoms dN undergoing radioactive transformation in the interval dt is

$$dN = \lambda N_0 e^{-\lambda t}\,dt \tag{8-17}$$

as obtained from Eqs. (8-3) and (8-6). The quantity dN may be taken as the number of life periods t within the interval dt. The total time is the sum of the periods for all atoms taken over all possible lifetimes. Then the average time τ will be this summation divided by the number of atoms present initially. Thus

$$\tau = \frac{1}{N_0}\int_{N_0}^{0} t\,dN = \frac{1}{N_0}\int_{0}^{\infty} t\lambda N_0 e^{-\lambda t}\,dt \tag{8-18}$$

From a table of integrals in the standard form, it is found that

$$\tau = \frac{1}{\lambda} = \frac{T}{0.693} = 1.443T$$

The mean life, then, corresponds to the time required for the disintegration rate to decrease by the factor e^{-1}.

The average life finds application in calculations of the total number of particles, e.g., beta particles, emitted by a given radioactive source during complete decay. For example, the total number of disintegrations obtained from 1 μc of Na^{24} ($T = 14.97$ hr) during complete decay would be simply the number of disintegrations per second, i.e., 3.7×10^4, multiplied by the average life of a radiosodium atom, i.e., 7.77×10^4 sec, since $N_0 = A_0/\lambda = A_0\tau$. This would be 2.88×10^9 disintegrations. The total number of beta particles emitted, assuming one beta particle per disintegration, would be 2.88×10^9. The same calculation for the case of 1 μc of P^{32} (14.2 days) leads to a value of 6.5×10^{10} beta particles emitted during complete decay.

For incomplete decay during the time t, the total number of disintegrations would be $N_0 - N$, or $N_0(1 - e^{-\lambda t})$, and $N_0 = A_0/\lambda$ as before.

In general, the cumulated disintegrations during the period t is given by the integral

$$A_0 \int_0^t e^{-\lambda t}\, dt$$

From the total number of beta particles, the total energy released by the source and absorbed by the surroundings may be calculated. Thus, the total energy corresponding to the total number of beta particles would be given by the product of the average beta-ray energy and the total number of beta rays. For Na^{24}, having an average beta-ray energy of 0.54 Mev, the total energy (as beta radiation only) from 1 μc would be 1.55×10^9 Mev. Such calculations are of importance, for example when moderately short-lived radionuclides are used for medical research and therapy.

It is of interest to note that, in medical and biological applications, a radionuclide is considered to have an "effective half-life" which takes into account the biological half-life in addition to the half-life T for radioactivity. The biological half-life T_b is equal to $0.693/\lambda_b$, where λ_b is the constant rate of elimination of the radionuclide. The "effective half-life" is then defined as $T_{eff} = TT_b/(T + T_b)$ for the case of constant rate of elimination.

Partial Half-lives. When more than one mode of decay is possible for a radionuclide, partial half-lives may be calculated for the various processes, provided the frequency of occurrence of each of the competitive processes is known. This phenomenon of multiple decay processes is referred to as branching. A classical example of branching is that of RaC, which may emit beta radiation to form RaC′ or alpha radiation to form RaC″. Occasionally, partial half-lives are calculated for the parallel branches in a complex disintegration scheme leading to the same decay product.

When there are two processes, for example, with disintegration constants λ_1 and λ_2, the over-all or total disintegration constant λ_{1+2} is the sum of the two independent constants. If f_1 is the measured fraction of the total events in a given time corresponding to λ_1, and f_2 is the fraction corresponding to λ_2, the ratio of the disintegration constants is given by the ratio of the frequencies with which the processes occur. In terms of half-lives, the above may be represented by two equations as follows:

$$\frac{1}{T_{1+2}} = \frac{1}{T_1} + \frac{1}{T_2} \tag{8-19}$$

and

$$\frac{T_1}{T_2} = \frac{f_2}{f_1} \tag{8-20}$$

By solving these equations simultaneously, the partial half-lives T_1 and T_2 may be calculated when the over-all half-life is known.

Determination of Half-life from Decay Measurements. *General Procedure.* By inspection of Eq. (8-10) it can be seen that an estimate of the half-life of a single radioactive species can be obtained from two measurements of the counting rate of a sample which are made at two times separated by the interval t. This interval should be chosen so that the ratio R/R_0 does not have a value close to unity, in order to minimize the uncertainty in the calculated half-life.

It is preferable to follow the decay of a radionuclide by making a series of counting-rate measurements over a period of several half-lives. For long-lived materials requiring a series of decay measurements that extend over a period longer than a few hours in a given day, it is good practice to make periodic, e.g., daily or twice daily, measurements of the counting rate of a very-long-lived reference source. The preparation of such a source is described in Expt. 5-1.

By means of the reference source, corrections can be made for trends in data which may result from slow changes in the operational characteristics of the counting equipment. The source may also serve as a means for normalizing data when Geiger tubes are changed or if some other variation in the experimental arrangement is introduced during the series of measurements. When the counting equipment is operating properly, inspection, e.g., a linear plot, of the data for the standard will show a normal random variation with time and no correction of other data is indicated. Sudden changes in the counting rate of the reference source may indicate that normalization is necessary or may indicate that the measurements are completely invalid.

Decay data obtained from a series of measurements may be analyzed by several methods. Commonly, these are the graphical method, the method of averages, and the method of least squares. The choice of method depends upon the reliability of the data. Obviously, only precise data are worthy of analysis by the more laborious methods. Helpful discussions of the general problems of curve fitting and the calculation of constants for equations are given by many authors (3–5). For the most part, in routine radiochemical work, the graphical method is adequate.

Since Eq. (8-16) is linear in the logarithm of the counting rate, a straight line is obtained when the decay data, corrected for background, coincidence losses, etc., are plotted as a function of time on semilogarithmic graph paper. The best straight line is drawn through the points, and by inspection the time required for any selected counting rate to decrease by 50 per cent is determined. In order that the slope $(-0.301/T)$ of the line may be well defined, the measurements should extend over a period of several half-lives. A typical plot is shown in Fig. 8-1.

As an indication of the reliability of each point, the uncertainty, e.g., the standard deviation, may be indicated on the semilogarithmic plot as a vertical extension above and below the point. These vertical extensions may be used in weighting the points when the best line is

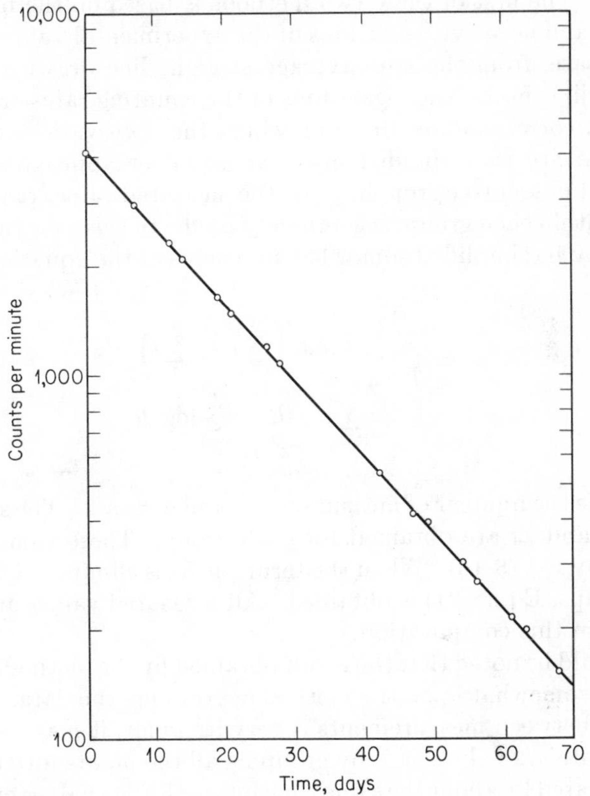

FIG. 8-1. Decay curve for P^{32}; $T = 14.3$ days.

drawn through the points. It should be noted that there is frequently a tendency to overweight the end points. Unless care is taken, the uncertainty for these two points may be relatively large, since in one case the counting rate is low and the statistical error may be large and, in the other case, the counting rate may be so high as to require considerable correction for counting losses in the detector. These conditions may be largely avoided, of course, by proper selection of detector and adjustment of sample size or by changing the position of the sample relative to the radiation detector. If, however, the sample is moved from one shelf to another to improve the counting rate during the course of a half-life investigation, the relative counting yields should be determined carefully from measurements made with the sample itself.

When a value for the half-life better than that obtainable graphically is desired, and when the precision of the data warrants the effort, the data may be analyzed by the method of averages or the method of least squares. The first of these two methods is based on the fact that the positive and negative deviations of the experimental values, i.e., log R in this case, from the true average straight line drawn through the points will cancel. The logarithms of the counting rates are tabulated with the corresponding times at which the observations were made. The data are then divided into two equal or approximately equal groups. Consecutive grouping, i.e., the measured values taken consecutively within each group, is commonly used. In this case the computations may be simplified somewhat by means of the equation

$$\bar{T} = \frac{0.301\left(\sum_{a+1}^{n} t - \sum_{1}^{a} t\right)}{\sum_{1}^{a} \log R - \sum_{a+1}^{n} \log R} \tag{8-21}$$

where n is the number of measurements and $a \approx n/2$. The summations Σ log R and Σt are obtained for each group. These summations are related by Eq. (8-16). When the term log R_0 is eliminated between the two groups, Eq. (8-21) is obtained. All measured values are weighted equally in this computation.

It should be noted that the result obtained by the method of averages depends somewhat upon the method of grouping the data. If the time interval between measurements is very irregular, it may be preferable to compute $n/2$ values of T by grouping all the points into pairs which are separated by about the same time interval. The values of T are then averaged. As indicated below, this same grouping procedure may be used to estimate the precision uncertainty in the final value of T.

The method of least squares is considered to be the most accurate one for analyzing very precise decay data. When the data show truly random variations, the half-life obtained by this method is the most probable. The principle is that the sum of the squares of the residuals, i.e., differences between the values calculated by the equation found to represent the data and the values actually observed, will be a minimum when the best constants for the equation are obtained. If the decay measurements are not all equally reliable, each point should be weighted according to its reliability. For radioactivity data the logarithm of each apparent activity may be weighted inversely as the square of its standard deviation, i.e., its variance, σ^2. The standard deviation is obtained from the relationship

$$\sigma_{\log R} = \frac{0.434\sigma_R}{R} \tag{8-22}$$

which follows from the law of propagation of errors.

Before considering the reliability of the half-life obtained from decay data, some attention should be given to the reliability of individual measurements. An observed precision measure such as the σ_R can be calculated for each decay point from observed deviations from an average value when each point is based on several measurements. If each point represents only a single measurement and if, as discussed in Chap. 3, it is assumed that the uncertainty is due entirely to the random occurrence of the nuclear disintegrations, the standard deviation in terms of $(R/t)^{1/2}$ may be used. Except for very-short-lived radionuclides, errors in timing can usually be reduced to negligible values for counting periods of 5 min or more. For those cases in which a reference source is used for normalization of decay data, the scattering of the data is generally magnified since the data for the reference source scatter also. The uncertainties introduced by normalization are calculated by the rules for the propagation of errors in ratios. As mentioned previously, the reference source is needed only for correcting discontinuities or trends (instrumental, etc.) which are outside the normal or expected scatter.

With respect to the reliability of the half-life values derived from the decay data, it should be recalled that, if the goal is to obtain the "best" value and its precision index from the data, the method of least squares is recommended. The formal methods for evaluating the standard deviation, probable error, nine-tenths error, etc., in the half-life value obtained by least squares are well established and are described in the texts previously cited. The values so calculated have a definite significance in accordance with the general statistical treatment of errors. However, when some other method is used to analyze the data, the evaluation of a formal precision index is frequently difficult and may not be worth the effort. For example, in the method of averages, it is usually adequate to calculate an approximate value for a precision index. This is of interest in the determination of the number of significant figures which are justified in the result. A reasonable measure of how well the curve (regression line) fits the data may be obtained in the following manner. First, as indicated for Eq. (8-21), the data are divided into two approximately equal groups. Then, a set of half-life values is calculated by taking pairs of corresponding points in each group. Thus, if there are n measurements and if $n/2 = a$, the pairs of equally spaced points i and j are $i = 1, j = a + 1$; $i = 2, j = a + 2$;

etc. This gives $n/2$ values for T which are compared with $\bar{T}$ to give the residuals ΔT_i. The standard deviation for $\bar{T}$ is then

$$\sigma_{\bar{T}} = \left[\frac{\Sigma(\Delta T_i)^2}{(0.5n)^2}\right]^{1/2} \tag{8-23}$$

In general this is a satisfactory measure of the goodness of fit of the decay curve corresponding to the half-life obtained by an averaging process.

When the half-life is determined by drawing a best line through the decay points plotted on semilogarithmic graph paper, the same procedure as that described above for the method of averages may be used to find a σ for the goodness of fit. The values of T_i for the equally spaced, fairly widely separated points in each pair may be obtained by calculation or by inspection from straight lines drawn through the pairs of points in each case. If, in drawing the original decay curve, two or three lines seem to fit the points, it is possible to decide on one in preference to the others by summing the squares of the deviations of the experimental points from the predicted points, i.e., the curve for each case. This sum will be a minimum for that curve of those considered which fits the data best.

Another method is sometimes used to estimate the reliability of a half-life value obtained from a graph. The precision measure, theoretical or observed, for each decay point may be used to estimate a range of values for the half-life. Extreme decay lines may be drawn through the terminal values of the vertical extensions representing the precision measures for two widely separated points. Thus, if one point is R_i with an uncertainty $\pm\epsilon_i$ and the other point is $R_j \pm \epsilon_j$, then one line is drawn between $(R_i + \epsilon_i)$ and $(R_j - \epsilon_j)$ and the other is drawn between $(R_i - \epsilon_i)$ and $(R_j + \epsilon_j)$. The half-life values obtained from several such lines may be compared with the chosen "best-curve" value, and a mean deviation calculated. This procedure will generally give a larger estimated uncertainty than that representing simply the goodness of fit to all the observed data. When the precision measure of the first and last few points is about the same, as may be the case for measurements of long-lived material, the extreme range of half-life values may be estimated by applying this graphical technique to the end points alone.

For accurate work, each decay point for a given source should be the average of several measurements, and several sources should be studied so that a grand average may be obtained for the half-life value. The reader is referred to the work of Peierls (6), who has suggested a counting schedule and a method of analyzing the data when a very accurate half-life value is sought.

Modified Procedure for Short Half-lives. For a radionuclide having a half-life in the range of a few minutes to a few hours, the time required for the measurement of the counting rate may be a significant fraction of the half-life. The observed counting rate, which is then an average over the counting period, is commonly associated with the time at the mid-point of the counting period. This is usually justifiable since the exponential decay may be taken as a linear function for the purposes of interpolation over the relatively small counting interval.

Decay measurements for a radionuclide with a half-life in the range of 10 to 1,000 sec may be carried out with ordinary counting equipment with relatively minor modification of procedure. It is no longer feasible, however, to reset the mechanical register between measurements. The counts are allowed to accumulate, and the total is observed at short intervals. An automatic recording device, of course, is convenient for this type of measurement.

The half-life may be determined by calculating the counting rate for each time of observation and plotting the rates vs. time on semilogarithmic graph paper as described earlier. When this is done, the points are likely to scatter badly since the statistical error for each point will generally be large, owing to the small total number of counts taken for each point. A better way of analyzing the data is to plot an "integral" decay curve.

The "integral" decay curve is constructed in the following manner. The accumulated count is observed at the end of successive short time intervals until the short-lived radionuclide has decayed completely, as far as detection is concerned. After correction for background or a long-lived contaminant is made, the difference between the total number of counts S_∞ obtained from the short-lived activity and the number of counts S_t accumulated at any one time of observation t is proportional to the amount of the radionuclide remaining at time t. This quantity, $S_\infty - S_t$, is plotted as a function of time on semilogarithmic graph paper. A "best" straight line is drawn through the points, and the half-life is obtained graphically as in the normal rate plot, or the method of averages, etc., may be used. For comparison, the two types of decay curves are illustrated in Fig. 8-2*a* and *b*, which are based on data for 1.17-min UX_2 (Expt. 8-3). Studier and Hyde (7) have described the application of the "integral" method to the determination of the half-life of 38-sec Ra^{222}. Many special techniques have been devised for obtaining decay data for short-lived radionuclides. These include the use of rotating wheels and pneumatic delivery tubes for rapidly transporting a sample from the point of radioactivation to the radiation detector. Several of these methods have been reviewed by Rowlands (8).

Determination of Half-life from Specific-activity Measurements. For very-long-lived radionuclides such as C^{14}, K^{40}, and U^{238}, the activity of a sample does not decrease sufficiently in an experimentally convenient time to make decay measurements of value in determining the half-life. If, however, the disintegration rate of a sample and

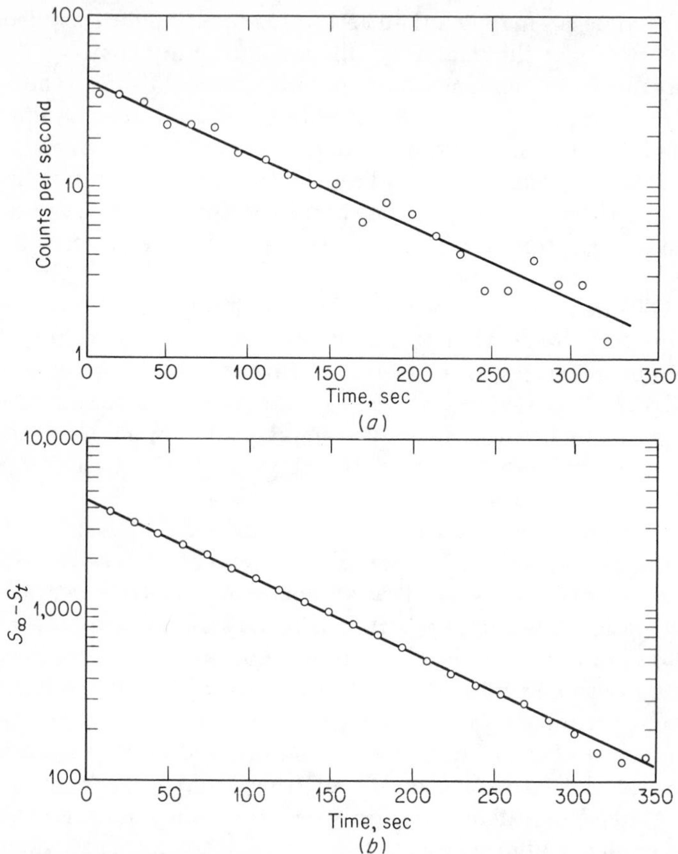

FIG. 8-2. Decay curves for 1.17-min UX_2. (a) Rate plot; (b) integral plot.

the number of atoms of the radionuclide are known, the half-life of the radionuclide may be obtained from Eq. (8-9), rewritten in terms of T as

$$A = \frac{0.693N}{T} \qquad (8\text{-}24)$$

"Absolute" counting techniques such as those described in Chap. 7 are used for measurement of the disintegration rate. The number of radionuclide atoms is obtained from a knowledge of the weight of the element, the atomic weight, and the isotopic percentage of the radionuclide in question. Applications of this method are numerous. Examples are the determinations of (1) the half-life of Th^{232} by Kovarik and Adams (9); (2) the half-life of C^{14} by Engelkemeir, Hamill, Inghram, and Libby (10); and (3) the half-life of Ra^{226} by Kohman, Ames, and Sedlet (11). Discussions of the experimental techniques and references to earlier work are presented in the papers describing the investigation of these three radionuclides.

Estimation of Half-life from Radiation Energy. It was apparent to the early workers that the radiation energy and the disintegration constant can be correlated for many of the naturally occurring radioactive substances. Two empirical relations were formulated. One of these, the Geiger-Nuttall relation for alpha emitters, is commonly written in the form

$$\log (\text{range}) = a + b \log \lambda \tag{8-25}$$

where the range is that in air, a is characteristic for each of the three natural series, and b is essentially the same for all series.

For beta emitters the disintegration constant and the maximum energy are correlated approximately by the Sargent rule, which is generally represented by the equation

$$\lambda = kE_{\text{max}}^5 \tag{8-26}$$

The value of k depends upon the nature of the beta transition and has been interpreted, by analogy with the Fermi theory of beta decay, as a measure of the degree of "forbiddenness" of the transition.

The Geiger-Nuttall and the Sargent relations are most commonly represented graphically as families of curves. Of the two, the former has had the greater use. It has served, for example, as the basis for estimation of the half-lives of very-short-lived alpha emitters which could not be determined accurately before the development of modern measurement techniques. At the present, with approximately one hundred alpha emitters known, the correlation of half-life and alpha-ray energy has been extended to include the neptunium series and the other artificially produced collateral series. Valuable information has been obtained by combining such correlations with certain concepts of periodicity in the properties and structure of nuclei (12). For example, in the synthesis of new heavy radionuclides it is of interest to estimate the magnitude of the half-life expected for a radionuclide whose alpha-ray energy has been measured. Furthermore, where there are several widely differing half-life values for a radionuclide reported in the literature, a decision can frequently be made in favor of one value on the basis of the alpha-ray energy. (The reverse calculation of alpha-ray energy from a half-life is also of interest, of course.) Various specific applications are discussed by Perlman, Ghiorso, and Seaborg (13) in a paper on the Systematics of Alpha-radioactivity.

8-2. Mixture of Independent Radionuclides

The total absolute activity A_{total} for a mixture of radioactive substances A, B, C, etc., which are decaying independently, e.g., Na^{24} and Cl^{38}, is equal to the sum of the individual activities. Thus

$$A_{\text{total}} = A_A + A_B + A_C + \cdots \tag{8-27}$$

and

$$A_{\text{total}} = (A_A)_0 e^{-\lambda_A t} + (A_B)_0 e^{-\lambda_B t} + (A_C)_0 e^{-\lambda_C t} + \cdots \tag{8-28}$$

where subscripts are used to denote the individual components. As the total activity of the mixture decreases, the contributions due to the individual radionuclides become negligible in the order of increasing half-life. Equations analogous to (8-27) and (8-28) may be written in terms of the counting rate of a mixture. Experimentally, however, the relative contribution of each component to the total counting rate will not agree in general with the relative contribution of each component to the total disintegration rate. The discrepancy results from differences in the counting yield Y, arising in turn from differences in the radiation characteristics of the radionuclides in the mixture. In general the radioactive species in a mixture are separated chemically or physically, and their half-lives are determined by the methods used for a single radionuclide. Occasionally, however, separation is not possible because of the presence of independent isomers or other radioactive isotopes, or it may not be feasible to carry out a complete radiochemical separation rapidly enough to recover a very-short-lived activity. Satisfactory half-life values can be obtained frequently in such cases by graphical analysis of the composite decay data.

Figure 8-3 shows the type of curve that is obtained when the observed corrected data are plotted as a function of time on semilogarithmic graph paper. As the short-lived radionuclides disappear, the apparent half-life of the sample increases until only the longest-lived substance remains. The observed composite curve could be constructed by adding the individual straight-line decay curves if these were known. The actual procedure is essentially the reverse of this. The apparent activity is followed until the decay curve becomes clearly linear on the logarithmic plot. This linear portion then represents the simple decay curve for the longest-lived component. The decay measurements must be continued until the slope of this straight line can be established accurately. The decay curve of the longest-lived component is extrapolated back to the first measurement of the series. Subtraction of the contribution of this radionuclide from the total apparent activity at various times leads to a curve representing the combined apparent activity due to the other components present in the original mixture. This process of subtracting or "peeling off" the extrapolated decay curve of the longest-lived component is continued until the straight-line decay curve for the radionuclide having the shortest half-life is obtained. The half-life of each component is determined by inspection of its decay curve.

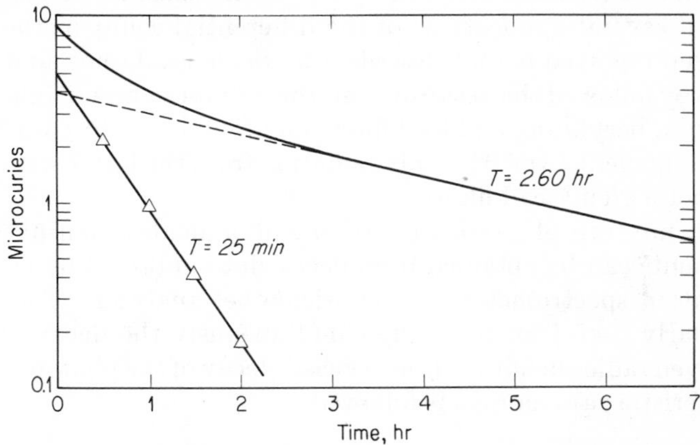

FIG. 8-3. Composite and resolved decay curves for two independent radionuclides.

There are certain objections and limitations to this method. As indicated above, it is necessary to follow the counting rate of the sample until only the longest-lived component remains in order to find the half-life of any of the other components. If the half-lives of the components of the mixture are not very different, resolution of the composite decay curve is difficult, if not impossible. Even when the half-lives differ by an order of magnitude, the uncertainties introduced in successive subtractions accumulate and can result in large errors in the values for the components of shorter half-life. Resolution of a composite decay curve representing more than three components either graphically or analytically is generally unsatisfactory; hence chemical separation is required.

Under certain conditions, it is feasible to follow the decay of the components of a mixture separately, without chemical separation, by the so-called differential-count method. When the radiation characteristics of the radionuclides in the mixture differ sufficiently, it is often possible to measure the apparent activity of the sample under conditions such that the radiation emitted by one of the radionuclides can be detected without interference from the other radionuclide. Suppose, for example, that the two components in a mixture are a pure-beta emitter and a beta-gamma emitter. If a lead absorber of suitable thickness is placed between the sample and the detector, the decay of the gamma-emitting radionuclide may be followed as if the other radionuclide were not present. Differential counting may be achieved also by proper selection of radiation detectors. Thus, for a mixture of an alpha emitter and a beta emitter, a proportional counter or an ionization chamber may be used to detect only the alpha rays, and a Geiger tube may be used for the beta rays. Ultimately the decay data corresponding to each type of radiation detected are analyzed by one of the usual methods.

One of several applications of the differential-count method which have been reported is that described by Seaborg, James, and Morgan (14). They followed the decay of deuteron-produced americium through aluminum, beryllium, and lead filters and found a 12-hr (Am^{239}) and a 50-hr component (Am^{240}). Only radiation from the latter was detected through a 5 g/cm^2 lead filter.

For a mixture of gamma-emitting radionuclides, half-lives of the components can be obtained from decay data obtained by means of a scintillation spectrometer or a multichannel analyzer. The latter is particularly useful for following simultaneously the decay of several short-lived radionuclides. In either case, decay of the photopeaks of the characteristic gamma rays is followed.

8-3. Formation of a Stable Daughter Nuclide

For the simple case $A \rightarrow B$ (stable), the rate of formation of the stable product is equal to the rate of disappearance of the parent radionuclide. Expressed in the form of an equation,

$$\frac{dN_B}{dt} = \lambda_A N_A = \lambda_A (N_A)_0 e^{-\lambda_A t} \tag{8-29}$$

When substance B is absent initially, this equation has the integrated form

$$N_B = (N_A)_0(1 - e^{-\lambda_A t}) \tag{8-30}$$

for the number of atoms of substance B which have been produced up to time t. The quantity N_B is, of course, simply the difference between $(N_A)_0$ and N_A.

8-4. Mixture of Genetically Related Radionuclides

General Equations. The successive transformations in a series or chain of radionuclides may be represented by the sequence $A \rightarrow B \rightarrow C \rightarrow D \cdots$, etc. For the case of two substances, namely A, the parent, and B, the daughter, the basic rate equation for the daughter is

$$\frac{dN_B}{dt} = \lambda_A N_A - \lambda_B N_B \tag{8-31}$$

This equation expresses the fact that the net rate of change of the number of daughter atoms is equal to the rate of production from the parent minus the rate of decay of the daughter. Since Eq. (8-31) is a linear first-order first-degree differential equation, it can be integrated readily by use of the integrating factor $e^{\lambda_B t}$. This method of integration is of general application for the differential equations which are obtained for the rates of radioactive processes, and therefore the integration of Eq. (8-31) is given in Appendix H as an illustrative example. Other methods of integration such as that described by Friedlander and Kennedy (15) may be used, of course, depending upon the preference of the reader.

Integration of Eq. (8-31) leads to

$$N_B = \frac{\lambda_A (N_A)_0}{\lambda_B - \lambda_A} (e^{-\lambda_A t} - e^{-\lambda_B t}) \tag{8-32}$$

when there are no daughter atoms present when $t = 0$, that is, $(N_B)_0 = 0$. If, on the other hand, the daughter radionuclide is present initially, a term $(N_B)_0 e^{-\lambda_B t}$ is added to this equation. In terms of activities, Eq. (8-32) may be written

$$A_B = \lambda_B N_B = \frac{\lambda_B (A_A)_0}{\lambda_B - \lambda_A} (e^{-\lambda_A t} - e^{-\lambda_B t}) \tag{8-33}$$

Similarly, in terms of half-lives, Eq. (8-33) becomes

$$A_B = \frac{T_A (A_A)_0}{T_A - T_B} (e^{-0.693t/T_A} - e^{-0.693t/T_B}) \tag{8-34}$$

Extending the series, we obtain the following equation for the activity of species C at any time t if $(N_B)_0 = (N_C)_0 = 0$:

$$A_C = \lambda_C N_C = \frac{\lambda_A \lambda_B \lambda_C (N_A)_0}{(\lambda_B - \lambda_A)(\lambda_C - \lambda_A)(\lambda_C - \lambda_B)} [(\lambda_C - \lambda_B) e^{-\lambda_A t} + (\lambda_A - \lambda_C) e^{-\lambda_B t} + (\lambda_B - \lambda_A) e^{-\lambda_C t}] \tag{8-35}$$

This equation may be extended for the general case of any member Q of a chain, or it may be written in the following alternative form:

$$A_Q = N_Q \lambda_Q = C_A e^{-\lambda_A t} + C_B e^{-\lambda_B t} + C_C e^{-\lambda_C t} + \cdots + C_Q e^{-\lambda_Q t} \tag{8-36}$$

where $$C_A = \frac{\lambda_A \lambda_B \lambda_C \cdots \lambda_Q (N_A)_0}{(\lambda_B - \lambda_A)(\lambda_C - \lambda_A) \cdots (\lambda_Q - \lambda_A)}$$

and $$C_B = \frac{\lambda_A \lambda_B \lambda_C \cdots \lambda_Q (N_A)_0}{(\lambda_A - \lambda_B)(\lambda_C - \lambda_B) \cdots (\lambda_Q - \lambda_B)}$$

As before, it has been assumed that initially all activities are zero except $(A_A)_0$. With respect to computations involving this equation, it should be recognized, of course, that the numerators in the coefficients $C_A, C_B, \ldots$ are identical and include $(A_A)_0$.

If, at $t = 0$, $(A_Q)_0 \neq 0$, the term $(A_Q)_0 e^{-\lambda_Q t}$ is added to Eq. (8-36). If any of the other precursors of Q (in addition to A) are present initially, the contribution to A_Q from each at time t is found by solving Eq. (8-36) separately for each precursor as parent. The sources of Q are thus treated independently.

The form of the general equation (8-36) for the nth member of a chain was described by Bateman (16) in 1910, and such equations (17), most commonly expressed in terms of numbers of atoms, are referred to as "Bateman equations." More recently a general equation has been derived by Watson (18) using matrix methods.

It is convenient to examine the general equations (8-32) to (8-34) for certain limiting cases. The special equations which result are discussed in the following sections.

Certain general conclusions concerning the relationship between parent and daughter activities may be drawn from Eq. (8-33). The three possible combinations are, of course, (1) $T_A > T_B$, or $\lambda_A < \lambda_B$; (2) $T_A = T_B$, or $\lambda_A = \lambda_B$; and (3) $T_A < T_B$, or $\lambda_A > \lambda_B$. It is customary to refer to two types of behavior—transient equilibrium and secular equilibrium—in describing the growth and decay of a radioactive daughter having a half-life less than that of its parent. Actually, secular equilibrium is approached as a limiting case of transient equilibrium, and it will be treated as such in the following sections.

Whether $T_A > T_B$ or $T_A < T_B$, an expression for the time at which the daughter activity reaches a maximum may be obtained by setting the derivative dA_B/dt equal to zero and solving for t. Thus

$$t_{(A_B)\max} = \frac{3.323 T_A T_B}{T_A - T_B} \log \frac{T_A}{T_B} \tag{8-37}$$

This time also coincides with the time at which the disintegration rates of the parent and daughter become momentarily equal, as may be shown by equating the expressions for A_A and A_B and solving for t.

The problem of determining the half-lives of genetically related radioactive substances was encountered very soon after the discovery of radioactivity, since most of the naturally radioactive substances are members of a series. It is a great credit to the early workers that they were able to unravel the three complex natural series by means of ingenious experiments depending upon relatively simple equipment.

With the discovery of artificial radioactivity, there arose the additional problem of analyzing complex mixtures of radioactive substances produced in irradiated targets.

In general, the mixture of radioactive substances obtained by activation of a target is composed of independent radionuclides such as are produced by competing reactions or by activation of impurities. There are many cases, however, in which genetically related substances are produced. For example, there are short chains such as

$$\mathrm{Te}^{130}(n,\gamma)\mathrm{Te}^{131} \xrightarrow[25\text{ min}]{\beta^-} \mathrm{I}^{131} \xrightarrow[8.0\text{ days}]{\beta^-,\,\gamma,\,e^-} \mathrm{Xe}^{131}\text{ (stable)}$$

and there are many cases of isomeric transitions in this classification. Tellurium may be used also for examples of the latter. Thus

$$\mathrm{Te}^{126}(n,\gamma)\mathrm{Te}^{127*} \xrightarrow[105\text{ days}]{\text{IT},\,e^-} \mathrm{Te}^{127} \xrightarrow[9.3\text{ hr}]{\beta^-} \mathrm{I}^{127}\text{ (stable)}$$

and the previous example is complicated by the reaction

$$\mathrm{Te}^{130}(n,\gamma)\mathrm{Te}^{131*} \xrightarrow[30\text{ hr}]{\text{IT},\,e^-} \mathrm{Te}^{131} \xrightarrow[25\text{ min}]{\beta^-} \mathrm{I}^{131},\text{ etc.}$$

In addition there are artificially produced series such as the neptunium series, the collateral branches of the natural series, and the fission-product chains.

As in the case of a mixture of independent radionuclides, an obvious approach to the problem of determining the half-lives of the components is to carry out radiochemical separations. As before, the presence of species which are difficult, if not impossible, to separate chemically is a limiting factor. Genetically related isomers are now added to the list of species separated with difficulty. In addition, the chemically separated parent does not show a simple decay curve, because of the growth of a daughter radionuclide. In the latter case it is assumed that the radiation from the daughter is detected along with that of the parent. Even when the half-life of a component can be determined satisfactorily after chemical separation, etc., analysis of a composite parent-daughter decay curve is of use in establishing genetic relationships. The differential-count and spectrometer techniques mentioned in the preceding section have considerable application in the study of mixtures of genetically related radionuclides.

Case I. Half-life of Parent Greater than That of Daughter. Systems for which $T_A > T_B$ have certain characteristics which may be recognized by examination of Eq. (8-33). For example, the term $e^{-\lambda_B t}$ approaches zero more rapidly than the term $e^{-\lambda_A t}$ with increasing time, eventually becoming negligible with respect to the latter, so that the relative amount of daughter and parent activity reaches an essentially constant value. *Thereafter*, both the parent and the daughter activity decay with the half-life of the parent. Thus

$$\frac{A_B}{(A_A)_0} = \frac{\lambda_B}{\lambda_B - \lambda_A} e^{-\lambda_A t} = \frac{T_A}{T_A - T_B} e^{-0.693t/T_A} \tag{8-38}$$

or

$$\frac{A_B}{A_A} = \frac{\lambda_B}{\lambda_B - \lambda_A} = \frac{T_A}{T_A - T_B} \tag{8-39}$$

and the total activity is given by

$$A_A + A_B = A_{\text{total}} = \left(1 + \frac{T_A}{T_A - T_B}\right) A_A \tag{8-40}$$

Prior to the time when steady state is reached, the total activity goes through a maximum value at the time

$$t_{(A_{total})\max} = \frac{3.323 T_A T_B}{T_A - T_B} \log \frac{T_A^2}{2T_A T_B - T_B^2} \tag{8-41}$$

This equation is obtained by setting the derivative $d(A_A + A_B)/dt$ [with A_B given by Eq. (8-34)] equal to zero and solving for t.

When the steady-state condition obtains, the daughter is said to be in "equilibrium" with the parent and decays at a rate equal to its rate of formation. This condition is not one of equilibrium in the sense of reversibility, of course. Furthermore, the time when steady state is reached is not a uniquely determined value, but may be taken arbitrarily as the time required for the contribution of the exponential term $e^{-\lambda_B t}$ to be essentially undetectable in the laboratory. The approach to steady state may be expressed in terms of the ratio $e^{-\lambda_B t}/e^{-\lambda_A t}$, which is a measure of the extent to which the system falls short of the steady-state condition. The time, expressed as half-lives of the daughter, for the ratio to have the values 0.10, 0.05, 0.01, and 0.001 for various ratios of T_A/T_B is shown in Fig. 8-4. Thus, from the figure, the ratio of exponential terms is 0.01 after eight half-lives of the daughter for a system with T_A/T_B equal to six.

If the rate of decay of the total activity of a system in the steady state is used to calculate the initial total activity or graphically extrapolate a decay curve, the result corresponds to the condition before purification of the parent substance and not to the actual activity of the parent alone. Thus from Eq. (8-40), for $t = 0$,

$$(A_{\text{total}})_{0,\,extrap} = \left(1 + \frac{T_A}{T_A - T_B}\right)(A_A)_0 \tag{8-42}$$

Similarly, the extrapolated initial daughter activity is

$$(A_B)_{0,\,extrap} = \frac{T_A}{T_A - T_B}(A_A)_0 \tag{8-43}$$

If the parent is sufficiently longer-lived than the daughter so that the change in amount of parent during the time for steady state to be reached is negligible, the steady-state condition is referred to as "secular equilibrium." On the other hand, if there is appreciable decay of the parent before the daughter reaches a steady state, the steady-state condition is referred to as "transient equilibrium." In terms of Eq. (8-38), the two types of "equilibrium" may be distinguished as follows:

Secular Equilibrium. For a system which can attain secular equilibrium, the term $e^{-\lambda_A t}$ is approximately unity for values of t up to at least

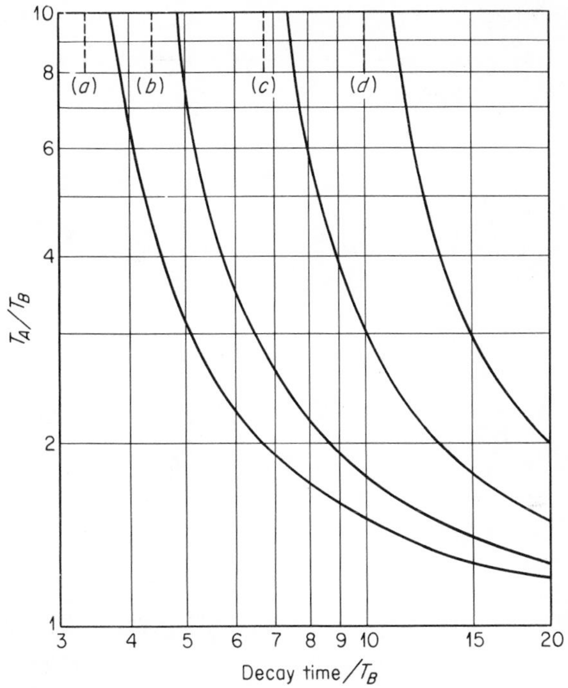

FIG. 8-4. Time required to establish the following values of $e^{-\lambda_B t}/e^{-\lambda_A t}$: (*a*) 0.10; (*b*) 0.05; (*c*) 0.01; (*d*) 0.001.

the time for attainment of the steady state, e.g., 7 to 10 times the half-life of the daughter, and the constant $\lambda_B/(\lambda_B - \lambda_A)$ is not significantly greater than unity, since λ_A is negligible relative to λ_B. Then, Eq. (8-34) becomes

$$A_B = (A_A)_0(1 - e^{-0.693t/T_B}) \tag{8-44}$$

and after steady state is reached $A_B = (A_A)_0$. This condition would hold for any system for which the half-life of the parent is, say as a specific example, 1,000 times greater than that of the daughter regardless of the actual values (seconds, minutes, hours, etc.) of the half-lives.

Two examples of systems which can attain secular equilibrium are 1,620-year $Ra^{226} \rightarrow$ 3.824-day Rn^{222}, illustrated in Fig. 8-5, and 1.0-year $Ru^{106} \rightarrow$ 30-sec Rh^{106}. During the initial growth period of the daughter, the difference $(A_A)_0 - A_B$ is a function of the half-life of the daughter and is equal to $(A_A)_0 e^{-0.693t/T_B}$, as may be readily seen from Eq. (8-44).

For very long decay times such that the decay of the parent after steady state has been reached is not negligible, Eq. (8-38) becomes

$$A_B = (A_A)_0 e^{-\lambda_A t} = A_A \tag{8-45}$$

For n nuclides in secular equilibrium, $A_A = A_B = A_C = A_D$, etc., and the total disintegration rate is nA_A, or $n(A_A)_0$ if decay of the parent is

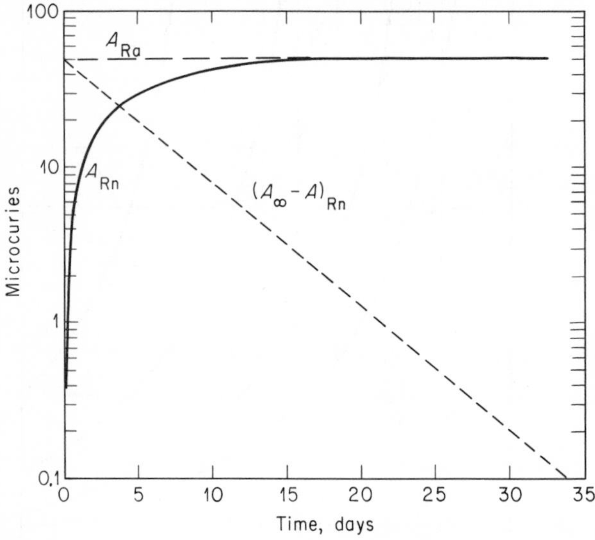

FIG. 8-5. Secular equilibrium: growth of Rn^{222} (3.824 days) from Ra^{226} (1,620 years).

negligible. For example, in that portion of the uranium $(4n + 2)$ series which is present in separated, aged, natural uranium compounds, four nuclides are in secular equilibrium. These are

$$_{92}U^{238} \xrightarrow[4.50 \times 10^9 \text{ years}]{\alpha} {}_{90}Th^{234} \xrightarrow[24.10 \text{ days}]{\beta^-} {}_{91}Pa^{234} \xrightarrow[1.175 \text{ min}]{\beta^-}$$

$$_{92}U^{234} \xrightarrow[2.48 \times 10^5 \text{ years}]{\alpha} {}_{90}Th^{230}, \text{ etc.}$$

Whereas all members of this series terminating with RaG (Pb^{206}) are present in uranium minerals, the series in refined uranium ends in effect with the long-lived U^{234}.

For a system which attains secular equilibrium and involves a very-long-lived parent, the half-life of the daughter can be determined from the rate of growth of the daughter. When the growth of the daughter is followed independently of the parent until secular equilibrium is essentially established, i.e., about $10T_B$, the value of T_B may be obtained by analysis, graphically or otherwise, of the data expressed in terms of the difference between the saturation or equilibrium apparent activity and the apparent activities observed at various times. The growth of the apparent activity of the daughter is expressed by the following equation, obtained from Eq. (8-44):

$$R_B = (R_B)_\infty(1 - e^{-0.693t/T_B}) \tag{8-46}$$

where $(R_B)_\infty$ is the equilibrium apparent activity and is equal to $Y_B(A_A)_0$. The difference $(R_B)_\infty - R_B$ is then

$$(R_B)_\infty - R_B = (R_B)_\infty e^{-0.693t/T_B} \tag{8-47}$$

which is simply an equation for the decay of the daughter (see Fig. 8-5).

The half-life of the daughter may be evaluated also from the slope of the growth curve obtained by plotting the growth data on rectangular coordinate paper. From Eq. (8-46) the slope of such a growth curve is found to be

$$\frac{dR_B}{dt} = \frac{0.693}{T_B}(R_B)_\infty e^{-0.693t/T_B} \tag{8-48}$$

The initial slope of the curve is then equal to $0.693(R_B)_\infty/T_B$, and the equation for the growth curve, if it followed the initial slope, would be

$$R_B - \frac{0.693t}{T_B}(R_B)_\infty = 0 \tag{8-49}$$

If the initial tangent is extended by means of this equation until it intersects the asymptote to the curve at $(R_B)_\infty$, the value of t at the intersection is simply $T_B/0.693$. This is illustrated in Fig. 8-6. Owing to the long extrapolation of the initial tangent, a small error in drawing the tangent will result in a large error in T_B.

The methods described above for analyzing growth data require a knowledge of the apparent activity of the daughter at equilibrium. In the event that an incomplete growth curve is obtained, the procedure for evaluating T_B is more difficult. A satisfactory method is based on plotting the slope of the growth curve as a function of time on semilogarithmic graph paper. According to Eq. (8-48) such a plot is linear, and T_B may be obtained by inspection. There are many well-known techniques for evaluating the slope at various points along a growth curve. The method of counting squares along the sides of a triangle whose hypotenuse is tangent to the curve and the method of predetermined angles are among the more simple ones. (In any case the original growth curve must be drawn with extreme care.) Briefly, the method of predetermined angles is as follows: Angles, relative to the abscissa, in the range of 10 to 90° and in intervals of 5° are marked off with the aid of a protractor in the lower portion of the graph paper. A straightedge that is set on the paper at one of the angles serves as a guide for a triangle. The triangle is moved along the straightedge until the former becomes tangent with the curve. The point of contact is found by approaching the curve from the convex side. The value of t is noted and

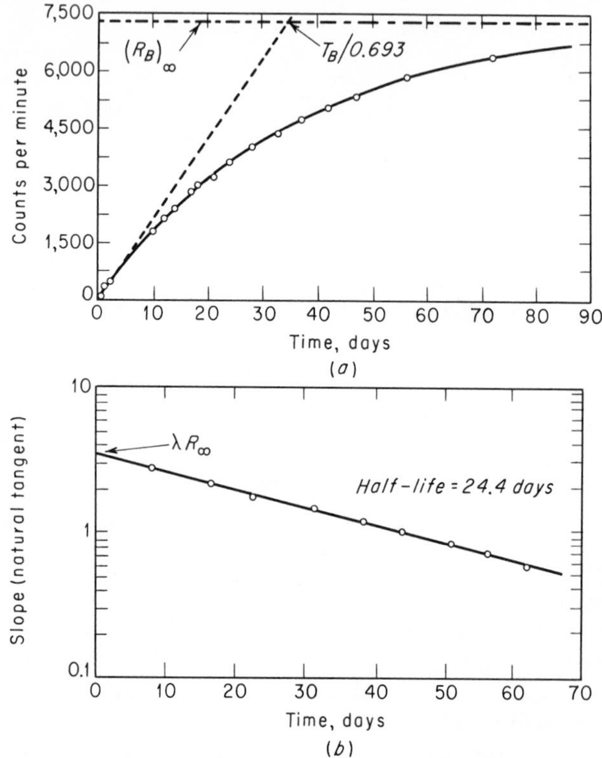

FIG. 8-6. Growth of UX_1 from U^{238}. (a) Growth curve; (b) slope of growth curve.

tabulated with the corresponding angle and its natural tangent. If desired, the value of $(R_B)_\infty$ may be calculated from T_B and the intercept on the ordinate.

The half-life of the long-lived parent does not appear in Eq. (8-48), and its value is not obtained from data for the growth of a short-lived daughter. However, there are cases for which the activity of a parent which emits weak radiation is conveniently measured in terms of the apparent activity of a short-lived daughter in equilibrium. One example is that of 1-year Ru^{106}–30-sec Rh^{106}.

When two radionuclides are in secular equilibrium, the half-life of one may be calculated from that of the other, since $N_B T_A = N_A T_B$. It is necessary to know either the weight of each species or the relative number of atoms. The latter may be determined for very-long-lived radionuclides by mass-spectrographic measurements. The half-lives of the naturally occurring isotopes of uranium determined by this method were reported by Nier (19) in 1939 and by Chamberlain, Williams, and Yuster (20) in 1946.

When the half-life for the second member is extremely short in a series such as $A \rightarrow B \rightarrow C$, coincidence-counting techniques can be used to determine the short half-life period. Several methods, based on coincidence measurements, have been used successfully.

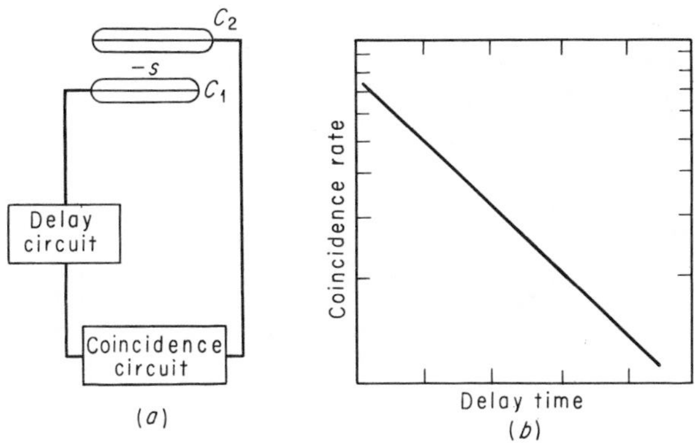

FIG. 8-7. Coincidence method of very short half-lives.

We shall consider the method of delayed coincidence as an example. A typical two-channel counting circuit is indicated in Fig. 8-7. A source s is placed between two radiation detectors, e.g., Geiger tubes. The pulses from one counter, C_1, are delayed electronically before entering the coincidence circuit. The pulses from the other counter enter the coincidence circuit directly. The coincidence counting rate is observed as a function of the time that the pulses from C_1 are delayed. A short-time measuring device such as an oscilloscope can be used to measure the delay time. When the logarithm of the observed coincidence counting rate is plotted as a function of the delay time, a typical straight-line decay curve is obtained. This is expected since the disintegration rate of the daughter radionuclide decreases exponentially as a function of the time after formation. The reference time is the instant of disintegration of the parent, and therefore the greatest number of coincidences per unit time are observed when the pulse from C_1 is not delayed. The observed coincidence rate, corrected for the known random coincidence rate, represents the rate for delayed pulses from C_1 due to radiation from radionuclide A arriving in coincidence with pulses from C_2 due to radiation from the short-lived radionuclide B.

DeBenedetti and McGowan (21) used the method of delayed coincidence to show the existence of a 22-μsec metastable state for Ta^{181} produced in the beta decay of Hf^{181}. Studier and Hyde (7) have described a relatively simple coincidence method which they used to measure the half-life of 0.019-sec Rn^{218}, the daughter of 38.0-sec Ra^{222}.

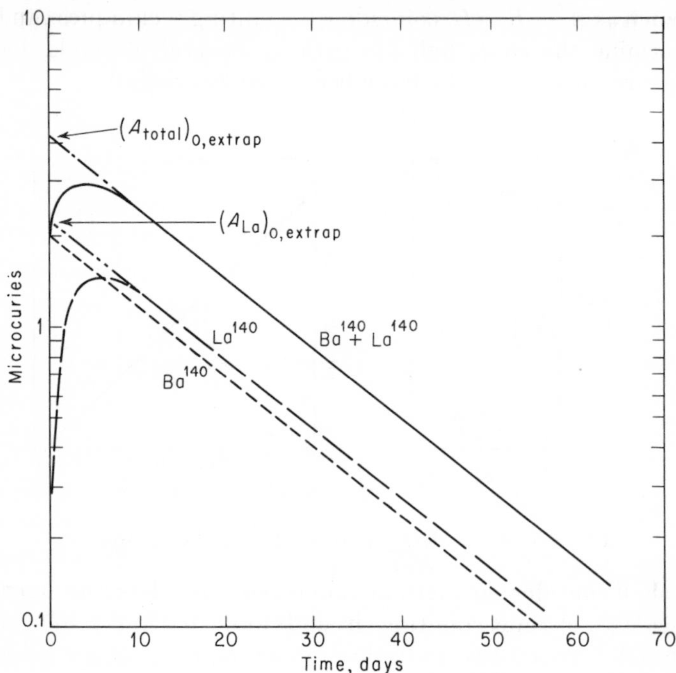

FIG. 8-8. Transient equilibrium: Ba^{140} (12.8 days)–La^{140} (40 hr).

Transient Equilibrium. For a system which can attain transient equilibrium, the decrease in the value of $e^{-\lambda_A t}$ below unity during the attainment of equilibrium cannot be neglected, and the values of λ_A and λ_B are sufficiently similar so that $\lambda_B/(\lambda_B - \lambda_A)$ is significantly greater than unity. The steady-state disintegration rate of the daughter exceeds that of the parent. Thus, for the fission-product chain

$$Ba^{140} \xrightarrow[\beta^-,\gamma]{12.80 \text{ days}} La^{140} \xrightarrow[\beta^-,\gamma]{40.0 \text{ hr}} Ce^{140} \text{ (stable)}$$

A_{La} is equal to 1.15 A_{Ba}, as illustrated in Fig. 8-8. The time after purification of Ba^{140} at which the La^{140} activity reaches a maximum is 5.67 days, or 1.40 times T_B. The total activity reaches a maximum after 3.92 days.

After transient equilibrium is established in a mixture of two genetically related radionuclides, the effective half-life is that of the parent. The half-life T_A is then obtained simply from the decay curve for the transient-equilibrium mixture.

The half-life of the daughter, when there are no other descendants, can be obtained generally by separating the daughter radionuclide radiochemically and carrying out decay measurements on the product.

The half-life of the daughter can be evaluated also from data for the growth of the daughter or from growth-decay data for the mixture. If we subtract Eq. (8-34) from Eq. (8-38), we obtain for the difference

$$\Delta A_B = \frac{T_A(A_A)_0}{T_A - T_B} e^{-0.693t/T_B} \tag{8-50}$$

which corresponds to subtracting the growth curve for the daughter from the straight line obtained by extrapolating the growth curve back to zero time after transient equilibrium has been established. The logarithms of the difference values are plotted against time, preferably with the time scale expanded relative to that for the growth curve. Since the value of T_B is found from the slope of the difference curve, which resembles a simple decay curve, it is not necessary to know the detection coefficients.

When the half-life of either the parent or the daughter is known, that of the other may be obtained from a composite growth-decay curve of the type illustrated in Fig. 8-8. It will be recalled that the time when the total disintegration rate reaches a maximum is given by Eq. (8-41), which may be solved for either T_A or T_B. In practice, however, it is difficult to obtain an accurate half-life value by this method, since $t_{\max}$ is subject to considerable uncertainty and a small error in $t_{\max}$ results in a large error in the calculated half-life. Thus, although the maximum increase in total absolute activity is a constant for a given system, both the observed increase in the apparent activity and the time corresponding to the maximum counting rate depend upon the type of detector used, the nature of the radiation emitted, the method of mounting the source, etc. An expression for $t_{(R_{\text{total}})\max}$ which includes Y_A and Y_B is

$$t_{(R_{\text{total}})\max} = \frac{3.323T_AT_B}{T_A - T_B} \log \frac{kT_A^2}{(k+1)T_AT_B - T_B^2} \tag{8-51}$$

where $k = Y_B/Y_A$. The possible range of values for $t_{(R_{\text{total}})\max}$ may be deduced quite simply. Thus, for $Y_B = 0$, $Y_A > 0$, the counting rate is greatest when $t = 0$ and never goes through a maximum. For $Y_B = Y_A$, $t_{(R_{\text{total}})\max}$ is the same as $t_{(A_{\text{total}})\max}$, given by Eq. (8-41). Finally, for $Y_B > 0$ but $Y_A = 0$, $t_{(R_{\text{total}})\max}$ is equal to $t_{(R_B)\max}$, which is greater than $t_{(A_{\text{total}})\max}$.

It will be recalled that Eq. (8-41) holds only for the case that the chemical separation used to prepare the sample of parent nuclide removes all the daughter nuclide. If $(N_B)_0 \neq 0$, the time for maximum total activity is shifted to lower values. The effect is readily calculated for the case $Y_A = Y_B$ by including the term $(A_B)_0 e^{-0.693t/T_B}$ in the total activity $A_A + A_B$ and deriving the expression for $t_{(A_{total})max}$.

Another method for finding T_A depends upon a knowledge of the half-life of the daughter and the time at which the daughter activity reaches a maximum. The data for the growth curve are obtained by making successive quantitative separations of the daughter radionuclide from the sample of the parent which has been freed of descendant radionuclides at a reference time $t = 0$. The counting rate of the daughter after each separation is added to the cumulated counting rate, adjusted for decay, for all previously separated samples. In this case, t_{max} is independent of the counting yield Y_B, provided, of course, that Y_B remains constant. Since T_B can be found directly from decay measurements for the separated daughter, Eq. (8-37) may be used to calculate T_A.

A value for T_A or T_B can be calculated from the initial counting rate of the parent, the extrapolated initial value for either the total activity or the daughter activity, and the other half-life. Again, the counting yields must be known, since Eq. (8-42), for example, when expressed in terms of the counting rate, becomes

$$(R_{total})_{0,extrap} = \left(1 + \frac{T_A}{T_A - T_B} \frac{Y_B}{Y_A}\right)(R_A)_0$$

It should be noted that any method depending upon properties of the system in a state of transient equilibrium is not very satisfactory as a practical matter unless the half-life of the parent is at least three times greater than that of the daughter.

When the half-life of T_A or T_B is known and the detection coefficient for each substance is known, the half-life of the second radionuclide may be estimated by selecting values of the half-life until a curve based on the calculated total activity fits the experimental curve. This general method of comparing a theoretical curve with an experimental one was used by Studier and Hyde (7) to determine the half-life of Pa^{230} (17 days) by following the growth of its 20.8-day daughter, U^{230}. In this case, the growth of U^{230} was followed by alpha counting without interference from the beta rays from Pa^{230}, and the theoretical curve was based on Eq. (8-33).

There are several genetically related isomers which belong to this case of $T_A > T_B$. Among these are the familiar Br^{80*} (4.4 hr)–Br^{80} (18 min) and Zn^{69*} (13.8 hr)–Zn^{69} (57 min). The bromine isomers can be separated chemically since the chemical bond involving the Br^{80*}

in a substance like ethyl bromide is broken when this radionuclide undergoes isomeric transition to the ground state.

Case II. Half-life of Parent Equal to That of Daughter. Admittedly the occurrence of a pair of related radionuclides having identical half-lives is most unlikely. There are, however, a few pairs for which T_A and T_B are not very different. For example, we have

$$\mathrm{RaB} \xrightarrow[26.8\ \mathrm{min}]{\beta^-,\gamma} \mathrm{RaC} \xrightarrow[19.7\ \mathrm{min}]{\beta^-,\alpha} \begin{matrix}\mathrm{RaC}' \\ \mathrm{RaC}''\end{matrix}, \text{ etc.}$$

It is mainly of academic interest to examine briefly the limiting case as the values of T_A and T_B approach each other. The case is illustrated in Fig. 8-9.

When the half-lives are identical, the general equations (8-33) and (8-34) assume an indeterminate form. However, if we go back to Eq. (8-31) and write it in the form

$$\frac{dN_B}{dt} = (A_A)_0 e^{-\lambda_A t} - \lambda_B N_B \quad (8\text{-}52)$$

and if we replace λ_A by λ_B and integrate with the condition that $(N_B)_0 = 0$, we have

$$N_B = (A_A)_0 t e^{-\lambda_B t} = A_A t \quad (8\text{-}53)$$

and $$A_B = \lambda_B A_A t$$

$$= 0.693 A_A \frac{t}{T_B} \quad (8\text{-}54)$$

The time for maximum absolute activity of the daughter, obtained as for the derivation of Eq. (8-37), is

$$t_{(A_B)\max} = \frac{1}{\lambda_B} = 1.443 T_B \quad (8\text{-}55)$$

and at this time, according to Eq. (8-54),

$$A_B = A_A = (A_A)_0 e^{-1} \quad (8\text{-}56)$$

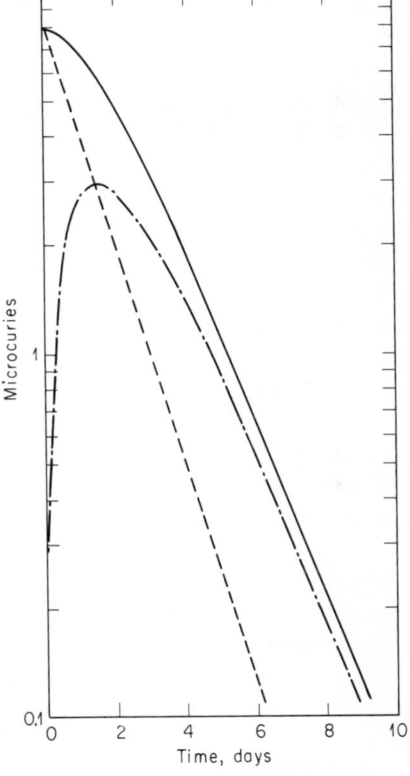

FIG. 8-9. Decay curves for parent and daughter of equal half-life ($T_A = T_B = 1$ day).

Finally, the total activity is at its maximum value at $t = 0$.

Case III. Half-life of Daughter Longer than That of Parent. Examples of a pair of genetically related radionuclides for which the half-life of the daughter is longer than that of the parent are Sr^{92} (2.7 hr)–Y^{92} (3.60 hr), Ce^{143} (33 hr)–Pr^{143} (13.7 days), and RaE (5.0 days)–RaF (138 days).

As for the case when $T_A > T_B$, $t_{(A_B)\max}$, the time at which the daughter activity has grown to the maximum value, is given by Eq. (8-37). The total absolute activity, however, is never greater than that of the parent initially, and a state of equilibrium is never reached.

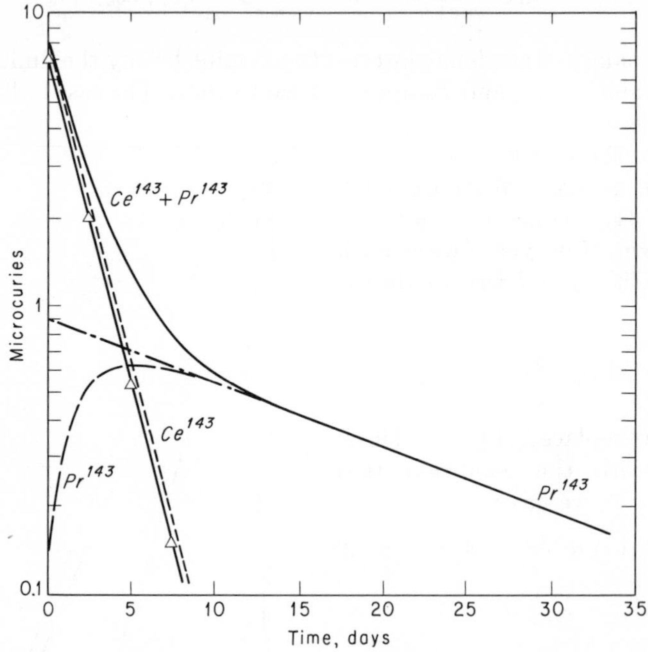

FIG. 8-10. Decay curves for Ce^{143} (33 hr)–Pr^{143} (13.8 days).

When T_B is at least an order of magnitude longer than T_A, the total absolute activity becomes, after a period of the order of $10T_A$, essentially equal to that of the daughter alone. Then we may write

$$A_B = A_{\text{total}} = \frac{T_A(A_A)_0}{T_B - T_A} e^{-0.693t/T_B} \tag{8-57}$$

since the exponential term involving T_A becomes negligible. From this equation an expression may be obtained for the extrapolated initial daughter or total absolute activity. Thus we have

$$(A_B)_{0,extrap} = \frac{T_A}{T_B - T_A} (A_A)_0 \tag{8-58}$$

The value of $(A_B)_{0,extrap}$ is then less than $(A_A)_0$. In Fig. 8-10, the system

Ce^{143} (33.0 hr)–Pr^{143} (13.7 days) is illustrated for an initial Ce^{143} activity of 8 μc.

If the daughter has a very long half-life, so that its decay may be neglected, Eq. (8-34) reduces to

$$A_B = \frac{T_A(A_A)_0}{T_B}(1 - e^{-0.693t/T_A}) \tag{8-59}$$

and accordingly the daughter grows in with the half-life of the parent. Similarly, Eq. (8-58) now becomes

$$(A_B)_{0,extrap} = \frac{T_A}{T_B}(A_A)_0 \tag{8-60}$$

The composite decay curve for this case (assuming the daughter to be absent initially) has the general appearance of that for a mixture of independent radionuclides. Inspection does not reveal that the longer-lived material is being produced from the shorter-lived one.

The half-life of the daughter may be obtained from the slope of the decay curve after the half-life of the mixture becomes essentially equal to that of the daughter alone.

The half-life of the parent can be found by extrapolating the decay curve for the daughter back to zero time, subtracting this curve from the observed composite decay curve, and plotting the difference. This is, of course, the same method used for the mixture of independent radionuclides. The semilogarithmic plot of the difference curve will give the proper half-life for the parent but an incorrect value for $(R_A)_0$. This may be seen from the equation for the difference curve, which is

$$(R_A)_0\left(1 - \frac{T_A}{T_B - T_A}\frac{Y_B}{Y_A}\right)e^{-0.693t/T_A} = R_{\text{total}} - R_B \tag{8-61}$$

Analysis by this method is not satisfactory if the half-life of the daughter is less than about three times that of the parent. In any case, the method of graphical resolution will not reveal that the radionuclides are genetically related.

Several methods discussed previously for the case when $T_A > T_B$ apply to this case equally well. For example, when T_B, $(R_B)_{0,extrap}$, and $(R_A)_0$ have been found from the composite decay curve, a value of T_A may be calculated from the equation

$$(R_B)_{0,extrap} = \frac{T_A}{T_B - T_A}\frac{Y_B}{Y_A}(R_A)_0 \tag{8-62}$$

Another previously discussed method for determining the half-life of the parent makes use of Eq. (8-37). This requires a knowledge of the half-life of the daughter and the time when the activity of the daughter reaches a maximum. Both of these values are obtained by radiochemically separating the daughter species from a given parent source and plotting a growth curve for the daughter. Quantitative separation is necessary, but a knowledge of the counting yield Y_B is not required. This method was used by Livingood and Seaborg (22) to estimate the half-life of Te^{131}, the parent of 8-day I^{131}. A value of 1.2 days was calculated for the half-life of the parent. A growth curve based on this value of 1.2 days was calculated for I^{131}. The calculated curve lay below the observed curve for the first few days. An additional short-lived parent was suspected and later reported by Seaborg, Livingood, and Kennedy (23). A parent with a 25-min half-life was found by using the same method and analyzing the growth curve during the early period of I^{131} growth. The tellurium isomers were shown to be genetically related, with the 1.2-day isomer assigned to the upper state.

Among the few examples of genetically related isomers with $T_B > T_A$ are Co^{60*} (10.7 min)–Co^{60} (5.3 years) and Y^{91*} (51.0 min)–Y^{91} (57 days).

Finally, when $T_B \gg T_A$, the value of T_A can be obtained directly from the decay of the parent or indirectly from the growth of the daughter (Eq. 8-59). The half-life of the daughter can be obtained from Eq. (8-60), provided the counting yields (or their ratio) are known so that absolute activities may be calculated from counting rates.

For the case in which the daughter is stable ($T_B = \infty$), the growth of the daughter may be calculated by means of Eq. (8-30). From a measured value of the ratio of the number of atoms of the stable daughter to the number of atoms of the parent at a given time, the half-life of the parent can be calculated. The ratio is simply

$$\frac{N_B}{N_A} = e^{\lambda_A t} - 1 \tag{8-63}$$

As an illustration of an application of this method we may refer to the work of Ahrens and Evans (24), who determined the decay constants of K^{40} by evaluating the ratio Ca^{40}/K^{40} in samples of lepidolite having a known potassium content and an age known to be 2.1×10^9 years. The total calcium content was determined spectrographically, and an average observed nonradiogenic calcium content was subtracted to give the calcium formed by beta decay of K^{40}. However, since K^{40} decays also by electron capture to form Ar^{40}, a modified form of Eq. (8-63) was employed.

If λ_1 is the constant for beta decay and λ_2 is the disintegration constant for decay by K capture, Eq. (8-63) becomes

$$\frac{N_B}{N_A} = \frac{\lambda_1}{\lambda_1 + \lambda_2} \left(e^{(\lambda_1 + \lambda_2)t} - 1\right) \tag{8-64}$$

The half-life for the electron-capture process was calculated from the value of the total half-life obtained and from recalculated published values for the half-life for the beta-decay process.

In order to determine the half-lives of some of the short-lived (of the order of seconds) noble-gas fission products with longer-lived radioactive descendants, Dillard, Adams, Finston, and Turkevich (25) and others have employed the charged-wire technique of Makower and Geiger (26). In their experiments the mixture of radioactive isotopes of krypton and xenon was passed at a known rate of flow through a tube containing a negatively charged wire along the length of which the radioactive descendants deposited exponentially. The wire was cut into sections which were analyzed radiochemically for each of the daughter radionuclides. A graph of the logarithm of the apparent activity of the daughter per unit length of wire as a function of the distance along the wire resulted in a simple decay curve. The half-life of the parent gas was calculated from the flow rate of the gas and the distribution of activity along the wire.

8-5. Synthesis of Radionuclides

General Equations. When a target is irradiated with projectiles such as neutrons, protons, deuterons, helium nuclei, photons, etc., the nuclear-reaction products may be either isotopes of the elements in the target or nuclides of other elements. Although both stable and radioactive products may be formed, the former will not be included in this discussion.

Consider the production of a single radionuclide by irradiation of a thin target with slow neutrons. Depending on the composition of the target, several reactions might occur. One reaction might be represented by an equation such as

$$_zE^A + {}_0n^1 \rightarrow {}_zE^{A+1} + \gamma$$

A specific example might be the reaction $Cu^{63}(n,\gamma)Cu^{64}$. For ease in writing the equations which follow, $_zE^A$ will be replaced by K, and $_zE^{A+1}$ by L. Then, the net rate of change of the number of L atoms is given by the expression

$$\frac{dN_L}{dt} = F_L - \lambda_L N_L \tag{8-65}$$

where F_L is the rate of formation of radionuclide L. In the derivation of this equation it is assumed that L is not present in the target before bombardment and that it is not removed by any nuclear transformation other than spontaneous disintegration. The effect of removal of L by reaction with neutrons is discussed later.

Before Eq. (8-65) can be integrated, the time dependence of F_L must be examined. Ideally, the rate of formation of L atoms is maintained constant throughout the irradiation period; otherwise F_L must be expressed as a known function of time. After integration with F_L constant, Eq. (8-65) becomes

$$N_L = \frac{F_L}{\lambda_L}(1 - e^{-\lambda_L t}) \tag{8-66}$$

and in terms of activity and half-life this is

$$A_L = F_L(1 - e^{-0.693t/T_L}) \tag{8-67}$$

At a time t' after removal from the neutron source, the disintegration rate of the radionuclide L is

$$A_L = F_L(1 - e^{-0.693t/T_L})e^{-0.693t'/T_L} \tag{8-68}$$

It should be noted that these equations are general and are not restricted to the (n,γ) reaction used as an example. For each product formed in a target an equation such as Eq. (8-68) with the appropriate constants applies.

The Rate of Nuclear Reaction in a Target. In the above equations the term F_L depends upon the number of projectiles incident upon the target per unit time, the number of target atoms which could react to form the desired radionuclide, and the probability that a fusion of the incident particle with the proper target nucleus will result in the formation of the specified product radionuclide. For the purpose of illustrating the evaluation of F_L, we shall continue to use an (n,γ) reaction as an example.

The number of particles of known energy striking the target per square centimeter per second is referred to as the flux, which we shall represent by ϕ. The neutron flux is also commonly written as nv, where n is the neutron density (number per cubic centimeter) and v is the neutron velocity. Slow-neutron fluxes up to 10^{15} neutrons/(cm^2)(sec) are attainable in nuclear reactors, with 10^{12} to 10^{13} common today. Ideally, the flux is uniform throughout the target. This condition may be approached somewhat more readily for a uranium reactor than for a cyclotron or a small neutron source (e.g., radium-beryllium type).

The reaction probability is expressed in terms of an effective area or cross section σ for the target nucleus. Although the cross section is not identical with the physical cross-sectional area, it is frequently of the same order of magnitude and is commonly expressed in barns, where 1 barn $= 10^{-24}$ cm^2. Weinberg and Wigner (27) prefer the word "fermi" for 10^{-24} cm^2 and use the symbol F. In principle, for every nuclide there is a separate cross section for each of the possible nuclear reactions. The various cross sections which are measured for neutron-induced processes are the following: absorption, σ_a; activation, σ_{act}; and scattering, σ_s. Activation cross sections are for absorption reactions which lead to radionuclide formation, for example, (n,γ), (n,p), (n,α) reactions. Cross sections are energy-dependent, and it is necessary to indicate the energy of bombarding particles. Each nuclide has its own characteristic absorption spectrum for each reaction, but at low energies, i.e., kinetic energies near that corresponding to thermal motion at room temperature, many cross sections follow a simple "$1/v$ law" for reactions such as radiative capture (n,γ). For such nuclides, σ varies inversely as the neutron velocity over the region of "$1/v$" dependence. For a thermal-neutron flux, thermal-neutron cross sections must be used. The latter are given for a neutron velocity of 2,200 m/sec, corresponding to an energy of 0.026 ev at a temperature of 300°K. This velocity is the most probable velocity for neutrons having a Maxwell-Boltzmann energy distribution at that temperature. In the region where the "$1/v$ law" applies, (σv) is constant; hence $nv\sigma$, or $\phi\sigma$, applies even though the neutrons are not monoenergetic.

Among the compilations of neutron cross sections available is that of Hughes and coworkers (28), which is periodically revised. A few thermal-neutron cross sections are listed in Appendix G.

The number of atoms N_K of a given isotope of a target element is calculated from the number of grams and the atomic weight of the element, Avogadro's number, and the percentage abundance, i.e., atom fraction f of the isotope K. The proper cross section to be used with this number of atoms is the isotopic cross section, i.e., that given for the particular isotope rather than the normal element when the element is not monoisotopic.

In terms of the above quantities, F is given by the product

$$\phi(\sigma_{act})_K N_K$$

which is the total number of reactions per second in the target leading to the formation of a particular nuclide. For F to be constant with time, as assumed in the derivation of Eq. (8-66), the flux must remain constant and the extent of depletion of the target nuclei must be negligible. Moreover, if the target is not a thin one, the flux may not be uniform throughout its entirety. Thus, very thin foils must be used if a uniform flux is requisite. This is especially true for target elements having a large absorption cross section. Since the attenuation of neutron flux with depth within the target is essentially exponential, suitable corrections can be applied when justified.

Certain analogies may be drawn between nuclear reactions and chemical reactions. When the rate of production of a nuclide is constant, the reaction is somewhat like a zero-order chemical reaction. Examples of the latter are reactions occurring on completely covered surfaces and certain photochemical reactions. Moreover, like chemical reactions which reach a steady state when the rate of a zero-order forward reaction becomes equal to that of a reverse first-order reaction, a steady state can be reached in the production of a radionuclide when the rate of production is equal to the rate of decay. Examination of Eq. (8-67) shows that, for an irradiation period which is long compared with the half-life of the radionuclide being produced, the activity becomes essentially equal to the rate of formation. The activity corresponding to this steady state is termed the "saturation" activity and is the maximum attainable for the given irradiation conditions.

Evaluation of F before an irradiation may not be feasible since ϕ or σ, or both, may not be known. Thus, for cyclotron bombardments it is common practice to refer to the observed activity yield for a radionuclide in terms of an excitation function in units such as millicuries per microampere-hour or milliampere-hour. Target yields for a number of reactions have been given by Garrison and Hamilton (29) and Martin and coworkers (30).

Indirect Synthesis of the Second Member of a Radioactive Series. As an illustration of the method of finding the amount of a radioactive daughter produced by decay of an ancestor that was produced by nuclear reaction, we may take the reaction

$$K(n,\gamma)L \xrightarrow{\beta^-} M \xrightarrow{\beta^-} N$$

An example of this is

$$\text{Pd}^{110}(n,\gamma)\text{Pd}^{111} \xrightarrow[\text{26 min}]{\beta^-} \text{Ag}^{111} \xrightarrow[\text{7.5 days}]{\beta^-} \text{Cd}^{111} \text{ (stable)}$$

The basic rate equation for the daughter M is

$$\frac{dN_M}{dt} = \lambda_L N_L - \lambda_M N_M \tag{8-69}$$

If $(N_L)_0 = 0$, if F does not vary with time, and if the loss of the parent or daughter by further nuclear reaction is neglected, Eq. (8-69) may be written in the form

$$\frac{dN_M}{dt} = F_L(1 - e^{-\lambda_L t}) - \lambda_M N_M \tag{8-70}$$

Integration of this equation with the condition that $(N_M)_0 = 0$ leads to

$$A_M = F_L\left(1 + \frac{\lambda_L e^{-\lambda_M t} - \lambda_M e^{-\lambda_L t}}{\lambda_M - \lambda_L}\right) \tag{8-71}$$

Rearranged and expressed in terms of half-lives, this becomes

$$A_M = F_L\left[\frac{T_L}{T_L - T_M}(1 - e^{-0.693t/T_L}) - \frac{T_M}{T_L - T_M}(1 - e^{-0.693t/T_M})\right] \tag{8-72}$$

General equations for more complicated cases including the production of radionuclides in a series with successive transmutation have been derived by Rubinson (31).

Removal of Product Nuclide by Multiple Independent Processes. In general it is not necessary to consider removal of the product nuclide in a target by methods other than radioactive decay. However, there are two other ways for removal of the product during irradiation which must be taken into account in certain cases. One of these is "burnout," or transformation of the product nuclide into another nuclide by nuclear reaction with the bombarding particles. This process is generally not significant (although always occurring) unless (1) the product nuclide has a very large absorption cross section (e.g., for Xe^{135} produced in fission, $\sigma_a = 2.7 \times 10^6$ barns) for thermal neutrons, (2) the flux is extremely high, or (3) both are significantly high.

The rate of burnout of L atoms would be $\phi(\sigma_a)_L N_L$, and Eq. (8-65) would become

$$\frac{dN_L}{dt} = F_L - \lambda_L N_L - \phi(\sigma_a)_L N_L \tag{8-73}$$

$$= \phi(\sigma_{act})_K N_K - N_L[\lambda_L + \phi(\sigma_a)_L] \tag{8-74}$$

and

$$N_L = \frac{\phi(\sigma_{act})_K N_K}{\lambda_L + \phi(\sigma_a)_L}(1 - e^{-[\lambda_L + \phi(\sigma_a)_L]t}) \tag{8-75}$$

where K is the stable target nuclide having the capture cross section $(\sigma_{act})_K$ leading to the formation of L. The quantity $\phi(\sigma_a)_L$ is analogous to the rate constant λ_L and represents the fraction removed per second.

The second additional removal process is the direct removal by physical or chemical separation, e.g., removal of a gaseous product by volatilization or of a nonvolatile product by continuous chemical processing of a fluid target. If a constant fraction k_L of the product nuclide is removed per unit time, the term $k_L N_L$ is subtracted from the right-hand side of Eq. (8-73), and the final equation, analogous to Eq. (8-75), becomes

$$N_L = \frac{\phi(\sigma_{act})_K N_K}{\lambda_L + \phi(\sigma_a)_L + k_L}(1 - e^{-[\lambda_L + \phi(\sigma_a)_L + k_L]t}) \tag{8-76}$$

It may be seen from Eqs. (8-75) and (8-76) that, when the other removal processes occur, the steady-state concentration of L is reduced and the steady state is reached more rapidly.

Determination of Half-life of Product from Yield Measurements. The half-life of a very-long-lived radionuclide can be determined from the yield, i.e., number of microcuries, and the number of atoms of the radionuclide produced by bombardment of a target. Measurement of the yield requires chemical separation of the product with a known chemical yield and use of a calibrated detector to measure the disintegration rate. For an irradiation time t, the number of atoms formed N_L is simply F_Lt, as may be seen from Eq. (8-66), since λ_Lt is very small. The rate of formation F_L can be evaluated from the size of sample, cross section or excitation function, and flux or beam current. When the uncertainties in F_L are appreciable, the method provides only an estimate of the half-life. Seaborg, James, and Morgan (14), for example, used the method to estimate the half-life of Pu^{241}. Brosi and Ketelle (32) also used the method to determine a value of $(6 \pm 2) \times 10^4$ years for the half-life of La^{137} produced by decay of its short-lived precursor, Ce^{137}, which was prepared by neutron irradiation of cerium oxide. In this case N_L represents the number of atoms of mass 137 produced.

Graves and Walker (33) activated indium foils by slow-neutron bombardment and calculated the half-life of the resulting 54-min In^{116} from a measured saturation activity and three measured time intervals, namely, the irradiation period, the interval between irradiation and start of counting period, and the counting period.

Fission yields have been used to determine the half-lives of some of the long-lived fission products. For a fission product the absolute activity at the end of an irradiation period t is given by Eq. (8-67), which may be written in the form

$$A = F'(1 - e^{-0.693t/T}) \tag{8-77}$$

When T is much greater than t, this equation may be simplified and rearranged to the form

$$T = \frac{0.693F't}{A} \tag{8-78}$$

where F' represents the product of the fission rate and the fission yield. A value for the fission rate may be obtained from the measured saturation disintegration rate of another fission product such as Ba^{140} having a well-established yield. The fission yield for the long-lived product may be estimated from the known smooth yield-mass curve for fission products. All disintegration rates are corrected for chemical yield. Using this method, Glendenin and Metcalf (34) estimated the half-life of Cs^{137} to be 33 ± 3 years.

Experiment 8-1
Determination of the Half-life of an Artificially Produced Radionuclide of Intermediate Half-life by Decay Measurement

The range of half-life intended by "intermediate" is from a few minutes to a few months. It is assumed that the radionuclide to be studied is not contaminated by other radionuclides. This implies that the radionuclide has been radiochemically purified with respect to radioactive impurities of about the same or longer half-life and that shorter-lived contaminants have decayed to an insignificant level. A few suggested radionuclides are listed below:

Radionuclide	*Half-life*	*Radionuclide*	*Half-life*
I^{128}	24.99 min	La^{140}	40.22 hr
Cl^{38}	37.29 min	Y^{90}	64.2 hr
In^{116}	53.99 min	Au^{198}	2.697 days
Ba^{139}	84.0 min	Bi^{210}	5.013 days
Ni^{65}	2.564 hr	I^{131}	8.08 days
Mn^{56}	2.576 hr	Mn^{52}	5.60 days
K^{42}	12.52 hr	P^{32}	14.22 days
Cu^{64}	12.80 hr	Fe^{59}	45.1 days
Ga^{72}	14.3 hr	Sr^{89}	50.5 days
Na^{24}	14.97 hr	Sb^{124}	60.9 days
W^{187}	24.0 hr	Y^{91}	57.5 days
As^{76}	26.4 hr	S^{35}	87 days
Br^{82}	35.87 hr		

For a similar experiment utilizing naturally occurring radioactive material, see Expt. 8-2.

Apparatus and Materials

Radiation-detection equipment
Radioactive material, e.g., neutron-irradiated indium foil; aqueous solution of $H_3P^{32}O_4$; etc.
Sample mounting materials or container
For source preparation by evaporation of a liquid:
- Micropipette with control
- Heat lamp
- Appropriate reagents for converting source to stable, nonhygroscopic form

Procedure

Prepare a suitable source by one of the methods described in Chap. 5. Follow the counting rate for as many half-lives as possible. The interval between successive measurements should be spaced to provide several measurements during each half-life period. A counting schedule based on an acceptable uncertainty in the results should be followed. If time permits, measurements may be made in duplicate or triplicate and averaged.

For fairly long-lived materials, the operation of the counting equipment should be checked by counting a reference source. The reference source data are not used except when normalization is required.

If the source is moved to higher shelf positions as the activity decreases, the relative counting yields for the various shelf positions should be obtained with the source itself.

Analysis of Data

The corrected counting-rate data should be plotted on semilogarithmic graph paper, and a straight line drawn through the points. A discontinuity in a decay curve may indicate faulty equipment, loss of part of the source, change in counting procedure, change in chemical composition, or increase or decrease in moisture content. A nonlinear decay curve (concave upward) indicates the presence of at least two radionuclides of different half-life.

The half-life can be determined from the slope of the decay curve by noting the time required for the counting rate to decrease by 50 per cent. The reliability of the value obtained should be estimated from the values that would be obtained by drawing other straight lines through the decay points. When sufficiently large to warrant it, a precision measure, e.g., the standard deviation, of each point should be indicated on the graph.

To illustrate the computation methods, the decay data should be analyzed also by the method of averages and the method of least squares. Typical decay data, obtained with an end-window G-M tube, are plotted in Fig. 8-1 for P^{32}. From the slope of the curve the half-life is 14.3 days. The half-life with standard deviation is 14.3 ± 0.1 days by the method of averages and 14.2 ± 0.2 days by the method of least squares.

Experiment 8-2

Determination of the Half-life of a Naturally Occurring Radionuclide of Intermediate Half-life by Decay Measurement. The Half-life of UX_1

Since UX_1 (Th^{234}) is readily obtained from common uranyl salts, it can be used conveniently to illustrate the determination of a half-life from decay measurements when an artificially produced radionuclide, such as those listed in Expt. 8-1, is not available. The decay of UX_1 can be followed by measuring the beta radiation emitted by the short-lived daughter UX_2, when the two radionuclides are in equilibrium. Because the 24.1-day half-life of UX_1 is relatively long, it is advisable to start this experiment relatively early in the course.

Various separation procedures are available for the preparation of UX_1 sources. To a limited extent, these have been used* in the past to prepare UX_1-UX_2 beta-ray standards for the calibration of counting equipment. In this experiment the UX_1 is separated from uranium by nonisotopic carrier precipitation with iron in the presence of excess carbonate, which holds the uranium in solution by complex formation. For the purpose of half-life determination, complete recovery of the UX_1 is not necessary but the UX_1 must be radiochemically pure.

Apparatus and Materials

- Radiation-measurement equipment
- Clinical-type centrifuge with 15-ml Pyrex tubes
- Hot plate and water bath
- Heat lamp
- Test-tube rack
- Volumetric pipettes
- Pipette control
- Slurry pipette
- Graduated cylinder (5 or 10 ml)
- Small wash bottle
- Stirring rods
- Source mounting material
- Reagent solutions
  - Uranyl nitrate (0.1 g uranium/ml, 0.25 *M* in HNO_3)
  - Ferric nitrate (3 mg iron/ml, acidified with HNO_3)
  - Ammonium carbonate (saturated, freshly prepared)
  - Hydrochloric acid (1 *N*) (in dropping bottle)
  - Ammonium hydroxide (6 *N*) (in dropping bottle)

Procedure

To a 15-ml centrifuge tube are added 1 ml of uranyl nitrate solution, 1 ml of iron carrier solution, 5 ml of distilled water, dilute ammonium hydroxide (dropwise, to neutralize most of the nitric acid but insufficient to produce a precipitate), and finally 1 to 2 ml (or at least an excess) of saturated ammonium carbonate solution. The resulting

* L. D. Norris and M. G. Inghram, The Half-life of Carbon 14, *Phys. Rev.*, vol. 73, pp. 350–360, 1948.

mixture is stirred and heated in a water bath to coagulate the ferric hydroxide. After centrifugation, the supernatant liquid is decanted and the residue is slurried with 5 ml of water containing a little ammonium carbonate. The solution is heated again and centrifuged, the supernatant is decanted, and the residue is dissolved in dilute hydrochloric acid. After dilution of the ferric chloride solution to about 5 ml, ferric hydroxide is reprecipitated by the addition of a slight excess of ammonium carbonate and then is centrifuged and washed as before. The ferric hydroxide is transferred with a slurry pipette to a flat or cupped mount, dried under a heat lamp, covered with collodion, and finally covered with a thin foil of aluminum or polystyrene.

The counting rate of the source and that of a long-lived reference source are measured once a week for as many half-lives as possible.

Analysis of Data

See Expt. 8-1.

In addition, calculate the half-life after each measurement, using Eq. (8-14). Plot the calculated values as a function of the age of the source.

Experiment 8-3

Determination of the Half-life of a Short-lived Radionuclide by Decay Measurement

The aim of this experiment is to illustrate the determination of the half-life of a radionuclide by simple decay measurements when the half-life is near the lower limit for which conventional counting equipment may be used. The readily available UX_2 (Pa^{234}) with a 1.175-min half-life is a convenient radionuclide to study. When irradiation facilities are at hand, other radionuclides such as 2.27-min Al^{28} may be preferred. In any case, it is obviously essential to use rapid procedures for chemical separation and for preparation of the source.

Several nonisotopic precipitation carriers, e.g., $Zr(OH)PO_4$ and MnO_2, may be used to separate UX_2 from uranium and its thorium parent, UX_1. In this experiment, MnO_2 is used. The latter is prepared by reduction of permanganate with manganous ion in nitric acid solution. The amount of MnO_2 formed is controlled by the amount of $KMnO_4$ added. Thorium (Th^{232}) holdback carrier is used to decrease the carrying of UX_1.

Loss of UX_2 by decay during the formation and separation of the carrier precipitate is avoided by adsorbing the UX_2 on a preformed mat of MnO_2. Time is still required, of course, to pass the UX_2-containing solution through the MnO_2 mat, but the total time from the beginning of the separation to the beginning of the activity measurement is only about 40 to 60 sec. Part of this time is consumed in washing and drying the source. A complete practice separation without activity should be carried out to ensure that all the apparatus is arranged in the most convenient manner for rapid manipulation.

Care must be taken to avoid chemical and radiochemical contamination of the various solutions. A given pipette or dropper should not be used for more than one solution.

Apparatus and Materials

Radiation-measurement equipment
Clinical centrifuge
Centrifuge tubes, 40 ml
Hot plate and water bath
Filtration unit
Filter flask
Heat lamp
Source-mounting materials, e.g., filter planchet, filter paper, and retaining ring described in Chap. 5
Pipettes with control or medicine droppers marked for 1 ml capacity
Graduated cylinders, 10 ml
Reagent solutions
  Uranyl nitrate (0.1 g uranium/ml, 0.25 *M* in HNO_3)
  Thorium nitrate (40 mg thorium/ml, 0.25 *M* in HNO_3)
  Manganous nitrate (15 mg manganese/ml)
  Potassium permanganate (5 mg manganese/ml)
  Nitric acid, 16 *M*
  Nitric acid, 2 *M* (in a dropping bottle)
  Distilled water (in a dropping bottle)
  Acetone (in a dropping bottle)

Procedure

1. *Purification of Thorium Holdback Carrier.* Using separate droppers or graduated cylinders add the following to a 40-ml centrifuge tube: 3 ml of $Th(NO_3)_4$ solution, 1 ml of 16 *M* HNO_3, and 2 ml of $Mn(NO_3)_2$ solution. Heat the mixture in a hot water bath and add 10 to 12 drops of $KMnO_4$ solution. Swirl the tube to mix the contents. Allow the MnO_2 to coagulate and then centrifuge the mixture. Decant the supernatant liquid into a labeled vessel, e.g., a centrifuge tube or small screw-cap bottle, for use in the UX_2 separation.

The MnO_2 contains radioactive substances which would have contaminated the UX_2. As a separate experiment, it is of interest to filter this MnO_2 on a filter-type source mount or transfer it as a slurry to a cupped planchet, dry the source, and measure its activity as a function of time with and without absorbers in order to identify it. (For either type of source the Th^{232} residue should be washed out of the MnO_2 with water when the source is prepared for counting.)

2. *Preparation of* MnO_2 *Filter Mat.* To a clean 40-ml centrifuge tube add 1 ml of 16 *M* HNO_3 and 2 ml of $Mn(NO_3)_2$ solution. Heat and add about 6 drops of $KMnO_4$. Swirl the tube to mix the contents and, after the precipitate has coagulated, filter the solution on the filter-paper disk contained in the filter planchet. The layer or mat of MnO_2 should cover the entire filter and should be fairly uniform in thickness. The layer of MnO_2 should *not* be dried sufficiently for cracks to form.

(When the centrifuge tube is cleaned, any MnO_2 adhering to the wall may be easily removed by addition of a little 10 per cent hydrogen peroxide and a few drops of dilute sulfuric acid.)

3. *Practice Separation.* Using a freshly prepared MnO_2 mat, carry out a practice UX_2 separation as described below except for the substitution of equivalent volumes of water for the $UO_2(NO_3)_2$ and $Th(NO_3)_4$. Note the time taken from the instant when the liquid is first poured onto the MnO_2 to the instant when the source is placed in position in the counter. It should be less than 1 min for this and for the actual separation.

Discard the MnO_2-covered filter paper.

4. *Separation of* UX_2. To a clean 40-ml centrifuge tube add 5 ml of $UO_2(NO_3)_2$ solution and 1 ml of purified $Th(NO_3)_4$ solution. Mix and pass the mixture through a moist MnO_2 mat using suction. As the last of the liquid passes through the filter, add successively with droppers 1 ml of 2 *N* HNO_3, 1 ml of H_2O, and 1 ml of acetone, allowing each to displace the residue of the preceding liquid. Turn on the heat lamp, which should be positioned directly above the filter. When the MnO_2 is dry, release the suction, remove any liquid on the bottom of the filter planchet by means of a piece of disposable tissue, insert a retaining ring to prevent curling of the paper, and place the source in position for counting.

5. *Decay Measurements.* A counting-rate meter with a suitable time constant can be used, preferably with a strip-chart recorder. An ordinary scaler and recorder can also be used. Data obtained with a scaler can be used to illustrate the differential and integral methods of analysis (see Sec. 8-1). When a scaler is used, the measurements are best made by two people. The number of accumulated counts is noted at exactly 15-sec intervals for a period of 10 min, at 30-sec intervals for an additional 10 min, and finally at 1-min intervals for an additional 20 min. This is done without resetting the mechanical register and requires estimation of the interpolation counts, where justified.

Analysis of Data

Method 1. Calculate the counting rate (in counts per minute) for each interval and assign it to the time of observation. Correct for coincidence losses if appropriate for the detector used. Subtract from each of the gross counting rates the constant rate corresponding to normal background plus any long-lived contamination observed after decay of all the UX_2. Plot the net counting rate as a function of time on semilogarithmic paper. Draw a "best" straight line through the points, evaluate the half-life, and estimate its reliability. (See Fig. 8-2*a*.)

Method 2. Correct the values of accumulated counts for coincidence loss, if necessary. Calculate and subtract the contribution of combined background and contamination to each of the observed accumulated counts. The difference is S_t, the accumulated count for UX_2 at each time of observation. S_t eventually reaches the total number of UX_2 counts, S_∞, with increasing time. S_∞ should also be equal to the difference between the total number of counts observed for the first 20-min period and that observed for the second 20-min period.

Plot the differences $S_\infty - S_t$ as a function of time on semilogarithmic graph paper. Draw the "best" line through the points and evaluate the half-life. (See Fig. 8-2*b*.) Compare the result with that obtained by method 1.

Experiment 8-4

Determination of the Half-life of Each of the Independent Components of a Mixture

As an extension of the procedure for studying a single radionuclide, an "unknown" mixture may be studied. This might be a synthetic mixture of available radionuclides, an activated salt, which provides two or three radionuclides, or a sample of a can or wrapper used as a container during the irradiation of a target. It is advisable to carry out a partial radiochemical separation if a prospective sample contains more than three components.

Apparatus and Materials

Radiation-measurement equipment
Sample of radioactive material
Reagents for necessary chemical processing
Source-mounting materials
(Long-lived reference source, if necessary)

Procedure

The counting rate of the source is followed first at short intervals, i.e., 5 min or so, to detect any very-short-lived components and then at regular intervals suitably spaced to provide several measurements during each period corresponding to 50 per cent reduction in total counting rate. The data should be plotted as a composite decay curve after each measurement, in order that the counting schedule may be adjusted as the apparent half-life increases. Measurements should be continued until the half-life of the longest-lived component can be established.

If the radiation characteristics of the components are readily distinguishable as shown by a few absorption measurements, it may be feasible to follow the decay of one or more of the components separately by placing suitable aluminum or lead absorbers between the source and the detector. For gamma emitters the use of a sodium iodide scintillation spectrometer makes it possible to follow the decay of the components separately by setting the spectrometer for the photopeak, for example, for each component and following the decrease in activity at that energy with time. It is assumed, of course, that the various photopeaks are resolvable.

Analysis of Data

If decay of the source is followed without differentiation of the radiation, plot the composite decay curve on semilogarithmic paper and resolve the components graphically, starting with the longest-lived radionuclide. Estimate the errors which arise in the successive subtractions.

If absorbers or a spectrometer is used, plot the decay curve for each set of data in addition to the composite curve. Be certain that all components are accounted for.

Experiment 8-5

Determination of the Half-lives of Two Genetically Related Radionuclides: Transient Equilibrium

Examples of genetically related radionuclides which satisfy the requirements for transient equilibrium are found among the fission products. A specific example is provided by the last two radioactive members of the mass-140 chain:

$$\mathrm{Ba}^{140} \xrightarrow[\beta,\gamma]{12.80\ \mathrm{days}} \mathrm{La}^{140} \xrightarrow[\beta,\gamma]{40.22\ \mathrm{hr}} \mathrm{Ce}^{140}\ \text{(stable)}$$

This chain is of interest because of its role in the discovery of the fission of uranium, in which reaction it is produced in a relatively high yield. Barium 140 and its daughter are used in this experiment.

The radiochemical separations used in this experiment illustrate the use of isotopic precipitation carriers and isotopic holdback carriers.

Apparatus and Materials

Radiation-measurement equipment
Clinical centrifuge
15- and 40-ml Pyrex centrifuge tubes
Heat lamp
Micropipettes with control
Test-tube holder and rack
Source-mounting materials
Solution of Ba^{140}-La^{140} equilibrium mixture
Sulfuric acid (6 *N*)
Hydrochloric acid (6 *N*)
Ammonium hydroxide (6 *N*)
Nitric acid (6 *N*)
Ammonium chloride (saturated solution)
Barium chloride (20 mg Ba/ml, 0.1 *M* HCl)
Lanthanum chloride (20 mg La/ml, 0.1 *M* HCl)
Transfer pipettes (capillary droppers) and slurry pipettes
Methyl red indicator solution
Stirring rods

Procedure

1. Prepare a collodion-covered counting source of Ba^{140}-La^{140} equilibrium mixture of suitable strength for decay and beta-ray absorption measurements. Measure the absorption of the radiation from the source in aluminum, using a range of thickness adequate to establish the slope of the gamma-ray portion of the absorption curve.

2. Prepare a second collodion-covered counting source of the equilibrium mixture of suitable strength for measurement of the absorption of the radiation in lead. Measure the absorption in lead for the whole range of absorbers available.

3. Prepare a source of La^{140} free of its parent as follows:
To a 15-ml Pyrex centrifuge add:
20 mg of La carrier
20 mg of Ba holdback carrier
Ba^{140}-La^{140} (twice the amount used for preparation of the beta source of the mixture)
H_2O to make about 10 ml total volume
Three of four drops of methyl red
NH_4Cl, about 1 ml

Heat the mixture in a hot water bath (90 to 100°C) and add NH_4OH dropwise while the solution is stirred. Add a few drops in excess after the indicator has turned yellow. Heat and stir the solution to coagulate the precipitate, adding more NH_4OH, if necessary, to compensate for loss by volatilization.

Centrifuge the sample and decant the supernatant liquid either to a radioactive waste bottle (properly labeled) or to a 40-ml centrifuge tube for recovery of Ba^{140}. (In the procedure described below, a fresh sample of the equilibrium mixture is taken for Ba^{140} separation because of the time limitation of a 3-hr laboratory period.)

Slurry the $La(OH)_3$ in 5 ml of H_2O containing a few drops of NH_4Cl and NH_4OH. Heat the mixture with stirring, centrifuge it, and decant the supernatant liquid to the waste bottle.

Dissolve the washed $La(OH)_3$ in a few drops of 6 *N* HCl. Add 20 mg of Ba carrier, about 1 ml of NH_4Cl, methyl red indicator, and water to make 10 ml. Heat and reprecipitate $La(OH)_3$ as before. Wash and dissolve the $La(OH)_3$ and reprecipitate $La(OH)_3$, adding Ba holdback carrier and proceeding exactly as before. After washing the final precipitate, dissolve it in a minimum ($\sim$1 ml) amount of acid (HNO_3 if source mount is a stainless-steel planchet, or HNO_3 or HCl if glass). Transfer the La^{140} activity to the source mount by means of a capillary transfer pipette. Cover the dried source with a thin film of collodion.

Measure the absorption of the La^{140} radiation in aluminum and lead. Follow the decay of the sample.

4. Prepare a source of Ba^{140} free of its La^{140} daughter as follows:

To a 15-ml centrifuge tube add:

20 mg of La carrier

20 mg of Ba carrier

Ba^{140}-La^{140} (amount as for La^{140} separation)

H_2O to make 10 ml total volume

Methyl red, 3 to 4 drops

NH_4Cl (1 ml)

Heat the mixture in a hot water bath and add a slight excess of NH_4OH dropwise. Heat and stir the solution. Centrifuge the solution and decant the supernatant liquid into a 40-ml graduated centrifuge tube. Wash the $La(OH)_3$ once with 5 ml of water containing a few drops of NH_4Cl and NH_4OH. Heat the mixture with stirring, centrifuge it, and decant the supernatant liquid into the 40-ml tube containing the first supernatant liquid. Dissolve the $La(OH)_3$ in dilute HCl and, if it is not to be used as a source of La^{140}, discard the solution to a radioactive waste bottle.

To the 40-ml centrifuge tube containing the Ba^{140} add a few drops of HCl to acidify the solution, heat the resulting solution, and slowly add dropwise, with stirring, a slight excess of 6 *N* H_2SO_4. Test for complete precipitation by allowing the $BaSO_4$ to settle and by adding a drop of H_2SO_4 to the clear liquid. Centrifuge the solution. Note the liquid volume and withdraw 1 ml with a pipette. Transfer the 1-ml sample to a labeled cupped planchet and dry the sample under a heat lamp. Either volatilize or neutralize any H_2SO_4 in the source with NH_3 vapor, and cover the source with a thin film of collodion. The remainder of the supernatant liquid should be transferred to the waste bottle.

Transfer the $BaSO_4$ to a labeled, cupped planchet by means of a slurry pipette using a minimum of water. Dry the source and heat to SO_3 fumes. Cool the source and cover with collodion.

Measure the counting rate of the $BaSO_4$ source and the dried portion of supernatant liquid. Calculate the loss of Ba activity in the supernatant liquid. Check the decay of this sample and compare it with the Ba^{140}. Measure the absorption of the Ba^{140} radiation in aluminum and lead before the La^{140} activity becomes significant. Follow the decay of the sample, making measurements at appropriate times to locate the growth curve as La^{140} activity grows in.

Analysis of Data

Plot all decay curves and absorption curves.

Determine (1) the half-life of Ba^{140} from the decay of the equilibrium mixture, (2) the half-life of La^{140} from the decay of the La^{140} source, (3) the time of maximum total Ba^{140}-La^{140} activity, and (4) the growth curve for La^{140} by subtracting a calculated Ba^{140} decay curve from the total activity. Compare the observed and calculated values for the times for maximum total and maximum daughter activities.

Find the beta- and gamma-ray energies for the equilibrium mixture and for the separate fractions, and compare the results.

Evaluate the loss of Ba^{140} activity when carried as $BaSO_4$.

Experiment 8-6

Determination of the Half-lives of Two Genetically Related Radionuclides: Secular Equilibrium

A convenient case of secular equilibrium occurs in the fission-product chain of mass 144, i.e.,

$$Ce^{144} \xrightarrow[\beta^-]{285 \text{ days}} Pr^{144} \xrightarrow[\beta^-]{17.27 \text{ min}} Nd^{144} \text{ (stable)}$$

Because of the relatively short life of Pr^{144}, a rather rapid precipitation method of separation is used (see Chap. 9). The cerium activity is carried isotopically as $Ce(IO_3)_4$;* the praseodymium activity is carried nonisotopically by $La(OH)_3$.† It is assumed that the starting material is the Ce-Pr equilibrium mixture free of significant amounts of other fission products. Otherwise, additional purification to remove zirconium and other contaminants such as the yttrium and the lanthanum-group elements would be required. Holdback-carrier techniques would then be needed.

Apparatus and Materials

- Radiation-detection equipment for beta radiation
- Micropipette and syringe or control
- Clinical centrifuge
- Graduated cylinders, 10 and 25 ml
- Hot water bath
- Centrifuge tubes, 40 ml
- Medicine droppers
- Test-tube rack or block
- Stirring rods
- Filtration device or slurry pipette
- Heat lamp
- Source-mounting materials
- Disposable tissue
- Labeled containers for liquid and solid Ce^{144}-Pr^{144} waste
- Reagent solutions
    - Nitric acid, concentrated, 16 *M*
    - Potassium bromate, 0.2- to 0.5-g portions
    - Potassium iodate, 0.35 *M*
    - Cerium carrier, 10 mg Ce/ml as ceric ammonium nitrate
    - Lanthanum carrier, 10 mg La/ml as nitrate
    - Ammonium hydroxide, concentrated, 15 *M*
    - Ethanol, 95 per cent
    - Acetone
    - Ce^{144}-Pr^{144} sample
    - (Hydrochloric acid, concentrated, 12 *M*)
    - (Hydrogen peroxide, 30 per cent)

* W. F. Boldbridge and D. N. Hume, Improved Determination of Cerium and Other Rare-earth Activities in Fission, in C. D. B. Coryell and N. Sugarman (eds.), "Radiochemical Studies: The Fission Products," book 3, paper 294, pp. 1693–1701, McGraw-Hill, New York, 1951.

† A. S. Newton, A. Kant, and R. E. Hein, Discovery of 17.5 m Pr^{144}, in C. D. B. Coryell and N. Sugarman (eds.), "Radiochemical Studies: The Fission Products," book 2, paper 185, pp. 1200–1205, McGraw-Hill, New York, 1951.

Procedure

1. Prepare a source of the Ce^{144}-Pr^{144} equilibrium mixture by drying an aliquot in a cupped planchet and covering the deposit with collodion. Measure the attenuation of the beta radiation in aluminum.

2. *Cerium Separation.* To a 40-ml centrifuge tube add 20 mg of cerium carrier, 20 mg of lanthanum carrier, Ce^{144}-Pr^{144} activity in an amount to provide adequate counting rates for the separated materials, and 8 ml of concentrated HNO_3. Mix the solution by swirling the tube and, without cooling, add 0.2 to 0.5 g of solid $KBrO_3$ to make certain that the cerium is in the (IV) oxidation state. Add, with mixing and cooling, 20 ml of KIO_3 solution to precipitate the cerium at room temperature. Swirl the tube or stir the solution until the light yellow precipitate of cerium iodate coagulates. Note the time at which the precipitation is carried out, and complete the subsequent operations as rapidly as possible.

Centrifuge the sample and transfer the supernatant liquid either to a labeled waste bottle or to a second 40-ml tube if the praseodymium fraction is to be processed at once. Wash the $Ce(IO_3)_4$ precipitate with 20 ml of water (break up any lumps of precipitate with a stirring rod), and after centrifugation transfer the supernatant liquid to the waste bottle. Slurry the precipitate with about 10 ml of 95 per cent ethanol and filter the sample on paper in a filtration-type source mount. Air-dry the source with suction and the heat lamp, if necessary. Cover the source with a thin film of collodion by placing a few drops of dilute collodion solution on the filter. Remove the mount from the holder, dry the bottom of the mount with disposable tissue (to be placed in the solids waste container for Ce^{144}-Pr^{144}), insert the clamping ring, and count the source. Alternatively, the precipitate, after the water wash, may be slurried in a minimum number of drops of 95 per cent ethanol, transferred to a cupped planchet by means of a slurry pipette, and dried under the heat lamp. The filtration procedure is likely to be the more rapid but may lead to greater loss of precipitate.

Note the time when the source is placed in the counter, and follow the growth of the Pr^{144} activity until secular equilibrium is established. Predict the minimum time required. Approximately 5 min will be required for chemical processing from the time of the cerium precipitation to that of the first activity measurement. Follow the decay of the Ce^{144} source for as many days as possible and estimate its half-life.

3. *Praseodymium Recovery.* After precipitation of the Ce^{144} as cerium iodate according to the above procedure, note the time and transfer the supernatant liquid containing the Pr^{144} to a second centrifuge tube. Heat the liquid in a water bath and, with stirring, very cautiously add concentrated ammonium hydroxide to a slight excess.

Centrifuge the sample, decant the supernatant liquid to the waste bottle, and wash the precipitate with about 15 ml of water. After centrifugation and transfer of the wash water to the waste bottle, slurry the $La(OH)_3$ precipitate with about 10 ml of acetone, and filter the sample on paper in a filtration-type source mount using suction and the heat lamp to dry the sample rapidly. Add a few drops of collodion solution, dry the source, remove it from the holder, dry the bottom with disposable tissue, insert the clamping ring, and count the source. Record the time. Alternatively, the precipitate, after the water wash, may be transferred to a cupped planchet as a slurry in acetone. Follow the decay of the sample until only the long-lived cerium contaminant remains. If the Pr^{144} fraction is counted on the same day as the Ce^{144}, the sources should be counted alternately, using appropriate counting times for each.

The experiment may be extended in several ways. For example, the recovery or yield of cerium may be determined gravimetrically for the conditions used. The effect of reprecipitation on the purity of the $Ce(IO_3)_4$ may be determined by rapidly dissolving the precipitate (after the water wash) by the addition of 1 drop of concentrated HCl and 1 to 2 drops of 30 per cent H_2O_2, followed by the addition of 8 ml of concentrated HNO_3, and then reprecipitating with 20 ml of KIO_3 solution after the addition of $KBrO_3$.

Analysis of Data

Plot the aluminum absorption curve and resolve the curve into its components. Evaluate the energies of the beta rays emitted by the Ce^{144}-Pr^{144} equilibrium mixture.

Plot the growth and decay curves for the separated cerium and praseodymium fractions respectively.

On the basis of the cerium growth curve, plot the difference between the total activity at any time and that at equilibrium, and from the resulting curve obtain the half-life of Pr^{144}.

From the decay curve of the Pr^{144} fraction determine the half-life of Pr^{144}.

From the counting rate of the sample of unseparated Ce^{144}-Pr^{144} equilibrium mixture, the counting rate of the separated Ce^{144} source after equilibrium has been reestablished, and the extrapolated counting rate of the separated Pr^{144} source, estimate the recovery of each radionuclide.

Making use of the aluminum absorption data and published information on the decay schemes of the two radionuclides, consider how a plot of the true activity for a Ce^{144}-Pr^{144} growth curve would differ from that of the observed activity.

Estimate the half-life of Ce^{144} from the decay of one of the cerium sources.

Experiment 8-7

Determination of the Half-life of a Naturally Occurring Radionuclide by Growth Measurements

The half-life of UX_1 may be obtained by following the increase in the beta-ray counting rate of a sample of a uranium compound previously freed of UX_1. As pointed out in Expt. 8-2, the energetic beta rays detected are emitted by UX_2. Alpha rays from the parent U^{238} are absorbed in the source cover and do not interfere.

Apparatus and Materials

Radiation-measurement equipment
Clinical-type centrifuge with 15-ml tubes
Hot plate, water bath
Heat lamp
Test-tube rack
Volumetric pipettes
Pipette control
Graduated cylinder (5 or 10 ml)
Small wash bottle
Stirring rods
Source-mounting materials
Long-lived reference source
Reagent solutions
  Uranyl nitrate (0.1 g U/ml, 0.25 *M* in HNO_3)
  Ammonium carbonate (saturated, freshly prepared)
  Hydrochloric acid (1 *N*) (in dropping bottle)
  Ammonium hydroxide (6 *N*) (in dropping bottle)
  Ammonium nitrate (about 1 per cent)
  Ethanol (95 per cent)

Procedure

The following are added to a 15-ml Pyrex centrifuge tube: 1 ml of uranyl nitrate, 1 ml of ferric nitrate, 5 ml of distilled water, and 1 to 2 ml (or at least a finite excess) of saturated carbonate solution. After the mixture has been heated in a water bath to coagulate the ferric hydroxide, the latter is separated by centrifugation. The supernatant liquid is decanted into a second centrifuge tube. About 0.5 ml of ferric nitrate is added, and ferric hydroxide is precipitated again with heating. After centrifugation, the supernatant liquid is decanted into a 40- or 50-ml Pyrex centrifuge tube. (If complete recovery of uranium is desired, so that the equilibrium activity may be calculated, the ferric hydroxide residues should be dissolved and reprecipitated, and the supernatants combined with the bulk of uranium.) Excess carbonate is removed by acidifying the solution with hydrochloric acid and heating to expel the carbon dioxide. To the hot carbonate-free solution, dilute ammonium hydroxide is added dropwise (with stirring) until precipitation of ammonium diuranate is complete. The sample is centrifuged, and the supernatant is discarded. The residue is washed once with 10 ml of dilute ammonium nitrate and finally with 5 ml of ethanol. The residue is then transferred, by means of a spatula or slurry pipette, to a cupped planchet and dried slowly under a heat lamp. If the drying is carried out below 100°C, the ammonium diuranate will not decompose appreciably and may be covered with a film of collodion. The mass of the source may be decreased by igniting at about 800°C in a furnace. Collodion is used as a binder for the resulting uranic oxide.

A thin (about 10 mg/cm^2) aluminum foil should be placed over the source. This is especially important if the detector used is sensitive to alpha particles. Counting-rate measurements should be made in a reproducible manner at 2- to 3-day intervals for approximately the first 3 weeks and at 1-week intervals thereafter for as many weeks as possible. A long-lived reference source should be counted also.

Analysis of Data

A growth curve is plotted on rectangular coordinate paper. The data are analyzed by one or more of the methods outlined in Sec. 8-4. The data for the long-lived source should be examined for irregularities, and corrections applied to the UX_1 data if necessary. An estimate of reliability of the half-life value obtained for UX_1 should be made.

A growth curve with the corresponding plot of the slope of the growth curve is presented in Fig. 8-6.

Experiment 8-8

Determination of the Half-life of a Long-lived Radionuclide by Specific-activity Measurement

The half-life of naturally occurring potassium 40 may be determined rather easily by measuring the specific activity of a pure potassium compound. Potassium chloride is a convenient salt to use.

Potassium 40 is of considerable interest since (1) the beta transition is a highly forbidden one leading to an unusually energetic beta ray for such a long-lived radionuclide and (2) it is of use as a "radioactive clock" in the determination of the age of minerals.

The following are some of the characteristic constants for K^{40}:

Per cent abundance in nature	0.0119 ± 0.0001
E_{β}, max	1.33 Mev
E_{γ} ($\sim$100 per cent with EC)	1.46 Mev
Per cent decay by EC	11
Per cent decay by β	89
Half-life (β decay)	1.39×10^9 years
Half-life (total)	1.25×10^9 years
Spin change	4 to 0

The corresponding decay scheme is as follows:

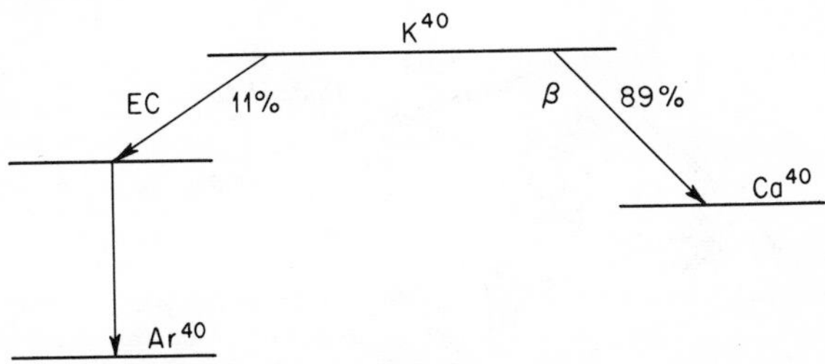

Only the decay by beta-ray emission is studied in this experiment. Because of the very long half-life and the very low abundance, it is necessary to use samples of potassium chloride weighing several milligrams in order that accurate counting data may be obtained in a reasonable length of time with a conventional end-window beta counter. Actually, this may be considered advantageous pedagogically, since it increases the scope of the laboratory exercise by introducing the need for making a self-absorption correction and also for planning a counting schedule to minimize counting errors for samples having a counting rate close to the natural background rate. The experiment illustrates the problems of calculating a disintegration rate from a counting rate.

Apparatus and Materials

Radiation-detection equipment (calibrated for beta radiation)
Analytical balance
Potassium chloride (reagent grade)
Source-mounting materials—1-in.-diameter flat metal planchets, 1-in.-OD and ¾-in.-ID rings about 0.016 in. thick; thin covering foil; cement
Source holder to provide high counting yield (see Fig. 8-11)

Procedure

1. *Preparation of Sources.* To correct for self-absorption, four sources of varied thicknesses corresponding to one, two, three, and four metal

rings are prepared. The rings are cemented together and to the backing to provide a shallow source. The effect of backscattering (which may be used to increase the counting rate) will depend on the selection of the backing, which may be thin aluminum foil (~4 mg/cm^2) or a copper or steel flat planchet (~300 mg/cm^2).

To the labeled and weighed planchets, finely (100 mesh or finer) ground KCl is added in a uniform layer leveled with the top of the mount. (Note that extreme care should be taken to preclude contamination of the KCl with other radionuclides, as might happen if KCl is ground in a contaminated mortar.) The source mount is reweighed and covered

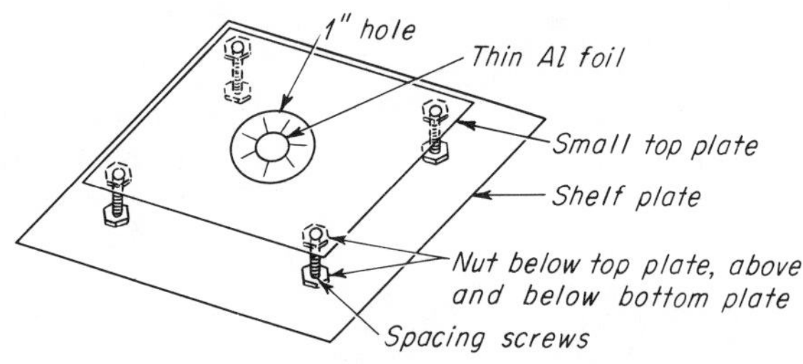

FIG. 8-11. Adjustable source mount (Expt. 8-8).

with thin polystyrene or aluminum without disturbing the KCl or allowing the cement used for holding the cover to reach the powder. Commonly, the four sources cover the range of thickness of 40 to 150 mg/cm^2.

2. *Source Holder.* To obtain the maximum counting rate for the sources, it is advantageous to raise the position of the source under the end-window tube nearer to the tube than the conventional first-shelf position, without disturbing the tube. The adjustable source holder illustrated in Fig. 8-11 has proved to be satisfactory, but it is only one of several possible designs.

Since sources vary in thickness, a thin flexible aluminum foil is cemented under the 1-in. hole of the top plate so that all sources may be positioned with their top surfaces flush with the top of the source plate. In this way the top surface of each sample is the same distance from the counter window. The source does not project above the plate and is thereby unable to damage the tube window. Flexibility of the aluminum foil is assured by cutting a ¾-in. circular opening concentric with the 1-in. hole and cutting a few radial slits in the foil.

3. *Measurement of Specific Activity.* It is advantageous to have sources prepared in advance if only a 3-hr period is available for counting.

Estimate, by taking a brief count, the counting rate for the thinnest and the thickest samples. With this information and a knowledge of the normal background rate, prepare a counting schedule for four sample measurements and two background measurements—one before and one after the four samples. Measure the background rate with the source holder in position. It is obviously desirable that the background rate be as low as possible in this experiment, since the sources will count about 0.3 cpm/mg KCl above background.

The distance between the source plate and the detector window should be measured carefully without damaging the latter.

Analysis of Data

From the net counting rates of the four samples, calculate the specific counting rates in counts per minute per milligram of KCl, and plot the values against sample weight or thickness (milligrams per square centimeter) on linear graph paper. Extrapolate the self-absorption curve to zero thickness and obtain a value for the counting rate. For comparison, estimate the self-absorption corrections from an estimate of the absorption coefficient for the K^{40} beta radiation. For K^{40}, an approximate absorption coefficient may be obtained from (1) aluminum absorption measurements for K^{40}, (2) a plot of μ (obtained from the low-absorber third of the aluminum absorption curves for nuclides such as UX_2, P^{32}, and RaE) as a function of the beta-ray energy, or (3) the known half-thickness of the radiation, which is about 50 mg/cm^2 of aluminum. The same information is needed to obtain the correction for external absorption of the K^{40} beta rays in the (1) sample cover, (2) air, and (3) detector window. If necessary, correct for backscattering using the data of Expt. 6-2. The fully corrected rate is converted to a disintegration rate by means of the calibration factors for the detector (see Expt. 7-2).

Calculate the half-life for beta decay for K^{40}.

The following are among the sources of uncertainty in the results:

1. Beta-ray counting—random fluctuations
2. Sample preparation—uniformity of thickness and area
3. Slight variations in the positioning of samples relative to the detector window
4. Purity of potassium chloride—chemical and radiochemical
5. Estimation of detection coefficient or counting yield
6. Self-absorption correction
7. Correction for absorption of radiation in the detector window
8. Backscattering correction
9. Detection of gamma rays emitted in the electron-capture process
10. Abundance of K^{40} in nature

Values for the half-life as reported in the literature range from

1.2×10^9 to 1.8×10^9 years. These values were obtained in the course of careful research rather than by laboratory exercises. Results obtained in this experiment are usually within the range of the literature.

Cited References

1. Kohman, T. P.: Measurement Techniques of Applied Radiochemistry, *Anal. Chem.*, vol. 21, pp. 352–364, 1949.
2. XVIth Conference, International Union of Pure and Applied Chemistry, *Chem. Eng. News*, vol. 40, pp. 4072–4082, 1951.
3. Worthing, A. G., and J. Geffner: "Treatment of Experimental Data," Wiley, New York, 1944.
4. Daniels, F. D.: "Mathematical Preparation for Physical Chemistry," McGraw-Hill, New York, 1928.
5. Daniels, F., J. H. Mathews, J. W. Williams, P. Bender, and R. A. Alberty: "Experimental Physical Chemistry," 5th ed., chap. 17, McGraw-Hill, New York, 1956.
6. Peierls, R.: Statistical Error in Counting Experiments, *Proc. Roy. Soc. (London)*, vol. 149A, pp. 467–486, 1935.
7. Studier, M. H., and E. K. Hyde: A New Radioactive Series—The Protactinium Series, *Phys. Rev.*, vol. 74, pp. 591–600, 1948.
8. Rowlands, S.: Methods of Measuring Very Long and Very Short Half-lives, *Nucleonics*, vol. 3, no. 3, pp. 2–13, 1948.
9. Kovarik, A. F., and N. I. Adams, Jr.: The Disintegration Constant of Thorium and the Branching Ratio of Thorium C, *Phys. Rev.*, vol. 54, pp. 413–421, 1938.
10. Engelkemeir, A. G., W. H. Hamill, M. G. Inghram, and W. F. Libby: The Half-life of Radiocarbon (C^{14}), *Phys. Rev.*, vol. 75, pp. 1825–1833, 1949.
11. Kohman, T. P., D. P. Ames, and J. Sedlet: The Specific Activity of Radium, in G. T. Seaborg, J. T. Katz, and W. M. Manning (eds.), "The Transuranium Elements," vol. II, pp. 1675–1699, McGraw-Hill, New York, 1949.
12. Perlman, I., and F. Asaro: Alpha Radioactivity, *Ann. Rev. Nuclear Sci.*, vol. 4, pp. 157–190, 1954.
13. Perlman, I., A. Ghiorso, and G. T. Seaborg: Systematics of Alpha-radioactivity, *Phys. Rev.*, vol. 77, pp. 26–50, 1950.
14. Seaborg, G. T., R. A. James, and L. O. Morgan: The New Element Americium, in G. T. Seaborg, J. T. Katz, and W. M. Manning (eds.), "The Transuranium Elements," pt. II, paper 22.1, McGraw-Hill, New York, 1949.
15. Friedlander, G., and J. W. Kennedy: "Nuclear and Radiochemistry," Wiley, New York, 1955.
16. Bateman, H.: Solution of a System of Differential Equations Occurring in the Theory of Radio-active Transformations, *Proc. Cambridge Phil. Soc.*, vol. 15, pp. 423–427, 1910.
17. Rutherford, E. R., J. Chadwick, and C. D. Ellis: "Radiations from Radioactive Substances," Cambridge, New York, 1930.
18. Watson, W. H.: A Method for Computing Transformations in Radioactive Series, *Can. J. Research*, vol. 25A, pp. 252–260, 1947.
19. Nier, A. O.: The Isotopic Constitution of Uranium and the Half-lives of the Uranium Isotopes. I, *Phys. Rev.*, vol. 55, pp. 150–153, 1939.
20. Chamberlain, O., D. Williams, and P. Yuster: Half-life of Uranium-234, *Phys. Rev.*, vol. 70, pp. 580–582, 1946.

21. DeBenedetti, S., and F. R. McGowan: A Metastable State of 22 Microseconds in Ta^{181}, *Phys. Rev.*, vol. 70, p. 569, 1946.
22. Livingood, J. J., and G. T. Seaborg: Radioactive Isotopes of Iodine, *Phys. Rev.*, vol. 54, pp. 775–782, 1938.
23. Seaborg, G. T., J. J. Livingood, and J. W. Kennedy: *Phys. Rev.*, vol. 57, p. 363, 1940.
24. Ahrens, L. H., and R. D. Evans: The Radioactive Decay Constants of K^{40} as Determined from the Accumulation of Ca^{40} in Ancient Minerals, *Phys. Rev.*, vol. 74, pp. 279–286, 1948.
25. Dillard, C. R., R. M. Adams, N. Finston, and A. Turkevich: Determination of Gas Half-lives by the Charged-wire Technique (II), in C. D. B. Coryell and N. Sugarman (eds.), "Radiochemical Studies: The Fission Products," book 2, paper 68, pp. 624–641, McGraw-Hill, New York, 1951.
26. Makower, W., and H. Geiger: "Practical Measurements in Radioactivity," p. 98, Longmans, New York, 1912.
27. Weinberg, A. M., and E. P. Wigner: "The Physical Theory of Neutron Chain Reactors," University of Chicago Press, Chicago, 1958.
28. Hughes, D. J., and R. B. Schwartz: Neutron Cross Sections, *U.S. Atomic Energy Comm. Rept.* BNL-325, 2d ed., July 1, 1958.
29. Garrison, W. M., and J. G. Hamilton: Production and Isolation of Carrier-free Radioisotopes, *Chem. Rev.*, vol. 49, pp. 237–272, 1951.
30. Martin, J. A., R. S. Livingston, R. L. Murray, and M. Rankin: Radioisotope Production Rates in a 22-Mev Cyclotron, *Nucleonics*, vol. 13, no. 3, pp. 28–32, 1955.
31. Rubinson, W.: The Equations of Radioactive Transformation in a Neutron Flux, *J. Chem. Phys.*, vol. 17, pp. 542–547, 1949.
32. Brosi, A. R., and B. H. Ketelle: Radioactive Decay of La^{137} and Ce^{137}, *Phys. Rev.*, vol. 103, pp. 917–920, 1956.
33. Graves, A. C., and R. L. Walker: A Method for Measuring Half-lives, *Phys. Rev.*, vol. 71, pp. 1–3, 1947.
34. Glendenin, L. E., and R. P. Metcalf: Estimation of the Half-life of 33y Cs^{137}, in C. D. B. Coryell and N. Sugarman (eds.), "Radiochemical Studies: The Fission Products," book 2, paper 152, pp. 1067–1069, McGraw-Hill, New York, 1951.

9

Radiochemical Separation Methods

9-1. Introduction

Except for separation by recoil, the methods used to separate radioactive substances are the same as those used for nonradioactive substances. The merits of any of the classical methods can be evaluated in terms of the yield or per cent recovery and the purity of the separated material. High purity and high recovery are generally inconsistent, although both are usually desired. In the presence of isotopic carrier, i.e., macro amounts of the same chemical species containing stable isotopes, the yields are the same as for the stable material. For carrier-free radioactive material, however, losses resulting from adsorption on the walls of vessels, etc., which are usually negligible percentagewise on a macro scale, may represent the major part of a sample at the tracer level.

Chemical purity and radiochemical purity are not synonymous terms. Because such small quantities of some radioactive materials are readily detected, a sample of material which is pure on the basis of macro behavior may be very impure radiochemically. Thus, a sample of sodium chloride containing 1 μc Na^{24} and 1 μc P^{32}/mg would, if free of stable phosphorus, contain only about 3×10^{-3} ppm of phosphorus, but it would be a very impure sample of Na^{24} and would become more impure with time. Moreover, at the tracer level, the effectiveness of a separation or purification method is not necessarily the same as that at the macro level, since there may be a strong dependence on concentration.

Before describing specific separation methods it is of interest to mention certain aspects which are common to all separation methods. In any of the methods, separation of the components of a mixture is achieved by providing conditions such that a driving force, e.g., concentration gradient, electromotive force, pressure drop, or solvent flow, causes a transfer of molecules, atoms, or ions from a region of initial composition to one of final composition. The regions are separated by a phase boundary, e.g., solid-liquid interface, or by a physical or potential barrier of some type. Thus the original sample becomes divided into at least two parts, which differ in composition. The separation or change in composition can be expressed in several ways. Commonly the effectiveness of a separation method is expressed in terms of the removal or separation or concentration change of one particular substance, and the change is usually expressed relative to the unseparated material. Thus the degree of separation of two substances by any method can be expressed in terms of a separation factor SF, which may be defined as

$$\mathrm{SF} = \frac{C'_A/C'_B}{C''_A/C''_B}$$

where C'_A and C'_B are concentrations of substances A and B in the sample before separation and C''_A and C''_B are the concentrations in the separated material. Thus A might be the contaminant and B the material desired in a pure form. In radiochemical work the degree of purification is often expressed in terms of a decontamination factor DF, which may be defined as

$$\mathrm{DF} = \frac{(\mathrm{cpm}\ A)'/(\mathrm{cpm}\ B)'}{(\mathrm{cpm}\ A)''/(\mathrm{cpm}\ B)''}$$

where the prime (′) refers to the material before separation and the double prime (″) to material afterward. The radioactivity of A may also be referred to a unit weight of B. This is convenient, for example, in the fission-product decontamination of neutron-irradiated uranium 235. Decontamination factors of 10^6 to 10^9 may be required for the decontamination of uranium-235 reactor fuel.

A separation factor or a decontamination factor may refer to a single-stage process or to a multistage process or to a sequence of different processes. The over-all DF attained in a countercurrent solvent-extraction process, an ion-exchange process, or a process involving repeated reprecipitation, etc., represents many repeated separations and is the DF per stage raised to a power equal to the effective number of stages. The DF per stage is not necessarily constant, because of various effects such as diffusion; hence the over-all DF cannot be increased indefinitely by adding more stages.

The number of specific separations of radioactive material which could be used to illustrate the methods described in this chapter is overwhelming. Only a limited number of illustrative examples have been cited. The texts and review papers listed in the supplementary references should provide a good basis for locating methods or details of techniques which have been used for a particular radionuclide.

In any of the separation methods, aliquoting and transferring of liquids containing radioactive material are achieved through the use of standard volumetric pipettes, measuring pipettes, and micropipettes. Techniques for using micropipettes are described in Chap. 5. All mouth pipetting of liquids in a laboratory containing radioactive material should be absolutely forbidden even though the liquid may not be radioactive. Several types of pipette controls are available from laboratory supply houses.

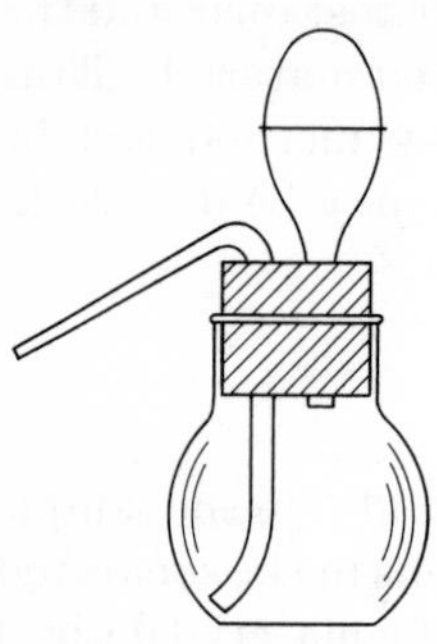

Fig. 9-1. Wash bottle.

Remote-control pipetters are commercially available for transfer of liquids behind a lead shield. Such a device may consist of a pantograph frame or a lightweight rod with a pipette clamped at one end and connected by means of flexible rubber or plastic tubing to a syringe at the other end. Manipulations behind the shielding can be observed by the use of one or more mirrors.

It is seldom, if ever, necessary to make precise measurements of carrier solutions used in separation procedures. Medicine droppers are convenient for volumes of about 1 ml. The droppers can be marked at ½- and 1-ml volumes by means of a file if the full capacity of the rubber bulb is not a suitable measure. Dropping bottles with ground-glass joints are satisfactory except for solutions which cause the joint to "freeze." As an alternative, the dropper can be placed in a small test tube taped to the side of a screw-cap bottle.

Various small wash bottles which can be held in the palm of the hand are commercially available. A simple one that can be easily made in the laboratory is illustrated in Fig. 9-1.

9-2. Precipitation Methods

Introduction. Separation by precipitation is familiar to everyone as one of the most commonly used classical methods of analytical chemistry. All the factors such as the type and excess of precipitating agent used, temperature, concentration, and rate of precipitation, which affect the purity of a precipitate and the completeness of precipitation apply when radioactive materials are involved.

In most cases, particularly at tracer level, in which the amount of radioactive material is small, the concentration in solution before precipitation is too low to permit precipitation by exceeding the solubility of a compound considered to be "insoluble." It is necessary that a carrier be present which can be removed from the solution by precipitation. The carrier is not simply a substance which can be precipitated. It must, as the name implies, carry the desired radioactive material with it from solution. Such a carrier may be present automatically as a constituent accompanying the radioactive material or it may be added just before the separation. It may be an isotopic or a nonisotopic carrier.

Mechanisms of Carrying. *Isotopic Carrying.* A salt containing the element to be carried is added to the radioactive material, and an insoluble compound characteristic of the substance is precipitated. For example, Ba^{140} can be carried from solution by adding a normal barium salt such as $BaCl_2$, mixing to give a uniform solution, and precipitating $BaSO_4$ by the addition of a sulfate. The isotopic ions are equivalent and are homogeneously incorporated in the $BaSO_4$ crystals. The per cent of Ba^{140} carried would be the same as the per cent of a total barium carrier precipitated. In the example cited, La^{140}, the 40-hr daughter of Ba^{140}, would be present in solution with the Ba^{140} and would also be present in the $BaSO_4$, which acts as a nonisotopic carrier for the La^{140}. The per cent of total La^{140} carried would be less than that for Ba^{140} and could be further decreased by addition of lanthanum "holdback" carrier. The term "holdback" carrier is an anomalous one which refers to an isotopic diluent for a substance whose carrying is undesirable. It does not prevent carrying of the contaminating element; rather it may increase the total number of atoms of the element carried. However, since the fraction of available contaminant atoms carried is decreased, the fraction of radioactive contaminant carried is decreased. The "holdback" carrier is used, then, to decrease contamination by a radioactive substance carried nonisotopically.

In the use of carriers for radioisotopes, as in the reverse process of using radioisotopes as tracers, it is essential that the isotopic carrier be in a chemical form identical with that of the radioactive material being carried. In the case of the example above, all the barium would normally be present as Ba^{++} and the problem does not appear. For substances which may be present in different oxidation states, e.g., Fe^{++} or Fe^{3+}, or different ionic species of the same oxidation state such as PO_4^{3-} or $P_2O_7^{4-}$, conversion of all the material to a common form before precipitation is necessary. Occasionally a long-lived radioisotope is used as an isotopic carrier for a shorter-lived one, as in the case of carrying Th^{234} with Th^{232}.

Nonisotopic Carrying. Nonisotopic carriers are often used to separate high-specific-activity material when it is desirable to retain the high specific activity. "Carrier-free" radioisotopes have no added isotopic carrier and approach the highest attainable specific activity, any stable isotopic material having been introduced as an impurity originally or during processing. For certain elements, for example, Po, no stable isotopic carrier exists.

Nonisotopic carrying is commonly classified into types according to the classification of Hahn (1), namely:

Isomorphous replacement. The ions of the carried element replace some of the carrier ions in isomorphous compounds and thereby form mixed crystals. The trace element is distributed either homogeneously or inhomogeneously throughout the crystal, depending upon the precipitation conditions. Homogeneous distribution is often referred to as the Berthelot-Nernst distribution. The corresponding distribution "law" is merely an expression for an equilibrium distribution ratio and has the form

$$D = \frac{\text{ratio of radioisotope to carrier in precipitate}}{\text{ratio of radioisotope to carrier in solution}}$$

A precipitate is enriched with respect to tracer if D is greater than unity; the solution is enriched for values of D less than unity. Such a distribution ratio can also be used in connection with the distribution of an impurity between the solid phase and the liquid phase in purifying an organic material by recrystallization.

For inhomogeneous distribution of the carried ion, the logarithmic or Doerner-Hoskins distribution law applies. It is of the form

$$D = \frac{\log \text{(fraction of tracer in precipitate)}}{\log \text{(fraction of carrier in precipitate)}}$$

(λ is sometimes used instead of D to distinguish this distribution ratio from that for the homogeneous case.) In this case the ratio of tracer to carrier in the surface of the growing crystal is proportional at any time to the changing ratio of tracer to carrier-ion concentration in the contacting solution. For a given fraction of carrier precipitated, the fraction of tracer carried is larger, the larger the value of D. The numerical values of the homogeneous and the logarithmic distribution ratios should be essentially the same and a characteristic constant for a given precipitation system. From the definitions of the two distribution ratios it can be seen that, when carrying is favorable, the per cent of tracer carried is greater for a given per cent precipitation of carrier for logarithmic carrying. For a given system, the type of distribution followed depends upon the conditions of precipitation.

Anomalous mixed crystal formation. Although the carrier and the tracer elements do not form isomorphous crystals of the compound precipitated at macro concentrations, the tracer is incorporated in the crystal in a homogeneous manner similar to that of isomorphous replacement. Thus, the carrier can incorporate the carried ion at trace concentrations of the latter even though this would not be predicted on the basis of behavior at macro concentrations. The distribution ratio used for isomorphous replacement applies to this case also.

Surface adsorption. Carrying can be effected by adsorption of the carried ions on the surface of the precipitate rather than by incorporation in the crystals. Adsorption carrying can also be effected by the use of suitable preformed precipitates. Although a distribution ratio and a separation factor can be calculated for a given experiment, the values obtained cannot be taken as characteristic of the separation method in general.

Internal adsorption. Carrying may occur as the result of adsorption during the growth of crystals to trap the carried ions within the crystals. This is not the same as the formation of mixed crystals, and the carried ions are distributed irregularly within the crystals. Calculated values of D and λ are meaningful for the particular precipitate alone.

The term "nonisotopic carrying" is often used interchangeably with "coprecipitation," which is generally classified into two types, namely, incorporation within the crystal and adsorption on the surface of the precipitate. The discussions of coprecipitation in textbooks on quantitative analysis are helpful in providing an understanding of nonisotopic carrying. As a rule, the analytical chemist is interested in minimizing coprecipitation of all impurities.

Factors to Be Considered in Designing, Evaluating, or Modifying a Precipitation Process. *Carrier.* The carrying observed for processes involving isomorphous replacement or anomalous mixed crystal formation is generally reproducible over a wide range of conditions, including the concentration of the ion being carried. Carrying by surface adsorption or by internal adsorption, however, is erratic and sensitive to precipitation conditions.

In the laboratory, carrier precipitations are seldom carried out under conditions such that the process can be described entirely as belonging to one of the four types described above. There are, in fact, many effective nonisotopic carriers for which the mechanism of carrying is not known. From a detailed knowledge of the behavior of several carriers it is possible to predict roughly how effective various possible carriers may be and how the precipitation conditions will affect the carrying.

Isotopic carriers. Isotopic carriers find wide applications except in cases where (1) isotope dilution is undesirable or (2) no suitable isotope exists. For laboratory application selection of a particular insoluble compound from several possible ones is based on:

1. Solubility and, therefore, yield

2. Selectivity—tendency to incorporate impurities
3. Ease of preparation and handling, particle size, corrosiveness of reagents, etc.
4. Ease of purification
5. Ease of conversion to final form desired in utilization of radioactive material
6. Toxicity and chemical hazards
7. Expense and availability of reagents

NONISOTOPIC CARRIERS. For a given chemical element the available insoluble compounds of all the other elements are potentially usable as nonisotopic carriers. In addition to the selection criteria listed for isotopic carriers, the most important criterion is that the precipitate must carry to a useful extent. Unlike the case of isotopic carrying there is seldom any guarantee that the precipitate will carry detectably. The limited class of isomorphous replacement carriers is predictable on the basis of the known behavior of the compounds of interest on a macro scale. Selectivity becomes a problem if the mixture to be separated contains more than one ion which can compete in isomorphous replacement. In a general way one can also predict that insoluble substances which form gelatinous or very finely divided precipitates will carry by surface adsorption. These are often referred to as "scavengers" and have the disadvantage of poor selectivity.

With respect to the extent of carrying by coprecipitation, the following generalizations are of interest:

1. A precipitate having an ionic lattice tends to adsorb from solution substances such as salts, acids, and bases, containing the lattice cation or anion.
2. The adsorbability of ions to form compounds with a lattice ion increases with decreasing solubility of the compound formed (Fajans-Paneth-Hahn adsorption rule) and with decreasing ionic dissociation of the adsorbed compound.
3. Adsorption exchange of ions with lattice ions may occur for solutes having no common ion.
4. Surface adsorption commonly occurs for precipitates which separate in the form of a flocculated colloid having a large surface area. Examples are hydrous oxides and metal sulfides. In general the fraction carried is larger, the larger the surface area, the more insoluble the carried compound, and the more highly charged the carried ion.

The above apply, of course, to any nonisotopic carrying, including the contamination of isotopically carried material by nonisotopically carried contaminants.

Precipitation Conditions. RATE OF PRECIPITATION. When isomorphous replacement occurs, rapid precipitation from an agitated supersaturated solution followed by digestion favors homogeneous distribution; slow precipitation by evaporation of a saturated (not supersaturated) solution and rapid precipitation from an agitated supersaturated solution, followed by immediate filtration, favor the logarithmic distribution; and precipitation by addition of a precipitating reagent can lead to the occurrence of both processes because of the local variations of concentration during the precipitation.

For carrying by surface adsorption, the carrying is greater the finer the particles of the precipitate. This condition is favored by rapid precipitation.

Temperature. The effect of the temperature of the solution at the time of precipitation is of importance primarily for the process of carrying by surface adsorption. Finer particles and greater adsorption can be expected when a precipitate is formed at room temperature rather than at a higher temperature. A precipitate so formed will usually be much more difficult to handle, i.e., separate, wash, etc. On the other hand, lower temperature usually corresponds to lower solubility and, therefore, increased yield because of more nearly complete precipitation of the carrier.

Digestion. Digestion of the precipitate favors a uniform distribution in the case of isomorphous incorporation but does not greatly change the amount carried. For carrying by surface adsorption, however, digestion, which results in recrystallization (release of carried material) and growth of crystals (reduction of surface area), can be expected to decrease the amount carried. Digestion is accelerated at elevated temperatures.

Agitation. When a precipitate is formed by adding a precipitating agent, some agitation is required for mixing purposes. Continued agitation promotes recrystallization and crystal growth and, therefore, less carrying by surface adsorption.

Concentration of carrier. In general, the higher the concentration at the time of precipitation, the finer the precipitate particles and the greater the resultant surface adsorption.

Effect of other solutes. The presence of an electrolyte in appreciable concentration decreases surface adsorption of ions at tracer concentration by (1) substitution and (2) promoting flocculation and crystal growth of charged colloidal particles. Depending upon the nature of the electrolyte, it can also interfere by substitution in isomorphous-replacement carrying of tracers.

The presence of an isotopic holdback carrier decreases the carrying of an undesired radioisotope in the same chemical form by substitution, although the total concentration of the element carried will usually be greater except for any effect on the particle size of the precipitate.

Holdback carriers are useful for decreasing the contamination of a desired substance regardless of the type of precipitate and carrying process used.

Complexing agents may be added to decrease the carrying of an undesired radioisotope by formation of a more soluble, less favorably carried complex. Such an additive may be considered to be a "nonisotopic holdback" carrier. Water-miscible, less polar organic solvents such as ethanol and acetone may be added to lower the solubility of the precipitate. Such additives may also affect the particle size.

For any particular separation problem the over-all precipitation conditions represent a compromise to obtain acceptable purity and yield within the time available. The latter is often limited by the half-life of the material being carried.

Techniques. *Precipitation, Centrifugation, Filtration.* As a rule, precipitates formed in a radiochemical purification process are separated from the supernate by centrifugation and decantation rather than by filtration. It is easier to avoid or at least control the loss (and simultaneous contamination of apparatus) of radioactive material in the precipitate if the precipitate is not transferred back and forth between the precipitation vessel and a filter for the necessary washing and reprecipitation steps. A second reason for preferring centrifugation is that the amount of precipitate may be quite small, so that filtration would be slower and less convenient even in the absence of radioactive material.

Filtration is often used, of course, in the preparation of counting sources, as described in Chap. 5. On occasion, precipitation and filtration may be convenient when separation and source preparation can be combined. Filter media and techniques are discussed in Chap. 5.

For routine low-level radiochemical work it is common to use standard glass, Lusteroid, or polyethylene centrifuge tubes in the capacity range of 12 to 50 ml. Glass tubes should be made of heat-resistant glass, and although they have a lower capacity, heavy-wall tubes are less apt to break and cause contamination of the centrifuge. Inner caps are available for the plastic tubes, and the glass tubes can be obtained with plastic screw caps or glass stoppers.

Conventional test-tube racks and blocks can be used to hold the centrifuge tubes. Similarly, for precipitation above room temperature, a conventional hot water bath, consisting of an electric hot plate (with adjustable temperature regulator) and a beaker with a metal cover having holes of the appropriate sizes for the centrifuge tubes, is adequate. Fire-polished stirring rods can be made readily from 2-mm heat-resistant glass rod.

Reprecipitation. Reprecipitation is a classical way to increase the purity of a precipitate, especially if the contaminant is carried by surface adsorption. The addition of holdback carriers helps "wash out" the impurity at each reprecipitation. The process can be repeated until adequate purity is attained, but usually at the expense of the yield.

Yield. The yield, or per cent recovery, of a radioactive substance in a precipitation process can be found in several ways. For isotopically carried material the recovery is the same as that of the carrier, which can be determined by weighing. Actually, it is not necessary to weigh the radioactive precipitate for each sample in a series if the separation is always done in exactly the same way. The yield for the method as used can be established in the absence of radioactive material.

For nonisotopic carrying the yield characteristic of a given separation procedure can be established by measuring the yield for a known amount of radioactive material. The known amount can be represented in terms of counts per minute. Any differences in self-absorption, etc., between the initial and final measurements must be taken into account in the yield calculation. The use of radioactive material to determine solubility, recovery, etc., is an important type of tracer application.

Experiments designed specifically to illustrate precipitation methods of separation have not been included in this chapter. The techniques are utilized in several experiments having different objectives and contained in the other chapters, e.g., Chap. 8.

Although the techniques used in forming, washing, and transferring a precipitate of radioactive material are to a large extent the same as those used for nonradioactive material, three precautions should be noted. First, there may be a radiation hazard making it unwise to hold the tube with one's fingers or to hold it close to one's eyes. Secondly, any of the radioactive liquid which finds its way to the outside of the tube, e.g., as the result of decantation, will contaminate tongs, fingers, etc. A stirring rod should be used when the supernate is decanted as in normal chemical practice. Thirdly, whenever gas is evolved from a liquid, as in the acidification of a carbonate or when dissolved air bubbles from a liquid being heated, the spray, if it escapes, will carry radioactive material with it. Although the mass of material which escapes is small or even invisible to the eye, serious contamination can result in the case of material having a very high specific activity. Whenever this problem may arise, an attempt should be made to minimize the escape of radioactive material by using a funnel, watch glass, or even a condenser, for example. If a large vessel is required, an erlenmeyer flask is preferable to a beaker. Furthermore, the whole operation should be conducted in a hood. These three precautions are not necessary for nonradioactive material unless, in the case of two of them, the material is toxic or pathogenic and, therefore, they are easily overlooked by a person with preformed habits.

9-3. Solvent-extraction Methods (Solvex)

Introduction. The term solvent extraction includes both liquid-liquid and solid-liquid extraction, but commonly, when used without qualification, the term refers to the former rather than to the process of leaching. In liquid-liquid extraction the process of contacting a solution containing one or more extractable solutes (organic or inorganic substances) with an "immiscible" extracting solvent leads to the distribution or partitioning of the extracted material between the two phases. Generally, for the extraction of inorganic substances, the original solvent is water and the extracting solvent is an immiscible, less polar organic liquid.

Solvent extraction on a micro or macro scale is a well-established process for the separation of organic or inorganic substances. It is of interest historically to note that the use of diethyl ether for the separation of uranium as uranyl nitrate from the other constituents of pitchblende for both analytical and large-scale production purposes on the Manhattan Project can be traced back to the use of ether by Peligot in 1842 to purify uranyl nitrate obtained from pitchblende. The classical application to analytical chemistry is, of course, the extraction of ferric chloride from hydrochloric acid solution by diethyl ether introduced by Rothe in 1892. Today, with a variety of ways of promoting solvent extraction available, almost every element in the periodic table has been found to undergo solvent extraction under suitable conditions. Many contributions to the development of methods, theory, and techniques of solvent extraction of inorganic substances have originated in the problems arising since the 1930s in connection with target chemistry associated with the production of artificial radioactivity, and more recently in connection with the utilization of nuclear energy for peaceful and military purposes.

Solvent-extraction Systems. In order that an inorganic substance may be distributed between an aqueous-organic solvent pair, the substance must obviously be present in a chemical form (usually a complex species) or forms soluble in both solvents. The conditions which lead to such a partitioning provide a basis for classifying the many examples of solvent extraction into types of systems. Morrison and Freiser (2) classify extraction systems for metal ions on the basis of the nature of the extractable species assumed to be uncharged molecules, e.g., coordination complexes or ion-association complexes.

Coordination complexes are formed by interaction between a metal electron-acceptor cation and an electron-donor coordinating group, or ligand. The relative tendencies for complex formation for some single ligands are shown in Table 9-1. The relative strengths of complexes formed with simple ligands of a similar type correlate in general with the relative strengths of the ligands as Lewis bases. For a given ligand the tendency to form a coordination compound depends upon the electronic configuration of the metal cation. Among the other coordination types of complexes which are of interest for solvent extraction are chelates,

TABLE 9-1*

TENDENCIES FOR COMPLEX FORMATION OF SOME SIMPLE LIGANDS†

$NH_3 > RNH_2 > R_2NH > R_3N$
$H_2O > ROH > R_2O > RCOR > RCHO$
$R_3As > R_3P > R_2S$
$CN^- > SCN^- > F^- > OH^- > Cl^- > Br^- > I^-$

* G. H. Morrison and H. Freiser, "Solvent Extraction in Analytical Chemistry," Wiley, New York, 1957.

† R = alkyl or aryl group.

which are formed by polyfunctional ligands or chelating agents such as dimethylglyoxime. Heteropoly acids such as silicomolybdic acid also belong in the class of coordination complexes which may undergo extraction.

Extractable ion-association complexes consist of ionic species, which are mostly individual ions in the aqueous phase but which may enter the organic phase by virtue of their formation of electrically neutral aggregates. The organic solvent, e.g., diethyl ether, is incorporated in the ion-association complex and adds to its stability. The formation of ion-association complexes has been discussed by Diamond (3) and Irving (4).

In summary, chelates are large, neutral complexes which have solubilities in nonpolar solvents characteristic of the chelating agent. For simple ligands the formation of a complex ion does not in itself lead to solubility in an organic solvent. It is necessary that the complex ion form, with the aid of the organic solvent, a soluble association complex. Thus, ferric iron readily forms halo complexes with chloride and fluoride ions, but the fluoride complexes are not extractable. For nonmetals such as the halogens, the covalent nature of the elemental species permits extraction into nonpolar solvents.

Distribution of a Solute between Solvents. The extent to which a given solute partitions is generally expressed in terms of a partition or extraction or distribution ratio which is variously represented by the symbols D, E, or $E_a{}^0$.

For solute A, the practical distribution ratio corresponding to the reaction $A_{aq} \rightleftharpoons A_{org}$ is defined as

$$D = \frac{(C_A)_{org}}{(C_A)_{aq}}$$

where $(C_A)_{org}$ and $(C_A)_{aq}$ are the total equilibrium concentrations of solute A in the organic solvent and in water, respectively. This is the ratio derived by Nernst in 1891. For an "ideal" system in which the solute does not dissociate or associate and the miscibility of the solvents is not altered by the dissolved substances, the distribution ratio is essentially independent of the total amount of extractable solute present. There are relatively few systems which are almost "ideal" in this sense over even a limited range of initial solute concentration. An example of a relatively ideal system is that involving the distribution of iodine (as I_2) between water and carbon disulfide reported by Jakowkin (5). The distribution ratio $(I_2)_{CS_2}/(I_2)_{H_2O}$ increases from 586.2 to 651.8 for a concentration change of 0.0518 to 0.2571 g/liter in H_2O and 30.36 to 157.6 g/liter in CS_2. For the extraction of $GaCl_3$ from hydrochloric acid solution (approximately 6 N) with diethyl ether, Grahame and Seaborg (6), in a classical paper on the solvent extraction of trace amounts of material, showed that the distribution ratio varied from an average of 18.2 at a $GaCl_3$ concentration of about 10^{-12} M to 16.9 at 1.6×10^{-3} M. In contrast, the distribution ratio for the extraction of ferric chloride from 5 M hydrochloric acid with isopropyl ether is relatively constant between the limits of 0.315 and 0.339 for the range of aqueous-equilibrium iron concentration from 4.05×10^{-5} to 2.78×10^{-3} M but then increases sharply to 13.40 at 3.5×10^{-2} M (7). The dependence of the distribution ratio on the aqueous iron concentration is believed to result from polymerization of the ethereal iron.

When derived on the basis of chemical thermodynamics, the distribution can be expressed in terms of chemical activities as

$$K_D = \frac{(a_A)_{org}}{(a_A)_{aq}}$$

where the K_D is a true constant—the distribution coefficient. Unfortunately the activities are seldom known.

In practice, it is often convenient to express the per cent extraction as a measure of the extractability for a given system. The per cent extracted and the distribution ratio are related as follows:

$$\text{Per cent extracted} = \frac{100D}{D + V_{aq}/V_{org}}$$

for a single equilibration resulting in the equilibrium volumes V_{aq} and

V_{org}. The effect of volume ratio is most pronounced, of course, for small values of D.

As a practical matter, the distribution ratio must be determined empirically for a variety of conditions for each extraction system. For a given extraction system, i.e., specified extractable material in a given oxidation state, solvent, and participating reagents, the value of the distribution ratio may vary markedly, depending upon the system, with the following variables:

1. Temperature—commonly D decreases with increasing temperature.
2. Concentration of the organic solvent when an inert diluent is used, e.g., per cent tri-*n*-butyl phosphate in carbon tetrachloride.
3. Concentration of participating reagents, e.g., chelating agent such as thenoyltrifluoroacetone (TTA) in the organic solvent, hydrochloric acid in the aqueous phase; common-ion type of salting agents.
4. Concentration of interfering substances which form nonextractable compounds with the desired material, e.g., phosphate interference in the extraction of uranyl nitrate.
5. Concentration of nonparticipating substances which change the ionic strength of the aqueous phase, thereby acting to alter the activity of the extracting substance or the activity of water, e.g., a bulk impurity.
6. Concentration of a substance which may or may not participate in the extraction of the desired solute but does itself extract to alter the properties of the extracting solvent, e.g., nitric acid in the extraction of uranyl nitrate.
7. Ratio of volumes of liquids contacted. This can be important when a second solute which participates in the desired extraction also extracts independently. Normally, for convenience, the initial organic-aqueous volume ratio is taken as 1 : 1 but may be 2 : 1 for some systems involving concentrated solutions of readily extracted substances.
8. Presence of solid.

The selectivity of a solvent-extraction process can be expressed in terms of a separation factor defined as

$$\alpha = \frac{D_A}{D_B}$$

in terms of distribution ratios. The separation factor relates the extraction of one substance relative to a second substance in the mixture to be separated. The desired constituent is usually extracted from the undesired one, as in the purification of uranium, although the reverse procedure is sometimes followed, as in the removal of iron used as a nonisotopic carrier for a radionuclide. A value of α greater than unity means that component A is preferentially extracted, and the greater the value of α, the purer the extract of A relative to substance B; a value of α of unity means no separation; and a value of α less than unity means that component A remains preferentially in the aqueous phase.

Factors to Be Considered in Designing, Evaluating, or Modifying an Extraction Process. When there is a choice of ligand and/or solvent for a particular separation problem, many factors in addition to those mentioned above as affecting the distribution ratio, separation factor, and recovery must be taken into account. The various factors are summarized below:

Ligand. STABILITY AND REACTIVITY. Included are sensitivity to oxidation or reduction by air or other substances in the system and attack of solvent or container.

AVAILABILITY AND COST. These are usually not very serious problems for small-scale laboratory work but should be kept in mind if the laboratory procedure is being considered for large-scale application.

TOXICITY. Toxic substances are generally controlled by the same techniques used in handling radioactive material.

Solvent. DENSITY AND VISCOSITY. The rate of separation of the phases after equilibration is generally greater, the greater the difference in density between the organic and the aqueous layer. A low viscosity favors rapid separation of phases. For tri-*n*-butyl phosphate an inert diluent such as carbon tetrachloride is frequently used to increase the density of the organic layer, or a hydrocarbon diluent is used to decrease the density. The diluent may also lower the viscosity. In any case, when a diluent is used, the concentration of active solvent is an important variable.

The relative densities and viscosities of the organic and aqueous phases are factors which are related to the formation of emulsions. The solvents should be equilibrated and tested for emulsion-forming characteristics in advance.

SOLUBILITY IN THE AQUEOUS PHASE. Substances dissolved in the two phases will generally alter the mutual solubilities of the solvents. Although no pair of solvents is absolutely immiscible, mutual solubilities beyond about 5 vol % are usually undesirable in terms of the separation factor and completeness of extraction. For a very expensive organic solvent its recovery would also become a problem. Some solvents are relatively less sensitive to the effect of acid on mutual solubility. β,β-Dichloroethyl ether, for example, may be used with higher hydrochloric acid concentration than di-isopropyl or diethyl ether.

STABILITY. Frequently small amounts of materials produced as the result of oxidation, halogenation, hydrolysis, cleavage, etc., of the organic solvent by reaction with acids, oxidants, etc., present in the system have an unfavorable effect on the separation factor. Although it is a rarer problem, radiation decomposition of solvents in the processing of highly radioactive materials producing a radiation energy density of the order of watts per gram can have an analogous deleterious effect. For extraction systems involving nitrates, perchlorates, or other strong oxidizing agents together with readily oxidized substances such as diethyl ether, certain precautions are obviously necessary to avoid concentration of the oxidizing substance before removal of the solvent. The damage which can result from the explosion of a few grams of such a mixture should not be underestimated.

EASE OF REMOVAL FROM PRODUCT. A volatile solvent such as diethyl ether can be removed readily (but cautiously) by evaporation. For high-boiling solvents it may be preferable to extract the solute from the organic phase with water.

FLAMMABILITY. Obvious precautions must be taken to avoid a fire when a flammable solvent is used.

TOXICITY. See comment relative to the ligand.

Salting Agent. Salting agents are commonly added to the aqueous phase to increase the distribution ratio for an extracting solute and in some cases to improve the separation factor as well. A salting agent may provide a high concentration of common ion, e.g., chloride ions supplied by LiCl in the extraction of a complex chloride, and, at the same time, may increase the escaping tendency of the extracting species both by electrostatic interaction and by having the cation compete with the extracting species for solvation water, thereby favoring incorporation of the organic solvent in an extractable ion-association complex.

Acidity. The hydrogen-ion concentration must be carefully adjusted in systems involving chelates, since their stability is pH-dependent. The acidity must be adjusted with some care for systems in which the extractable species is an acid, e.g., $HFeCl_4$. For such systems the acidity must be adjusted after each successive extraction. It is similarly true for systems in which an extractable acid such as HNO_3 must be present in sufficient amount to prevent hydrolysis and possible precipitation of the extracting substance or some other substance in the aqueous phase.

Oxidation States of Solute. The higher oxidation states for elements generally favor the formation of extractable complexes. Separation of two substances can be enhanced by taking advantage of differences in redox potentials. An example is the purification and separation of uranium and plutonium. These two elements coextract from nitrate solution when they are in the (VI) state. The extract mixture can be transferred to an aqueous solution, and the uranium (VI) extracted away from the plutonium after the latter has been reduced to the (III) state. Similarly iron extracts from hydrochloric acid solution when in the (III) state but not when in the (II) state.

Masking Agents. Complex formation may be used to prevent extraction of an unwanted constituent in a mixture. Addition of a reagent such as fluoride, tartrate, etc., leads to the formation of stable complexes which, for some elements, mask or prevent the formation of extractable complexes which would otherwise form in the extraction system. Assuming that the extractability of the desired constituent is not affected, an improvement in separation factor results.

Backwashing or Scrubbing. The concentration of coextracted impurities in the organic phase can be lowered for impurities with a lower D by contacting the organic phase with a portion of an aqueous wash solution having the proper concentration of extraction reagent, acid, salting agent, etc. Care must be taken to keep the loss of the desired material in the washing process to a level consistent with purity requirements, since some of it will also transfer to the aqueous wash solution.

Successive Extraction and Reextraction. If the recovery is not adequate in a single contact, the aqueous phase, after adjustment of reagent concentrations, may be contacted successively with fresh solvent. Repeated extraction with small portions of solvent is preferable to one extraction with a large volume. If the combined extract does not meet purity requirements, the solute can be back-extracted into water (or the solvent removed by evaporation) and reextracted after adjustment of reagent concentrations. A scrubbing step may be inserted before the reextraction step.

Emulsion Formation. The tendency to form emulsions may be an inherent characteristic of the mixture of solvents and reagents used in an extraction system, or it may be attributed to the sample of material to be separated. The presence of suspended material such as silica at the interfacial boundary is frequently considered to be a cause of emulsification. The amount and effect of such suspended material will vary from sample to sample of aqueous feed solution.

Commonly, emulsification presents an easily recognized problem, namely, the slow coalescence of the two phases. At times, however, there is reasonably rapid separation of the bulk phases, which then show a turbidity which disappears slowly. Occasionally the phases appear clear to the naked eye but contain fine droplets of the other solvent which are detected by means of a magnifying lens. Unless observed, the latter two conditions can lead to a product of unsatisfactory radiochemical purity, particularly if the undesired constituents have a high specific activity.

Among the techniques which may be used to break emulsions are:

1. Addition of an inert diluent
2. Addition of a surface-active agent, although there is risk of promoting emulsification with these agents and the effect of any additive on the selectivity must be ascertained
3. Filtration to remove solid material
4. Centrifugation

Apparatus and Techniques. The choice of apparatus is governed by such factors as volumes of phases; techniques to be used, e.g., backwashing; relative density of aqueous and organic layer; possible attack of container; tendency toward emulsification; and radiation hazard of the sample. Typical vessels for batch extraction consist of separatory funnels; pipettes; stoppered or capped test tubes, centrifuge tubes, and cylinders; and special micro extractors (8). Some of these are illustrated in Fig. 9-2.

In using apparatus for batch extraction, the following comments should be noted:

1. Leakage around stoppers and stopcocks is a constant source of contamination of hands and bench top. For many nuclides, depending upon the radiation emitted, extractions can be done by hand for radioactivity levels into the millicurie range. The use of rubber gloves is advisable, particularly if it is necessary to minimize or even avoid the use of a stopcock lubricant. Sometimes it is adequate to use an absorbent hood over the stopper. Such a hood consists of several layers of absorbent paper contained in a layer of nonabsorbent, solvent-insoluble material such as rubber or metal foil. If the vessel is held with tongs because of the radiation level, all stopcocks and the stoppers should be clamped or wired in position.
2. Low-boiling solvents, e.g., diethyl ether, should be vented cautiously after equilibration. Spray will carry contamination. In some extraction systems, e.g., when concentrated acids are present, considerable heat is evolved during the equilibration, resulting in appreciable pressure generation.
3. Equilibration time should be checked for adequacy by successive equilibration and sampling of an extraction mixture. Commonly, less than 5 min of vigorous agitation is required. Agitation can be achieved by stirring instead of shaking the mixture. For cases in which successive extraction of an aqueous solution is necessary, it is a convenience, when vessels with a bottom outlet are used, to have a solvent whose density is greater than that of the aqueous solution because the aqueous phase does not have to be removed from the separatory funnel. β,β-Dichloroethyl ether is such a solvent.

Sampling or withdrawal of a phase for vessels without bottom outlets can be done with an ordinary volumetric or measuring pipette of suitable size or a capillary pipette. In each case a suitable pipette control is used. It is generally advisable to remove all of the upper layer and a portion of the lower layer before sampling the lower layer with a clean

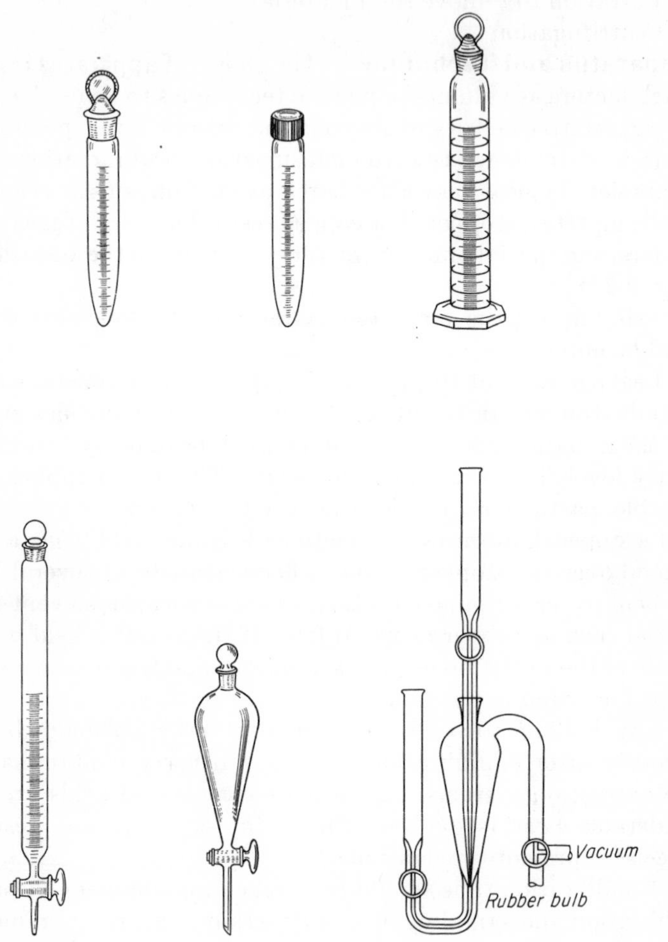

FIG. 9-2. Extraction vessels. [*Microextractor from Kirk and Danielson* (8).]

pipette. When the whole of each phase is required, a portion of the lower layer can be withdrawn with the last of the upper phase and then carefully drained (to the interface) into a separate container.

Examples of continuous-extraction apparatus are shown in Fig. 9-3. Continuous extraction is more convenient than batch extraction when several successive extractions are needed and when many samples of material are to be extracted.

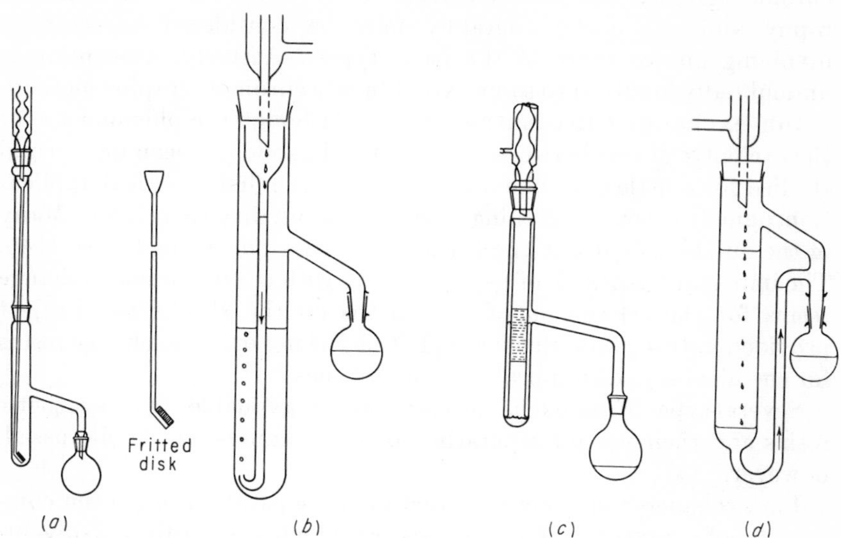

FIG. 9-3. Continuous extractors. (*a*) Continuous extractor for use with a solvent lighter than water; (*b*) Kutscher–Steudel extractor for use with solvents lighter than water; (*c*) continuous extractor for use with a solvent heavier than water; (*d*) Wehrli extractor for solvents heavier than water. [*From Morrison and Frieser* (2). (*d*) *From Wehrli, Helv. Chim. Acta, vol.* 20, *p.* 927, 1937.]

9-4. Chromatographic Methods

Introduction. The term "chromatography" is commonly applied to the separation of substances by selective distribution between a flowing fluid and an insoluble solid known as the support. Chromatographic methods may be used for processing macro amounts of material for preparative purposes or micro amounts for assay purposes.

As used by Tswett over 50 years ago, chromatography consisted of a method of separating naturally occurring dyestuffs by selective adsorption from solution onto powdered calcium carbonate to form a system of colored bands known as a chromatogram. The various chromatographic methods in use today, however, are not limited to the separation of colored substances or to selective adsorption. Unfortunately there is no consistent scheme for classifying and naming the numerous types of chromatographic methods. For the purposes of presentation in this chapter it is convenient to separate the methods according to the type of chemical process which predominates. Accordingly, the three basic types are taken to be ion-exchange chromatography, adsorption chromatography, and partition chromatography. Electrochromatography and gas chromatography may be considered as methods involving one or more of the basic types. Actually, adsorption is undoubtedly involved to some extent in any chromatographic method.

Ion-exchange Chromatography. Although the phenomenon of the exchange of ions between a solution and a solid has been known and studied for a little over one hundred years, the first practical application, namely in water softening, was made about fifty years later. Many of the numerous current applications have been developed since 1940. The important series (9) of papers dealing with the use of ion-exchange resins for the separation of rare earths on the Manhattan Project provided a strong stimulus for exploiting the use of ion-exchange resins for chemical-separation problems of all types.

Several types of ion-exchange materials are available. Only synthetic resins and their use for separating ionic substances will be discussed, however.

Ion-exchange resins may be used in the separation of (1) the components of a mixture of ionic species or (2) ionic species from a solvent. Under suitable conditions the process of separation is also one of concentration.

The separation may be carried out either by contacting the solution containing the ionic material with the resin in a batchwise mixing process or by passing the solution through a bed of resin contained in an ion-exchange column. The former technique is useful for equilibrium distribution studies, but the nonequilibrium column technique is generally used for actual separations.

There are two techniques for separating ions by means of a column, namely, the breakthrough technique and the elution technique. In the former case, as the solution of ionic species is passed through the column, the ions migrate down the column at a rate dependent upon their exchange affinities. The first ion to appear in the effluent is the one most weakly adsorbed. The other ions appear in order of increasing adsorption. Breakthrough curves are obtained when the concentration or the fraction of a given ion is plotted as a function of the volume of effluent or the milliequivalents of ions passed through the column. These curves have an asymmetric sigmoidal shape and may overlap in the case of poor separation.

The elution technique is frequently referred to as ion-exchange chromatography. The ions are first adsorbed from a dilute solution in a narrow band at the top of the column and then removed by the addition of an eluting agent or an elutriant which causes the band of adsorbed ions to separate, as it moves down the column, into a number of bands corresponding to the number of ionic species being separated. The degree of separation depends upon the nature of the eluting agent as well as the resin. For radiochemical separations, chromatographic elution is the more important technique.

Types of Ion-exchange Resins. An ion-exchange resin consists of a polymeric framework of an insoluble hydrocarbon to which ionizable groups are attached. The resin may be visualized as an insoluble polyelectrolyte. As examples, polymers may be obtained by polymerization of phenol and formaldehyde or by copolymerization of styrene and divinylbenzene. Specific ionizable groups are introduced to provide the desired exchange properties.

Ion-exchange resins are classified as either cation-exchange resins or anion-exchange resins, depending upon the nature of the ionizable or exchangeable group. These may be further classified as "strong" or "weak," in the sense of a strong or weak acid or base, according to the characteristics of the ionizable group. The strong functional groups are well suited for inorganic separations, and the weak groups for organic separations, e.g., mixtures of amino acids.

Through the processes of adsorption and diffusion an ion in solution in contact with an ion-exchange resin can exchange with or replace an ion supplied by the functional or "ion-active" group of the resin. Thus, for a cation-exchange resin, functional groups in the acid form, such as the sulfonic acid ($—SO_3H$) and carboxylic acid groups ($—COOH$), can ionize and reversibly exchange H^+ for cations such as Na^+, Ca^{++}, La^{3+}, Th^{4+}, etc., in appropriate stoichiometric ratio. The same functional groups in the salt form, e.g., $—SO_3Na$ and $—COONa$, can undergo exchange with H^+ or other metal cations. The strong acid, e.g., sulfonic acid, type of resin is completely ionized and exchanges rapidly in both acid and salt forms. The weak acid, e.g., carboxylic acid, type is partially ionized in the acid form and completely ionized in the salt form. Exchange is rapid for the salt form and slow for the acid form.

For anion-exchange resins, quaternary ammonium bases ($\gtrless N—OH$) and amines ($—NH_2$, $>NH$, $\equiv N$) are typical strong and weak functional groups, respectively. The strong quaternary ammonium base type of resin exchanges rapidly with anions, e.g., Cl^-, $FeCl_4^-$, in the base or the salt form.

The exchange capacity depends upon the type of polymer and the type of functional group. The capacity of weak acid or weak base types is dependent upon the pH of the contacting solution. For strong functional groups the capacity is independent of pH except for effects arising from weak groups which may also be present in the resin to a minor extent. At very high acidity the capacity of a cation-exchange resin is decreased for ions of low affinity.

Ion-exchange capacity may be expressed in several ways, e.g., milliequivalents per gram of dry resin or milliequivalents per milliliter of wet resin. For Dowex-50 (10) cation-exchange resin, for example, these would be approximately 5 and 1.9 meq respectively. For this resin the water content is about 45 per cent by weight for 20- to 50-mesh particles.

Distribution of Solute between Resin and Solution. Various theoretical approaches have been used to describe the behavior of ion-exchange resins. Thus, the Donnan equilibrium theory, the mass-action law, and the adsorption theories of Freundlich and Langmuir have been used to account for the distribution of ions between an ion-exchange resin and an external solution. These theoretical treatments have been summarized by Samuelson (11).

For tracer concentrations a useful expression derived by Tompkins and Mayer (12) for the equilibrium distribution ratio for an adsorbed cation A in terms of measured quantities is

$$D = \frac{(\% A)_{\text{resin}}}{(\% A)_{\text{solution}}} \frac{\text{volume of solution}}{\text{mass of resin}}$$

Thus, D is the ratio of the amount per kilogram of dry resin to the amount per liter of solution. The valence of the ion is not involved in the calculation. As defined above, D is reasonably constant with concentration for a given ion.

Distribution ratios and therefore their ratios, i.e., selectivities, depend upon the following factors:

Nature of adsorbed ion. In general for solutions under 0.1 N the affinity for a cation exchanger increases with charge on the cation and decreases with increasing size of the hydrated cation. The exchange affinity has been correlated (13) with $\mathring{a}$, the closest distance of approach of cations in the Debye-Huckel equation for the activity coefficient of an electrolyte. Assuming $\mathring{a}$ to be a measure of hydrated-ion size, a correlation is observed between ion-exchange affinity and $1/\mathring{a}$ obtained from activity-coefficient data. In terms of nonhydrated-ion size, the larger ions (which are hydrated to a lesser degree) are held more strongly.

The order of relative exchange affinity depends upon the resin and the experimental conditions. With respect to the effect of the resin, the major differences in order are observed when resins with strong functional groups are compared with resins with weak functional groups. The following series may be taken as indicative for dilute solutions:

Cations, strong resin functional group, e.g., —SO_3H

(Trivalent) lanthanum > cerium > praseodymium > neodymium > promethium > samarium > europium > gadolinium > terbium > dysprosium > yttrium > holmium > erbium > thulium > ytterbium > lutecium; yttrium > scandium > aluminum.

(Divalent) barium > strontium > calcium > nickel > copper > zinc > magnesium > beryllium; magnesium > manganese > cadmium.

(Univalent) silver > thallium > cesium > rubidium > ammonium > potassium > sodium > hydrogen > lithium.

Anions, strong resin functional group, e.g., quaternary ammonium base

(Polyvalent) citrate > sulfate > oxalate > chromate; (univalent) iodide > bisulfate > nitrate > bromide > cyanide > bisulfite > nitrite > bromate > chloride > bicarbonate > dihydrogen phosphate > formate > acetate > hydroxyl* > fluoride.

OTHER SOLUTES. Other solutes do not have a serious effect on the selectivity of an ion exchanger in a specified form for a given ion unless the other solutes result in (1) appreciable conversion of the resin to a different ionic form or (2) formation of complex ions or molecules in the aqueous solution. Complex-ion formation may enhance or decrease the distribution ratio for a given ion. In the absence of complex-forming solutes the distribution ratios for two ions may be sufficiently similar to make the separation poor. The additional separation factor which can arise from differences in stability of a given type of complex ion may result in excellent separation.

Ions which form complex anions can be separated from ions which do not by means of an anion exchanger. Thus cobalt and nickel can be separated (see Expt. 9-2) by contacting a strong hydrochloric acid solution of nickel and cobalt with an anion exchanger. The cobalt is adsorbed as a chloro complex, but the nickel remains in cationic form as Ni^{++} and is not adsorbed.

The classical example of the use of complexing agents to enhance separation by means of cation resins is the separation of rare earths in the presence of citrate, which forms nonadsorbable complex ions. An over-all separation factor α for two cations A and B can be written as

$$\underset{\text{Over-all}}{\alpha_{A/B}} = \underset{\text{Resin}}{\alpha_{A/B}} \times \underset{\text{Complex}}{\beta_{A/B}}$$

where α_{resin} is the ratio of distribution ratios for the resin and β_{complex} is the ratio of dissociation constants for the complexes. The observed

* The position of hydroxyl in this series is characteristic of Dowex-1. In the case of Dowex-2, however, hydroxyl affinity is between chloride and bicarbonate.

over-all separation ratio would be the ratio of distribution ratios observed with citrate present. Commonly ions with greater exchange affinity form weaker complexes. Thus for separation of cerium (Ce^{3+}) and yttrium (Y^{3+}) on a cation resin for which α_{resin} (Ce/Y) was 1.55, $\alpha_{\text{over-all}}$ was 4.5 in the presence of citrate for which β_{complex} was 2.9 (14).

This effect of complexing agents is frequently used to advantage in the elution of ions from a resin bed.

Resin functional groups. For a given type of resin (cation or anion) some variations in distribution can be attributed to the nature of the functional group, particularly its behavior as a strong or weak acid or base. If, for specific ions, ion affinities relative to H^+ or OH^- remain unchanged, the separation is not altered.

In general, for separation of inorganic ions, strongly acidic or strongly basic functional groups are preferable.

Extent of resin-ion conversion. Although the thermodynamic distribution ratio for a given ion and a given resin is independent of concentrations, the ratio computed from concentrations generally decreases with increasing ratio of adsorbed to resin ions in the resin and tends to be more sensitive to extent of conversion the larger the value of D.

Total concentration of electrolyte in solution. The distribution ratio for an ion (cation or anion) decreases with increasing concentration of bulk electrolyte. The sensitivity to concentration change depends upon the valence of the ion and the total concentration. Thus, for a resin in univalent-ion form exchanging with univalent, divalent, or trivalent ions, the observed dependence is roughly the zeroth, first, and second power, respectively, of the ratio of total equivalents per unit quantity of resin to total equivalents per unit quantity of solution. Dilution effects are greater the more dilute the solution.

As a general rule, the more dilute the solution, the better the separation, provided, of course, that there are no complications from hydrolysis or colloid formation at very low concentrations.

Factors to Be Considered in Selecting an Ion-exchange Resin. The choice between an anion and a cation exchanger is governed by the particular separation problem. A few elements may be adsorbed in either cationic or complex anionic form.

In selecting a particular resin within each of the two classes, consideration must be given to selectivity, exchange capacity, solubility, chemical stability, swelling, mechanical strength, particle size, and particle shape. For small-scale laboratory work mechanical strength is not usually a problem. For a given type of exchanger, i.e., specified polymer and functional group, usually a choice is to be made with respect to the degree of cross linkage and the particle size.

Cross linkage. For copolymer resins, the extent of cross linkage can be varied during preparation of the copolymer. The greater the cross linkage, the tighter the resin structure. The extent of cross linkage is usually expressed as the per cent content of one of the materials copolymerized, e.g., 8 per cent divinylbenzene. In general, the lower the per cent cross linkage, (1) the greater the swelling (or shrinking) resulting from the adsorption of water, (2) the lower the mechanical strength, (3) the higher the capacity for exchanging ions of high molecular weight, (4) the faster the internal diffusion rates, (5) the lower the selectivity, (6) the lower the exchange capacity on a volume basis, (7) the higher the solubility, and (8) the greater the influence of flow rate on the exchange process.

Particle size and shape. The over-all rate of separation by ion exchange is determined by the rate of diffusion of ions through the resin particles rather than by the rapid exchange of ions at the functional groups. The resin is more effectively used when in the form of small particles. For example, the over-all exchange rate is more rapid, separations are sharper, and less elutriant is required. Since flow rates decrease with decreasing particle size, the improved separation is at the expense of time. Resins available in commercial quantities are generally rather coarse—about 20 to 50 mesh (0.84 to 0.297 mm respectively). For research applications, particles 200 mesh (0.074 mm) or finer are available and are preferable.

Resins are commonly available in spherical granules. These provide minimum free volume and offer, therefore, considerable resistance to flow when very small. There is less chance for channeling with spherical particles than with irregularly shaped particles.

Apparatus and Techniques. As mentioned above, ion-exchange separation may be conducted as a batch operation or a column operation. The latter is more commonly used, although a combination of the two may be advantageous for a separation problem in which column operation in the initial stages of the separation would be difficult because of the evolution of gas or precipitation of solids.

Examples of ion-exchange columns are shown in Fig. 9-4. Basically the column consists of a tube provided with means for supporting the resin bed and for controlling the flow of solution. The necessary column length depends upon the difficulty of the separation, the quantity of ions involved, and the resin particle size (the smaller the particles, the shorter the column). The length needed may be between 10 and 100 times the diameter, with the latter varying from a few millimeters to a centimeter or two. For small-diameter tubes the resin particles must be sufficiently small to provide distributed flow without channeling.

The simplest apparatus is one in which the resin is supported on a glass-wool plug in a tube which is made of glass, plastic, or any other chemically resistant material and has a constricted bottom outlet to control the flow rate. As an example, a burette of suitable length may

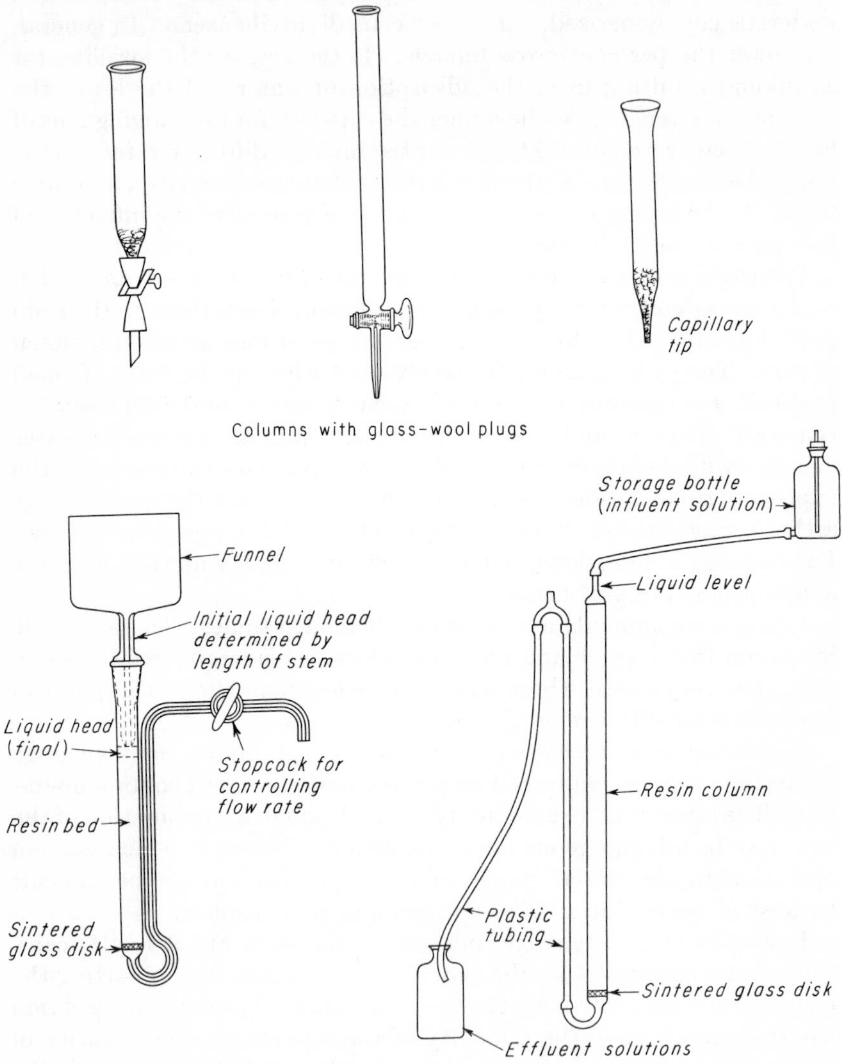

FIG. 9-4. Ion-exchange columns. [*Continuous columns from Tompkins* (15).]

be used. Such a simple apparatus requires constant attention when in use in order to prevent the liquid level from falling below the top of the resin bed and thereby allowing air to become entrapped in the resin bed.

The entrapped air slows down the flow rate and causes channeling. It is often necessary to remove all the resin from the column and reconstitute the bed in order to remove entrapped air. The addition of a side-arm overflow tube prevents the liquid level from falling too low. For a fixed bed height the side arm may be constructed of glass; for a variable bed height it may be made of flexible plastic tubing having suitable chemical stability and equipped with a glass outlet tube. In any case, the side arm should have a small bore to minimize liquid holdup.

Commercially available units of the type illustrated in Fig. 9-4 are all glass and are equipped with a removable funnel and a fritted plate for supporting the resin.

Ion-exchange columns are usually constructed for operation at room temperature but may be equipped with a heating jacket for operation at higher temperature. In general an increase in temperature, e.g., to 100°C, results in increased diffusion rates and less resistance to flow because of the lower viscosity of the solution. The time necessary for the adsorption, washing, and elution steps may then be shortened. Decomposition of the resin and hydrolysis become more important problems with increased temperature, however.

PREPARATION AND CONDITIONING OF THE RESIN BED. The resin is normally obtained and stored in a wet form. It should not be dried.

In preparing a resin bed it is convenient to transfer the resin to the column in the form of a slurry in water. Some workers fill the column with water before adding the slurry. All gas bubbles should be removed from the slurry, and precautions should be taken in the transfer operation to avoid entrapping air in the resin bed. It is important, as mentioned above, that the bed always be covered with a layer of liquid.

Extremely fine resin particles which greatly increase the resistance to liquid flow may be removed while the resin is being slurried or after it is in the column by allowing water to flow upward through the column, i.e., by backwashing, at a rate which causes the very fine particles to float away but does not cause the loss of larger particles.

Before the adsorption step, the resin should be saturated with monovalent ions, usually hydrogen ions, if it is not already in the desired form. Strong cation resins are commonly supplied in H^+ or Na^+ form, strong anion resins in OH^- or Cl^- form. The hydrogen-ion form is especially convenient if the solute tends to hydrolyze. On the other hand, ammonium ions may be used it acidic conditions are unsuitable.

Traces of iron or other acid-soluble impurities which may color the effluent may be removed by pretreatment with hydrochloric acid. Excess acid or other conditioning reagents should be removed with distilled water.

ADSORPTION. A dilute solution, e.g., 10^{-1} to 10^{-3} M or less, is allowed to flow through the resin bed at a controlled rate which is generally in the range from 10 down to 0.1 ml/cm^2/min or less. The optimum flow rate for a given separation will depend upon the resin particle size, concentration of solute, etc.

Solutions containing cations which readily hydrolyze should be acidified but not without limit because at high acidities more resin is needed to provide adequate exchange capacity. Acidity above a few hundredths normal may make adsorption of monovalent ions difficult.

When adsorption of a complex anion, e.g., $CoCl_3^-$, is involved, the necessary complexing reagents at the proper concentration must be added to the solution.

After the adsorption step the nonadsorbed material is displaced from the resin bed with distilled water or weak acid or a special reagent if hydrolysis or anion decomposition is a problem.

ELUTION. Hydrochloric acid is commonly used as the elutriant for cation exchangers. The optimum concentration is generally about 3 to 4 M HCl. The quantity of acid required depends upon the nature of the cation to be eluted, the more strongly adsorbed higher-valent cations requiring more acid. Elution flow rates are usually about the same as adsorption rates.

Salts and complexing agents may also be used as elutriants. Complexing agents may be used to (1) enhance the separation of similar ions or (2) elute very strongly adsorbed ions. Separation of the elutriant from the desired ions may be a problem except in the case of the volatilizable hydrochloric acid.

For anion resins, alkaline, neutral salt, or acidic solutions may be used for elution.

For either type of resin an elution curve is obtained by plotting the concentration of each eluted ion as a function of effluent volume or time for constant flow rate. Changes in the concentrations of radioactive materials are readily determined radiometrically either by passing the effluent stream through a counter for liquid sources or by measuring the radioactivity of separate fractions of effluent. Depending upon the ions and the elutriant, the individual ion peaks, as shown in Fig. 9-5, may be sharp and well separated or they may be broad and overlapping.

An interesting application of ion-exchange chromatography which illustrates both the separation of C^{14}-labeled amino acids and the extent to which the isotope effect can occur in ion-exchange chromatography has been described by Piez and Eagle (16).

Adsorption Chromatography. Separation of substances by adsorption chromatography involves the repeated partitioning of the substances between a solid adsorbent and a solvent. The extent of separation depends upon differential migration, i.e., differences in the migration rates of the substances. For a given adsorbent and a given solvent, the migration rate of a well-behaved substance can be characterized by the constant R, which is defined as

$$R = \frac{\text{distance moved by solute}}{\text{distance moved by solvent}}$$

For the case of columnar chromatography the adsorbent consists of a substance such as activated alumina, calcium carbonate, silica gel,

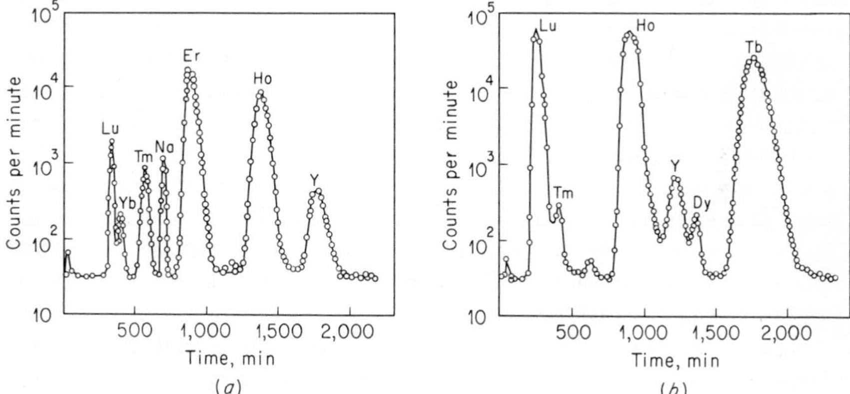

FIG. 9-5. Ion-exchange elution curves. [*From Ketelle and Boyd* (14).]

activated charcoal, etc. The solvent may be a hydrocarbon, an alcohol, etc., depending upon the solutes. Separation can be achieved by a batch process or a continuous process.

Since the method is very sensitive to small structural differences among organic molecules, it is very selective. Applications have generally been limited to organic substances of the nondissociating type.

The adsorbents mentioned above are essentially inactive in the sense of participating in a chemical reaction. If the adsorbent is chemically active, e.g., a chelating agent, the method is sometimes referred to as chemichromatography and can be applied to inorganic substances.

Partition Chromatography. *Introduction.* Separation by partition chromatography involves partitioning of substances between a mobile organic solvent phase and a water phase associated with the support. Thus, the predominating process is solvent extraction.

The support may be a column of a material such as cellulose in the form of filter-paper pulp, or it may be a piece of filter paper. The latter is convenient for trace amounts of material. Organic solvents and various solvent mixtures commonly used have been selected rather empirically, although there is some correlation with their solvent-extraction behavior.

Filter-paper Chromatography. In the preparation of a filter-paper chromatogram a drop (about 10 to 50 λ) of solution (aqueous in most cases) containing on the order of 50 μg of each substance to be separated is placed on the paper to form a spot at a predetermined, marked location. For example, the spot may be placed about 3 to 6 cm from the edge of the paper which is in contact with the solvent, or it may be at the center of a paper disk. When two or more samples are processed at the same time on a strip of paper, the spots are placed about 2 to 3 cm apart on the starting line. After being dried, the paper is placed in contact with a suitable solvent mixture in a closed vessel to maintain a solvent-saturated atmosphere. As the solvent travels along the paper, the partitioning substances migrate in the same direction at different rates and are thus separated into individual spots.

The migration behavior of a particular substance, e.g., organic molecule, inorganic anion, or cation, is characterized by R_f, the ratio of the distance from the starting point traversed by the substance to that traversed by the solvent. The numerical value of R_f, a number between and including 0 and 1, depends strongly on the solvent system and the concentrations of reagents such as acids, bases, and complexing agents. It depends to a lesser extent on the method of application of the solvent, the temperature, and the method of measuring the migration distance. Commonly, migration distances are measured to the center of density of the migrating spot. Uncertainty in the location of the center of the spot may arise because of distortion of the shape of the spot as it migrates. When the solvent system leads to two solvent fronts, the one corresponding to the greater distance is used. Extensive tables of R_f values are given by Lederer and Lederer (17) and Pollard and McOmie (18).

The separability of two substances by a given procedure can be expressed in terms of ΔR_f. Then, the difference in migration distance for the two substances, i.e., their linear separation, is equal to the distance traveled by the solvent multiplied by ΔR_f. The minimum linear separation required will depend on the shape and size of the original spot and on the changes during migration in shape and size of the spots of the various substances. Thus, if the solvent travels 20 cm, a ΔR_f of 0.05 is needed for a linear separation of 1 cm. This simple estimate is based on the assumption that the substances partition independently, so that the R_f values for the single substances apply to the mixture. From a knowledge of R_f values, prediction can be made of the feasibility of separating substances by partition chromatography on filter paper or in a column. It should be noted that it is not practicable to improve a separation indefinitely by merely increasing the migration distance because of the counteraction of diffusion.

In certain cases separation is enhanced by two-dimensional chromatography. The chromatogram is prepared by first allowing a solvent to flow in one direction along the paper and then allowing a second solvent to flow at right angles to the direction of the first.

Filter-paper chromatograms are classified according to the method of applying the solvent and by the shape of the piece of paper used. Thus the solvent may be allowed to ascend or descend a piece of filter paper which may be in the shape of a narrow strip or a large sheet. Several filter papers are suitable for use in chromatography; use for chromatography should be specified. Examples are Whatman No. 1, No. 3 MM, and No. 4 and Schleicher and Schuell Nos. 589 and 595. Glass-fiber paper and paper impregnated with materials such as aluminum oxide, silica gel, and even ion-exchange resin have also been used.

In the preparation of an ascending chromatogram the bottom edge of the paper, which is supported at the top, dips into a container holding the solvent. In the case of a descending chromatogram, the paper is supported at the top where it dips into the solvent in an open trough. For either type of chromatogram the whole assembly is placed inside a simple enclosure, e.g., stoppered test tube or glass cylinder with a watch-glass cover, to prevent loss of the volatile solvent and permit control of the humidity—a critical factor for some systems.

A disk chromatogram is prepared by applying the solvent to the center of a filter-paper disk. The solvent travels outward radially to produce concentric rings rather than spots of the separated substances. Various arrangements have been used to enclose the paper and permit application of the solvent. As examples, the disk may be placed (1) between a petri dish and its cover after a thin radial strip has been cut and folded down from the center of the disk so that it dips down into the solvent contained in the dish; (2) in a container such as a vacuum desiccator with a pipette or delivery tube penetrating the cover at the center; or (3) between two glass plates with a hole drilled at the center of one.

Solvents include alcohols, ethers, ketones, esters, chlorinated hydrocarbons, organic bases, and organic acids. The less stable ones must be freshly purified before use. Commonly, for "water-immiscible" solvents such as *n*-butanol the organic solvent is mixed with excess water or acid, if appropriate, to form a two-liquid-phase system. After separation, the water-saturated organic phase is used to produce the chromatogram, and the aqueous phase to control the humidity, if necessary.

Depending upon the choice of solvent and paper, the time required for preparation of a chromatogram may range from about 1 hr to about 24 hr or longer.

In the absence of radioactive substances, the spots or bands of separated substances are located by difference in color or ultraviolet fluorescence. If the substances themselves are not colored, a colored or fluorescent derivative is formed by spraying on a suitable reagent with an atomizer. The latter process is referred to as development of the chromatogram, although the term is also used for the partitioning step. The latter is also known as the washing step.

For rough quantitative work the areas of the spots may be correlated with the quantity of separated material. After location of the spots the substances can be extracted from the filter paper and determined by standard trace methods such as polarography or spectrophotometry. When radionuclides are present, autoradiographic and instrumental scanning techniques can be utilized for both qualitative and quantitative measurements. For a chromatogram obtained by plotting the response of a detector vs. position on the paper, the amount of a separated material is proportional to the area under its peak on the tracing.

As for any other method, it is usually advantageous to compare the behavior of the unknown sample with that of a reference or standard sample. In this case the two samples are allowed to migrate in parallel on the same piece of paper.

An example of the use of filter-paper chromatography for the separation of labeled organic substances is that described by Benson and coworkers (19) as part of a study of photosynthesis involving the use of C^{14}-labeled carbon dioxide. An application of radioisotope techniques to the separation of inorganic ions by paper chromatography has been described by Frierson and Jones (20).

Electrochromatography. There are many varieties of electrochromatographic methods of separation. Basically, they involve a combination of electromigration of ions and simultaneous flow of a solvent. When a d-c potential is applied to an electrolytic solution, the ions migrate toward the electrodes, and for ions having different migration rates in the direction of a given electrode, separation occurs. This can be used as a separation process without flow of the solvent by placing a support for the solution such as paper, gelatin, powdered glass, or ion-exchange resin between two electrodes.

In the procedure used by Strain and Sullivan (21) a sheet of paper is held vertically between two glass plates one of which is grooved to accept two platinum electrodes. As the current flows across the paper, solvent flows downward. Strips of paper protruding below the glass plates provide drip channels for keeping the effluent fractions separate.

Voltages applied may be from 100 to 400 volts, with currents of 50 to 100 ma.

Gas Chromatography. In gas chromatography, substances are separated from a gas flowing through a column either by adsorption on a solid or by partition between the gas phase and an absorbent liquid held on an inert support. Typical adsorbents for gas-adsorption chromatography are activated charcoal, activated alumina, and silica gel. For gas-liquid partition chromatography a typical absorbent is a very-high-boiling liquid such as dioctyl phthalate deposited on a support such as kieselguhr, e.g., Celite 545.

The column is charged with a mixture of substances which are separated by elution with an inert carrier gas or by displacement with a more strongly retained gas. In the more commonly used elution technique, nitrogen is often used as the carrier gas. As the inert gas passes through the column, the components of the mixture move along the column more slowly than the carrier gas and with individual velocities. In the case of gas-liquid partition there is a partition coefficient and a corresponding retention time for each substance. The appropriate chromatographic constant R_f may be defined in terms of the rate of movement of one constituent relative to that of the gas phase.

A chromatogram usually consists of a pen-and-ink recording of the response of a detector vs. time. The quantity of each separated substance is proportional to the area under its peak.

Gas chromatography has been used to assay tritium and C^{14}-labeled compounds by Wolfgang and Rowland (22).

9-5. Other Methods

Electrolysis. Electrolysis can be used for source preparation, as described in Chap. 5, and for the separation of the components of a mixture. Either the impurities or the desired material can be electrodeposited. The following elements can be removed from aqueous solution by cathodic electrodeposition: Ag, Am, Au, Bi, Cd, Cm, Co, Cr, Cu, Fe, Ga, Ge, Hg, In, Ir, Mn, Mo, Ni, Np, Pb, Pd, Po, Pt, Pu, Re, Rh, Ru, Sb, Se, Sn, Tc, Te, Th, Tl, U. These are deposited in elemental form except for Am, Cm, Np, Pu, Th, and U, which are separated as hydrous oxides (23). The elements Co, Mn, Pb, and Po can also be deposited anodically as oxides. For Pb, this is the preferred method. Not all the elements listed are deposited easily or completely. Furthermore, complete removal for nonradioactive material usually means a final solution concentration of about 10^{-6} M. Addition of isotopic carrier is necessary, therefore, for short-lived carrier-free material. The amount remaining in solution after electrolysis can be lowered by increasing the applied potential, but usually at the expense of the purity of the deposit.

When the mixture contains two or more elements depositable on the same electrode, separation can often be obtained by control of the applied potential, the acidity, the ionic concentration of one element by means of a complexing agent, or a combination of all of these.

Bromide, chloride, and iodide can be deposited on a silver anode to form the corresponding silver halide.

If a mercury cathode is used, the elements listed above can be deposited at higher acidity and even elements such as sodium and potassium can be deposited, if the solution is strongly alkaline. The advantages of a mercury cathode are (1) the high hydrogen overvoltage and (2) the relatively small change in electrode surface characteristics during deposition of an element which dissolves, diffuses into the liquid mercury, or forms an amalgam. Recovery of the deposited material is not always simple; hence the mercury cathode is probably of more interest as a receptacle for unwanted contaminants.

Internal electrolysis is a means for separating elements without an external source of potential. It is particularly useful for the removal of small amounts of one material from large amounts of a second material. The reactive anode, commonly a metal which is a major constituent of the solution and is above the element to be deposited in the electromotive series, is connected externally to the cathode where deposition occurs. Platinum is usually used for the cathode. The electrode solutions are separated by a porous membrane.

Volatilization. Separation of organic compounds by distillation or vaporization is standard practice. An example of an application to radioactive material is the fractional distillation of labeled alkanes using carrier gas (24).

A few inorganic substances have also been separated by volatilization. Examples are the distillation of iodine as I_2 from an aqueous solution containing tellurium or fission products (25), ruthenium as RuO_4 from a perchloric acid solution of fission products (26), and technetium as Tc_2O_7 from a concentrated sulfuric acid solution of other elements (27). Yttrium (Y^{90}) has been separated from Sr^{90} by vacuum evaporation (28).

Recoil. Separation of certain naturally occurring radionuclides by alpha-ray recoil has been known for over 50 years. An example is the collection of ThC″ on a negatively charged plate placed near a source of ThC (29). As the ThC″ atoms are formed, they are ejected from the ThC as positively charged ions which may then be collected on the negatively charged electrode. A recent application is that described by Sun and Pecjak (30).

The Szilard-Chalmers process (31) is often referred to as a means of separation. It does not provide a separation in the sense used in this chapter, but it does bring about a type of separation which makes it possible to use one of the usual methods such as precipitation or solvent extraction. For example, when an organic halide, e.g., C_2H_5Br, is irradiated with thermal neutrons, the radioactive halogen atoms produced in the (n,γ) process are ejected from the molecule by the recoil energy associated with the process. Unless the "hot" atoms so produced recombine with the inactive organic fragments, they can be readily separated from the organic halide by extraction into water.

Experiment 9-1
Radiochemical Separation by Solvent Extraction

In this experiment radiochemical separation by solvent extraction is illustrated through the use of the readily available radionuclide P^{32}. Phosphorus is extracted from aqueous solution into an organic solvent as molybdophosphoric acid.* This type of separation from nonextractable radioactive substances has been used in the determination of P^{32} in the effluent cooling water from the Hanford reactors.†

Apparatus and Materials

Radiation-measurement equipment
Two glass-stoppered 10-ml graduated separatory funnels or graduated cylinders
Support stands for separatory funnels
Micropipette with control
Four volumetric pipettes, 0.50 or 1.00 ml, with control
Source-mounting materials, e.g., glass-cupped planchets
P^{32} tracer
Waste container for P^{32}
Reagent solutions
- Sulfuric acid, 6 *N*
- Ammonium molybdate, 10 per cent
- Phosphate carrier, e.g., H_3PO_4, 50 mg/ml
- Ethyl acetate
- Ammonium hydroxide, 6 *N*

Two 5-ml pipettes with control
Two 15-ml centrifuge tubes with rack or block support
Heat lamp

* G. H. Morrison and H. Freiser, "Solvent Extraction in Analytical Chemistry," Wiley, New York, 1957.

† W. B. Silker, Radiochemical Determination of Phosphorus-32, *Anal. Chem.*, vol. 28, pp. 1782–1783, 1956.

Procedure

To a 10-ml graduated separatory funnel or cylinder add 3.0 ml of distilled water, 3 drops of H_2SO_4, phosphate carrier (one of the following amounts: 0.5, 1.0, 5.0, or 10 mg), and P^{32} in an amount sufficient to provide satisfactory counting rates. To a second funnel add exactly the same materials except for the carrier, which should be replaced by distilled water. Mix the solution and add 4 drops of ammonium molybdate solution. Mix the solution again. Add 3.0 ml of ethyl acetate and shake the funnel vigorously for 1 to 2 min. Be certain the stopper is tightly seated, and use rubber gloves. Allow the layers to separate, and record the volume of each.

Carefully transfer the contents of the funnel to a 15-ml centrifuge tube and separate the phases by centrifugation. Using separate pipettes withdraw aliquots, e.g., 0.5 ml, of the organic and aqueous phases from each tube. Take the sample from the organic phase first, avoiding contact with the lower aqueous layer. Next remove the remainder of the organic layer plus a little of the aqueous layer and finally take an aliquot of the aqueous layer with a clean pipette. The unused portions of each layer should be transferred to the waste container. The aliquots for counting should be dried carefully in labeled glass-cupped planchets. It is important that the organic layers be dried very slowly under the heat lamp to avoid creepage of the liquid to the top of the planchet. The latter behavior may be detected visually for the sample with added carrier, since the molybdophosphoric acid is yellow. When the sources appear to be about dry, add 4 drops of ammonium hydroxide to neutralize the acid and dry the sources completely. Measure the counting rates of all four samples in a like manner.

Analysis of Data

Calculate the distribution ratio and the per cent extraction for each extraction system. When this experiment is performed by several laboratory groups, the results for the carrier-free system should be compared and the results for various carrier concentrations collected and presented graphically to show the dependence on initial phosphate concentration (moles per liter) in the aqueous phase.

Experiment 9-2

Radiochemical Separation by Ion Exchange

The usual situation in the laboratory requiring radiochemical separation involves the separation of two or more radioactive materials. To illustrate this is not easy in a laboratory demonstration, since some type of differential counting is required to demonstrate the difference in the components as they are eluted from the column. In this experiment, advantage is taken of the color of nickel dimethylglyoxime as an indicator of the presence of nickel, but the radioactivity of cobalt is used as the indicator for this element. This experiment was introduced into one of the authors' courses by R. H. Firminhac.

Apparatus and Materials

Twenty-five 1-in. watch glasses or other suitable containers
One 20-λ micropipette
Four counting-sample holders
One enamel tray
One ion-exchange column (approximately 8 cm long with 2 to 5 mm ID)
Concentrated NH_4OH in dropping bottle
Dimethylglyoxime in ethyl alcohol (1 per cent) in dropping bottle
10 N hydrochloric acid
Solution containing approximately 1 mg/ml each of Co(II) and Ni(II) as chlorides and approximately 2.5 μc Co^{60}/ml
Dowex-1 anion-exchange resin (150 to 200 mesh)

Procedure

The resin should first be suspended in a water slurry and passed into the ion-exchange column, which has a small plug of glass wool or a sintered filter disk in the lower portion. After a column of resin about 5 cm long has been collected in the tube, it may be tapped to eliminate bubbles that may have been trapped. Do not permit the resin to become dry after the tube is filled. Pass at least five column volumes of 10 N HCl through the column to make certain it is thoroughly "chloride-conditioned." The tube may be left in this condition for several days before it is used if liquid is left remaining over the resin.

At the time of the experiment, the solution above the resin is removed and 20 λ of the Co^{60}-Ni solution is added directly above the resin. The 10 N HCl is then passed through the column, and each drop is collected in a separate watch glass. Each sample is tested for the presence of nickel by adding 5 drops of NH_4OH and then 2 drops of dimethylglyoxime. Number the watch glasses and observe which watch glass shows the deepest red color. Continue until there is no color reaction, which indicates that the nickel has all been eluted from the column.

When the effluent no longer gives indication of the presence of nickel, remove the HCl above the resin with a pipette. Pass distilled water through the column to elute the cobalt. Collect each drop on a separate watch glass or planchet. Dry the samples and count with a suitable radiation-detection instrument.

Analysis of Data

The data are plotted with the amount of element present in each sample against the number of drops. Unless colorimetric determinations are made on the nickel, there is no quantitative measure of the amount of nickel present, although a rough indication of the color might be plotted for each of the drops of the HCl solutions. The counting rate for each sample may be plotted against the number of drops for the cobalt samples. Determine the half-width value at half-height of the curve to give a measure of the resolution of the resin for this particular experiment.

It is probable that the ions present in the solutions are negative complex cobalt ions* and Ni^{++}. The positive nickel ion is not absorbed on the resin under these conditions, whereas the negative cobalt ion exchanges with the chloride on the resin. Upon addition of water the cobalt reverts to the Co^{++} cation and is eluted.

Experiment 9-3

Radiochemical Separation by Filter-paper Chromatography

Filter-paper chromatography is illustrated in this experiment† for the separation of two radionuclides, e.g., Co^{60} and P^{32}. Counter scanning techniques as well as autoradiography are used to locate the separated materials. (See also Expt. 2-6.)

Apparatus and Materials

- Radiation-detection equipment
  - Count-rate meter
  - Detector with shielded slit
- Glass culture tube, 25 by 200 mm, with screw cap
- Filter-paper strip, e.g., Whatman No. 1, about 2 by 20 cm
- Stand or block to support culture tubes
- Micropipette (5 λ) with control
- Heat lamp
- X-ray film, e.g., Eastman No-Screen, as strips slightly larger than filter paper

* G. E. Moore and K. A. Kraus, Anion Exchange Studies. IV, Cobalt and Nickel in Hydrochloric Acid Solutions, *J. Am. Chem. Soc.*, vol. 74, pp. 843–844, 1952.

† L. B. Rockland and M. S. Dunn, A Capillary-ascent Test Tube Method for Separating Amino Acids by Filter Paper Chromatography, *Science*, vol. 109, pp. 539–540, 1949.

Solution of mixture of radionuclides (may also contain added dye mixture, e.g., ink)
Separatory funnel
Scissors
Aluminum or lead foil
Cardboard backing and black wrapping paper of appropriate size to prepare autoradiogram
Labels
Adhesive tape
Millimeter graph paper
Darkroom equipment: trays, tongs, safelight
Reagent solutions
Hydrochloric acid, 2 *N*
n-Butanol
Photographic solutions: X-ray developer, X-ray fixer, acetic acid short-stop bath

Procedure

1. The *n*-butanol–HCl solvent is prepared by equilibrating equal volumes of *n*-butanol and 2 *N* HCl. After the aqueous layer is withdrawn from the separatory funnel, the organic layer is transferred to a centrifuge tube for clarification.

2. With a pencil draw a line across the strip of filter paper about 3 cm from one end. Place 5 λ of the solution of radioactive material on the paper. The deposit should be centered on the line. An attempt should be made to keep the area of the deposit as small as possible. Dry the paper near a heat lamp.

Place 5 ml of the *n*-butanol–HCl solvent in a labeled culture tube, and then insert the filter-paper strip with the deposit of radioactive material at the bottom. The bottom of the strip should dip into the liquid but should not rest on the bottom of the tube. Support the paper at the top under the cap, using adhesive tape if necessary. Place the cap on the tube and mount the tube in a support. The paper should clear the wall of the tube. Avoid disturbing the apparatus as the solvent ascends the paper.

Allow the separation to proceed for about 3 hr. Remove the paper, mark the position of the solvent front, and dry the paper near a heat lamp. (The solvent will migrate about 12 cm in 3 hr.)

In a darkroom, place a piece of X-ray film in contact with one side of the filter-paper strip. On the other side, place a suitable absorbing metallic foil to allow a distinction to be made between the Co^{60} and the P^{32}, and then place a piece of X-ray film over the foil. To facilitate matching the autoradiogram with the chromatogram later, align the top edge of the paper with one end of the film and cut one of the corners at that edge. Wrap the assembly in cardboard and black paper. Label the packet and set aside for a suitable exposure time, i.e., 3 to 18 hr, depending upon the level of activity used.

Process the film in accordance with the manufacturer's instructions.

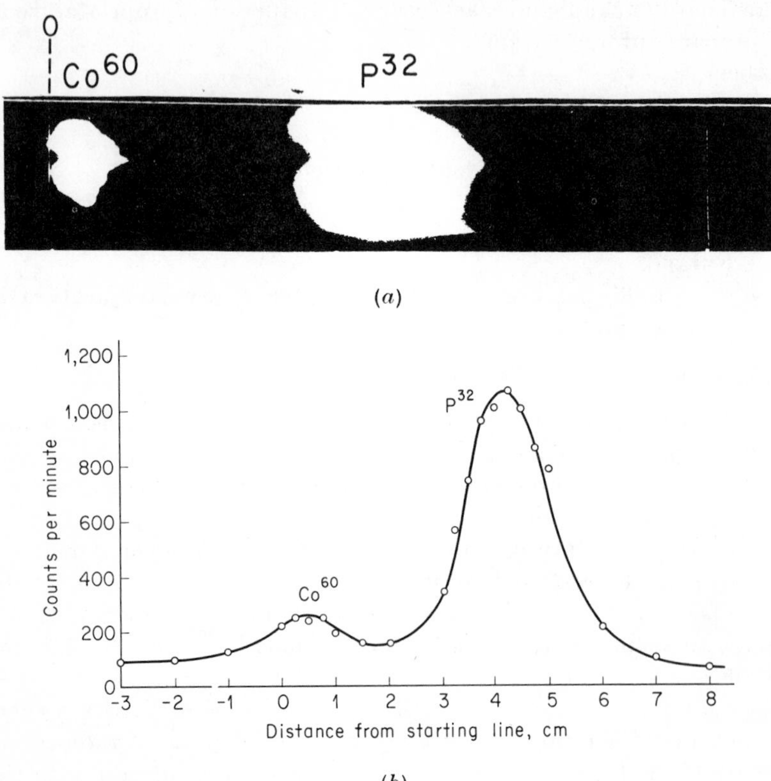

FIG. 9-6. Separation of Co^{60} and P^{32} by filter-paper chromatography (Expt. 9-3). (*a*) Autoradiogram of chromatogram; (*b*) scan of chromatogram.

After the autoradiogram has been prepared, mount the strip of filter paper, by means of adhesive tape, on a piece of millimeter graph paper, which, in turn, is mounted on a stiff piece of cardboard. Number the centimeter divisions on the graph paper, allowing about 3 cm of graduations to the left of zero, and align the starting line on the filter paper with zero on the graph paper. Pass the filter-paper chromatogram slowly across the slit of the detector. Note the counting rate at various distances from the reference point, using 0.5-cm spacing where the counting rate is high. Identify the separated materials by means of absorbers.

Automatic scanning devices should be used, if available.

Analysis of Data

Plot the counting rate as a function of the distance from the starting line on the filter-paper strip. Correlate the plot with the autoradiogram (see Fig. 9-6).

Note the position of any colored materials in the original sample.

Determine R_f for each constituent.

Experiment 9-4
Identification of an "Unknown" Radioactive Material

In identifying the radionuclides in a sample of radioactive material, information must be obtained on the type and energy of emitted radiation, half-life, and chemical characteristics. Information concerning the occurrence in nature or its general method of production, if artificial, is obviously of value also.

The following considerations should be kept in mind:

1. Several radionuclides may be present which may or may not be genetically related.

2. There may be several kinds of radiation emitted and several energy groups for each type. The radiation types include α, β^-, β^+, e^- (conversion electrons), X, and γ.

3. The sensitivities of available radiation detectors for various types of radiation may differ appreciably. Conversion ratios and β/γ ratios may be valuable.

4. In estimating a half-life from decay measurements (when the activity of a sample decreases detectably but slowly with time), consider the error in the estimated value and set limits on the half-life.

5. When information concerning the type and energy of radiation and half-life has been obtained, refer to sources such as the following and select the most likely radionuclides:

A Table of Radionuclides Arranged According to Half-life*
Table of Isotopes†
"Chart of the Nuclides"‡
"Nuclear Data Sheets"§

6. Radionuclides are identified by carrying out chemical reactions

* H. M. Clark and D. E. Neil, A Table of Radionuclides Arranged According to Half-life, *U.S. Atomic Energy Comm. Rept.* AECU-3144, December, 1955.

† D. Strominger, J. M. Hollander, and G. T. Seaborg, Table of Isotopes, *Revs. Modern Phys.*, vol. 30, pp. 585–904, 1958.

‡ General Electric Company, Educational Division, Schenectady, N.Y. (1956 and any later revisions).

§ "Nuclear Data Sheets," National Academy of Sciences–National Research Council, Washington.

which are specific for the elements involved. More than one radioisotope of an element may be involved. The activity separated by a chemical process is compared with the original in respect to radiation and half-life. The chemical identity should be confirmed by at least two independent chemical reactions which are specific for the element. Separations by precipitation, ion exchange, solvent extraction, electrolytic deposition, paper chromatography, and distillation should be evaluated. Isotopic or nonisotopic carrier precipitation is generally not specific and should be confirmed in several ways, including (if possible for the element) the carrying or absence of it for various oxidation states.

7. Under certain conditions the radioactive constituents of the "unknown" may be converted to volatile form through chemical reactions or through heating. These conditions should be borne in mind not only because of possible loss of material, but also because of possible health hazard.

Apparatus and Materials

Radiation-detection equipment
Samples of "unknown" radioactive material
Source-mounting materials, radiochemical apparatus, reagents

Procedure

Prepare a source of the material for counting. In the absence of specific recommendations, proceed with caution and check for loss of activity by volatilization. Also, count the first source with care since the quantity of activity taken the first time may be too great for the instrument. A variety of source intensities and mounts may be required for satisfactory detection of the components of a complex mixture of radiation.

Identify the types of radiation emitted and estimate their energy, using Feather analysis (Expt. 6-1) and spectrometer data (Expt. 6-5) where possible. Estimate the half-life of each component. From the table of half-lives select those radionuclides for which the half-life, radiation, and methods of production are in reasonable agreement with the findings.

After the selected list has been prepared, draw up at least two proposed separations to identify the chemical elements involved. Have the proposed chemistry approved before proceeding.

Analysis of Data

Show the absorption data and decay data in both tabular and graphical form where applicable in order to evaluate radiation energy and half-life.

Indicate your conclusions and give proof of identity.

Cited References

1. Hahn, O.: "Applied Radiochemistry," Cornell University Press, Ithaca, N.Y., 1936.
2. Morrison, G. H., and H. Freiser: "Solvent Extraction in Analytical Chemistry," Wiley, New York, 1957.
3. Diamond, R. M.: The Solvent Extraction Behavior of Inorganic Compounds. II, General Equations, *J. Phys. Chem.*, vol. 61, pp. 69–74, 1957.
4. Irving, H.: Solvent Extraction and Its Applications to Inorganic Analysis, *Quart. Revs.* (*London*), vol. 5, pp. 200–226, 1951.
5. Jakowkin, A. A.: Zur Frage über die Verteilung eines Stoffes zwischen zwei Losungsmitteln, *Z. physik. Chem.*, vol. 18, pp. 585–594, 1895.
6. Grahame, D. C., and G. T. Seaborg: The Distribution of Minute Amounts of Material between Liquid Phases, *J. Am. Chem. Soc.*, vol. 60, pp. 2524–2528, 1938.
7. Myers, R. J., D. E. Metzler, and E. H. Swift: The Distribution of Ferric Iron between Hydrochloric Acid and Isopropyl Ether Solutions. I, The Compound Extracted and the Extraction at Constant Acid Concentration, *J. Am. Chem. Soc.*, vol. 72, pp. 3767–3771, 1950.
8. Kirk, P. L., and M. Danielson: A Liquid-Liquid Microextractor for Solvents Lighter than Water, *Anal. Chem.*, vol. 20, pp. 1122–1123, 1948.
9. The Separation of Rare Earth, Fission Product and Other Metal Ions and Anions by Adsorption on Ion-exchange Resins, *J. Am. Chem. Soc.*, vol. 69, pp. 2769–2881, 1947.
10. Bauman, W. C., R. E. Anderson, and R. M. Wheaton: Ion Exchange, *Ann. Rev. Phys. Chem.*, vol. 3, pp. 109–130, 1952.
11. Samuelson, O.: "Ion Exchangers in Analytical Chemistry," Wiley, New York, 1953.
12. Tompkins, E. R., and S. W. Mayer: Ion Exchange as a Separations Method. III, Equilibrium Studies of the Reactions of Rare Earth Complexes with Synthetic Ion Exchange Resins, *J. Am. Chem. Soc.*, vol. 69, pp. 2859–2865, 1947.
13. Boyd, G. E., J. Schubert, and A. W. Adamson: The Exchange Adsorption of Ions from Aqueous Solutions by Organic Zeolites. Ion-exchange Equilibria, *J. Am. Chem. Soc.*, vol. 69, pp. 2818–2829, 1947.
14. Ketelle, B. H., and G. E. Boyd: The Exchange Adsorption of Ions from Aqueous Solutions by Organic Zeolites. IV, The Separation of the Yttrium Group Rare Earths, *J. Am. Chem. Soc.*, vol. 69, pp. 2800–2812, 1947.
15. Tompkins, E. R.: Laboratory Applications of Ion-exchange Techniques, *J. Chem. Educ.*, vol. 26, pp. 32–38, 92–100, 1949.
16. Piez, K. A., and H. Eagle: Systematic Effect of C^{14}-labeling on Ion-exchange Chromatography of Amino Acids, *Science*, vol. 122, pp. 968–969, 1955.
17. Lederer, E., and M. Lederer: "Chromatography: A Review of Principles and Applications," 2d ed., Elsevier, Houston, Tex., 1957.
18. Pollard, F. H., and J. F. W. McOmie: "Chromatographic Methods of Inorganic Analysis," Butterworth, London, 1953.
19. Benson, A. A., J. A. Bassham, M. Calvin, T. C. Goodale, V. A. Haas, and W. Stepka: The Path of Carbon in Photosynthesis. V, Paper Chromatography and Radioautography of the Products, *J. Am. Chem. Soc.*, vol. 72, pp. 1710–1718, 1950.

20. Frierson, W. J., and J. W. Jones: Radioactive Tracers in Paper Partition Chromatography of Inorganic Ions, *Anal. Chem.*, vol. 23, pp. 1447–1452, 1951.
21. Strain, H. H., and J. C. Sullivan: Analysis by Electromigration plus Chromatography, *Anal. Chem.*, vol. 23, pp. 816–823, 1951.
22. Wolfgang, R., and F. S. Rowland: Radioassay by Gas Chromatography of Tritium and Carbon-14-labeled Compounds, *Anal. Chem.*, vol. 30, pp. 903–906, 1958.
23. Ko, R.: Electrodeposition of the Actinide Elements, *Nucleonics*, vol. 15, no. 1, pp. 72–77, 1957.
24. Wolfgang, R., J. Eigner, and F. S. Rowland: Studies of the Recoil Tritium Labeling Reaction. II, Methane and Ethane, *J. Phys. Chem.*, vol. 60, pp. 1137–1138, 1956.
25. Ballentine, D. S., and W. E. Cohn: The Preparation of Carrier-free I^{131}, *U.S. Atomic Energy Comm. Rept.* MDDC-1600, 1947.
26. Newton, A. S.: The Fission of Thorium with Alpha Particles, *Phys. Rev.*, vol. 75, pp. 17–29, 1949.
27. Hackney, J. C.: Technetium—Element 43, *J. Chem. Educ.*, vol. 28, pp. 186–190, 1951.
28. Sherwin, C. W.: Vacuum Evaporation of Radioactive Materials, *Rev. Sci. Instr.*, vol. 22, pp. 339–341, 1951.
29. Rutherford, E., J. Chadwick, and C. D. Ellis: "Radiations from Radioactive Substances," Cambridge, New York, 1930.
30. Sun, K. H., and F. A. Pecjak: Recoil Separation of Isotopes, *Nucleonics*, vol. 14, no. 11, pp. 122–126, 1956.
31. Maddock, A. G.: The Szilard-Chalmers Effect, *Endeavour*, vol. 12, pp. 95–100, 1953.

Supplementary References

Aronoff, S.: "Techniques of Radiobiochemistry," Iowa State College Press, Ames, Iowa, 1956.

Ashley, S. E. Q.: Electroanalysis, *Anal. Chem.*, vol. 21, pp. 70–75, 1949.

———: Electroanalysis, *Anal. Chem.*, vol. 24, pp. 92–95, 1952.

Block, R. J., E. L. Durrum, and G. Zweig: "Manual of Paper Chromatography and Paper Electrophoresis," Academic Press, New York, 1955.

Boyd, G. E.: Ion Exchange, *Ann. Rev. Phys. Chem.*, vol. 2, pp. 309–342, 1951.

Broda, E.: "Advances in Radiochemistry," Cambridge, New York, 1950.

Cassidy, H. G.: "Fundamentals of Chromatography," Interscience, New York, 1957.

Clegg, D. L.: Paper Chromatography, *Anal. Chem.*, vol. 22, pp. 48–59, 1950.

Cohn, W. E., G. W. Parker, and E. R. Tompkins: Ion Exchangers to Separate, Concentrate, and Purify Small Amounts of Ions, *Nucleonics*, vol. 3, no. 5, pp. 22–33, 1948.

Coryell, C. D., and N. Sugarman: "Radiochemical Studies: The Fission Products," 3 vols., McGraw-Hill, New York, 1951.

Craig, L. C.: Extraction, *Anal. Chem.*, vol. 21, pp. 85–87, 1949.

———: Extraction, *Anal. Chem.*, vol. 22, pp. 61–64, 1950.

———: Extraction, *Anal. Chem.*, vol. 23, pp. 41–44, 1951.

———: Extraction, *Anal. Chem.*, vol. 24, pp. 66–70, 1952.

———: Extraction, *Anal. Chem.*, vol. 26, pp. 110–115, 1954.

———: Extraction, *Anal. Chem.*, vol. 28, pp. 723–729, 1956.

Cramer, F.: "Paper Chromatography," 2d ed., St. Martin's, New York, 1955.

DeFord, D. D.: Electroanalysis, *Anal. Chem.*, vol. 26, pp. 135–140, 1954.

———: Electroanalysis, *Anal. Chem.*, vol. 28, pp. 660–666, 1956.

——— and R. C. Bowers: Electroanalysis and Coulometric Analysis, *Anal. Chem.*, vol. 30, pp. 613–619, 1958.

Evans, J. B., and J. E. Willard: Use of Gas Chromatography for the Separation of Mixtures of Carrier Free Radioactive Substances: Products of Chemical Reactions Activated by Nuclear Processes, *J. Am. Chem. Soc.*, vol. 78, pp. 2908–2909, 1956.

Finston, H. L., and J. Miskel: Radiochemical Separation Techniques, *Ann. Rev. Nuclear Sci.*, vol. 5, pp. 269–296, 1955.

Frierson, W. J., P. F. Thompson, and H. P. Raaen: Elution Chromatography with Thick Filter Paper, *Anal. Chem.*, vol. 26, pp. 1210–1211, 1954.

Garrison, W. M., and J. G. Hamilton: Production and Isolation of Carrier-free Radioisotopes, *Chem. Revs.*, vol. 49, pp. 237–272, 1951.

Glendenin, L. E., and E. P. Steinberg: Fission Radiochemistry (Low Energy Fission), *Ann. Rev. Nuclear Sci.*, vol. 4, pp. 69–80, 1954.

Gordon, C. L.: Nucleonics, *Anal. Chem.*, vol. 21, pp. 96–101, 1949.

———: Nucleonics, *Anal. Chem.*, vol. 23, pp. 81–86, 1951.

———: Nucleonics, *Anal. Chem.*, vol. 26, pp. 176–181, 1954.

Gray, I.: Detection of Tritiated Compounds in Paper Chromatography, *Rev. Sci. Instr.*, vol. 21, p. 1022, 1950.

Haissinsky, M.: "Electrochimie des substances radioactives et des solutions extrêmement dilueés," Masson, Paris, 1946.

———: "La Chimie nucleaire et les applications," Masson, Paris, 1957.

Hildebrand, J. H., and R. L. Scott: "The Solubility of Nonelectrolytes," 3d ed., Reinhold, New York, 1950.

Horne, R. A., C. D. Coryell, and L. S. Goldring: Generalized Acidity in Radiochemical Separations, *Ann. Rev. Nuclear Sci.*, vol. 6, pp. 163–178, 1956.

Kahn, M.: Enrichment of Antimony Activity through the Szilard-Chalmers Separation, *J. Am. Chem. Soc.*, vol. 73, pp. 479–480, 1951.

Kitchener, J. A.: "Ion-exchange Resins," Methuen, London, 1957.

Kokes, R. J., H. Tobin, Jr., and P. H. Emmett: New Microcatalytic-Chromatographic Technique for Studying Catalytic Reactions, *J. Am. Chem. Soc.*, vol. 77, pp. 5860–5862, 1955.

Kraus, K. A., and F. Nelson: Radiochemical Separations by Ion Exchange, *Ann. Rev. Nuclear Sci.*, vol. 7, pp. 31–46, 1957.

Kunin, R.: Ion Exchange, *Anal. Chem.*, vol. 21, pp. 87–96, 1949.

———: Ion Exchange, *Anal. Chem.*, vol. 22, pp. 64–65, 1950.

———: Ion Exchange, *Anal. Chem.*, vol. 23, pp. 45–46, 1951.

———: Ion Exchange, *Anal. Chem.*, vol. 24, pp. 64–66, 1952.

———: "Ion Exchange Resins," 2d ed., Wiley, New York, 1958.

——— and F. X. McGarvey: Ion Exchange, *Anal. Chem.*, vol. 26, pp. 104–109, 1954.

———, ———, and A. Farren: Ion Exchange, *Anal. Chem.*, vol. 28, pp. 729–735, 1956.

———, ———, and D. Zobian: Ion Exchange, *Anal. Chem.*, vol. 30, pp. 681–686, 1958.

Lederer, M.: "Introduction to Paper Electrophoresis and Related Methods," Elsevier, Houston, Tex., 1955.

Meinke, W. W.: Chemical Procedures Used in Bombardment Work at Berkeley, *U.S. Atomic Energy Comm. Rept.* D-2738 (UCRL-432), 1949.

Meinke, W. W.: Nucleonics, *Anal. Chem.*, vol. 28, pp. 736–756, 1956.

———: Nucleonics, *Anal. Chem.*, vol. 30, pp. 686–728, 1958.

Morrison, G. H.: Role of Extraction in Analytical Chemistry, *Anal. Chem.*, vol. 22, p. 1388, 1950.

——— and H. Freiser: Extraction, *Anal. Chem.*, vol. 30, pp. 632–640, 1958.

Nachod, F. C.: "Ion Exchange, Theory and Application," Academic Press, New York, 1949.

Noyes, A. A., and W. C. Bray: "A System of Qualitative Analysis for the Rare Elements," Macmillan, New York, 1948.

Nuclear Chemistry and Effects of Irradiation, *Proc. Intern. Conf. Peaceful Uses Atomic Energy*, vol. 7, United Nations, New York, 1956.

Osborn, G. H.: "Synthetic Ion-exchangers," Macmillan, New York, 1956.

Phillips, C.: "Gas Chromatography," Academic Press, New York, 1956.

Roberts, H. R., and F. J. Carleton: Determination of Specific Activity of Carbon-14-labeled Sugars on Paper Chromatograms Using an Automatic Scanning Device, *Anal. Chem.*, vol. 28, pp. 11–16, 1956.

Schubert, J.: Analytical Applications of Ion Exchange Separations, *Anal. Chem.*, vol. 22, pp. 1359–1368, 1950.

Shaver, K. J.: Coprecipitation of Rare Earth Iodates with Thorium Iodate Precipitated from Homogeneous Solution, *Anal. Chem.*, vol. 28, pp. 2015–2019, 1956.

Smith, O. C.: "Inorganic Chromatography," Van Nostrand, Princeton, N.J., 1953.

Stevenson, P. C., and H. G. Hicks: Separation Techniques Used in Radiochemistry, *Ann. Rev. Nuclear Sci.*, vol. 3, pp. 221–234, 1953.

Strain, H. H.: "Chromatographic Adsorption Analysis," Interscience, New York, 1945.

———: Chromatographic Separations, *Anal. Chem.*, vol. 21, pp. 75–81, 1949.

———: Chromatography, *Anal. Chem.*, vol. 22, pp. 41–48, 1950.

———: Chromatographic Systems, *Anal. Chem.*, vol. 23, pp. 25–38, 1951.

———: Chromatography, Analysis by Differential Migration, *Anal. Chem.*, vol. 30, pp. 620–629, 1958.

——— and G. W. Murphy: Chromatography and Analogous Differential Migration Methods, *Anal. Chem.*, vol. 24, pp. 50–60, 1952.

——— and T. R. Sato: Chromatography and Electrochromatography, *Anal. Chem.*, vol. 28, pp. 687–694, 1956.

———, ———, and J. Engelke: Chromatography and Analogous Differential Migration Methods, *Anal. Chem.*, vol. 26, pp. 90–100, 1954.

Wahl, A. C., and N. A. Bonner: "Radioactivity Applied to Chemistry," Wiley, New York, 1951.

Weil, H.: Chromatographic Technology in Radioisotope Separation, *Atomics*, vol. 1, pp. 230–234, 345–356, 1950.

Willard, J. E.: Chemical Effects of Nuclear Transformations, *Ann. Rev. Nuclear Sci.*, vol. 3, pp. 193–220, 1953.

Zechmeister, L.: "Progress in Chromatography, 1938–1947," Chapman & Hall, London, 1950.

——— and L. Cholnoky: "Principles and Practice of Chromatography," Wiley, New York, 1948.

10

The Utilization of Radioisotopes

10-1. Special Applications of Radioisotope Techniques

Analytical Techniques. One of the primary reasons for the usefulness of radioisotopes lies in the high sensitivity of their detection. This is brought about by the fact that, for intermediate half-lives ranging from hours to years, the amount of radioactive element present in a counting sample is of the order of 10^{-16} to 10^{-19} g. It is evident that in no case can one actually have such a "carrier-free" sample because of the trace contamination of all materials by other elements. However, it is possible, under certain conditions, to detect 10^{-11} to 10^{-14} g of a number of common elements such as phosphorus, sodium, calcium, cobalt, zinc, silver, and many others. With this sensitivity a very large number of phenomena can be investigated with this analytical tool in any chemical or physical state.

There are a number of different types of analytical procedures which have been given various names in the literature. Two examples are activity analysis and radiometric analysis. Although these terms are often used interchangeably, Meinke (1, 2) and other writers have distinguished between them by using the term activity analysis to refer to the simple determination of the amount of radioactive material in a sample. Meinke uses the term radiometric analysis for the assay of a given nonradioactive substance by the addition of a radioactive tracer. For example, silver could be determined directly in a sample by analysis of radioactive silver, or the amount of silver could be determined by radiometric analysis by precipitating AgCl with radioactive chloride ions. In general, activity analysis is used much more extensively. An example of radiometric assay is the development of a paper chromatogram with radioactive hydrogen sulfide. The location of the metal sulfide could then be determined directly on the paper using a radiation detector.

The development of scintillation counters within the last few years has revolutionized many activity measurements. Newer measurement techniques have also permitted workers to assay mixtures of radioactive materials to a degree which was not formerly considered possible. It is probable that developments of low-counting-rate techniques will make major revisions in analytical applications. For example, it has been suggested that labeling petroleum up to the natural background level of C^{14} would permit widespread industrial tagging techniques, since oil has negligible C^{14} because of its great age. The references listed by Meinke in his thorough articles indicate how the analytical interest in the nuclear field has expanded between 1953 and the present.

There are two analytical techniques that are primarily dependent on nuclear phenomena. One of these is the direct analysis of elements by the radioactivity produced in a nuclear irradiation. The other is the technique known as isotope dilution, which is a method of determining the quantity present by measuring the change in concentration or specific activity of isotopes of the same element in chemical processes.

Activation Analysis. Although several studies (3) were reported earlier, the first use of the term and the first systematic presentation of radioactivation analysis as a method were made by Clark and Overman (4) in 1947. A number of papers have appeared with applications in many fields (5–7). Because of the demand for assays and the limited number of reactors available, the analytical group at the Oak Ridge National Laboratory (8–10) began in 1953 to offer a commercial analytical service using this technique. As reactors and accelerators become more common, it is likely that the technique will become routine at other locations.

As in all methods of analysis, certain elements are more readily determined than others. The chief limitations in this case, however, have their origin in the nuclear properties of the atom. The method is capable of high sensitivity and accuracy for many elements which are not conveniently determinable by standard methods of trace analysis. Furthermore, if an element is present in sufficient quantity to permit identification of its half-life and radiation energy, it is a straightforward matter to determine its concentration at the same time. Analysis with a nuclear reactor will be described here, although the procedures can be followed with any type of nuclear-irradiation device.

In a reactor activation the sample to be analyzed is placed in a uniformly high flux of slow neutrons for a length of time sufficient to produce a measurable amount of radioisotope of the element X to be determined. The activity A_t (disintegrations per second) present for a given isotope of an element at time t after the start of the irradiation is given by the expression

$$A_t = N\phi\sigma\left[1 - \exp\left(-0.693\,\frac{t}{T}\right)\right] \tag{10-1}$$

where N = total number of nuclei of element X present in sample; weight in grams times Avogadro's number divided by gram atomic weight

ϕ = slow-neutron flux, neutrons/cm²/sec, assumed to be constant; frequently written nv, in which n is neutron density and v is velocity of neutrons

σ = activation cross section, barns (10^{-24} cm²), for normal element for slow neutrons in reaction leading to formation of radioisotope used in measurement*

T = half-life of radioisotope of interest

In terms of the weight of the element, Eq. (10-1) becomes

$$X\text{ (g)} = \frac{A_t M}{\phi \times 0.602 \times 10^{24} \times \sigma \times [1 - \exp(-0.693t/T)]} \tag{10-2}$$

where M = chemical atomic weight of desired element.

Using typical values for the cross sections of various nuclei and known half-life values, it is a simple matter to calculate the activity by Eq. (10-2) which would result from the (n,γ) activation of 1 μg of an element for various assumed values of a slow-neutron flux. Taking Mn, Cu, I, and Au as examples, the activities, expressed as disintegrations per minute, which would be produced at saturation are given in Table 10-1.

TABLE 10-1

CALCULATED SATURATION ACTIVITIES FOR SOME REACTOR-PRODUCED RADIOISOTOPES

Isotope	*Saturation activity, dpm/μg (flux of 10^{12} neutrons/cm²/sec)*
Mn^{56}	8.8×10^6
Cu^{64}	1.7×10^6
I^{128}	1.6×10^6
Au^{198}	1.7×10^7

It should be noted that, for the monoisotopic elements such as manganese, iodine, and gold, the cross section for the normal element used in Eq. (10-1) is the same as the isotopic cross section. In the case of copper, however, the cross section for the normal element for the production of Cu^{64} is only 69.1 per cent of the isotopic cross section, since the Cu^{63} has this per cent abundance. Cross-section values are

* It has been suggested that a better combination of reactor terms would be to consider σv as a constant characteristic of a nucleus (valid except in resonance-absorption regions) and to consider the neutron density n a constant which is characteristic of a given reactor position.

sometimes listed as "per atom of normal element" or "per atom of isotope." Care should be taken to use the proper value.

According to Table 10-1, 1 μg of manganese after a 24-hr irradiation in a flux of 10^{12} neutrons/cm^2/sec would give 2.2×10^6 beta counts per minute, assuming a counting yield of 25 per cent. As little as 0.00005 μg, or 5×10^{-11} g, of Mn under the same conditions would still give 105 cpm above background. An air-cooled graphite reactor may have positions where the flux is 5×10^{11} neutrons/cm^2/sec.

The first step in measuring the activity or activities in an irradiated sample usually consists in dissolving the sample in an appropriate solvent. If the activity of the element of interest is great enough to be obtained by analysis of a composite decay curve, an aliquot of the solution containing the dissolved sample is transferred to a mount, dried, and counted. However, if the activity to be counted is only a small fraction of the total activity or is mixed with another activity of about the same half-life, it is necessary to isolate the desired activity by a chemical separation. A simple group separation is sometimes adequate for this purpose. It is sometimes possible to determine the amounts of various components of a mixture directly, using a scintillation spectrometer. It should be noted that inert carrier may be added after the irradiation without affecting the amounts originally activated.

One of the frequent problems in this type of analysis is the identification of unknown contaminants in the sample. In general, the half-life, beta-ray energy, and gamma-ray energies are sufficient to identify a given nuclide, although chemical methods are also frequently required for a firm identification. Several sources of information are extremely helpful in making this type of identification in addition to the usual sources of nuclear-decay-scheme information. The various charts of nuclides which are available present much information in a simple way, although identification of an unknown may require the inspection of several hundred nuclides. Since the half-life is a key characteristic, the table of nuclides arranged in order of half-life by Clark and Neil (11) is quite helpful. Likewise, the set of Nuclear Data Sheets (12) which are published by the National Academy of Sciences–National Research Council furnish a means of screening isotopes for several characteristics. (See Expt. 9-4.)

Radioactivation analysis may be performed in one of two ways, depending on the information which is available to the analyst. If a calibrated counter or other method for determining the absolute activity of a sample is available and if the flux can be determined by a monitor of some type, it is possible to measure the activity and determine the amount of material present by the absolute method. The determination of the other parameters, i.e., the half-life, cross section, atomic weight, and irradiation time, usually offers no difficulties. For precise work there are other factors such as the optimum length of irradiation time, the presence of resonance neutron capture, and similar factors which may give difficulties in certain cases. However, it is usually possible to make absolute analyses which may be accurate to 15 per cent. This is frequently quite acceptable for trace-level impurities.

Most of the difficulties encountered in the absolute method can be avoided through the use of a known weight of a standard in a comparative method. The known, or standard, sample should have the same general composition as the unknown, but this requirement is not a rigid one provided the self-absorption is negligible in all samples. The standard sample can be subjected to the same chemical separation as the unknown, although in many cases it is possible to choose a standard material such that the activity of the element to be determined is the predominant one.

To find the weight of the element X it is merely necessary to compare the counting rate of the unknown with that of the standard at a given time. Then

$$\frac{\text{Total cpm of } X \text{ in unknown}}{\text{Total cpm of } X \text{ in standard}} = \frac{\text{g of } X \text{ in unknown}}{\text{g of } X \text{ in standard}} \tag{10-3}$$

The deviations in the results obtained by the comparative method will usually arise mainly from the statistical uncertainty of the radiation measurement and are much less than those in the absolute method. Typical analyses and surveys of the method are included in the References at the end of the Chapter and in the Selected Bibliography on Radioisotope Applications in Sec. 10-3.

Isotope-dilution Methods. The second technique which exploits the power of nuclear characteristics is that of analysis by isotope dilution. This technique can be employed using either stable or radioactive isotopes of an element. Suitable methods for determining the atom per cent in the case of stable isotopes or the specific activity of the radioactive forms must be available. The methods are particularly useful when quantitative separations are not available for the systems under study. A number of examples of this technique appear in the literature (13–16).

The principle of this method may be shown by using a balance sheet such as that given by Rosenblum (17). In order to assay a sample of a certain size containing x g of a given compound, y g of the isotopic form of the unknown being sought is added with an initial specific activity SA_i. After thorough mixing, a small amount of pure compound is separated, and its final specific activity SA_f is determined. Since the total activity remains constant, the balance sheet shows the following:

Weight	*Specific activity*
x g of compound	0
y g of labeled compound	SA_i
$(x + y)$ g of mixture	SA_f

or

$$(x + y)SA_f = ySA_i \tag{10-4}$$

which transforms to

$$x = y\left(\frac{SA_i}{SA_f} - 1\right) \tag{10-5}$$

It is seen that only two specific activities and the weight of the added labeled compound must be known in order to apply the method. The calculation is similar but somewhat more complex if atom per cent values are used for stable isotopes rather than specific activities of radioactive tracers.

A variation of the direct isotope-dilution technique usually called the inverse dilution technique is necessary if it is desired to determine the amount of radioactive material in a system. In order to determine x g of product with a specific activity SA_i, y g of nonradioactive material of the same element can be added, a small quantity of pure isotopic mixture can be isolated, and its specific activity SA_f can be determined. The balance sheet for this case is as follows:

Weight	*Specific activity*
x g of compound	SA_i
y g of carrier	0
$(x + y)$ g of mixture	SA_f

The amount of the original radioactive material is then given by the equation

$$x = y\frac{1}{(SA_i/SA_f) - 1} \tag{10-6}$$

which reduces to

$$x = y\frac{SA_f}{SA_i} \tag{10-7}$$

for large amounts of carrier.

Modifications such as the double-dilution technique (18) and applications of these methods are quite extensive and have been invaluable particularly in biochemistry, where simple quantitative chemical-separation methods are frequently not available. The cited and supplementary references at the end of this chapter should give an adequate entry into the theory and application of this method. The general references in the analytical section of the bibliography in Sec. 10-3 include considerable information also.

Geological Dating and Low-level Measurement. The constancy of the decay constant of radioactive materials has been one of the outstanding phenomena examined by a number of workers. For practical purposes this constant is independent of the chemical or physical state of the material and is not affected by any but the most extreme conditions. Quite early in the study of these rates it was evident that valuable information about the age of various materials could be ascertained for certain materials. For example, it was found possible to extract and measure the volume of the helium gas from various uranium-bearing ores. This gave a direct measure of the age of the ore if the assumption was made that the helium represents only the alpha particles emitted from uranium or its decay products. A number of other, similar techniques for the dating of various geological samples have been widely accepted as reliable methods for these determinations even though there is not complete agreement as to the validity of the assumptions made by various workers. Some of these have been discussed in a volume edited by Faul (19) and in a review paper by Kohman and Saito (20).

Many of these dating techniques make use of procedures which are quite useful to the tracer-laboratory worker, but one of the methods has attained considerable importance, not only because of its unique contribution to the dating problems but also because it has opened the field of low-level sample counting of tracers. This is the technique of low-level measurement as applied to radiocarbon dating which was developed by Libby (21) and has given rise to a number of radiocarbon-dating laboratories and the publication of numerous lists of dates obtained by this method.

The basis of the radiocarbon-dating method is the assumption that the radioactive C^{14} which is formed in the atmosphere by the bombardment of N^{14} by cosmic rays is in equilibrium between the atmosphere and living matter. That is, if carbon enters the respiratory system of plants and animals, there is an ultimate equilibrium value for the specific activity of this living material. One widely accepted world-wide specific-activity value calculated for radioactive carbon is 16.1 ± 0.5 dpm/g of carbon in exchange equilibrium at the earth's surface. If the assumption is made that there has been no change in the specific activity of the living material or the intensity of the cosmic radiation during the last several tens of thousands of years, a complete balance is considered to obtain between the rate of uptake of radioactive carbon atoms in the life cycle and the rate of disintegration of the carbon atoms. When the organism dies, however, the uptake or the assimilation by the plant or animal ceases abruptly, whereas the disintegration of the radiocarbon continues.

Libby has shown that the biological specific activity of carbon is 15.3 dpm/g of carbon, based on the known ages of a number of samples for which the specific activity has been determined. The value of the half-life of C^{14} for these measurements is taken to be 5,568 $\pm$ 30 years. Based on this value, the age of a given sample or the length of time since the death of the organism from which the sample was taken is given by the following equation:

$$SA_{C^{14}} = 15.3 \exp\left(-0.693 \frac{t}{5{,}568}\right)$$

in which t is the age of the organic material in years and $SA_{C^{14}}$ is the observed specific activity of the sample in disintegrations per minute per gram of carbon. A number of assumptions are commonly made in regard to the validity of such calculations. A discussion of these, together with references to the papers of interest to a worker in this field, is given in the book by Libby.

As in most radioactivity work, two steps are involved in making the age determinations, i.e., the preparation of the sample and its measurement. Although setting up an age-dating laboratory is quite a specialized procedure, the main points of Libby's procedure are included here because of its application to the measurement of other low-level samples. The apparatus is described in detail in the original reference, and it is apparent that some of the steps apply only to carbon-dating samples.

1. The sample must be separated free from any possible source of modern carbon and then physically cleaned if possible.

2. The sample is then tested with 1 N hydrochloric acid to determine whether any carbonate is present in the sample. If any effervescence is noted, the sample is treated for several hours with the acid to remove the carbonate, since it would not have the same isotopic composition as the organic material in the sample.

3. The next step is the controlled combustion of the sample. If the sample is organic in nature, it is burned to carbon dioxide, but if it is a shell or other carbonate sample being measured for control purposes, it is treated with hydrochloric acid to generate the carbon dioxide. The particular system used commonly for this combustion differs from usual combustion trains in that only the portion of the sample actually burning is heated and the hot gases are not passed over the unburned portion of the sample. The sample size must be chosen to give between

10 and 12 g of elemental carbon, which would generate approximately 24 liters of carbon dioxide. For a sample of shell approximately 100 g would be required for the sample. It is suggested that at least 1 oz of material per sample be utilized for the measurement.

4. The mixture of gases collected in the trap is then chemically separated to yield pure carbon dioxide. This may be done by precipitating the carbon dioxide as calcium carbonate and then removing it by an acid-generation step. The pure carbon dioxide is then ready for the reduction to carbon.

5. The reduction of the carbon dioxide is carried out in a tube filled with magnesium turnings, with cadmium turnings as a catalyst. The reduction begins to take place at about 660°C, when the magnesium is heated, and continues as the carbon dioxide is added from the storage bulbs.

6. The mixture of carbon, magnesium oxide, and unreacted magnesium is removed and moistened with distilled water. Concentrated hydrochloric acid is then added to remove the magnesium oxide and the metal. After repeated washings and acid purifications the black carbon residue is placed into weighing bottles and weighed.

7. The final step before counting the sample is that of grinding it to a very fine powder in an agate mortar and determining the amount of ash in a weighed portion of the material. Corrections for the ash are made in the specific-activity calculations.

The problems of the measurement of low-level samples are much the same as the other types of measuring problems, with the exception that extreme care must be taken to eliminate or compensate for background effects. In addition, those working with low-energy beta-ray emitters must also eliminate or compensate for the self-absorption and external-absorption factors in the measurement. The early work in carbon dating was performed with a Geiger-Müller counter using solid samples such as the elemental carbon samples described above.

One of the standard methods of measuring solid samples involves their introduction into a Libby screen-wall counter. This type of G-M counter tube consists of an envelope about 8 in. long and about 2 in. in diameter surrounding the usual type of center wire. However, between the envelope and the wire is interposed a wire grid structure which can act effectively as the outer wall or anode of the counter when no sample is in place in the detector. In making the measurement a brass holder is used as a support for the solid sample and the sample itself functions as the counter wall. In one type of detector, the sample holder is arranged in a fashion which permits it to slide into a counting position at one end; then it may be tilted mechanically to slide the sample into a shielded position for a background measurement. The counting rate is then determined at the two positions. The samples are routinely measured for 48 hr with appropriate alteration in position to permit the measurement of the background to attain suitable statistical accuracy for both the sample and background measurements.

It is apparent that one of the chief problems in this type of measurement is that of the reduction of the background to the lowest feasible intensity. The background radiation consists of two main components, the alpha radiation present in the construction materials of the detector and the electromagnetic radiation representing cosmic rays and gamma rays from the surrounding materials. For a typical unshielded screen-wall counter, the background may be of the order of 500 cpm. Eight inches of iron shielding (used because of the low naturally occurring radioactive contamination) would reduce this to about 100 cpm. Mercury is also used in special shielding problems.

To reduce this background further, it is common practice to employ a ring of Geiger counters surrounding the sample detector and connected with it by an anticoincidence circuit. The ring may typically consist of 11 counters, each 18 in. long and 2 in. in diameter, in tangential contact with one another. The electrical circuit is so designed that, when any of the surrounding counters register a pulse, the screen-wall counter is inactivated for about a millisecond. The total counting rate of the shielding counters might be 800 cpm. The use of such an anticoincidence ring together with the iron shield reduces the background to about 5 cpm. For a sample of wood which gives 6.7 cpm above background, the total counting rate of sample plus background would be 11.7 cpm, giving a measurement valid to about 2 per cent σ in 48 hr.

There have been a number of modifications and innovations in the field of low-level measurements, including the use of mercury shielding, improved devices for sample positioning, and improvements in sample handling and preparation techniques. These techniques will doubtless continue to be used for many types of measurements, not only for carbon-dating samples but for low-level samples of sulfur, phosphorus, and other beta-ray-emitting isotopes.

There are, however, developments in several other areas which hold promise. Two techniques that have received wide attention are gas-phase measurement and scintillation counting, particularly in liquid-scintillation media. A number of investigators have measured the activity of carbon dioxide as a gas in a proportional counter or a G-M counter. Several groups of workers have prepared other carbon-containing gases, for example, acetylene, and have reported good results. It is probable that the scintillation counters described by Arnold (22) will prove to be of great benefit in both radiocarbon and other types of beta measurements.

10-2. Problems of Experiment Design

It is quite apparent that a number of novel and sometimes complex factors are to be èxamined in designing experiments involving radioisotopes. Although the potential hazard of radioactive material is one of the prime reasons for considering the problems of working with these materials, there are also several specific areas which need to be considered in planning experiments. These have been mentioned by a number of workers, and many of them have been treated in some detail in this book. However, it will be the purpose of this section to bring together some of these factors and problems for consideration preparatory to applying these techniques. Proper interpretations of results require a consideration of many of these factors before the experiment is undertaken. Some of these have been mentioned by Comar (23) in his chapter on Basic Difficulties in Tracer Methodology, but he deals more with the chemical nature of the systems under study. Fluharty (24) likewise has a chapter entitled Tracer Experiments in which he outlines some of the pitfalls and difficulties from the standpoint of the laboratory worker which make the actual problems of designing an experiment quite complex. The following sections are an attempt to summarize some of the factors which are important from the standpoint of both the experiment and the experimenter.

Nature of the Systems Involved. When radioisotopes are used in dynamic chemical or mechanical systems, one of the common difficulties is that of failure to interpret data properly from a nonequilibrium system. One safeguard is to require that a complete activity balance be determined for the experiment.

Another type of problem which many workers face is that of the chemical nature of the system. For example, in biological experiments it is quite important that the material administered to the animal or plant conform to the chemical acceptability of such materials by the organism. Such materials when added should not be toxic in the quantities administered, should be free from pyrogenic materials, and should be administered at physiological concentrations of salts and at normal acidities when possible. Likewise, the mass of material added to any system as a tracer should not be an amount which appreciably changes the nature of the system. Conversely, it is sometimes necessary to add carriers in order that the tracer may react in a satisfactory chemical manner. For example, carrier-free iodine will not volatilize or extract as will macro quantities unless additional inert iodine is added. For demonstrations of plant uptake of P^{32} it is also necessary for micro amounts of phosphate to be present.

Radiochemical Problems. *Radiochemical Equivalence and Purity.* One of the prime requirements of any tracer application is to make certain that the measured activity represents only the component of interest. The basic assumption of all tracer work is that the tracer behaves in the system like the corresponding nonradioactive element. This may be a valid assumption under proper conditions (except for the isotope effect, which will be discussed below) if utmost care is taken to make certain that the chemical and physical state of the tracer is identical with the stable form.

Deviations in chemical state may arise as the result of either "hot-atom" or recoil reactions, or it may be that the material supplied to the worker does not exist in the same physical state or have the proper valence to become homogeneous with the material under study. For example, when NaH_2PO_4 was furnished for a plant experiment, an anomalous uptake was observed which could be accounted for only when it was determined that approximately 22 per cent of the active P^{32} was in the PO_3^{3-} state. Other experiments have shown that a wide variety of valence states are present in samples which have been irradiated in the solid state. In these cases it is necessary for the tracer to be dissolved along with the inert material and then treated with suitable oxidizing or other reagents to bring the radioisotope into chemical identity with the stable components. This factor should be considered in mixing solids for application directly, as is done in synthesizing radioactive fertilizers. This is less of a problem when inorganic material goes into solution, since many compounds ionize readily in water and exchange rapidly with the tracer. It is a considerable problem with organic compounds, and it is usually necessary to obtain labeled material of the same constitution as that being studied in order to obtain homogeneity. This is particularly true if the position of a given radioactive label in a molecule is significant.

One of the difficulties in inorganic chemical systems is that of the formation of radiocolloids. This has been a problem of considerable importance in fission-product studies and also in the utilization of carrier-free fission-product mixtures and even separated fission products. The nature of these colloids has been studied considerably, and it is generally agreed that the nature of the colloid formed is not strongly dependent on the radiation factors but is more dependent on the chemical history of the solution. The possibility of radiocolloid formation should be considered in any study involving very-high-specific-activity radioisotopes, particularly since they are often adsorbed on glass surfaces. Schweitzer and Jackson (25) have published a survey and bibliography on some of the factors in this problem. An interesting use of colloids is based on the fact that the distribution of certain materials in the animal lymphatic system can be controlled by adjusting the particle size of the injected colloid. This is of considerable interest in medical diagnosis and radiotherapy.

In many classical studies involving work with natural radioactive materials, one of the most difficult problems was that of determining the growth and decay rates of various members of radioactive chains. Many fission-product materials likewise have descendants which may be detected in the system unless proper steps are taken to exclude them. Several such pairs are in common use, including Sr^{90}-Y^{90} and Ba^{140}-La^{140}. The possibility of a different distribution of the daughter activity from the parent must be considered in such studies. It is sometimes possible to make chemical separations of the mixtures and make sufficiently rapid measurements on the separated fractions to make certain that no daughter activity is measured, but in other cases it is necessary to compensate for the presence of one or the other activity by using the decay laws discussed in Chap. 8. Interesting problems have arisen in several laboratories in which selective decontamination of the daughter took place, leaving the parent as a residual contamination.

Another requirement of radiochemical purity is to make certain that no foreign or extraneous radioactivity is present in the sample which will interfere with the measurement. For example, it is nearly impossible to obtain sodium and potassium chemically free from each other. The cross sections of the two materials and the per cent abundance of the isotopes responsible for the (n,γ) reaction are such that chemical potassium impurity in sodium does not produce sufficient potassium activity to be significant. However, in the case of chemical sodium impurity in potassium, a considerable difference arises both in the amount of initial activity formed and in the activity remaining after a period of time. Since the half-life of the K^{42} is 12.4 hr and that of Na^{24} is 15.0 hr, the sodium activity gains in relative abundance in time and after several days the activity of a sample with a very small amount of sodium initially may be predominantly sodium. The presence of impurities is particularly important in distribution studies such as cellular-metabolism research.

Two possibilities present themselves when such impurities are found. In some cases it is possible to measure one isotope in the presence of another by suitable instrumental techniques such as gamma-ray spectrometry. In other cases it is necessary to make a separation of the materials using any of the appropriate methods described in Chap. 9. The best procedure, of course, is to use pure materials for the irradiation, but this is not always feasible.

Radiation Effects on the System. This factor is not usually a problem at tracer-research levels, although it is particularly important for biological studies at high radiation level in which radiation effects might have a physiological effect on the organism under study. The problem of these effects is becoming more important as larger amounts of radioactive materials are being prepared and used. For example, multicurie amounts of tritium are being used in certain applications, and it is observed that this level of activity may produce changes in the system. Likewise, one of the most important problems in high-level reactor design is the effect of the radiation on the reactor construction materials. Many water-cooled or water-moderated reactors require apparatus to recombine the hydrogen and oxygen formed by the radiation decomposition of the water. Another compound usually produced by radiation on water is H_2O_2, which may have marked chemical or biological effects. (See the section on chemical dosimetry in Chap. 2.) These radiation effects are also a problem in organic solutions of C^{14} or other compounds used in radiation fields. Likewise, observations have been made as to chemical changes taking place in highly radioactive solutions of short-lived alpha emitters. It might be pointed out that a number of interesting industrial applications using radiation effects to initiate reactions are being developed.

A word of warning may be issued on this point. Substances which are highly radioactive, such as tritium or radium solution, should not be kept in tightly stoppered bottles with little gas space above the surface. It is quite possible that such solutions may form sufficient gas pressure to cause an explosion.

Radiochemical Exchange with Stable Compounds. Although homogeneity is essential in making certain that the tracer is actually tracing the material under investigation, there are situations in which exchange of the tracer with materials in the system is not desirable. Wahl and Bonner (26) list a large number of exchange reactions which have been studied, and a number of good papers and reviews of the subject are available (see bibliography in Sec. 10-3). One example was a study to determine the part played by $AlCl_3$ in the Friedel-Crafts synthesis. It was found that labeled acetyl chloride exchanged rapidly with the catalyst. It was thus not possible to determine whether the product chlorine comes from the organic chloride or the catalyst.

Isotope Effect. The isotope effect is a factor which must be considered in certain types of experiments. It was pointed out above that the basic assumption of all tracer work is that the radiotracer behaves in a fashion identical to the nonradioactive form. This is only approximately correct, since the masses of the nuclei vary and, according to kinetic theory, the rates of movement of atoms of different masses differ. If the energy of the two atoms is the same, it would be expected that the velocity should vary inversely as the square root of their mass.

It is apparent that this difference in rate would be quite considerable with hydrogen, deuterium, and tritium, with a rate difference of 73 per cent expected between H^3 and H^1. The difference in rate of movement would be about 7 per cent between C^{14} and C^{12} but would represent only about 1.5 per cent difference between I^{131} and stable I^{127}. The mass differences may exert their effect either upon the equilibrium constant or upon the rate of a reaction. In general, one may say that this effect is rarely significant in distribution studies when equilibrium conditions are approached, although it can be observed with compounds containing different isotopes of low mass number.

In conclusion, it is apparent that one of the fundamental problems in working with radioactivity is the question as to whether it is possible to obtain a given labeled material in a desired physical and chemical state. If it is not possible to obtain the material desired in the form needed, the investigator must consider the possibility of transforming the available material into a suitable chemical or physical form. Many times, as in problems involving the synthesis of labeled organic compounds, a major part of the research time for a given experiment is used in this step. Information as to the availability of various kinds of labeled material, such as that supplied in "The Isotope Index" (27), is quite helpful

Operational Problems in Tracer Experiments. In order to summarize a number of factors which are involved in the planning and organization of a tracer experiment, the following questions might be presented to serve as a check list of pertinent details.

1. Is there an isotope available with the appropriate decay characteristics to give answers to the problems raised in the research? These characteristics would be a half-life which is long enough to obtain the information desired but not sufficiently long to create disposal, storage, or contamination difficulties following the experiment. This factor might be quite important if the material is to enter commercial supplies. The proper energies of radiation must be considered in circumstances offering special measuring problems, as for *in vivo* measurements and in industrial systems. Many times such factors as the presence of annihilation photons and other secondary radiation emissions may be considered in making the selection of the isotope.

2. Is the available instrumentation suitable for the problem at hand? This includes such items as determining the best method to detect and measure the isotope selected as the tracer. In case of alternative possibilities for measurement a number of other factors must be considered. These include such considerations as cost, reliability, stability, linearity, availability of instrument maintenance facilities, gas supplies in the case of flow counters, the number and frequency of samples to be measured, the advisability of using automatic instrumentation as

against the use of a technician, and the manner in which the information is to be obtained from the measuring device. In the instances in which specific instrumentation is to be used, it is of importance that adequate information be available as to its operating condition and the availability of spare components such as detectors. For example, it is frequently desirable to know the ratio of counting rates for two detectors of differing window thickness with a given isotope in case a change is necessary during the course of the experiment.

3. Can the experiment be performed by a method such that the data have significance within the limits required for their interpretation? Calculations may involve losses of sample in chemical manipulations, the available specific activity, the efficiency of the detection system, the desired statistical level of confidence, particularly with respect to the background level, and the time available for making measurements.

4. Can the experiment be performed with due regard for radiological safety? These factors are of paramount importance, since the potential health hazard is the prime reason for requiring special training and experience in the use of these materials. In this category fall the problems of the design of the laboratory or working space, the availability of the proper kinds and amounts of shielding materials, and the presence of remote-handling devices where required or of special laboratory materials such as rubber gloves to minimize the radiation hazard. Where it is expected that experiments with different isotopes are to be carried out, the problems of cross contamination among the various experiments should be considered and the probability minimized. Suitable precautions to prevent the radioactivity from being transferred to any area other than the working space should be required even in the case of low levels of radioactivity. The most important factor is to make certain that suitable monitoring instrumentation is available and is in operating condition during the experiment.

5. Can the radioactive material be easily prepared in a form suitable for detection and measurement with the instrumentation selected for the experiment? This refers primarily to the chemical and physical form of the final sample for measurement. In addition to the normal chemical and physical problems associated with the preparation of the samples, it is frequently desirable to consider the amount of time required for the preparation of the sample and the number or frequency of samples to be measured. It is also necessary to consider the problems of self-absorption and scattering in the case of solid and liquid samples and the availability of safe and proper facilities for the preparation of gaseous samples.

6. Can the significant radioactive measurements be made and interpreted properly? Under this heading, one must consider the necessity

for the identification of the material or for the identification of impurities which might be present. Although it is frequently not necessary actually to confirm the nature of the radioactive material, it is important that absorbers and other types of equipment be available should such a contingency arise. Facilities should be available for the exact reproduction of the positioning of samples for comparative measurements. This is particularly necessary in industrial plant practice, where it is often difficult to obtain such reproducibility.

7. If any type of absolute measurement is to be performed or if results of the experiment are to be compared with those of any other laboratory, are suitable procedures and techniques available for such comparisons to be made? This is of particular importance for the medical administration of radioisotopes or for other problems in which the dosage must be known. It is highly desirable that standard sources and calibration values be available even if a commercial supplier is used as the source of the radioactive materials. These standardization or calibration techniques may be relatively simple, but they should be available to the laboratory workers.

8. Are techniques available for compensating for the loss or growth of a daughter radioactivity by radioactive decay? This factor would, obviously, be negligible in the case of C^{14} or a long-lived naturally occurring material, but it would be essential for short-lived materials and for those naturally occurring materials or fission products which form radioactive decay chains. Often the simplest solution is to compare all samples with a standard sample of the same radioisotope.

9. Are there suitable techniques and procedures to permit the separation of the materials of interest from other radioactive or inert materials? For example, many semimicro techniques are employed in chemical processes such as organic syntheses and separation processes. Techniques should be chosen which can be used to give radioactive samples in a form suitable for measurement with the available instrumentation.

10. Does the tracer material accurately and adequately represent the true state of the system under investigation? Here are included the factors outlined above, such as radiochemical equivalence, purity, and the effects of the radiation on the system itself.

The Estimation of Radioactivity Requirements. One of the first requirements in the initiation of any tracer experiment usually is the calculation of the amount of radioactivity which is needed. These calculations may range from simple dilution calculations on the amount of sample to take from a shipment for assay to complex industrial problems, such as the calculation of the strength of a cobalt source needed to serve as a level gauge when the radiation must pass through a

Experimental steps	*Factors to be evaluated*
Modification of chemical-physical state, volume, or weight of source material	1. Dilution factor Volume or weight basis Specific-activity change 2. Loss factors Side products Chemical yields
Activity added to system under investigation	1. Dilution factor 2. Loss factors
Sample processing	1. Dilution factor 2. Loss factors Chemical yield Mechanical loss
Radiation measurement	1. Accuracy desired 2. Time requirements 3. Counting yield Geometry Absorption, self-absorption, and shielding Detector efficiency 4. Decay losses 5. Distance losses
Determination of desired information	1. Counts per mintue 2. Volts 3. Divisions per second 4. Feedback-control signals

FIG. 10-1. Diagram illustrating the estimation of numerical factors in activity requirements. Factors which may be included in calculation are listed at right. The desired information must be validated in terms of the design criteria, i.e., radiochemical purity, etc., described in the text.

given thickness of liquid in a tank with steel walls of a given thickness to give a reading of a certain accuracy.

Although the various factors are considered in detail elsewhere in the book, the activity-balance diagram in Fig. 10-1 is an attempt to summarize the kind of calculations which are required in any such problem. In such a schematized experiment, the source material is obtained and then modified in whatever way is required for it to be introduced into the system to be studied. During these modifications, dilution by changes in volume or weight would be common, as would a change of specific activity in the case of an organic synthesis. Likewise, there may well be mechanical and chemical losses. In a similar manner there may be dilution and possible losses when the material is introduced into the system.

After the system has reached the point of equilibrium required by the investigation, samples are removed or some type of measurement device is introduced into the system which will detect the radiation. Here again dilution and mechanical losses may occur or a chemical-yield loss may be involved if chemical manipulation is necessary to prepare the sample for measurement. In the detection and measuring step, many factors come into play, such as the counting yield of the detector, the statistical accuracy required, and the decay loss during the course of the experiment.

As pointed out above, the simple case of taking an aliquot of a shipment of a radioactive material requires only the calculation of the volume dilution factor, although in certain cases the decay losses and mechanical losses by spattering would need to be considered. In making numerical estimates of these various factors in planning the experiment, some of the factors will be known directly from the laboratory equipment used, as in the case of making volumetric dilutions. A few of the factors, such as the statistical accuracy desired and any time limitations on the experiment or counting periods, may be determined arbitrarily, but many of the factors such as chemical synthesis or precipitation yields need to be determined independently. Upper or lower limits of many of the factors can be estimated by a trained worker in his field by making reasonable assumptions. For example, the investigator can assume uniform distribution of the activity throughout the system to estimate the dilution factor in the process itself. It should be pointed out that, although it is necessary to make numerical estimates of many of these factors to plan the experiment, one of the most powerful attributes of the tracer method is that these various factors may be determined quite precisely during the experiment using the tracer. If it is necessary to study any of the experimental parameters more thoroughly, it can usually be done quite well with the tracer even though this might be outside the scope of the main experiment. It is, of course, apparent that the actual values for these various factors determined during the experiment should be used in final calculations of the experimental results.

As can be seen from Fig. 10-1, it is possible to work in either direction. That is, if one has a given amount of activity initially, it is possible to make estimates of the amount of material which may be available for measurement in the final step. In most cases, however, the final measuring step is the critical one from the standpoint of the efficiency of the detection instrument or the statistical accuracy required, so that it is usual to begin at this point by specifying the required final measurement activity desired and working backward to determine the amount of activity which would be required initially. Loss and dilution factors are usually expressed either in ratios or in percentage yields. The usual procedure is to transform each of the estimates into fractions such that the final calculation involves a straightforward multiplication of the activity required by the cumulative loss factor. Fortunately, most detection instruments have sufficient latitude in their measurement range so that the estimates will bring the final sample into a usable range. It is for this reason that many laboratories prefer the flexibility of detectors with various shelf positions to permit a wider variation in sample strengths.

As an example of this type of calculation, one might estimate the total amount of radioactivity required to perform an experiment to determine the distribution of a certain compound in an animal. It is also assumed that the compound must be synthesized. Table 10-2 shows the estimates of the loss factor in the various steps and the calculation of the amount of activity which would be required to initiate such an experiment.

It is apparent that not all experiments require the evaluation of all these estimates. Simple assays, for example, require the consideration only of the counting yield of the instruments, decay losses, and dilution factors. However, the principle of this approach should be satisfactory for most tracer-experiment calculations in laboratory, clinical, and industrial applications.

The question arises as to ways of decreasing the loss factor in an experiment such as this. In preparing material for addition to the animal feed, it is doubtful if significant increases in the chemical yield are feasible. If the lower limit of the size of the sample is reached with such an amount that much more feed must be made up than finally appears in the animal, there would be no satisfactory way of reducing the loss factor in the feed-administration step. It might be possible to use semimicrosynthesis techniques to prepare a smaller amount of feed

TABLE 10-2

ESTIMATE OF TOTAL ACTIVITY REQUIRED PER ANIMAL TO PERFORM AN ANIMAL NUTRITION EXPERIMENT

Problem: Estimate the total amount of activity which is required to perform a tracer experiment involving the C^{14} synthesis of an organic compound which is fed to animals. This is followed by assay of the entire animal to give a solid sample with a counting rate of not less than 300 cpm above background, with a standard deviation of 2 per cent and a maximum counting time of 10 min per sample.

	Per cent	Loss factor
Chemical modification:		
Chemical yield of synthesis	65	1.5
Purification yield	4	25
Experimental system:		
Amount obtained from feed	0.2	500
Retained after respiration losses	40	2.5
Sampling aliquot	100	1
Radiation measurement:		
Counting yield	4	25
Decay (C^{14})	0	1
		1.2×10^6 (cumulative)

$$\text{Initial total activity required} = \frac{\text{total dpm}}{\text{dpm/mc}} = \frac{300 \times 1.2}{2.22 \times 10^9} \times 10^6 = 0.16 \text{ mc}$$

with a consequent reduction in the feed loss factor. The other possible method for decreasing the activity required would be to use a counting instrument with more than 4 per cent counting yield. If liquid-counting methods could be used, this loss factor might be materially reduced. It seems reasonable that by suitable modification of the experiment it might be possible to decrease the loss factor considerably; this would permit the experiment to be performed with microcurie quantities of activity.

10-3. Applications of Radioisotopes

General Sources of Information on Radioisotope Applications. The use of radioactive isotopes has proliferated so greatly in the last few years that it would be impossible to mention all the many and ingenious applications to which they have been put in hospitals, laboratories, and industrial organizations. There are a number of different ways of classifying these types of applications, depending on the particular nuclear properties being utilized. One popular classification is that of describing an application as being based on (1) the use of the radioactive material as a tracer, (2) the effect of the radiation on matter, and (3) the effect of matter on the radiation.

The first category makes use of the nuclear radiations emitted from the radioactive source in an effort to locate the material in question. Such uses range from the tracer studies in the study of thyroid metabolism to the location of a scraper in an oil pipeline.

The second category takes advantage of the radioactive material as a source of energy. Although much speculation has been offered as to methods of obtaining direct energy release from such materials as fission products and some success has been obtained with nuclear batteries which are capable of producing micromicroampere currents at potentials of several thousand volts, most of the uses of radiation in this field have taken advantage of the ionization produced by radiation. This ionization can be used directly, as in the case of static-electricity eliminators. In general, the indirect effect of the radiation has been more useful in fields such as the initiation of chemical reactions by radiation, the sterilization of food and drugs, and the use of radioactive materials at therapeutic radiation levels in clinical practice.

The most extensive use in terms of direct economic benefits has stemmed from the third category in the form of gauges and instruments of various types in which the radiation intensity gives information as to the amount of matter in the path of the radiation. Of great practical importance, likewise, is the field of industrial radiography, in which the effect of the material in the path of the radiation is recorded on a photographic plate or film.

Although a systematic treatment of uses may follow the categories mentioned above, it has been decided to outline isotope applications by including in this chapter a limited bibliography arranged by fields of scientific interest rather than by specific uses. It should be pointed out that many techniques in a given field are applicable in another and it is this "cross fertilization" of ideas and techniques that has characterized the development of nuclear science. It is hoped that the papers chosen will serve as a point of entry for a worker in any field having potential applicability of radioisotopes.

Of special importance are the general bibliographies, papers, and sources of information on radioisotope applications listed in the first part. "The Isotope Index" lists commercial suppliers, and the catalogues of the Oak Ridge and other national laboratories list isotopes, services available, and much information about shipping and packaging the materials.

The "International Bibliography" with its supplements is quite useful as a guide to non-United States literature, although it exhibits some time lag with the current periodicals. The *Proceedings of the Geneva Conferences* likewise offer world-wide survey papers, a number of which contain excellent bibliographical material. The best compilation of papers from United States workers as of 1955 is the Eight-year Summary, which lists about 7,000 papers published using radioisotopes from the United States. These are grouped in 30 scientific categories. The Five-year Summary has a number of papers listed also and should be consulted for work prior to 1952 since the eight-year report is not cumulative and does not duplicate the five-year listings. (See Appendix J.)

For current papers a worker has several sources of information of special interest to the nuclear field. One of these is the *Nuclear Science Abstracts* published by the Atomic Energy Commission. This is an excellent abstracting service, although the abstracts do not attempt to cover the field of isotope applications and techniques so well as they attempt to cover other problems of importance to reactor- and other nuclear-research programs. Of particular interest is the British report Sources of Information in Atomic Energy. This includes sections on information from Britain, the United States, Russia, and other countries.

Also included in this bibliography is a selected listing of journals devoted primarily to nuclear work. It should be noted also that most of the current applications are reported in the journals of a given scientific discipline, since it is normally the results of the radioisotope work which are of interest rather than the techniques themselves.

Radioisotope Applications in Research and Industry. The use of radioisotopes in many chemical fields is expanding rapidly. Much of the early work was in the fields of the analytical techniques discussed in Sec. 10-1 and in the study of theoretical analytical chemistry and the elucidation of mechanisms of organic chemical reactions. It is probable that the chief advances in biochemistry within the last 10 years have arisen primarily from information gained by the use of radioactive materials.

In the chemical General References are a review article on using isotopic tracers in chemical systems and two volumes discussing radioactivity as applied directly to chemistry. The book by Hevesy also describes many biological techniques. These contain a large amount of information which should be familiar to chemists interested in this field. The bibliography of organic syntheses is quite helpful.

The field of radiation chemistry is one which is now developing considerable interest. The survey articles in the *Annual Review of Physical Chemistry* and *Annual Review of Nuclear Science* cover the basic-science aspects of the radiation chemistry quite well. Allen's

Geneva Conference paper contains a good list of references to the basic aspects of the field. Of particular interest in the industrial field are the surveys listed in the Eight-year Summary in its section on applied industrial uses of radioisotopes. For example, in Section CC of the Eight-year Summary are listed survey and research papers on the following uses of radioisotopes in industry: textiles, wax testing, petroleum, nondestructive testing, food sterilization, metal cleaning, elastomers, detergency, gauges, beta-measuring methods, pipelines, catalysis, wear studies, paints, flow testing, process instrumentation, industrial control, pulp and paper, glass, and radiography.

In addition to the "practical" or plant uses of isotopes there are a number of industrial laboratories making routine studies in the fields of reaction mechanisms, separation efficiencies, mechanisms of crystal growth, the determination of the roles of catalysts and modifiers in reactions, problems of corrosion, and the determination of surface concentration and areas of various solids. There is also considerable industrial interest in theoretical studies of chemical systems such as those involved in absorption, coprecipitation, and precipitation aging phenomena.

Several excellent volumes dealing with biological applications of radioisotopes are available. Of particular interest are Comar's chapter on General Procedures for Radioassay, which includes considerable information on experimental techniques particularly applicable to biological systems, and his chapter on Properties and Procedures for Individual Isotopes. The latter chapter includes discussion on intake levels, radioassay, form of isotope available, cost, specific activity, chemistry, typical methods of analysis and use, and references to work done with some 55 elements.

Probably the largest single group of scientists using isotopes with respect to both the number of workers and the number of shipments received is physicians. In general, medical interest lies in research and diagnostic problems, although there is wide interest in radioisotope therapy in a limited number of conditions such as hyperthyroidism and certain types of cancer and blood dyscrasias. A large amount of clinical research is being carried on in practically all fields of medicine and physiology. The measurement of thyroid function with radioactive iodine is the method of choice in a large number of hospitals. In addition to the medical listings, the summary volumes described in the section on biology also have much material of interest to medical researchers. There are several books having to do with the clinical uses of isotopes. A number of other books are available with excellent sections dealing with various special fields of medicine such as radiology, internal medicine, hematology, and others.

One of the most complete surveys of the clinical field as of 1953 is published under the title "Radioisotopes in Medicine." This is a transcript of a course given at the Oak Ridge Institute of Nuclear Studies in September, 1953, and is edited by Andrews, Brucer, and Anderson. A somewhat similar transcript of a seminar at Oak Ridge in 1956 in the field of supervoltage therapy is also available. It has the title "Roentgens, rads, and Riddles" and is edited by Friedman and Brucer.

It is hoped that the following tabulation will serve as a useful introduction to the research literature in the reader's field of interest. To the experienced worker, it is hardly necessary to suggest that this list is only for purposes of orienting a newcomer and is not expected to take the place of intensive reading of the literature in the worker's own field.

Selected Bibliography on Radioisotope Applications*

General References on Radioisotope Applications and Availability

Anthony, L. J.: "Sources of Information in Atomic Energy," AERE Lib/Ll, 2d ed., Atomic Energy Research Establishment, Harwell, Berkshire, England, 1957.

"An International Bibliography on Atomic Energy," vol. II, "Scientific Aspects," with supplements, United Nations, Atomic Energy Commission Group, New York, 1951– (United Nations Document AEC/INF/10/Rev. 1).

"The Isotope Index: The Complete Purchasing Guide to the Isotopes," Scientific Equipment Company, Indianapolis, Ind.

Proceedings of the International Conference on the Peaceful Uses of Atomic Energy, Held in Geneva 8 August–20 August 1955, vol. 10, Radioactive Isotopes and Nuclear Radiations in Medicine; vol. 15, Applications of Radioactive Isotopes and Fission Products in Research and Industry, United Nations, New York, 1956.

"Radioisotopes, Special Materials and Services," Oak Ridge National Laboratory, Oak Ridge, Tenn.

U.S. Atomic Energy Commission: "Isotopes: A Five-year Summary of Distribution, with Bibliography," Government Printing Office, Washington, 1951.

———: "Isotopes: An Eight-year Summary of U.S. Distribution and Utilization, with Bibliography," Government Printing Office, Washington, 1955.

———: *Nuclear Science Abstracts*, Government Printing Office, Washington.

The Applications of Radioisotopes in Chemistry

General References

Calvin, M., C. Heidelberger, J. C. Reid, B. M. Tolbert, and P. F. Yankwich: "Isotopic Carbon: Techniques in Its Measurement and Chemical Manipulation," Wiley, New York, 1949.

Edwards, R. R.: Isotopic Tracers in Chemical Systems, *Ann. Rev. Nuclear Sci.*, vol. 1, pp. 301–342, 1952.

Hahn, O.: "Applied Radiochemistry," Cornell University Press, Ithaca, N.Y., 1936.

* See also Appendix J.

Hevesy, G. von: "Radioactive Indicators: Their Application in Biochemistry, Animal Physiology, and Pathology," Interscience, New York, 1948.

Johnston, J. E., R. A. Faires, and R. J. Millett (eds.): "Radioisotope Conference, Second, Oxford, 1954," vols. I and II, Academic Press, New York, 1954.

Popjak, G.: Chemistry, Biochemistry, and Isotopic Tracer Techniques, *Roy. Inst. Chem. (London), Lectures, Monographs, Repts.*, 2, 1955.

Wahl, A. C., and N. A. Bonner (eds.): "Radioactivity Applied to Chemistry," Wiley, New York, 1951.

Yankwich, E.: Radioactive Isotopes as Tracers, *Anal. Chem.*, vol. 21, pp. 318–321, 1949.

ANALYTICAL CHEMISTRY

Boyd, G. E., and D. N. Hume: Radiochemical Analytical Methods, in C. J. Rodden (ed.), "Analytical Chemistry of the Manhattan Project," pp. 662–692, McGraw-Hill, New York, 1950.

Cabell, M. J., and A. A. Smales: Radiochemical Methods in Analysis, *Research (London)*, vol. 9, pp. 214–219, June, 1956.

Calkins, G. D.: Radioactive Methods of Analysis, *Ohio J. Sci.*, vol. 52, pp. 151–160, May, 1952.

Gordon, C. L.: Nucleonics, *Anal. Chem.*, vol. 23, pp. 81–86, January, 1951.

———: Nucleonics, *Anal. Chem.*, vol. 26, pp. 176–181, January, 1954.

Rodden, C. J.: Analytical Nuclear Chemistry, *Ann. Rev. Nuclear Sci.*, vol. 1, pp. 343–362, 1952.

PHYSICAL AND ORGANIC CHEMISTRY

Begun, G. M., and R. Allen (comps.): Isotope Separation and Isotope Exchange: A Bibliography of Unclassified Literature, *U.S. Atomic Energy Comm. Rept.* TID-3036, 1953.

Conference on Isotopic Exchange Reactions and Chemical Kinetics, December 1–3, 1948, Brookhaven National Laboratory Chemistry Conference 2, *U.S. Atomic Energy Comm. Rept.* AECU-226, n.d.

Daudel, P.: Application de la méthode des isotopes radioactifs à l'étude des mécanismes des réactions chimiques, *Bull. soc. chim. France*, 1952, pp. 23D–27D.

Henriques, F. C., Jr., G. B. Kistiakowsky, C. Margnetti, and W. G. Schneider: Radioactive Studies, *Ind. Eng. Chem., Anal. Ed.*, vol. 18, pp. 349–353, June, 1946.

Horne, R. A., C. D. Coryell, and L. S. Goldring: Generalized Acidity in Radiochemical Separations, *Ann. Rev. Nuclear Sci.*, vol. 6, pp. 163–178, 1956.

Nevenzel, J. C., R. F. Riley, D. R. Howton, and G. Steinberg (comps.): Bibliography of Syntheses with Carbon Isotopes, *U.S. Atomic Energy Comm. Rept.* UCLA-316, 1954.

BIOCHEMISTRY

Aronoff, S.: "Techniques of Radiobiochemistry," Iowa State College Press, Ames, Iowa, 1956.

Borg, W. A. J.: Isotopen bij het biochemisch onderzoek, *Chem. Weekblad*, vol. 47, pp. 708–717, September, 1951.

Chaikoff, I. L., and D. B. Zilversmit: Radioactive Phosphorus: Its Application to the Study of Phospholipid Metabolism, *Advances in Biol. and Med. Phys.*, vol. 1, pp. 322–352, 1948.

Dubois, K. P., and D. F. Peterson: Biochemical Effects of Radiation, *Ann. Rev. Nuclear Sci.*, vol. 4, pp. 351–376, 1954.

Engelhardt, V. A.: Ycpekhl i Prospekty Vo Izpol'zananiya Radioaktivnykh Izotopov V Biokhimiya, *Sessiya Akad. Nauk S.S.S.R. Mirnomu Ispol'zovaniyu Atomnoĭ Energii, Moscow, July 1–5, 1955, Zasedan. Otdel. Biol. Nauk,* pp. 1–13.

Heidelberger, C.: Discussion of Biochemical Tracer Applications: Major Problems, Limitations, Perspective and Future Objective, *Proc. 2d Natl. Cancer Conf.*, vol. II, pp. 1576–1581, American Cancer Society, New York, 1954.

Radin, N. S.: Isotope Techniques in Biochemistry. I, *Nucleonics*, vol. 1, no. 1, pp. 24–33, September, 1947; II, vol. 1, no. 2, pp. 48–59, October, 1947; V, vol. 2, no. 2, pp. 33–45, February, 1948.

Sacks, J.: "Isotopic Tracers in Biochemistry and Physiology," McGraw-Hill, New York, 1953.

Villee, C. A.: Radioisotopes in Biochemical and Medical Research, *Ann. Rev. Nuclear Sci.*, vol. 1, pp. 525–568, 1951.

RADIATION CHEMISTRY

Allen, A. O.: Radiation Chemistry, *Ann. Rev. Phys. Chem.*, vol. 3, pp. 57–80, 1952.

———: A Survey of Recent American Research in the Radiation Chemistry of Aqueous Solutions, *Proc. Intern. Conf. Peaceful Uses Atomic Energy, Geneva, 1955*, vol. 7, pp. 513–520, United Nations, New York, 1956.

Dainton, F. S.: Radiation Chemistry, *Ann. Rev. Nuclear Sci.*, vol. 5, pp. 213–240, 1955.

Hart, E.: Radiation Chemistry, *Ann. Rev. Phys. Chem.*, vol. 5, pp. 139–162, 1954.

Hochanadel, C. J., and S. C. Lind: Radiation Chemistry, *Ann. Rev. Phys. Chem.*, vol. 7, pp. 83–106, 1956.

Lind, S. C.: "The Chemical Effects of Alpha Particles and Electrons," 2d ed., Reinhold, New York, 1928. (American Chemical Society Monograph 2.)

Magee, W. G.: Radiation Chemistry, *Ann. Rev. Nuclear Sci.*, vol. 3, pp. 171–192, 1953.

Radiation Chemistry, *Discussions Faraday Soc.*, no. 12, 1952.

Weiss, J.: Radiation Chemistry, *Ann. Rev. Phys. Chem.*, vol. 4, pp. 143–166, 1953.

Willard, J. E.: Chemical Effects of Nuclear Transformation, *Ann. Rev. Nuclear Sci.*, vol. 3, pp. 193–220, 1953.

———: Radiation Chemistry and Hot Atom Chemistry, *Ann. Rev. Phys. Chem.*, vol. 6, pp. 141–170, 1955.

Applications in Metallurgy

Bever, M. B.: Radioactive Tracers in Physical Metallurgy Research, *Trans. Am. Soc. Metals*, vol. 45A, pp. 278–311, 1953.

Carr, J. S.: Radioactive Isotopes in Mineral Dressing Research, *Atomic Energy Research Establ.* (*G. Brit.*) *Rept.* AERE CE/R-912, 1952.

Rogers, B. A., and F. H. Spedding: Progress in Metallurgy, *Ann. Rev. Nuclear Sci.*, vol. 1, pp. 441–464, 1952.

Shuttleworth, R.: The Use of Radioactive Isotopes in Metallurgy, *Brit. J. Appl. Phys.*, vol. 4, pp. 326–329, November, 1953.

Simnad, M. T.: Radioisotopes in the Study of Metal Surface Reactions in Solutions, in "Properties of Metallic Surfaces: A Symposium Organized by the Institute of Metals . . . London, on 19 November 1952," Institute of Metals, London, 1953. [*Inst. Metals* (*London*) *Monograph and Rept. Ser.* 13.]

Industrial Applications of Radioisotopes

Aebersold, P. C.: Industrial Applications of Radioisotopes, *Non-Destructive Testing*, vol. 9, no. 3, pp. 10–16, winter, 1950–1951.

——— and C. E. Crompton: Growth of Radioisotope Utilization in Industry and Engineering, *Chem. Eng. Progr. Symposium Ser.*, no. 13, 1954 (*Nuclear Engineering*, pt. III, pp. 105–114).

Bradford, J. R. (ed.): "Radioisotopes in Industry," Reinhold, New York, 1953.

Crompton, C.: Industrial Applications, *Nucleonics*, vol. 12, no. 10, p. 72, October, 1954.

———: The Versatility of Radiation Applications Involving Penetration or Reflection, *Proc. Intern. Conf. Peaceful Uses Atomic Energy, Geneva, 1955*, vol. 15, pp. 124–134, United Nations, New York, 1956.

D'yachenko, P. E.: Radioaktivnye Izotopy v Tekhnike, *Vestnik Akad. Nauk S.S.S.R.*, vol. 25, no. 10, pp. 39–47, 1955.

Fearnside, K.: The Application of Isotopes to the Examination of Industrial Materials, *Proc. Isotope Techniques Conference, Oxford, July, 1951*, vol. 2, pp. 138–144, H.M. Stationery Office, London, 1952.

Gueron, J.: Exemples d'applications industrielles de la radioactivité, *J. phys. radium*, vol. 15, pp. 65A–75A, May, 1954.

Guest, G. H.: "Radioisotopes: Industrial Applications," Pitman, New York, 1951.

"Industrial Uses of Radioactive Materials: A Selected Bibliography," Arthur D. Little, Inc., Cambridge, Mass., 1949. (Also published as *U.S. Atomic Energy Comm. Rept.* NP-3968.)

Kelly, R. C.: Industrial Applications of Radioisotopes, University of Tennessee master's thesis, Knoxville, Tenn., June, 1954.

Kramish, A., and E. M. Zuckert: "Atomic Energy for Your Business," McKay, New York, 1956.

Manowitz, B.: The Industrial Future of Radiation Chemistry, *Nucleonics*, vol. 11, no. 10, pp. 18–20, October, 1953.

Seligman, H.: Radioisotopes in Industry, *Atomics*, vol. 5, pp. 299–302, 318, November, 1954.

Shteinbok, N. I.: Osnovnye Voprosy Primeneniya Radioaktivnykh Izluchenii v Izmeritel'noi Teknike, *Uspekhi Fiz. Nauk*, vol. 54, pp. 231–284, 1954.

"Symposium on Radioactivity: An Introduction; Radioisotopes, Laboratories, Personnel, Radiation, Management Problems, ASTM Work," American Society for Testing Materials, Philadelphia, 1954.

Thomas, B. W.: Radioactivity Plays an Important Role in Many Types of Industrial Instrumentation, *Ind. Eng. Chem.*, vol. 45, no. 9, pp. 89A–91A, September, 1953.

Applications in Biology and Agriculture

Benigno, P.: Impiego degli isotopi in microbiologia e in chemioterapia, *Arch. ital. sci. farmacol.*, vol. 2, pp. 5–40, 1952.

Collier, P. A.: The Use of Isotopes in Agricultural Research. I, *Chem. & Ind.* (*London*), vol. 51, pp. 1122–1124, December, 1951.

Comar, C. L.: "Radioisotopes in Biology and Agriculture," McGraw-Hill, New York, 1955.

——— (ed.): "Atomic Energy and Agriculture," American Association for the Advancement of Science, Washington, 1957. (*Publ. Am. Assoc. Advance Sci.* 49.)

Comar, C. L., and S. L. Hood (comps.): The Role of Atomic Energy in Agricultural Research, *Proc. 4th Ann. Oak Ridge Summer Symposium, August 25–30, 1952.* (*U.S. Atomic Energy Comm. Rept.* TID-5115, 1953.)

Conference on the Use of Isotopes in Plant and Animal Research, Held on June 12, 13, and 14, 1952, *U.S. Atomic Energy Comm. Rept.* TID-5098, 1953.

Heidelberger, C.: Application of the Carbon Isotopes to a Study of Animal Metabolism, *Advances in Biol. and Med. Phys.*, vol. 2, pp. 78–131, 1951.

Hendricks, S. B., and L. A. Dean: Radioisotopes in Soils Research and Plant Nutrition, *Ann. Rev. Nuclear Sci.*, vol. 1, pp. 597–610, 1951.

Kamen, M. D.: "Isotopic Tracers in Biology: An Introduction to Tracer Methodology," 3d ed., Academic Press, New York, 1957.

Rachinskii, V. V.: Mechenye Atomy v Izuchenii Zhizni Rastenii, *Uspekhi Sovremennoĭ Biol.*, vol. 31, pp. 376–390, May–June, 1951.

Tolbert, N. E., and P. B. Pearson: Atomic Energy and the Plant Sciences, *Advances in Agron.*, vol. 4, pp. 279–303, 1952.

Applications in Medicine

Aebersold, P. C.: Development of Medical Use of Radioisotopes, *Nucleonics*, vol. 10, no. 3, pp. 50–51, March, 1952.

———: Survey of Isotope Utilization in the Study and Treatment of Cancer, *Acta Unio Intern. Contra Cancrum*, vol. 9, no. 1, pp. 19–28, 1953.

Andrews, G. A., M. Brucer, and E. B. Anderson (eds.): "Radioisotopes in Medicine," Government Printing Office, Washington, 1953.

Bartelstone, H. J.: Survey of the Use of Radioactive Isotopes in Dentistry, *N.Y.J. Dentistry*, vol. 20, pp. 320–334, August–September, 1950.

Behrens, C. F.: "Atomic Medicine," Nelson, New York, 1949.

Beierwaltes, W. H., P. C. Johnson, and A. J. Solari: "The Clinical Use of Radioisotopes," Saunders, Philadelphia, 1957.

Copp, H. D.: Implications of Atomic Energy in Medicine and Dentistry. I, Radioactive Isotopes as Research Tools, *Oral Surg. Oral Med. Oral Pathol.*, vol. 3, pp. 598–621, May, 1950.

Fields, T., and L. Seed: "The Clinical Use of Radioisotopes: A Manual of Technique," Year Book Publishers, Chicago, 1957.

Francis, G. E., W. Mulligan, and A. Wormall: "Isotopic Tracers: A Theoretical and Practical Manual for Biological Students and Research Workers," Athlane, London, 1954.

Friedman, M., and M. Brucer (eds).: Roentgens, rads, and Riddles: A Symposium on Supervoltage Radiation Therapy, *U.S. Atomic Energy Comm. Rept.* TID-7538, 1959.

Frimmer, M.: Die Anwendung von radioaktiven und stabilen Isotopen in der pharmakologischen Forschung, *Angew. Chem.*, vol. 64, pp. 638–642, Dec. 7, 1952.

Ignat'ev, A. (ed.): "Trudy Po Primeneniiu Radioaktivnykh Izotopov v Meditsine," 2d ed., Medgiz, Moscow, 1955.

Low-Beer, B. V. A.: "The Clinical Use of Radioactive Isotopes," Charles C Thomas, Springfield, Ill., 1950.

Mayneord, W. V.: Some Applications of Nuclear Physics to Medicine, *Brit. J. Radiol.*, *suppl.* 2, 1950.

Quimby, E. H.: Radioactive Isotopes in Clinical Diagnosis, *Advances in Biol. and Med. Phys.*, vol. 2, pp. 243–268, 1951.

Tabern, D. L., J. D. Taylor, and G. I. Gleason: Radioisotopes in Pharmaceutical and Medical Studies. I, *Nucleonics*, vol. 7, no. 5, pp. 3–23, November, 1950.

Wainwright, W. W.: Survey of Dental Uses of Radioactive Materials for 1952, *J. Am. Dental Assoc.*, vol. 47, pp. 656–660, December, 1953.

———: Dental Uses of Radioisotopes, *Proc. Intern. Conf. Peaceful Uses Atomic Energy, Geneva, 1955*, vol. 10, pp. 440–452, United Nations, New York, 1956.

Wasserman, L. R., and R. Loevinger: Uses of Radioactive Isotopes in Medicine, *Advances in Internal Med.*, vol. 5, pp. 77–161, 1950.

Selected Journals in the Nuclear Science Field*

Argentine Republic Comision Nacional de Energia Atomica. Publicacione: Serie Fisica, Serie Matematica, Serie Quimica, Buenos Aires

Atom, United Kingdom Atomic Energy Authority, London

Atombrief, Regensburg, Germany

Atomes, Atomes, Paris

Atomic Digest, Institute of Atomic Information for the Layman, London

Atomic Scientists Journal, Taylor & Francis, London

Atomkernenergie, Verlag Karl Thiemig Kg, Munich, Germany

Atompraxis, Verlag G. Braun, Karlsruhe, Germany

Atomwirtschaft, Verlag Handelsblatt, Düsseldorf, Germany

Atoom (*Wetenschak en Samenleving*), V. W. O. Rijn, Leiden, Netherlands

British Nuclear Energy Conference Journal, London

Energia nucleare, Milan, Italy

Industries atomiques, Editions de la Grange-Batelière, Paris

Institute of Nuclear Sciences, Boris Kidrich Institute, Belgrade, Yugoslavia

International Journal of Applied Radiation and Isotopes, Pergamon Press, New York

IRE Transactions on Nuclear Science, Institute of Radio Engineers, New York

Journal of the American Nuclear Society, Academic Press, New York

Journal of Inorganic & Nuclear Chemistry, Pergamon Press, New York

Journal of Nuclear Energy, Pergamon Press, New York

Journal de physique et le radium, Société française de physique, Paris

Nuclear Physics, North-Holland Publishing Co., Amsterdam

Nuclear Science and Engineering, Academic Press, New York

Nucleonics, McGraw-Hill Publishing Company, New York

Radiation Research, Academic Press, New York

Soviet Journal of Atomic Energy (translation), Consultants Bureau, New York

Technisches Zentralblatt. Abteilung Kerntechnik, Akademie-Verlag, Berlin

Of the myriad experiments that could be devised based on the various applications referred to in the above references, only a few representative ones are included here. There are several reasons for this selection, but the effort in formal courses is generally placed on those types of experiments which have wide application as methods rather than on those which show the details of a specific field of interest. For example, the isotope-dilution technique has wide applicability in many fields of science. It is felt that the experiments included here will be suggestive of the tremendous potential of the application of radioisotope techniques and that the worker will be in a position to extend his experimentation directly into his own field of scientific interest.

* Excluding journals concerned primarily with nuclear power and medicine.

Experiment 10-1
Analysis by Isotope Dilution

In this experiment a nonradioactive "unknown" amount of material is analyzed quantitatively by determining the change in specific activity of chemically identical, labeled material added to the unknown. The analysis of a sulfuric acid solution for sulfate is typical, because it serves to illustrate the lack of need for complete recovery of the separated material, $BaSO_4$. This agent is well known for its tendency to pass through even the finest filter paper unless particles are coarsened by prolonged digestion. It also serves as a companion experiment for Expt. 6-3, in which data for self-absorption correction for S^{35} in $BaSO_4$ are obtained.

Apparatus and Materials

Beta counter—G-M or proportional tube
Labeled H_2SO_4 solution of known H_2SO_4 concentration—assumed to be 0.110 M in procedure below and assumed to have a counting rate of about 5,000 cpm at a counting yield of 10 per cent for a sample of BaS^*O_4 having a thickness of 50 mg/cm^2—for convenience, the same solution used in Expt. 6-3
"Unknown" sulfuric acid solution—assumed to be of such concentration in the following procedure that the specific activity of the labeled H_2SO_4 can be reduced by about 50 per cent with a reasonable aliquot of the unknown
$BaCl_2$ solution (0.2 to 0.5 M)
Filtration unit, suitable source mounts
Centrifuge tubes, 40 ml
Analytical balance
Hot water bath
Stirring rods
Heat lamp
Pipettes

Procedure

Prepare duplicate samples for analysis by pipetting accurately into each of two 40-ml centrifuge tubes (1) a sample of the unknown (in the range of 2 to 5 ml) and (2) an aliquot (in the range of 2 to 5 ml) of the labeled sulfuric acid (0.110 M). Add 10 ml of distilled water and heat the sample in the water bath. Slowly add, with stirring, a slight excess of $BaCl_2$. Complete precipitation is not necessary, but it can be checked by allowing each precipitate to settle, adding a few drops of $BaCl_2$, and noting the formation or absence of additional $BaSO_4$.

After the precipitates have been allowed to digest in the hot water bath for a few minutes, they should be filtered through similar weighed filter mounts (forming an even layer), washed with water, and dried. The filter mounts should then be reweighed.

If this experiment is done in conjunction with Expt. 6-3 (using the same labeled H_2SO_4), the two samples should be counted exactly as for the BaS^*O_4 samples in that experiment. Necessary data for the specific activity of the labeled H_2SO_4 and self-absorption corrections, needed to normalize the isotope-dilution samples to those of the undiluted BaS^*O_4, are obtained from Expt. 6-3.

If this experiment is not done in conjunction with Expt. 6-3, at least two additional BaS^*O_4 samples should be prepared by the procedure of this experiment using the labeled H_2SO_4 alone. The sample size (in milligrams per square centimeter) for these BaS^*O_4 sources should be chosen to fall near and on either side of the isotope-dilution sources, so that the necessary self-absorption corrections can be made.

Analysis of Data

From the average specific activity for the duplicate samples and the specific activity for the labeled H_2SO_4, calculate the grams of H_2SO_4 per milliliter of "unknown" solution. Discuss the reliability of the results.

Experiment 10-2
Use of Isotope Exchange in Kinetic Studies

Many important exchange reactions take place in chemical systems. Some take place in very short time periods, but others go at a very slow rate. Radioactive tracers offer a direct method for determination of both qualitative and quantitative aspects of such exchange processes. The particular reaction under study is the exchange of I^{131} ions from sodium iodide with iodine atoms in *n*-butyliodide. The experiment has been developed by several members of the Special Training Division of ORINS, including Dr. Elizabeth Rona.

Apparatus and Materials

Five 2-ml volumetric flasks
One 5-ml volumetric flask
One 400-ml beaker
Thermostatically controlled water bath
Five micropipettes (100 λ)
One slurry pipette
Ten counting cups or sample mount for liquid samples
Linear graph paper

NaI aqueous solution, 0.08 M
NaI in 90 per cent acetone, 0.08 M (in glass stopper bottle)
I^{131} activity (approximately 10,000 cpm in 100 λ) as iodide
n-Butyliodide in 90 per cent acetone, 0.08 M (in glass stopper bottle)
Benzene

Procedure

All solutions except the radioiodide should be in the thermostatted water bath. Place five 2-ml volumetric flasks in a beaker filled with ice, and add to each 1 ml of the NaI aqueous solution and 1 ml of benzene. Place one 5-ml volumetric flask in the thermostatted bath, and add 1 ml of the NaI-acetone, the radioactive I^{131}, and 1.1 ml of the butyliodide-acetone. Replace stoppers in stock bottle immediately. If the experiment is being performed by two or more groups, two or more thermostats should be used with different bath temperatures. Convenient temperatures are 25 and 35°C. The time when the n-butyliodide is added to the tagged sodium iodide solution should be noted, and becomes the starting time of the experiment. Shake gently for about 1 min and replace in the bath. At appropriate intervals (about 20 to 25 min at 25°C and about 15 min at 35°C), take out a 100-λ sample of the mixture and add to a benzene–sodium iodide mixture in the ice bath. Shake each sample vigorously for 1 to 2 min. If an emulsion forms, the layers may be centrifuged for a few minutes. Take out the benzene (upper) layer *carefully* with a slurry pipette and deposit the benzene in the counting cup. Transfer the aqueous layer to a counting cup and count the gamma radiation from both fractions. The benzene layer will contain the butyliodide, which has gained the activity by exchange. The activity of this layer is denoted by x.

Estimate the half-time of the reaction. If results from two temperatures are available, calculate the experimental activation energy.

Analysis of Data

The reaction is of the general form

$$AX + BX^* \rightleftharpoons AX^* + BX \tag{10-8}$$

If the molar concentration of AX is denoted by a, that of BX by b, the amount of radioactive ion in compound AX^* by x, the amount of radioactive ion in compound BX^* by y, and the rate constant by R', the rate equation may be written as follows:

$$\frac{dx}{dt} = R'\left(\frac{y}{b} - \frac{x}{a}\right) = \frac{R'}{ab}(ay - bx) \tag{10-9}$$

Since the sum of the two activities is constant,

$$x + y = x_f + y_f$$

where the subscript denotes the conditions at equilibrium.

When equilibrium has been reached, the activities are uniformly exchanged. But $y_f/b = x_f/a$ and $y = x_f + (b/a)x_f - x$, and

$$\frac{x}{x_f} = \frac{a+b}{a} \frac{\text{act. in } C_4H_9I}{\text{act. in } C_4H_9I + \text{act. in NaI}}$$

Substituting and rearranging the rate equation, we have

$$\frac{dx}{x_f - x} = R' \frac{a+b}{ab} dt$$

On integrating and substituting the value of the integration constant for $t = 0$,

$$-\ln\left(1 - \frac{x}{x_f}\right) = R' \frac{a+b}{ab} t \qquad (10\text{-}10)$$

or expressing the activities as percentages and using common logarithms,

$$-\log\left(100 - 100\frac{x}{x_f}\right) = \frac{R'}{2.3} \frac{(a+b)}{ab} t \qquad (10\text{-}11)$$

The half-time of the reaction may be determined by plotting this equation on linear or semilog graph paper. One usually plots the term $\log(100 - 100x/x_f)$ as the ordinate and t as the abscissa. The velocity constant for a given temperature is given by the slope, denoted by $\boldsymbol{k}$.

If the experiment is carried out at two temperatures, the experimental activation energy ΔE may be calculated from the slopes of the respective curves k_1 and k_2 using the following equation:

$$\Delta E = 2.3R \frac{T_2 T_1}{T_2 - T_1} \log \frac{k_2}{k_1}$$

R in this instance is the universal gas constant of 1.98 cal/°K/mole. T_1 and T_2 are the temperatures of the two reactions in degrees absolute (degrees centigrade + 273).

Experiment 10-3
Distribution of Radioactive Phosphorus in a Rat (Wet-ashing and Liquid-counting Techniques)

This experiment is suitable for biological workers who are experienced in the dissection of the laboratory rat. Other animals or plants may be used since the wet-digestion technique and liquid counting are quite generally applicable. This particular experiment was used extensively by C. L. Comar in the Oak Ridge courses. Other radioactive isotopes may be used if the beta-ray energy is sufficiently high so that undue losses in the liquid-counting system are not realized or if gamma-detection equipment is available.

Apparatus and Materials

Standard detection apparatus (G-M, scintillation counter, or Landsverk electrometer)
Stand for holding 10-cm petri dish or other container at suitable distance from detector
Roller-Smith balance (or other simple balance) of about 1 g capacity
One balance of about 300 g capacity
One laboratory rat (other animal or plant which has been given P^{32})
Hypodermic needle and 1-ml syringe
Suitable scalpels and other surgical instruments
Five 50-ml graduated cylinders
Five 10-ml pipettes
Five 50-ml beakers
Five 10-ml petri dishes (10 cm diameter)
Electric hot plate
Chloroform
Concentrated HNO_3
P^{32} in physiological saline solution (concentration about 20 mc/ml)
P^{32} standard solutions (concentrations of about 10,000 cpm/ml)

Procedure

Calibration of Liquid-counting Samples (Self-absorption Curve). The counting arrangement is calibrated prior to the experiment by adding a known amount of activity to varying amounts (10 ml, 20 ml, etc.) of water in the petri dish. A self-absorption curve is plotted as counts per minute vs. concentration. A modification of this technique is to add the radioactive solution (in the amounts to be injected into the rat later) to various volumes of water. Ten milliliters of each of the dilutions is counted in the petri dish. A curve is plotted of the percentage of the administered dose against counts per minute. [See Comar (23), pp. 176–177.]

Injection and Dissection of Rat. Weigh the rat to the nearest gram. Inject 0.5 ml of the radioactive solution intramuscularly into the left hind leg. After the designated time (½ hr or less, although different times are recommended for each student if more than one rat is used), the rat is sacrificed with chloroform. Tissues from five organs are removed, taking care to avoid contamination from the site of injection. Suggested organs are brain, femur, liver, kidney, and a smooth muscle such as the gastrocnemius.

Samples (not over 1 g each) are weighed on the Roller-Smith balance and placed in separate beakers. Cover the samples with concentrated HNO_3 in a hood, and heat gently until the tissue is dissolved. Make up to 50 ml in a graduated cylinder, mix, and pipette 10 ml into the petri dish for counting. Count each sample, being careful to remove rubber gloves when handling the counting setup, and avoid spilling solution on the detector or counting stand.

Analysis of Data

From information given by the instructor and from values derived from calibration curves, calculate the following:

1. Activity administered to the rat (microcuries)
2. Weight of phosphorus administered to the rat (micrograms)
3. Concentration in rat (per cent of dose per gram of fresh tissue based on 300-g rat)
4. Specific activity in rat (per cent of dose per milligram of phosphorus based on 300-g rat)

Use average analytical values given below:

Organ	*P, mg/g freshly cut tissue*
Brain	2.0
Femur	100.0
Liver	3.1
Kidney	2.5
Gastrocnemius muscle	1.6

Experiment 10-4
Analysis by Radioactivation

The details of this experiment will of necessity vary depending on the type of equipment available. The activation device may be a nuclear reactor, although a cyclotron or other accelerator can be used if the proper cross-section or excitation-function values are known. Although it is possible to perform the experiment as an analytical procedure for a trace element, the experiment is frequently simplified by irradiating an unknown weight of a pure element or compound. A common variation of the experiment is to make an identification of the material from its radiation characteristics as well as to determine its weight. (See Expt. 9-4.) The experiment may also be performed using the "relative" method.

Apparatus and Materials

Nuclear-activating device such as reactor or other thermal-neutron source

A selection of chemical glassware for making proper dilutions

A selection of micropipettes and syringes

Sample cards on which to mount either thin plastic or thick silver sample holders
RaD-E-F standard (NBS standard or secondary standard)
Samples of a suitable element or compound for activation [e.g., MnO_2, $NaCl$, NH_4Br, In, $Ba(NO_3)_2$, $La(NO_3)_3$, $Cu(NO_3)_2$, KCl, As_2O_3, Zn]
Detection equipment (beta or beta and gamma)
Gamma standards (if gamma spectrometer is used)
Shielding
Remote-handling equipment

Procedure

The procedure consists in activating a sample and then determining the half-lives, the beta energies, the gamma energies, and an absolute measure of the disintegration rate of the samples. To make this determination, the sample is placed in the thermal-neutron field and the time is noted. Likewise, the time of removal is recorded. The sample is then monitored and transferred to the laboratory as soon as possible using whatever safety procedures are indicated by the radiation level of the source. The sample is dissolved as rapidly as possible in an appropriate solvent (water, HCl, or NaOH may be tried in order). Several aliquots (10, 20, 50, 100, and 1,000 μl) should be made up to have samples of different counting rates in order to have sufficiently strong sources to measure on the second or third day. Samples should be prepared as rapidly as possible to obtain one which can be used to determine the presence of very-short-lived radioactivity. If such a short-lived activity is observed, an attempt should be made to obtain an approximation of a beta absorption curve in order to make an estimate of its beta-ray energy. A gamma-ray spectrum should be made if possible. It is probable that such short-lived components will have complicated decay schemes and the information will be somewhat difficult to correlate. The decay data should be plotted as soon as they are taken in order to ascertain the portions of the curve corresponding to single components.

During each of these periods, absorption measurements and spectrometric measurements should be taken in order to have beta- and gamma-ray-energy values corresponding to each of the half-lives which will be determined, after the over-all curve has been resolved into its components. The time at which each measurement is made should be noted in the data record so that corrections can be made for decay as the energy measurements are made. If the sample is decaying rapidly, a good technique is to start with the thicker absorbers first in taking an absorption curve. In this way the lower portion of the curve will have better statistical accuracy.

If possible, it is also desirable to prepare a sample for absolute measurement during each of the periods when the decay curve is not changing rapidly. These measurements are frequently made according to the procedure in Expt. 7-2, although any type of absolute measurement can be performed.

Analysis Data

The decay data are first plotted and the half-lives of the various components determined by the resolution of the semilogarithmic curve (see Expt. 8-4). The absorption curves are plotted for the various components after making proper corrections for decay during the absorption measurements. Feather analysis (see Expt. 6-1) is performed on each component, and an estimate of the maximum beta-ray energy corresponding to each half-life is made. The gamma-ray spectra are likewise plotted for each half-life. From this information it should be possible to determine the beta-ray maximum energy and gamma-ray energies corresponding to each radioactive element in the sample. The gamma-ray spectra are usually much more reliable than the beta-ray-energy values, although valuable information may be gained from the beta-ray curves. The identification of the unknown material may be made by using the various tables and charts mentioned in Expt. 9-4.

For a quantitative measure of the activity it is usually better to make calculations for each of the half-lives even though the half-life values seem to arise from the same element. This permits a check on the calculations and plotting of the data. Proper corrections are made for all the factors outlined in Chap. 7, and an absolute measure of the radioactivity in the original sample at the time of removal from the reactor is calculated. The weight of the substance giving rise to the particular radioactivity studies is given by Eq. (10-2). The weight may be reported as grams of element or as the weight of the compound, if it has been identified.

If the sample being studied consists of a mixture of known elements in unknown amounts, the comparative method may be used. Equation (10-3) then applies. If time permits, a sample of the material may be analyzed qualitatively first and a second sample may then be analyzed quantitatively by the comparative method.

Experiment 10-5
Determination of the Solubility of a Slightly Soluble Substance

The use of radioisotopes in the determination of the solubility of a slightly soluble substance represents one of the early classical tracer applications of radioisotopes. In this experiment the principle of the method is illustrated for the case of lead iodide, PbI_2, labeled with I^{131}.

Briefly, the solubility is determined by comparing the activity of an aliquot of a saturated solution of a slightly soluble, labeled substance with that of a known weight of the labeled material. All radioactivity measurements are made under conditions as nearly identical as possible. For I^{131} the material may be beta- or gamma-counted. The latter type of measurement is conveniently carried out with a well-type scintillation counter.

The solubility of PbI_2 is 44.2 mg/100 g of water at 0°C and 436 mg at 100°C.

As an alternative slightly soluble substance, $MgNH_4PO_4 \cdot 6H_2O$ labeled with P^{32} can serve to illustrate the method. For the preparation of pure $MgNH_4PO_4 \cdot 6H_2O$, see Kolthoff and Sandell.*

Apparatus and Materials

- Radiation-detection equipment
- Clinical centrifuge
- 40-ml centrifuge tube
- Micropipette and syringe or other control
- Volumetric pipettes and control
- Two 15-ml centrifuge tubes with tightly fitting stoppers or caps
- Test-tube racks or blocks
- Stirring rods
- Source-mounting materials
- Disposable tissue
- Radioactive-waste containers for I^{131} for solid and liquid
- Reagent solutions
  - Lead acetate, about 0.5 *M*
  - Glacial acetic acid
  - Potassium iodide, about 0.5 *M*
  - I^{131} tracer
- Optional: constant-temperature bath or suitable means for controlling the temperature of the samples; solutions of foreign and complexing ions

Procedure

Preparation of Labeled PbI_2. To a 40-ml centrifuge tube add 5 ml of KI solution, I^{131} tracer (sufficient to provide 500 to 1,000 cpm per aliquot of saturated solution), 25 ml of water, and 5 ml of glacial acetic acid. Evaluate the radiation hazard with a survey meter. After the solution has been mixed by stirring, add, with stirring, 6 ml of lead

* I. M. Kolthoff and E. B. Sandell, "Textbook of Quantitative Inorganic Analysis," 3d ed., chap. 22, Macmillan, New York, 1952.

acetate solution. Allow the precipitate to coagulate and settle to the bottom of the tube. Complete the phase separation by centrifugation. Decant the supernatant liquid into a properly labeled I^{131} liquid-waste container.

Transfer the precipitate to a 250-ml flask and add a minimum amount of water to dissolve the lead iodide at about 100°C. Cool the solution in an ice bath, allow the crystals to settle out, decant most of the liquid to the I^{131} waste bottle, and transfer the solid to a 40-ml centrifuge tube. After centrifugation and decantation of the liquid to the waste bottle, slurry the lead iodide with 10 to 15 ml of 95 per cent ethanol. Either filter off the solid and dry it on the filter or centrifuge the mixture, decant the ethanol into the waste bottle, and dry the solid in the tube.

Carefully transfer the solid to a weighing bottle (equipped with a female cap) or a screw-cap vial properly labeled to indicate the radioactivity of the contents. By means of a survey meter, evaluate the radiation hazard associated with handling the labeled PbI_2. Store the sample behind adequate shielding.

Measurement of Solubility. 1. DETERMINATION OF THE SPECIFIC ACTIVITY OF THE PbI_2. Label a cupped planchet and weigh it to the nearest 0.1 mg on an analytical balance. Add 10 to 20 mg of labeled PbI_2 and determine the exact amount. Add a few drops of water, slurry the solid to distribute it evenly on the bottom of the planchet, and finally dry the source slowly under a heat lamp. Cover the deposit with a thin film of collodion. Measure the activity of the source as for the saturated-solution sources described below.

2. DETERMINATION OF THE ACTIVITY OF THE SATURATED SOLUTION. Transfer at least 10 mg (weighed approximately) of labeled PbI_2 to each of two 15-ml centrifuge tubes, and add 10 ml of distilled water. Heat the tubes briefly to about 50°C in a water bath. Stopper the tubes and shake the mixtures. Rubber gloves are recommended because of the chance of leakage around the stopper. Note the time when the samples are prepared. Agitate the samples periodically. The vessels may be stored at room temperature, or preferably in a thermostatted bath, particularly if the room temperature fluctuates rapidly. In the procedure described, a room temperature of about 25°C has been assumed. For higher temperatures larger quantities of PbI_2 must be taken, of course, to provide excess solid.

The approach to equilibrium (saturation) may be followed by periodically centrifuging the mixtures and withdrawing a sample, e.g., 1 ml, from each. The samples should be transferred to labeled cupped planchets, dried slowly, covered, and counted. If the approach to equilibrium is followed for more than a few hours, the sample of known weight should be counted each time to correct for decay of the I^{131}.

Analysis of Data

Determine the solubility and the solubility product of PbI_2 at the temperature of measurement. Discuss the agreement between results for the duplicate samples.

Additional samples may be prepared initially to show the effect of common ions, foreign ions, and complexing ions at various known concentrations on the solubility.

If facilities are available for determining the solubility at two temperatures, the heat of solution in calories per mole, ΔH_{sol}, may be calculated from the solubility S at each temperature by the equation

$$\log \frac{S_2}{S_1} = \frac{\Delta H_{sol}}{4.581} \frac{T_2 - T_1}{T_1 T_2}$$

where T_1 and T_2 are the absolute temperatures. In the derivation of this equation it is assumed that the heat of solution is constant over the range of temperature.

Experiment 10-6

Determination of the Specific Surface Area of an Insoluble Crystalline Substance by Isotope Exchange

When crystals of an insoluble substance are contacted with a saturated solution of the substance, there is a rapid exchange of ions between the surface of the solid and the solution. If the material in solution is initially labeled with a radioisotope, the extent of exchange, which depends upon the surface area of the crystals, can be determined.* At steady state,

$$\frac{\text{Total radioactive atoms on surface}}{\text{Total radioactive atoms in solution}} = \frac{\text{total amount material on surface}}{\text{total amount material in solution}}$$

Among the many substances which can be used to illustrate the method are the sulfates of calcium, strontium, barium, and lead. Mixed solvent or even nonaqueous systems may also be used for solids which are relatively soluble in water.

Apparatus and Materials

Radiation-detection equipment

Two stoppered or capped bottles (or flasks or cylinders) having a volume in excess of 10 ml

Crystalline solid, e.g., $CaSO_4 \cdot 2H_2O$ or CaF_2

* F. Paneth, "Radio-elements as Indicators," McGraw-Hill, New York, 1928.

Saturated solution of substance containing tracer, e.g., Ca^{45}
Micropipette with control
Pipettes, 10 ml and 0.1 or 0.5 or 1.0 ml, with control
Heat lamp
Cupped planchets

Procedure

1. To a saturated solution (free of any solid phase) of the substance to be studied, add tracer to provide a satisfactory counting rate for an aliquot in the range 0.1 to 1.0 ml. Note that (*a*) the added tracer solution should be of high specific activity in order that the small volume required may cause negligible reduction in concentration of the unlabeled material, and (*b*) the added tracer must be in exactly the same chemical form as the unlabeled material.

After the solution has been thoroughly mixed, withdraw an aliquot and evaporate it to dryness in a cupped planchet. Determine the specific activity of the solution, e.g., in counts per minute per milliliter.

2. Transfer 0.5 to 1.0 g (or sufficient to result in a 40 to 60 per cent reduction in counting rate) of the crystalline material to each of two screw-cap bottles. Weigh the solid to the nearest milligram. Pipette 10.0 ml of labeled, saturated solution into the bottle, cap the bottle tightly, and shake the mixture vigorously for about 2 min. (Rubber gloves should be worn, particularly if glass-stoppered vessels are used.) After the solid has settled in one of the containers, transfer a portion of the liquid to a centrifuge tube and centrifuge it briefly to separate any suspended solid. Determine the specific activity of the supernatant liquid in the manner used for the labeled, saturated solution.

Shake the second container for an additional 2-min period and then proceed as for the first sample.

3. The following alternative procedure, based on a modification of (1) and (2) above, may be used if preferred. To the vessels containing the weighed solid, pipette 10.0 ml of unlabeled, saturated solution. Add, by means of a micropipette, a known amount of tracer, i.e., a known number of counts per minute based on assay by the counting procedure to be used for the aliquot of the equilibrated solution. The mixing and sampling steps are as for procedure 2.

Analysis of Data

From the radioactivity measurements and the known total amount of substance in solution (based on actual gravimetric analysis or taken as the tabulated solubility at the temperature of saturation), calculate (1) the weight of substance in the surface of the solid sample and (2) the number of molecules in the surface.

Using the known crystal structure of the substance or assuming the molecules to be cubic, calculate the area per molecule. For a cube,

$$\text{Area per molecule} = \left(\frac{\text{mol. wt}}{6.02 \times 10^{23}} \frac{1}{d}\right)^{2/3} \qquad \text{cm}^2$$

in terms of the molecular weight and the density d. The specific area in square centimeters per gram is the product of the number of molecules in the surface and the area per molecule divided by the weight of the sample. Depending upon the particular sample, a value of 10^4 to 10^5 cm^2/g may be expected.

Compare the results obtained with the two samples and discuss the factors which could affect the agreement. Predict the effect of prolonged equilibration.

Show how the calculations would be modified if an exchangeable nonisotopic tracer, e.g., Sr^{89}, were used to determine the surface area of a calcium salt.

Cited References

1. Meinke, W. W.: Review of Fundamental Developments in Analysis (from 1953 to date): Nucleonics, *Anal. Chem.*, vol. 28, pp. 736–756, April, 1956.
2. Meinke, W. W.: Nucleonics, *Anal. Chem.*, vol. 30, pp. 686–728, 1958.
3. Seaborg, G. T., and J. J. Livingood: Artificial Radioactivity as a Test for Minute Traces of Elements, *J. Am. Chem. Soc.*, vol. 60, pp. 1784–1786, August, 1938.
4. Clark, H. M., and R. T. Overman: Determination of Trace Amounts of Elements by Radioactivation Analysis, *U.S. Atomic Energy Comm. Rept.* MDDC-1329, 1947.
5. Boyd, G. E.: Method of Activation Analysis, *Anal. Chem.*, vol. 21, pp. 335–347, 1949.
6. Tobias, C. A., and R. W. Dunn: Analysis of Microcomposition of Biological Tissue by Means of Induced Radioactivity, *Science*, vol. 109, pp. 109–113, Feb. 4, 1949.
7. Smales, A. A.: The Scope of Radioactivation Analysis, *Atomics*, vol. 4, pp. 55–63, 74, March, 1953.
8. Leddicotte, G. W., and S. A. Reynolds: Activation Analysis with the Oak Ridge Reactor, *Nucleonics*, vol. 8, no. 3, pp. 62–65, 78, March, 1951.
9. Brooksbank, W. A., G. W. Leddicotte, and H. A. Mahlman: Analysis for Trace Impurities by Neutron Activation, *J. Phys. Chem.*, vol. 57, pp. 815–819, November, 1953.
10. Leddicotte, G. W., and S. A. Reynolds: Neutron Activation Analysis: A Useful Analytical Method for Determination of Trace Elements, *U.S. Atomic Energy Comm. Rept.* AECD-3489, 1953.
11. Clark, H. M., and D. E. Neil: Radionuclides Arranged According to Half-life, *U.S. Atomic Energy Comm. Rept.* AECU-3144, 1955.
12. "Nuclear Data Sheets," National Academy of Sciences–National Research Council, Washington (available on subscription).
13. Gest, H., M. D. Kamen, and J. M. Reiner: The Theory of Isotope Dilution, *Arch. Biochem.*, vol. 12, pp. 273–281, February, 1947.

14. Radin, N. S.: Isotope Techniques in Biochemistry. I, *Nucleonics*, vol. 1, no. 1, pp. 24–33, September, 1947; II, vol. 1, no. 2, pp. 48–59, October, 1947; V, vol. 2, no. 2, pp. 33–45, February, 1948.
15. Pinajian, J. J., J. E. Christian, and W. E. Wright: The Isotope Dilution Procedure of Analysis. I, Historical and Literature Survey, *J. Am. Pharm. Assoc., Sci. Ed.*, vol. 42, pp. 301–304, May, 1953.
16. Christian, J. E., and J. J. Pinajian: The Isotope Dilution Procedure of Analysis. II, Procedure, *J. Am. Pharm. Assoc., Sci. Ed.*, vol. 42, pp. 304–307, May, 1953.
17. Rosenblum, C.: Applications of Radioisotope Techniques, in J. R. Bradford (ed.), "Radioisotopes in Industry," pp. 87–117, Reinhold, New York, 1953.
18. Mayor, R. H., and C. J. Collins: The Use of Double Dilution for the Simultaneous Determination of Yield and Activity of Radioactive Compounds, *J. Am. Chem. Soc.*, vol. 73, pp. 471–472, January, 1951.
19. Faul, H. (ed.): "Nuclear Geology," Wiley, New York, 1954.
20. Kohman, T. P., and N. Saito: Radioactivity in Geology and Cosmology, *Ann. Rev. Nuclear Sci.*, vol. 4, pp. 401–462, 1954.
21. Libby, W. F.: "Radiocarbon Dating," 2d ed., University of Chicago Press, Chicago, 1955.
22. Arnold, J. R.: Scintillation Counting of Natural Radiocarbon. I, The Counting Method, *Science*, vol. 119, pp. 155–157, Jan. 29, 1954.
23. Comar, C. L.: "Radioisotopes in Biology and Agriculture," McGraw-Hill, New York, 1955.
24. Fluharty, R.: Tracer Experiments, in J. R. Bradford (ed.), "Radioisotopes in Industry," pp. 191–226, Reinhold, New York, 1953.
25. Schweitzer, G. K., and M. Jackson: Radiocolloids, *U.S. Atomic Energy Comm. Rept.* ORO-48, n.d.
26. Wahl, A. C., and N. A. Bonner (eds.): "Radioactivity Applied to Chemistry," Wiley, New York, 1951.
27. "The Isotope Index: The Complete Purchasing Guide to the Isotopes," Scientific Equipment Company, Indianapolis, Ind.

Supplementary References

Albert, P., M. Caron, and G. Chaudron: Analyse des traces de Na, Cu, et des terres rares dans l'aluminium de haute pureté par la méthode d'activation à la pile, *Compt. rend.*, vol. 233, pp. 1108–1110, November, 1951.

Alpher, R. A., and R. C. Herman: Theory of the Origin and Relative Abundance Distribution of the Elements, *Revs. Modern Phys.*, vol. 22, pp. 153–212, April, 1950.

——— and ———: The Primeval Lead Isotopic Abundances and the Age of the Earth's Crust, *Phys. Rev.*, vol. 84, pp. 1111–1114, Dec. 15, 1951.

Anderson, E. C., and W. F. Libby: World-wide Distribution of Natural Radiocarbon, *Phys. Rev.*, vol. 81, pp. 64–72, Jan. 1, 1951.

Bloch, K., and H. S. Anker: An Extension of the Isotope Dilution Method, *Science*, vol. 107, p. 228, Feb. 27, 1948.

Keston, A. F., S. Udenfriend, and R. K. Cannan: A Method for the Determination of Organic Compounds in the Form of Isotopic Derivatives. I, Estimation of Amino Acids by the Carrier Technique, *J. Am. Chem. Soc.*, vol. 71, pp. 249–257, January, 1949.

Kulp, J. L., and L. E. Tryon: Extension of the Carbon 14 Age Method, *Rev. Sci. Instr.*, vol. 23, pp. 296–297, June, 1952.

Meinke, W. W., and R. E. Anderson: Activation Analysis Using Low Level Neutron Sources, *Anal. Chem.*, vol. 25, pp. 778–783, May, 1953.

——— and ———: Activation Analysis of Several Rare Earth Elements: A Comparison with Spectrophotometric Procedures, *Anal. Chem.*, vol. 26, pp. 907–909, May, 1954.

——— and R. S. Maddock: Neutron Activation Cross-section Graphs, *Anal. Chem.*, vol. 29, pp. 1171–1174, 1957.

Moore, F. D.: Determination of Total Body Water and Solids with Isotopes, *Science*, vol. 104, pp. 157–160, Aug. 16, 1946.

Pitzer, K. S.: Carbon Isotope Effect on Reaction Rates, *J. Chem. Phys.*, vol. 17, pp. 1341–1342, December, 1949.

Rittenberg, D., and G. L. Foster: A New Procedure for Quantitative Analysis by Isotopic Dilution, with Application to the Determination of Amino Acids and Fatty Acids, *J. Biol. Chem.*, vol. 133, pp. 737–744, 1940.

Rona, E., L. O. Gilpatrick, and L. M. Jeffrey: Uranium Determination in Sea Water, *Trans. Am. Geophys. Union*, vol. 37, pp. 697–701, December, 1956.

Ropp, G. A., and O. K. Neville: Review of the Uses of Isotopic Carbon in Organic Chemical Research. Dilution Method Analysis, *Nucleonics*, vol. 9, no. 2, pp. 33–36, August, 1951.

Suess, H. E.: Natural Radiocarbon Measurements by Acetylene Counting, *Science*, vol. 120, pp. 5–7, July 2, 1954.

Weigl, J. W., and M. Calvin: An Isotope Effect in Photosynthesis, *J. Chem. Phys.*, vol. 17, p. 210, February, 1949.

Yankwich, P. E., and M. Calvin: Effect of Isotopic Mass on the Rate of a Reaction Involving Carbon-Carbon Bond, *J. Chem. Phys.*, vol. 17, pp. 109–110, January, 1949.

Problems

1. The following observations were made on the quantity Q as the variable v was changed:

Q	v	Q	v	Q	v
95.0	0	44.1	5	20.0	10
81.8	1	37.6	6	17.1	11
69.9	2	32.2	7	14.8	12
60.0	3	27.4	8	12.6	13
51.5	4	23.4	9	10.8	14

Plot these values as follows:

(*a*) Q versus v on linear graph paper.
(*b*) $\ln Q$ versus v on linear graph paper.
(*c*) $\log Q$ versus v on linear graph paper.
(*d*) Q versus v on semilog graph paper.

The above data could be represented by the equation $Q = Q_0 \exp(-cv)$, where Q_0 is the value of Q at $v = 0$, the exponent is the base of the natural logarithms, and c is a constant.

(*e*) Determine the value of c for the above data and describe its significance.

2. (*a*) Calculate the velocity of a 3.32-Mev alpha particle.

(*b*) Calculate the wavelength of a 4.4-ev photon.

(*c*) Calculate the wavelength of light that has just sufficient energy to remove a photoelectron from the surface of a clean piece of metallic sodium (work function $= 3 \times 10^{-12}$ erg). If the sodium is illuminated with light of wavelength 2,537 A, what is the maximum velocity of the ejected photoelectrons?

3. What isotope is formed in each of the following reactions? Indicate whether it is stable or radioactive.

$Mg^{24}(n,\gamma)$ ———
$S^{32}(p,n)$ ———
$Fe^{56}(d,2n)$ ———
$Ti^{48}(\alpha,p)$ ———
$Bi^{209}(\alpha,6p7n)$———

4. In the reaction $N^{14}(n,p)C^{14}$ the masses of the particles are given as follows:

N^{14}	14.00752	p^1	1.00813
n^1	1.00897	C^{14}	14.00768

Is the reaction exoergic or endoergic, and by how much energy in Mev?

5. Construct a possible decay scheme for the following decay data:

Isotope	$T_{1/2}$, hr	Radiation	Mev	Branching, %
Ni^{65}	2.56	β_1	0.60	29
		β_2	1.01	14
		β_3	2.10	57
		γ_1	0.37	29
		γ_2	1.12	43
		γ_3	1.49	29

6. From *NBS Circular* 499 or other sources obtain the following information for Mn^{56} and As^{74}:

(*a*) What are the types of radiation emitted, and how many of each per disintegration?

(*b*) What is the energy of each of these radiations?

(*c*) In what per cent of the disintegrations is each of these present?

(*d*) To what do these isotopes decay?

(*e*) What are their half-lives?

(*f*) Is X radiation emitted?

(*g*) How can these isotopes be produced?

7. Calculate the current produced in an air ionization chamber by 500 α particles per second if the α energy is 4.5 Mev. Assume that all the energy is dissipated within the chamber and that all ions are collected.

8. A total of 100 r full scale is to be read on an ionization chamber. The capacitance of the chamber is 4×10^{-10} farad, and full-scale deflection corresponds to a 50-volt drop across electrodes of the ionization chamber. What should the chamber volume be to satisfy these conditions?

9. Calculate the change in voltage across a 10^{-11}-farad parallel-plate air chamber when all the ion pairs formed by a 5-Mev α particle are collected.

10. Suppose a proportional counter which has a gas amplification factor of 10^5 at the operating voltage is to be used for measuring 5-Mev α particles. What is the theoretical number of these α particles that can be counted with this counter? Assume a filling of methyl alcohol and argon with partial pressures of 1 and 9 cm Hg respectively. Counter volume $= 100$ cm^3.

11. Why is there a saturation phenomenon in both backscattering (activity vs. thickness of backing material) curves and self-absorption (activity vs. weight of sample at constant specific activity) curves?

12. Why is no saturation observed in a self-absorption curve of activity vs. thickness of sample at constant total activity?

13. An investigator has an absorption curve for a beta-ray-emitting sample of unknown energy and finds that the counting rate drops by approximately half at the following density-thickness values: 100, 190, 280, 370, 460, 550. If he assumes that the transmission factor of one-half represents one-tenth of the range, what is the estimated β energy of the unknown?

14. Cesium^{137} has a 0.661-Mev γ ray associated with its decay scheme. What should be the energy of the 180° backscattered Compton photon?

15. An experiment is performed to determine the relationship between half-thickness and energy for γ rays. The experiment is performed in two ways:

(*a*) With absorbers halfway between the detector and a collimated γ-ray source, which are 1 m apart.

(*b*) With the source and detector as close together as possible with absorbers placed between.

Explain the differences in the resulting half-thickness-vs.-energy curves.

16. A Geiger counter has a resolving time of 300 μsec. What is the true counting rate if the observed counting rate is 60,000 cpm? What is the upper limit of the count rate for not more than 1 per cent coincidence loss?

17. An average value for a series of observations is 20. What is the probability that a value of 16 will occur for the next observation assuming (*a*) a Gaussian or normal distribution, (*b*) a Poisson distribution?

18. The counting rate of a sample plus the background is about four times the background rate, and it is desired to determine the activity of the sample with 20 min counting. How must time be distributed between the counting of the background and that of background plus sample in order that the error in determining the sample activity may be a minimum?

19. In Prob. 18 the fractional standard deviation is desired to be (*a*) 0.10 and (*b*) 0.01. How long should the sample be counted if the background is 30 cpm?

20. If two values are 74.3 ± 0.8 and $19.2 \pm 0.6\ \sigma$, give the result and the error in the result if they are (*a*) added, (*b*) subtracted, (*c*) multiplied, and (*d*) divided.

21. Ten 1-min counts were made with these results: 2,046, 2,105, 2,011, 2,072, 2,014, 2,037, 2,043, 2,141, 2,021, and 2,010. Calculate the standard deviation and compare with the square root of the average value.

22. In the series of values given in Prob. 21, should any of these values be rejected on the basis of being suspiciously large? If so, which ones?

23. Calculate the numerical relation between the decay constant and the "third life" (i.e., the time required to reduce the activity to one-third of its original value)?

24. If one has 1 mc of two isotopes of approximately the same atomic weight differing in half-life, which will weigh more, the short or the long-lived activity?

25. If 1 mc each of two isotopes with the same decay scheme but different half-lives is injected in an animal, which would give the greater total radiation dose? Assume that each has the same residence time in the animal.

26. Why is it not possible to determine a universal conversion factor between the number of milliroentgens per hour at a given distance and the number of millicuries in a radioactive source?

27. Explain the use of a reference source in correcting the following data:

Sample count	*Reference source count*
1,482	5,091
1,692	5,202
1,513	5,109
1,612	5,197

What is the average sample count, corrected for variations in counter response?

28. Two isotopes, emitting fairly weak betas, are to be counted. One of the isotopes has sufficient energy to count satisfactorily in a thin-end-window G-M tube. Its half-life is 2½ years. The other isotope's half-life is 11 months. Would you expect it to count satisfactorily in the same setup?

29. A 10-λ aliquot of an iodine sample is placed in a watch glass, dried, and counted. Its count measures 12,000 cpm on an end-window proportional counter; 100 λ of the sample is placed in a 100-ml volumetric flask and filled to the mark with appropriate diluting solution. A 1-ml aliquot is placed in a stainless-steel counting cup, dried, and counted in the same counter at the same geometry. Do you expect to get a count of 1,200 cpm? If not, do you expect a count greater or less than 1,200 cpm?

30. An iodine-131 standard solution is obtained from the National Bureau of Standards. The following information is supplied concerning the solution: Assay of iodine 131, 0800 hours, Jan. 1 $= 2.09 \times 10^4$ dps/ml $\pm$ 2 per cent.

On Jan. 15, at 0800 hours, a sample of iodine 131 is counted in your laboratory. This sample has been obtained from a shipment in the following way: 20 λ of the shipment was diluted in a volumetric flask to 25 ml; 100 λ of this solution is in turn diluted to 10 ml; 50 λ of this solution is withdrawn, mounted on polystyrene, dried, and counted. The activity so measured is 4,280 cpm (corrected for background).

At the same time (0800 hours, Jan. 15) a 50-λ sample of the NBS standard iodine solution, mounted, dried, and counted in the same manner, is assayed. Its activity measures 1,213 cpm.

(*a*) What is the specific activity, in millicuries per milliliter, of the iodine-131 shipment at the time measured?

(*b*) What is the "geometry," or counting yield, in per cent, of the particular counting arrangement used for iodine 131 mounted on polystyrene?

31. In the reaction $AX + BX^* = AX^* + BX$, if the initial concentration of the isotope X^* is expressed as 100 per cent, the mole concentration of AX is 0.02 mole/liter, and that of BX is 0.04 mole/liter, what per cent of the isotope will be transferred from BX^* to AX (*a*) at the end of the reaction, (*b*) at the half-time?

32. Explain the reason for the different results obtained in the following experiments:

(*a*) When surviving liver slices of rat liver were incubated in Krebs saline solution containing S^{35}-labeled methionine, it was found that about 1 per cent methionine sulfur was replaced during the time of the experiment (2 hr). Homogenization of the tissue and inactivation of the enzyme reduced the uptake of labeled methionine to a very low value.

(*b*) A similar experiment was carried out with rat liver slices and labeled cystine. (1) Liver slices were incubated with saline solution containing S^{35}. (2) Tissue samples were first homogenized, and labeled cystine was added afterward. Both resulted in an equal uptake of S^{35} by the protein.

33. Given a flux of 10^{12} neutrons/cm^2/sec, what would be the specific activity of iridium after an irradiation of 1 week? Consider the formation of the 19-hr and 74-day activities.

34. Calculate the weight of bromine impurity in a reagent from its Br^{82} isotope, produced by neutron irradiation with a flux of 10^{12} neutrons/cm^2/sec. The activity of the radioisotope is 60 cps and the counting yield in the G-M tube is 8 per cent. The sample was irradiated for 40 hr and counted immediately.

35. Total fatty acids of two rat carcasses were hydrolyzed, two aliquots were taken, and the total deuteropalmitic acid, containing 21.5 per cent deuterium, was added.

Total fatty acids, g	Palmitic acid added, g	Deuterium content of samples isolated, %
14.641	0.2163	1.28
14.135	0.1757	1.28

Calculate the palmitic acid content in per cent.

36. A shipment contains 20 mc of radioactive I^{131} in a volume of 1 ml. It is necessary to prepare a sample counting approximately 5,000 cpm for assay. Enumerate the steps required in making the dilutions if the counting yield of the detector is 8 per cent. The glassware which is available consists of 10-, 20-, and 50-λ micropipettes; 1-, 2-, 5-, and 10-ml pipettes; and 10-, 50-, and 100-ml volumetric flasks. The final volume to be deposited on the sample mount should not be more than 50 λ.

Appendix A

Tables of Negative Exponential Functions

Table A-1
Selected Exponential Functions

x	e^{-x}	x	e^{-x}
0.05	0.951	1.3	0.272
0.10	0.904	1.4	0.247
0.15	0.861	1.5	0.223
0.20	0.819	1.6	0.202
0.25	0.779	1.7	0.183
0.30	0.741	1.8	0.165
0.35	0.705	1.9	0.150
0.40	0.670	2.0	0.135
0.45	0.638	2.2	0.111
0.50	0.607	2.4	0.091
0.55	0.577	2.6	0.074
0.60	0.549	2.8	0.061
0.65	0.522	3.0	0.050
0.70	0.497	3.5	0.030
0.75	0.472	4.0	0.018
0.80	0.449	4.5	0.011
0.85	0.427	5.0	0.007
0.90	0.407	5.5	0.004
0.95	0.387	6.0	0.0025
1.00	0.368	6.5	0.0015
1.1	0.333	7.0	0.0009
1.2	0.301		

For small values of x, e^{-x} approaches $1 - x$.

TABLE A-2

EXPONENTIAL FUNCTIONS FOR SELECTED RATIOS

q/Q (e.g., fractions of half-life or half-thickness)	$e^{-0.693q/Q}$	$1 - e^{-0.693q/Q}$
0.1	0.933	0.067
0.2	0.870	0.130
0.3	0.811	0.189
0.4	0.758	0.242
0.5	0.705	0.295
0.6	0.659	0.341
0.7	0.615	0.385
0.8	0.573	0.427
0.9	0.534	0.466
1.0	0.500	0.500
1.1	0.466	0.534
1.2	0.435	0.565
1.3	0.406	0.594
1.4	0.379	0.621
1.5	0.353	0.647
1.6	0.330	0.670
1.7	0.307	0.693
1.8	0.287	0.713
1.9	0.267	0.733
2.0	0.250	0.750
2.5	0.177	0.823
3.0	0.125	0.875
3.5	0.088	0.912
4.0	0.062	0.938
5.0	0.031	0.969
6.0	0.016	0.984
7.0	0.0078	0.9922
8.0	0.0038	0.9962
9.0	0.0019	0.9981
10.0	0.0009	0.9991

Appendix B

Multiplication Tables

SCALE OF 64

	0	1	2	3	4	5	6	7	8	9
0	0	64	128	192	256	320	384	448	512	576
10	640	704	768	832	896	960	1,024	1,088	1,152	1,216
20	1,280	1,344	1,408	1,472	1,536	1,600	1,664	1,728	1,792	1,856
30	1,920	1,984	2,048	2,112	2,176	2,240	2,304	2,368	2,432	2,496
40	2,560	2,624	2,688	2,752	2,816	2,880	2,944	3,008	3,072	3,136
50	3,200	3,264	3,328	3,392	3,456	3,520	3,584	3,648	3,712	3,776
60	3,840	3,904	3,968	4,032	4,096	4,160	4,224	4,288	4,352	4,416
70	4,480	4,544	4,608	4,672	4,736	4,800	4,864	4,928	4,992	5,056
80	5,120	5,184	5,248	5,312	5,376	5,440	5,504	5,568	5,632	5,696
90	5,760	5,824	5,888	5,952	6,016	6,080	6,144	6,208	6,272	6,336
100	6,400	6,464	6,528	6,592	6,656	6,720	6,784	6,848	6,912	6,976
110	7,040	7,104	7,168	7,232	7,296	7,360	7,424	7,488	7,552	7,616
120	7,680	7,744	7,808	7,872	7,936	8,000	8,064	8,128	8,192	8,256
130	8,320	8,384	8,448	8,512	8,576	8,640	8,704	8,768	8,832	8,896
140	8,960	9,024	9,088	9,152	9,216	9,280	9,344	9,408	9,472	9,536
150	9,600	9,664	9,728	9,792	9,856	9,920	9,984	10,048	10,112	10,176
160	10,240	10,304	10,368	10,432	10,496	10,560	10,624	10,688	10,752	10,816
170	10,880	10,944	11,008	11,072	11,136	11,200	11,264	11,328	11,392	11,456
180	11,520	11,584	11,648	11,712	11,776	11,840	11,904	11,968	12,032	12,096

SCALE OF 256

	0	1	2	3	4	5	6	7	8	9
0	0	256	512	768	1,024	1,280	1,536	1,792	2,048	2,304
10	2,560	2,816	3,072	3,328	3,584	3,840	4,096	4,352	4,608	4,864
20	5,120	5,376	5,632	5,888	6,144	6,400	6,656	6,912	7,168	7,424
30	7,680	7,936	8,192	8,448	8,704	8,960	9,216	9,472	9,728	9,984
40	10,240	10,496	10,752	11,008	11,264	11,520	11,776	12,032	12,288	12,544
50	12,800	13,056	13,312	13,568	13,824	14,080	14,336	14,592	14,848	15,104
60	15,360	15,616	15,872	16,128	16,384	16,640	16,896	17,152	17,408	17,664
70	17,920	18,176	18,432	18,688	18,944	19,200	19,456	19,712	19,968	20,224
80	20,480	20,736	20,992	21,248	21,504	21,760	22,016	22,272	22,528	22,784
90	23,040	23,296	23,552	23,808	24,064	24,320	24,576	24,832	25,088	25,344
100	25,600	25,856	26,112	26,368	26,624	26,880	27,136	27,392	27,648	27,904
110	28,160	28,416	28,672	28,928	29,184	29,440	29,696	29,952	30,208	30,464
120	30,720	30,976	31,232	31,488	31,744	32,000	32,256	32,512	32,768	33,024
130	33,280	33,536	33,792	34,048	34,304	34,560	34,816	34,072	35,328	35,584
140	35,840	36,096	36,352	36,608	36,864	37,120	37,376	37,632	37,888	38,144
150	38,400	38,656	38,912	39,168	39,424	39,680	39,936	40,192	40,448	40,704
160	40,960	41,216	41,472	41,728	41,984	42,240	42,496	42,752	43,008	43,264
170	43,520	43,776	44,032	44,288	44,544	44,800	45,056	45,312	45,568	45,824
180	46,080	46,336	46,592	46,848	47,104	47,360	47,616	47,872	48,128	48,384

Appendix C

Logarithms to Base 10

Natural numbers	0	1	2	3	4	5	6	7	8	9	Proportional parts 1	2	3	4	5	6	7	8	9
10	0000	0043	0086	0128	0170	0212	0253	0294	0334	0374	4	8	12	17	21	25	29	33	37
11	0414	0453	0492	0531	0569	0607	0645	0682	0719	0755	4	8	11	15	19	23	26	30	34
12	0792	0828	0864	0899	0934	0969	1004	1038	1072	1106	3	7	10	13	17	21	24	28	31
13	1139	1173	1206	1239	1271	1303	1335	1367	1399	1430	3	6	10	13	16	19	23	26	29
14	1461	1492	1523	1553	1584	1614	1644	1673	1703	1732	3	6	9	12	15	18	21	24	27
15	1761	1790	1818	1847	1875	1903	1931	1959	1987	2014	3	6	8	11	14	17	20	22	25
16	2041	2068	2095	2122	2148	2175	2201	2227	2253	2279	3	5	8	11	13	16	18	21	24
17	2304	2330	2355	2380	2405	2430	2455	2480	2504	2529	2	5	7	10	12	15	17	20	22
18	2553	2577	2601	2625	2648	2672	2695	2718	2742	2765	2	5	7	9	12	14	16	19	21
19	2788	2810	2833	2856	2878	2900	2923	2945	2967	2989	2	4	7	9	11	13	16	18	20
20	3010	3032	3054	3075	3096	3118	3139	3160	3181	3201	2	4	6	8	11	13	15	17	19
21	3222	3243	3263	3284	3304	3324	3345	3365	3385	3404	2	4	6	8	10	12	14	16	18
22	3424	3444	3464	3483	3502	3522	3541	3560	3579	3598	2	4	6	8	10	12	14	15	17
23	3617	3636	3655	3674	3692	3711	3729	3747	3766	3784	2	4	6	7	9	11	13	15	17
24	3802	3820	3838	3856	3874	3892	3909	3927	3945	3962	2	4	5	7	9	11	12	14	16
25	3979	3997	4014	4031	4048	4065	4082	4099	4116	4133	2	3	5	7	9	10	12	14	15
26	4150	4166	4183	4200	4216	4232	4249	4265	4281	4298	2	3	5	7	8	10	11	13	15
27	4314	4330	4346	4362	4378	4393	4409	4425	4440	4456	2	3	5	6	8	9	11	13	14
28	4472	4487	4502	4518	4533	4548	4564	4579	4594	4609	2	3	5	6	8	9	11	12	14
29	4624	4639	4654	4669	4683	4698	4713	4728	4742	4757	1	3	4	6	7	9	10	12	13
30	4771	4786	4800	4814	4829	4843	4857	4871	4886	4900	1	3	4	6	7	9	10	11	13
31	4914	4928	4942	4955	4969	4983	4997	5011	5024	5038	1	3	4	6	7	8	10	11	12
32	5051	5065	5097	5092	5105	5119	5132	5145	5159	5172	1	3	4	5	7	8	9	11	12
33	5185	5198	5211	5224	5237	5250	5263	5276	5289	5302	1	3	4	5	6	8	9	10	12
34	5315	5328	5340	5353	5366	5378	5391	5403	5416	5428	1	3	4	5	6	8	9	10	11
35	5441	5453	5465	5478	5490	5502	5514	5527	5539	5551	1	2	4	5	6	7	9	10	11
36	5563	5575	5587	5599	5611	5623	5635	5647	5658	5670	1	2	4	5	6	7	8	10	11
37	5682	5694	5705	5717	5729	5740	5752	5763	5775	5780	1	2	3	5	6	7	8	9	10
38	5798	5809	5821	5832	5843	5855	5866	5877	5888	5899	1	2	3	5	6	7	8	9	10
39	5911	5922	5933	5944	5955	5966	5977	5988	5999	6010	1	2	3	4	5	7	8	9	10
40	6021	6031	6042	6053	6064	6075	6085	6096	6107	6117	1	2	3	4	5	6	8	9	10
41	6128	6138	6149	6160	6170	6180	6191	6201	6212	6222	1	2	3	4	5	6	7	8	9
42	6232	6243	6253	6263	6274	6284	6294	6304	6314	6325	1	2	3	4	5	6	7	8	9
43	6335	6345	6355	6365	6375	6385	6395	6405	6415	6425	1	2	3	4	5	6	7	8	9
44	6435	6444	6454	6464	6474	6484	6493	6503	6513	6522	1	2	3	4	5	6	7	8	9
45	6532	6542	6551	6561	6571	6580	6590	6599	6609	6618	1	2	3	4	5	6	7	8	9
46	6628	6637	6646	6656	6665	6675	6684	6693	6702	6712	1	2	3	4	5	6	7	7	8
47	6721	6730	6739	6749	6758	6767	6776	6785	6794	6803	1	2	3	4	5	5	6	7	8
48	6812	6821	6830	6839	6848	6857	6866	6875	6884	6893	1	2	3	4	4	5	6	7	8
49	6902	6911	6920	6928	6937	6946	6955	6964	6972	6981	1	2	3	4	4	5	6	7	8
50	6990	6998	7007	7016	7024	7033	7042	7050	7059	7067	1	2	3	3	4	5	6	7	8
51	7076	7084	7093	7101	7110	7118	7126	7135	7143	7152	1	2	3	3	4	5	6	7	8
52	7160	7168	7177	7185	7193	7202	7210	7218	7226	7235	1	2	2	3	4	5	6	7	7
53	7243	7251	7259	7267	7275	7284	7292	7300	7308	7316	1	2	2	3	4	5	6	6	7
54	7324	7332	7340	7348	7356	7364	7372	7380	7388	7396	1	2	2	3	4	5	6	6	7

LOGARITHMS TO BASE 10 (*Continued*)

Natural numbers	0	1	2	3	4	5	6	7	8	9	Proportional parts								
											1	2	3	4	5	6	7	8	9
55	7404	7412	7419	7427	7435	7443	7451	7459	7466	7474	1	2	2	3	4	5	5	6	7
56	7482	7490	7497	7505	7513	7520	7528	7536	7543	7551	1	2	2	3	4	5	5	6	7
57	7559	7566	7574	7582	7589	7597	7604	7612	7619	7627	1	2	2	3	4	5	5	6	7
58	7634	7642	7649	7657	7664	7672	7679	7686	7694	7701	1	1	2	3	4	4	5	6	7
59	7709	7716	7723	7731	7738	7745	7752	7760	7767	7774	1	1	2	3	4	4	5	6	7
60	7782	7789	7796	7803	7810	7818	7825	7832	7839	7846	1	1	2	3	4	4	5	6	6
61	7853	7860	7868	7875	7882	7889	7896	7903	7910	7917	1	1	2	3	4	4	5	6	6
62	7924	7931	7938	7945	7952	7959	7966	7973	7980	7987	1	1	2	3	3	4	5	6	6
63	7993	8000	8007	8014	8021	8028	8035	8041	8048	8055	1	1	2	3	3	4	5	5	6
64	8062	8069	8075	8082	8089	8096	8102	8109	8116	8122	1	1	2	3	3	4	5	5	6
65	8129	8136	8142	8149	8156	8162	8169	8176	8182	8189	1	1	2	3	3	4	5	5	6
66	8195	8202	8209	8215	8222	8228	8235	8241	8248	8254	1	1	2	3	3	4	5	5	6
67	8261	8267	8274	8280	8287	8293	8299	8306	8312	8319	1	1	2	3	3	4	5	5	6
68	8325	8331	8338	8344	8351	8357	8363	8370	8376	8382	1	1	2	3	3	4	4	5	6
69	8388	8395	8401	8407	8414	8420	8426	8432	8439	8445	1	1	2	2	3	4	4	5	6
70	8451	8457	8463	8470	8476	8482	8488	8494	8500	8506	1	1	2	2	3	4	4	5	6
71	8513	8519	8525	8531	8537	8543	8549	8555	8561	8567	1	1	2	2	3	4	4	5	5
72	8573	8579	8585	8591	8597	8603	8609	8615	8621	8627	1	1	2	2	3	4	4	5	5
73	8633	8639	8645	8651	8657	8663	8669	8675	8681	8686	1	1	2	2	3	4	4	5	5
74	8692	8698	8704	8710	8716	8722	8727	8733	8739	8745	1	1	2	2	3	4	4	5	5
75	8751	8756	8762	8768	8774	8779	8785	8791	8797	8802	1	1	2	2	3	3	4	5	5
76	8808	8814	8820	8825	8831	8837	8842	8848	8854	8859	1	1	2	2	3	3	4	5	5
77	8865	8371	8876	8882	8887	8893	8899	8904	8910	8915	1	1	2	2	3	3	4	4	5
78	8921	8927	8932	8938	8943	8949	8954	8960	8965	8971	1	1	2	2	3	3	4	4	5
79	8976	8982	8987	8993	8998	9004	9009	9015	9020	9026	1	1	2	2	3	3	4	4	5
80	9031	9036	9042	9047	9053	9058	9063	9069	9074	9079	1	1	2	2	3	3	4	4	5
81	9085	9090	9096	9101	9106	9112	9117	9122	9128	9133	1	1	2	2	3	3	4	4	5
82	9138	9143	9149	9154	9159	9165	9170	9175	9180	9186	1	1	2	2	3	3	4	4	5
83	9191	9196	9201	9206	9212	9217	9222	9227	9232	9238	1	1	2	2	3	3	4	4	5
84	9243	9248	9253	9258	9263	9269	9274	9279	9284	9289	1	1	2	2	3	3	4	4	5
85	9294	9299	9304	9309	9315	9320	9325	9330	9335	9340	1	1	2	2	3	3	4	4	5
86	9345	9350	9355	9360	9365	9370	9375	9380	9385	9390	1	1	2	2	3	3	4	4	5
87	9395	9400	9405	9410	9415	9420	9425	9430	9435	9440	0	1	1	2	2	3	3	4	4
88	9445	9450	9455	9460	9465	9469	9474	9479	9484	9489	0	1	1	2	2	3	3	4	4
89	9494	9499	9504	9509	9513	9518	9523	9528	9533	9538	0	1	1	2	2	3	3	4	4
90	9542	9547	9552	9557	9562	9566	9571	9576	9581	9586	0	1	1	2	2	3	3	4	4
91	9590	9595	9600	9605	9609	9614	9619	9624	9628	9633	0	1	1	2	2	3	3	4	4
92	9638	9643	9647	9652	9657	9661	9666	9671	9675	9680	0	1	1	2	2	3	3	4	4
93	9685	9689	9694	9699	9703	9708	9713	9717	9722	9727	0	1	1	2	2	3	3	4	4
94	9731	9736	9741	9745	9750	9754	9759	9763	9768	9773	0	1	1	2	2	3	3	4	4
95	9777	9782	9786	9791	9795	9800	9805	9809	9814	9818	0	1	1	2	2	3	3	4	4
96	9823	9827	9832	9836	9841	9845	9850	9854	9859	9863	0	1	1	2	2	3	3	4	4
97	9868	9872	9877	9881	9886	9890	9894	9899	9903	9908	0	1	1	2	2	3	3	4	4
98	9912	9917	9921	9926	9930	9934	9939	9943	9948	9952	0	1	1	2	2	3	3	4	4
99	9956	9961	9965	9969	9974	9978	9983	9987	9991	9996	0	1	1	2	2	2	3	3	4

Appendix D

Periodic Chart

In this periodic chart, mass numbers are indicated by brackets and the atomic numbers of unknown elements are enclosed in parentheses. Comparison of this periodic chart with others currently available will reveal certain differences which arise from a lack of general acceptance of the names and symbols for some of the elements. Well-known as well as newly discovered elements are involved. Examples are elements 18, 41, 74, 99, 101, and 102.

In addition, there is variation in the practice of listing atomic weights for radioactive elements. In some cases the mass number of the longest-lived isotope is used. It is also of interest to note that consideration is being given to the unification of atomic-weight scales. (See *Chem. Eng. News*, vol. 36, pp. 76–81, Sept. 8, 1958.)

For information on the discovery and properties of some of the new elements, see Symposium: The New Elements, *J. Chem. Educ.*, vol. 36, pp. 2–44, 1959; J. J. Katz and G. T. Seaborg, "The Chemistry of the Actinide Elements," Methuen, London, 1957; and G. T. Seaborg and J. J. Katz, "The Actinide Elements" (National Nuclear Energy Series, div. IV, vol. 14A), McGraw-Hill, New York, 1954.

Periodic Chart of the Elements

1 **H** 1.0080																	2 **He** 4.003
3 **Li** 6.940	4 **Be** 9.013											5 **B** 10.82	6 **C** 12.011	7 **N** 14.008	8 **O** 16.000	9 **F** 19.00	10 **Ne** 20.183
11 **Na** 22.991	12 **Mg** 24.32											13 **Al** 26.98	14 **Si** 28.09	15 **P** 30.975	16 **S** 32.066	17 **Cl** 35.457	18 **Ar** 39.944
19 **K** 39.100	20 **Ca** 40.08	21 **Sc** 44.96	22 **Ti** 47.90	23 **V** 50.95	24 **Cr** 52.01	25 **Mn** 54.94	26 **Fe** 55.85	27 **Co** 58.94	28 **Ni** 58.71	29 **Cu** 63.54	30 **Zn** 65.38	31 **Ga** 69.72	32 **Ge** 72.60	33 **As** 74.91	34 **Se** 78.96	35 **Br** 79.916	36 **Kr** 83.80
37 **Rb** 85.48	38 **Sr** 87.63	39 **Y** 88.92	40 **Zr** 91.22	41 **Nb** 92.91	42 **Mo** 95.95	43 **Tc** [99]	44 **Ru** 101.1	45 **Rh** 102.91	46 **Po** 106.4	47 **Ag** 107.88	48 **Cd** 112.41	49 **In** 114.82	50 **Sn** 118.70	51 **Sb** 121.76	52 **Te** 127.61	53 **I** 126.91	54 **Xe** 131.30
55 **Cs** 132.91	56 **Ba** 137.36	57–71 **La** series	72 **Hf** 178.50	73 **Ta** 180.95	74 **W** 183.86	75 **Re** 186.22	76 **Os** 190.2	77 **Ir** 192.2	78 **Pt** 195.09	79 **Au** 197.0	80 **Hg** 200.61	81 **Tl** 204.39	82 **Pb** 207.21	83 **Bi** 209.00	84 **Po** 210	85 **At** [210]	86 **Rn** 222
87 **Fr** [223]	88 **Ra** 226.03	89–103 **Ac** series	(104)	(105)	(106)												

Lanthanide series	57 **La** 138.92	58 **Ce** 140.13	59 **Pr** 140.92	60 **Nd** 144.27	61 **Pm** [145]	62 **Sm** 150.35	63 **Eu** 152.0	64 **Gd** 157.26	65 **Tb** 158.93	66 **Dy** 162.51	67 **Ho** 164.94	68 **Er** 167.27	69 **Tm** 168.94	70 **Yb** 173.04	71 **Lu** 174.99
Actinide series	89 **Ac** 227.04	90 **Th** 232.05	91 **Pa** 231.05	92 **U** 238.04	93 **Np** [237]	94 **Pu** [242]	95 **Am** [243]	96 **Cm** [247]	97 **Bk** [249]	98 **Cf** [251]	99 **E** [254]	100 **Fm** [253]	101 **Mv** [256]	102 **?**	(103)

Appendix E

Characteristic *K* X-ray Emission Energies*

Element	*Kev*	*Element*	*Kev*	*Element*	*Kev*
11 Na	1.04	37 Rb	13.4	62 Sm	40.2
12 Mg	1.26	38 Sr	14.2	63 Eu	41.7
13 Al	1.49	39 Y	15.0	64 Gd	43.0
14 Si	1.74	40 Zr	15.8	65 Tb	44.6
15 P	2.01	41 Nb	16.6	66 Dy	46.1
16 S	2.31	42 Mo	17.5	67 Ho	47.7
17 Cl	2.63	43 Tc	18.3	68 Er	49.2
19 K	3.32	44 Ru	19.3	69 Tm	50.8
20 Ca	3.70	45 Rh	20.2	70 Yb	52.6
21 Sc	4.09	46 Pd	21.2	71 Lu	54.1
22 Ti	4.52	47 Ag	22.2	72 Hf	55.8
23 V	4.96	48 Cd	23.2	73 Ta	57.6
24 Cr	5.41	49 In	24.2	74 W	59.3
25 Mn	5.90	50 Sn	25.3	75 Re	61.3
26 Fe	6.42	51 Sb	26.4	76 Os	63.2
27 Co	6.92	52 Te	27.5	77 Ir	64.9
28 Ni	7.51	53 I	28.7	78 Pt	67.0
29 Cu	8.05	55 Cs	31.1	79 Au	68.8
30 Zn	8.64	56 Ba	32.3	81 Tl	72.9
31 Ga	9.25	57 La	33.5	82 Pb	75.1
32 Ge	9.91	58 Ce	34.8	83 Bi	77.4
33 As	10.6	59 Pr	36.1	90 Th	93.9
34 Se	11.3	60 Nd	37.4	92 U	98.3
35 Br	11.9	61 Pm	38.8		

* From J. M. Cork (comp.), "Chemical Rubber Handbook," 40th ed.

Appendix F

Equipment and Materials Used for Experiments

TABLE F-1

DETECTION EQUIPMENT USED FOR EXPERIMENTS

Expt.	G-M counter	Window-less counter	Scintilla-tion counter	Spectrom-eter	Portable detector	Beta counter	Personnel monitor or films	Absorber mount
2-1								
2-2	x							x
2-3	x							
2-4		x						
2-5			x					
2-6								
3-1	x	x	x				x	
3-2	x	x	x					
3-3	x	x	x					
4-1					x			
4-2					x		x	
4-3					x			
5-1	x	x						
5-2								
5-3						x		
5-4								
6-1	x					x		x
6-2	x					x		x
6-3	x					x		x
6-4	x							x
6-5	x		x	x				
7-1	x					x		
7-2	x					x		x
7-3	x					x		x
7-4	x		x			x		
7-5					x		x	
7-6							x	
8-1	x	x	x	x				
8-2	x	x						
8-3	x	x						
8-4	x	x	x	x				
8-5	x	x	x	x				x
8-6	x	x						
8-7	x	x				x		
8-8	x	x				x		
9-1	x	x	x	x				x
9-2	x	x	x	x				
9-3	x	x						x
9-4	x	x	x	x				x
10-1	x	x				x		
10-2	x	x	x	x				
10-3	x	x				x		
10-4	x	x	x	x			x	x
10-5	x	x	x	x				
10-6	x	x	x					

TABLE F-2

CHEMICAL EQUIPMENT USED FOR EXPERIMENTS

Expt.	Source mounts	Analytical balance	Electrolysis apparatus	Filtration apparatus	Centrifuge	Micropipettes	Muffle furnace	Petri dishes	Films	Shielding
2-1										x
2-2	x									
2-3	x									
2-4	x									
2-5	x									
2-6	x								x	
3-1	x					x				
3-2	x					x				
3-3	x									
4-1						x				
4-2									x	
4-3									x	
5-1	x	x								
5-2	x	x	x				x			
5-3						x		x		
5-4										
6-1	x					x				
6-2	x					x				
6-3	x	x		x	x	x				
6-4	x					x				
6-5	x					x		x		
7-1	x		x			x				
7-2	x					x				
7-3	x					x				
7-4	x					x				
7-5										x
7-6									x	x
8-1	x					x				
8-2	x				x	x				
8-3	x			x	x	x				
8-4	x					x				
8-5	x				x	x				
8-6	x				x	x				
8-7	x	x								
8-8	x	x								
9-1	x				x	x				
9-2	x					x				
9-3						x			x	
9-4	x					x				
10-1	x	x		x	x	x				
10-2	x					x				
10-3	x	x				x		x		
10-4	x					x				x
10-5	x				x	x				
10-6	x				x	x				

TABLE F-3

REAGENTS AND RADIOISOTOPES USED FOR EXPERIMENTS

Expt.	Reagents	Radioisotopes (minimum or suggested)
2-1		Nonstandard and standard Co^{60} or I^{131}
2-2		RaD-E-F or U_3O_8
2-3		RaD-E-F
2-4		RaD-E-F or U_3O_8
2-5		Standard Co^{60}, I^{131}
2-6		P^{32}, RaD-E-F, or Co^{60}
3-1		P^{32} or RaD-E-F
3-2		R^{32} or RaD-E-F
3-3		U_3O_8 or RaD-E-F
4-1	Acid cleaners, detergents, "Radiac wash"	Na^{24}, Fe^{59}, I^{131}, P^{32}
4-2		P^{32}, Co^{60}, I^{131}
4-3		Co^{60}, Sb^{124}, or Ir^{192}
5-1		U_3O_8
5-2	HNO_3, NaF	U_3O_8
5-3		P^{32}
5-4	H_3PO_4, N_2, dry ice or liquid N_2, acetone	$BaC^{14}O_3$
6-1		
6-2		RaD-E-F, P^{32}, or Co^{60}
6-3	$BaCl_2$	$H_2S^{35}O_4$
6-4		Co^{60}
6-5		Cr^{51} and "unknown" energy
7-1	Ag powder, HCl	RaD-E-F
7-2		Standard RaD-E-F, standard Co^{60}
7-3	Ethyl ether, HCl, NH_4OH, I reducing solution	Standard RaD-E-F, I^{131}
7-4		Fe^{59}, standard Co^{60}
7-5		Standard 10 to 100 mg of Ra^{226} or Co^{60}
7-6		Standard 10 to 100 mg of Ra^{226} or Co^{60}
8-1		I^{131} or P^{32}
8-2	$Fe(NO_3)_3$, HCl, NH_4OH, $(NH_4)_2CO_3$	Uranyl nitrate
8-3	$Th(NO_3)_3$, acetone, $KMnO_4$, $Mn(NO_2)_3$, H_2O_2, NH_4OH, HNO_3	Uranyl nitrate
8-4		P^{32}-I^{131}, Na^{24}-Cl^{38}
8-5	H_2SO_4, HCl, NH_4OH, HNO_3, NH_4Cl, $BaCl_2$, $LaCl_3$	Ba^{140}-La^{140}

TABLE F-3

REAGENTS AND RADIOISOTOPES USED FOR EXPERIMENTS (*Continued*)

Expt.	Reagents	Radioisotopes (minimum or suggested)
8-6	HNO_3, $KBrO_3$, KIO_3, HCl, NH_4OH, NH_4NO_3, C_2H_5OH, acetone, ceric ammonium nitrate, $La(NO_3)_3$	Ce^{144}-Pr^{144}
8-7	$(NH_4)_2CO_3$, HCl, NH_4OH, NH_4NO_3, C_2H_5OH	Uranyl nitrate
8-8	KCl	
9-1	H_2SO_4, sodium phosphate, ammonium molybdate, ethyl acetate, NH_4OH	P^{32}
9-2	Dowex-1 resin, $CoCl_2$, $NiCl_2$, NH_4OH, HCl, dimethylglyoxime in C_2H_5OH	Co^{60}
9-3	HCl, *n*-butanol	Co^{60}, P^{32}
9-4	As required	As available
10-1	H_2SO_4 (known and unknown concentrations)	$H_2S^{35}O_4$
10-2	NaI, acetone, *n*-butyliodide	I^{131}
10-3	Laboratory animal, $CHCl_3$, HNO_3, saline solution	P^{32}
10-4	Sample for activation (MnO_2, NaCl, etc.)	Standard RaD-E-F, Co^{60}
10-5	Lead acetate, KI, glacial acetic acid	I^{131}
10-6	$CaSO_4 \cdot 2H_2O$	Ca^{45}

TABLE F-4

GENERAL LIST OF MATERIALS AND SUPPLIES FOR EXPERIMENTS

Standard chemical glassware
Pipettes and pipetters (e.g., propipette)
Infrared lamps and holders
Hot plates
Scissors
Forceps
Microscope slides
Cardboard
Plastic wrap (e.g., Saran)
Cellulose tape (e.g., Scotch brand)
Cement (e.g., Duco)
Aluminum foil
Meter sticks
Stirring rods
Separatory funnels
Graduated cylinders
Tongs
Wash bottles (glass or plastic)
Dry-cell batteries
Test-tube racks
Watch glasses
Assorted planchets and counting cups
Graph paper
- Linear (millimeter)
- Semilogarithmic, 1, 2, and 3 cycles; 10 and 12 divisions/in.

"French" drawing curves
Straightedges

Appendix G

Isotopic Thermal-neutron Activation Cross Sections*

Target isotope	Abundance, %	Half-life† of product isotope	Isotopic activation cross section for (η,γ) reaction, barns‡ or fermis
H^2	0.015	12.26 years	0.57 ± 0.01 mb
Li^7	92.48	0.841 sec	33 ± 5 mb
Be^9	100	2.5×10^6 years	9 ± 3 mb
C^{13}	1.11	5,568 years	0.9 ± 3 mb
N^{15}	0.37	7.35 sec	$(24 \pm 8) \times 10^{-3}$ mb
O^{18}	0.204	29.4 sec	0.21 ± 0.04 mb
F^{19}	100	10.7 sec	9 ± 2 mb
Ne^{22}	8.82	40.2 sec	36 ± 15 mb
Na^{23}	100	14.97 hr	536 ± 10 mb
Mg^{26}	11.29	9.45 min	27 ± 5 mb
Al^{27}	100	2.27 min	0.21 ± 0.02
Si^{30}	3.05	2.62 hr	110 ± 10 mb
P^{31}	100	14.22 days	0.19 ± 0.01
S^{34}	4.215	87 days	0.26 ± 0.05
S^{36}	0.017	5.04 min	0.14 ± 0.04
Cl^{35}	75.4	3.08×10^5 years	30 ± 20
		87 days $S^{35}(n,p)$	0.19 ± 0.05
Cl^{37}	24.6	1.0 sec	5 ± 3 mb
		37.29 min	0.56 ± 0.12
Ar^{36}	0.34	35.0 days	6 ± 2
Ar^{38}	0.063	265 years	0.8 ± 0.2
Ar^{40}	99.600	110 min	0.53 ± 0.02
K^{39}	93.08	1.25×10^9 years	3 ± 2
K^{41}	6.91	12.52 hr	1.1 ± 0.1
Ca^{44}	2.06	164 days	0.67 ± 0.07
Ca^{46}	0.0033	4.7 days	0.25 ± 0.10
Ca^{48}	0.185	8.8 min	1.1 ± 0.1

Isotopic Thermal-neutron Activation Cross Sections* (*Continued*)

Target isotope	Abundance, %	Half-life† of product isotope	Isotopic activation cross section for (η,γ) reaction, barns‡ or fermis
Sc^{45}	100	19.5 sec	10 ± 4
		83.9 days	12 ± 6
Ti^{50}	5.34	5.79 min	0.14 ± 0.03
V^{51}	99.76	3.76 min	4.5 ± 0.9
Cr^{50}	4.31	27.8 days	13.5 ± 1.4
Cr^{54}	2.38	3.52 min	0.38 ± 0.04
Mn^{55}	100	2.576 hr	13.3 ± 0.2
Fe^{54}	5.84	2.60 years	2.5 ± 0.4
Fe^{58}	0.31	45.1 days	0.98 ± 0.10
Co^{59}	100	10.47 min	16 ± 3
		5.24 years	20 ± 3
Ni^{64}	1.16	2.564 hr	1.6 ± 0.2
Cu^{63}	69.1	12.80 hr	4.3 ± 0.2
Cu^{65}	30.9	5.10 min	1.8 ± 0.4
Zn^{64}	48.89	245 days	0.44 ± 0.05
Zn^{68}	18.56	13.8 hr	97 ± 10 mb
		57 min	1.0 ± 0.2
Zn^{70}	0.62	2.2 min	85 ± 20 mb
Ga^{69}	60.2	21.1 min	1.4 ± 0.3
Ga^{71}	39.8	14.3 hr	4.0 ± 0.7
Ge^{70}	20.55	11.4 days	3.9 ± 1.2
Ge^{74}	36.74	48 sec	40 ± 8 mb
Ge^{76}	7.67	54 sec	80 ± 20 mb
		11.3 hr	80 ± 20 mb
As^{75}	100	26.4 hr	5.4 ± 1.0
Se^{74}	0.87	121 days	26 ± 6
Se^{76}	9.02	18 sec	7 ± 3
Se^{80}	49.82	56.8 min	30 ± 10 mb
		18.2 min	0.5 ± 0.1
Se^{82}	9.19	70 sec	50 ± 25 mb
		25 min	4 ± 2 mb
Br^{79}	50.52	4.38 hr	2.9 ± 0.5
		17.6 min	8.5 ± 1.4
Br^{81}	49.48	35.87 hr	3.1 ± 0.5
Kr^{78}	0.35	34.5 hr	2.0 ± 0.5
Kr^{80}	2.27	13 sec + 2.1 × 10^5 years	95 ± 15
Kr^{84}	56.90	4.36 hr	0.10 ± 0.03
		10.3 years	60 ± 20 mb
Kr^{86}	17.37	78 min	60 ± 20 mb
Rb^{85}	72.15	18.66 days	0.80 ± 0.08
Rb^{87}	27.85	17.8 min	0.12 ± 0.03

ISOTOPIC THERMAL-NEUTRON ACTIVATION CROSS SECTIONS* (*Continued*)

Target isotope	Abundance, %	Half-life† of product isotope	Isotopic activation cross section for (η,γ) reaction barns‡ or fermis
Sr^{84}	0.56	70 min	1
		64.0 days	1.0 ± 0.3
Sr^{86}	9.86	2.80 hr	1.3 ± 0.4
Sr^{88}	82.56	50.5 days	5 ± 1 mb
Y^{89}	100	64.2 hr	1.26 ± 0.08
Zr^{94}	17.40	65 days	0.09 ± 0.03
Zr^{96}	2.80	17.0 hr	0.10 ± 0.05
Nb^{93}	100	6.6 min	1.0 ± 0.5
Mo^{92}	15.86	6.95 hr	6 mb
Mo^{98}	23.75	66.0 hr	0.45 ± 0.10
Mo^{100}	9.62	14.61 min	0.20 ± 0.05
Ru^{96}	5.7	2.88 days	0.21 ± 0.02
Ru^{102}	31.3	39.8 days	1.44 ± 0.16
Ru^{104}	18.3	4.5 hr	0.7 ± 0.2
Rh^{103}	100	4.4 min	12 ± 2
		44 sec	140 ± 30
Pd^{102}	0.8	17.0 days	4.8 ± 1.5
Pd^{108}	26.7	13.5 hr	10 ± 2
Pd^{110}	13.5	22 min	0.3 ± 0.1
Ag^{107}	51.35	2.3 min	45 ± 4
Ag^{109}	48.65	253 days	3.2 ± 0.4
		24 sec	113 ± 13
Cd^{106}	1.22	6.7 hr	1.0 ± 0.5
Cd^{110}	12.39	48.6 min	0.2 ± 0.1
Cd^{112}	24.07	5.1 years	30 ± 15 mb
Cd^{114}	28.86	43 days	0.14 ± 0.03
		53 hr	1.1 ± 0.3
In^{113}	4.23	50.0 days	56 ± 12
		72 sec	2.0 ± 0.6
In^{115}	95.77	53.99 min	155 ± 10
		13 sec	52 ± 6
Sn^{112}	0.95	119 days	1.3 ± 0.3
Sn^{116}	14.24	14.0 days	6 ± 2 mb
Sn^{118}	24.01	250 days	10 ± 6 mb
Sn^{120}	32.97	Long	1 ± 1 mb
		27.5 hr	0.14 ± 0.03
Sn^{122}	4.71	136 days	1.0 ± 0.5 mb
		39.5 min	0.16 ± 0.04
Sn^{124}	5.98	9.5 min	0.2 ± 0.1
		94 days	4 ± 2 mb
Sb^{121}	57.25	2.80 days	6.8 ± 1.5
Sb^{123}	42.75	21 min	30 ± 15 mb
		1.3 min	30 ± 15 mb
		60.9 days	2.5 ± 0.5

ISOTOPIC THERMAL-NEUTRON ACTIVATION CROSS SECTIONS (*Continued*)

Target isotope	Abundance, %	Half-life† of product isotope	Isotopic activation cross section for (η,γ) reaction, barns‡ or fermis
Te^{122}	2.46	104 days	1.1 ± 0.5
Te^{124}	4.61	58 days	5 ± 3
Te^{126}	18.71	105 days	90 ± 20 mb
		9.4 hr	0.8 ± 0.2
Te^{128}	31.79	33.5 days	15 ± 5 mb
		72 min	0.13 ± 0.03
Te^{130}	34.49	30 hr	8 mb
		24.8 min	0.22 ± 0.05
I^{127}	100	24.99 min	5.6 ± 0.3
Xe^{132}	26.89	5.270 days	0.2 ± 0.1
Xe^{134}	10.44	9.13 hr	0.2 ± 0.1
Xe^{136}	8.87	3.9 min	0.15 ± 0.08
Cs^{133}	100	3.2 hr	17 ± 4 mb
		2.07 years	30 ± 1
Ba^{130}	0.101	11.5 days	10 ± 1
Ba^{132}	0.097	7.2 years	7 ± 2
Ba^{138}	71.66	84.0 min	0.5 ± 0.1
La^{139}	99.911	40.22 hr	8.2 ± 0.8
Ce^{136}	0.19	34.5 hr	0.6 ± 0.2
		8.7 hr	6.3 ± 1.5
Ce^{138}	0.26	55 sec	7 ± 5 mb
		140 days	0.6 ± 0.3
Ce^{140}	88.48	33.1 days	0.31 ± 0.10
Ce^{142}	11.07	33 hr	0.95 ± 0.05
Pr^{141}	100	19.2 hr	10 ± 3
Nd^{146}	17.1	11.06 days	1.8 ± 0.6
Nd^{148}	5.72	2.0 hr	3.7 ± 1.2
Sm^{144}	3.16	340 days	2
Sm^{152}	26.63	47.1 hr	140 ± 40
Sm^{154}	22.53	23.5 min	5.5 ± 1.1
Eu^{151}	47.77	9.2 hr	1,400 ± 300
Eu^{153}	52.23	12.7 years	420 ± 100
Gd^{152}	0.20	236 days	125
Gd^{158}	24.87	18.0 hr	4 ± 2
Gd^{160}	21.90	3.6 min	0.8 ± 0.3
Tb^{159}	100	72.3 days	722
Dy^{164}	28.18	1.25 min	510 ± 20
		139.2 min	2,100 ± 300
Ho^{165}	100	27.3 hr	60 ± 12
Er^{168}	27.1	9.4 days	2.0 ± 0.4
Er^{170}	14.9	7.8 hr	9 ± 2
Tm^{169}	100	129 days	130 ± 30
Yb^{168}	0.140	31.8 days	11,000 ± 3,000
Yb^{174}	31.84	101 hr	60 ± 40

Isotopic Thermal-neutron Activation Cross Sections (*Continued*)

Target isotope	Abundance, %	Half-life† of product isotope	Isotopic activation cross section for (η,γ) reaction, barns‡ or fermis
Yb^{176}	12.73	1.9 hr	5.5 ± 1.0
Lu^{175}	97.40	3.71 hr	35 ± 15
Lu^{176}	2.60	6.75 days	$4{,}000 \pm 800$
Hf^{180}	35.44	44.6 days	10 ± 3
Ta^{181}	99.988	16.5 min	30 ± 10 mb
		115.1 days	19 ± 7
W^{180}	0.14	145 days	10 ± 10
W^{184}	30.6	75.8 days	2.1 ± 0.6
W^{186}	28.4	24.0 hr	34 ± 7
Re^{185}	37.07	88.9 hr	100 ± 20
Re^{187}	62.93	16.7 hr	75 ± 15
Os^{184}	0.018	93.6 days	200
Os^{190}	26.4	16.0 days	8 ± 3
Os^{192}	41.0	30.6 hr	1.6 ± 0.4
		1.42 min	260 ± 100
Ir^{191}	38.5	74.37 days	700 ± 200
Ir^{193}	61.5	19.0 hr	130 ± 30
Pt^{190}	0.012	3.00 days	0.76 ± 0.10
Pt^{192}	0.78	4.3 days	90 ± 40
Pt^{196}	25.4	18 hr	0.8 ± 0.1
Pt^{198}	7.2	31 min	3.9 ± 0.8
Au^{197}	100	2.697 days	96 ± 10
Hg^{202}	29.80	46.9 days	3.8 ± 0.8
Hg^{204}	6.85	5.5 min	0.43 ± 0.10
Tl^{203}	29.50	3.56 years	8 ± 3
Tl^{205}	70.50	4.19 min	0.10 ± 0.03
Pb^{204}	1.48	5×10^7 years	0.7 ± 0.2
Pb^{208}	52.3	3.30 hr	0.6 ± 0.2 mb
Bi^{209}	100	5.013 days	19 ± 2 mb

* From D. J. Hughes and R. B. Schwartz, Neutron Cross Sections, *U.S. Atomic Energy Comm. Rept.* BNL-325, July 1, 1958.

† From D. Strominger, J. M. Hollander, and G. T. Seaborg, Table of Isotopes, *Revs. Modern Phys.*, vol. 30, pp. 585–904, 1958.

‡ mb = millibarn, 10^{-3} barn.

Appendix H

Integration by the Integrating-factor Method

The integrating-factor method may be used to integrate linear differential equations of the first order such as Eq. (8-31), namely,

$$\frac{dN_B}{dt} = \lambda_A N_A - \lambda_B N_B \tag{H-1}$$

where λ_A and λ_B are constants and N_A is either constant or a function of time only. The factor has the form $e^{\int \lambda_B dt}$, which is $e^{\lambda_B t}$. When Eq. (H-1) is multiplied by $e^{\lambda_B t}$ and the terms are collected, the result is

$$e^{\lambda_B t}\frac{dN_B}{dt} + \lambda_B N_B e^{\lambda_B t} = \lambda_A N_A e^{\lambda_B t} \tag{H-2}$$

Since the two terms on the left-hand side of Eq. (H-2) are equivalent to

$$\frac{d(N_B e^{\lambda_B t})}{dt}$$

the equation may be written as

$$d(N_B e^{\lambda_B t}) = \lambda_A N_A e^{\lambda_B t}\, dt \tag{H-3}$$

and

$$\int d(N_B e^{\lambda_B t}) = \int \lambda_A N_A e^{\lambda_B t}\, dt \tag{H-4}$$

Integration with

$$N_A = (N_A)_0 e^{-\lambda_A t}$$

leads to

$$N_B e^{\lambda_B t} = \frac{\lambda_A (N_A)_0}{\lambda_B - \lambda_A} e^{(\lambda_B - \lambda_A)t} + C \tag{H-5}$$

Solving for N_B, we obtain

$$N_B = \frac{\lambda_A (N_A)_0}{\lambda_B - \lambda_A} e^{-\lambda_A t} + Ce^{-\lambda_B t} \tag{H-6}$$

Recalling that, in formulating Eq. (8-32), $(N_B)_0 = 0$ at $t = 0$,

$$C = \frac{-\lambda_A (N_A)_0}{\lambda_B - \lambda_A} \tag{H-7}$$

After substitution for C, the final equation [Eq. (8-32)] is

$$N_B = \frac{\lambda_A (N_A)_0}{\lambda_B - \lambda_A}(e^{-\lambda_A t} - e^{-\lambda_B t}) \tag{H-8}$$

Appendix I

Licensing Requirements for Radioisotope Procurement

The Atomic Energy Commission has set up specific rules and regulations which govern the sale and use of radioactive materials. AEC Form 313, entitled "Application for By-product Material License," must first be submitted to the AEC for approval. These forms may be obtained from the AEC or from commercial suppliers. They request such information as quantity and type of isotope, training and experience of the user, and facilities and radiation-monitoring instrumentation available. The completed forms are submitted directly to the Division of Licensing and Regulation, U.S. Atomic Energy Commission, Washington, D.C. Upon approval of this application the AEC issues to the applicant an "AEC By-product Material License," which will then permit him to purchase the radioactive materials from any supplier. The AEC license number must be furnished with the purchase order and is valid for 2 years.

Large-quantity users may obtain specific licenses for multiple quantities and types of radioisotopes.

In the case of foreign orders for radioactive materials of atomic number 3 to 83 inclusive, no AEC authorization is required. Likewise, no AEC authorization is required for "generally licensed quantities." In general, these are microcurie quantities of nonhazardous materials. The current listing and quantities are available from the AEC or the *Federal Register*.

Appendix J

Additional References

Bayhurst, B. P., and R. J. Prestwood: A Method for Estimating Beta-counting Efficiencies, *Nucleonics*, vol. 17, no. 3, pp. 82–85, March, 1959.

Beaufait, L. J., Jr., and H. R. Lukens, Jr.: Handbook of Radiochemical Analysis, vol. I, Radiochemical Techniques, *U.S. Atomic Energy Comm. Rept.* NP-5056, 1953. (Also available from Department of Commerce, Office of Technical Services, as PB-121690.)

——— and ———: Handbook of Radiochemical Analysis, vol. II, Radiochemical Procedures, *U.S. Atomic Energy Comm. Rept.* NP-5057, 1952. (Also available from Department of Commerce, Office of Technical Services, as PB-121689.)

"Bibliography for Biological Data" (published for the ICRP), Pergamon, New York, in press.

Blatz, H. (ed.): "Radiation Hygiene Handbook," McGraw-Hill, New York, 1959.

Bryant, E. A., J. E. Sattizahn, and B. Warren: Strontium-90 by an Ion Exchange Method, *Anal. Chem.*, vol. 31, pp. 334–337, March, 1959.

Bunney, L. R., N. E. Ballou, J. Pascual, and S. Foti: Quantitative Radiochemical Analysis by Ion Exchange, *Anal. Chem.*, vol. 31, pp. 324–326, March, 1959.

Dzelepov, V. S., and L. K. Peker: Decay Schemes of Radioactive Isotopes, *U.S. Atomic Energy Comm. Rept.* AECL-457, 1957 (translation from a publication of the Academy of Sciences, U.S.S.R., Moscow-Leningrad, 1957).

Finston, H. L.: "Radiochemical Separations Compilation: Procedures Covering about 20 Elements," 1954–1958. (Available from H. L. Finston, Radiochemical Analytical Section, Brookhaven National Laboratory, Upton, Long Island, N.Y.)

Gibbs, R. C., and K. Way: "A Directory to Nuclear Data Tabulations," Nuclear Data Project, National Academy of Sciences–National Research Council, Washington, 1958.

Handley, T. H., and C. L. Burros: Determination of Radioactive Cesium, *Anal. Chem.;* vol. 31, pp. 332–334, March, 1959.

Hentz, R. R.: Limitations of the Radioactive Tracer Method, *J. Chem. Educ.*, vol. 35, pp. 625–628, December, 1958.

Hoisington, D. B.: "Nucleonics Fundamentals," McGraw-Hill, New York, 1959.

Holt, B. D.: Determination of Hydrogen in Alkali Metals by Isotope Dilution Method, *Anal. Chem.*, vol. 31, pp. 51–54, January, 1959.

Kennedy, M. R.: Health Physics Manual of Radiochemical and Chemical Analysis and Procedures, *U.S. Atomic Energy Comm. Rept.* KAPL-A-HP-3, 1957.

Lutwak, L.: Estimation of Radioactive Calcium-45 by Liquid Scintillation Counting, *Anal. Chem.*, vol. 31, pp. 340–342, March, 1959.

Mann, W. B., and H. H. Seliger: Preparation, Maintenance, and Application of Standards of Radioactivity, *Natl. Bur. Standards Circ.* 594, 1958.

"Measurements and Standards of Radioactivity: Proceedings of an Informal Conference Held October 9–11, 1957," *Natl. Research Council, Nuclear Sci. Series Rept.* 24, National Academy of Sciences–National Research Council, Washington, 1958.

Meinke, W. W.: Sensitivity Charts for Neutron Activation Analysis, *Anal. Chem.*, vol. 31, pp. 792–795, May, 1959.

Nokes, M. C.: "Radioactivity Measuring Instruments: A Guide to Their Construction and Use," Philosophical Library, New York, 1958.

Proceedings of the Second United Nations International Conference on the Peaceful Uses of Atomic Energy, Held in Geneva 1 September–13 September 1958, United Nations, Geneva, 1958:

Vol. 19, The Use of Isotopes: Industrial Use
Vol. 20, Isotopes in Research
Vol. 21, Health and Safety: Dosimetry and Standards
Vol. 22, Biological Effects of Radiation
Vol. 23, Experience in Radiological Protection
Vol. 24, Isotopes in Biochemistry and Physiology, Part I
Vol. 25, Isotopes in Biochemistry and Physiology, Part II
Vol. 26, Isotopes in Medicine
Vol. 27, Isotopes in Agriculture
Vol. 29, Chemical Effects of Radiation

Proceedings of the Sixth Scintillation Counter Symposium, January 27–28, 1958, *IRE Trans. on Nuclear Sci.*, vol. NS-5, no. 3, December, 1958.

"Recommendations of the International Commission on Radiological Protection: Report of the Committee on Permissible Dose for Internal Radiation" (1958 revision), Pergamon, New York, in press.

Regier, R. B.: Radiometric Determination of Krypton-85, *Anal. Chem.*, vol. 31, pp. 54–55, January, 1959.

Rickard, R. R., and E. I. Wyatt: Radiochemical Determination of Fission Ruthenium in Aqueous Solutions: A Nondistillation Technique, *Anal. Chem.*, vol. 31, pp. 50–51, January, 1959.

Ross, C. P.: Particle Size Analysis by Gamma-ray Absorption, *Anal. Chem.*, vol. 31, pp. 337–339, March, 1959.

"Safe Handling of Radioisotopes," International Atomic Energy Agency, Vienna, 1958.

Schindewolf, U.: Ionenaustauscher in der analytischen Chemie Entwicklungen in den letzten Jahren, *Angew. Chem.*, vol. 69, pp. 226–236, Apr. 7, 1957. (*U.S. Atomic Energy Comm.* translation AEC-tr-2975, Recent Developments in Ion Exchangers in Analytical Chemistry.)

Scintillation Counting—1958, *Nucleonics*, vol. 16, no. 6, pp. 54–62, June, 1958.

Slack, L., and K. Way: Radiations from Radioactive Atoms in Frequent Use, *U.S. Atomic Energy Comm. Rept.*, 1959.

Sugihara, T. T., H. I. James, E. J. Troianello, and V. T. Bowen: Radiochemical Separation of Fission Products from Large Volumes of Sea Water: Strontium, Cesium, Cerium, and Promethium, *Anal. Chem.*, vol. 31, pp. 44–49, January, 1959.

Sunderman, D. N., I. B. Ackermann, and W. W. Meinke: Radiochemical Separations of Indium, *Anal. Chem.*, vol. 31, pp. 40–44, January, 1959.

Appendix K

Useful Constants and Conversion Factors

Avogadro's number = 6.02×10^{23} atoms per gram atomic weight
Charge on the electron = 4.80×10^{-10} esu = 1.60×10^{-19} coulomb
Planck's constant = 6.63×10^{-27} erg-sec
Velocity of light = 3×10^{10} cm/sec
1 angstrom unit (A) = 10^{-8} cm
1 millimicron (mμ) = 10^{-7} cm
Wavelength of violet light $\approx$ 4,000 A = 400 mμ
1 atomic mass unit (amu) = 1.66×10^{-24} g (physical scale)

$$\frac{\text{Physical atomic weight } (O^{16} = 16.0000)}{\text{Chemical atomic weight } (O^{16,17,18} = 16)} = 1.000272$$

1 atomic mass unit (amu) = 931 Mev = 1.49×10^{-3} erg = 3.56×10^{-11} cal
1 Mev = 1.07×10^{-3} amu = 1.60×10^{-6} erg = 3.82×10^{-14} cal
1 erg = 671 amu = 6.25×10^{5} Mev = 2.39×10^{-8} cal
Radius of nucleus = $1.2A^{1/3} \times 10^{-13}$ cm, where A is mass number
Radius of atom $\approx 10^{-8}$ cm
Mass of electron = 9.1066×10^{-28} g = 0.000549 amu = 0.511 Mev
Mass of proton = 1.67248×10^{-24} g = 1.007594 amu
Mass of neutron = 1.6751×10^{-24} g = 1.008986 amu
Mass of α particle = 6.60×10^{-24} g = 4.002777 amu
Wavelength associated with 1 ev = 12,394.8 A
1 gamma = 10^{-6} g
1 lambda (λ) = 10^{-6} liter = 10^{-3} ml
1 curie = 3.700×10^{10} disintegrations per second (dps)
= 2.22×10^{12} disintegrations per minute (dpm)
1 millicurie (mc) = 3.700×10^{7} dps = 2.22×10^{9} dpm
1 microcurie (μc) = 3.700×10^{4} dps = 2.22×10^{6} dpm
roentgen = 1 esu of charge per cubic centimeter (0.001293 g) of dry air at STP
= 1.61×10^{12} ion pairs/g air
= charge equivalent to 2×10^{9} electrons/cm^3 air
1 rad = 100 ergs/g
1 rep = 93 ergs/g absorbed in tissue
1 ev/molecule = 23.060 kcal/mole
96,500 coulombs (ampere-seconds) of charge = 6.02×10^{23} electrons
1 day = 8.64×10^{4} sec
1 year = 3.156×10^{7} sec
1 barn = 10^{-24} cm^2
Density of lead = 11.342 g/cm^3
Density of aluminum = 2.70 g/cm^3

Index